INTERNATIONAL SERIES OF MONOGRAPHS IN

PURE AND APPLIED MATHEMATICS

VOLUME 88

INTEGRAL EQUATIONS AND THEIR APPLICATIONS

Volume I

Parts 1, 2 and 3

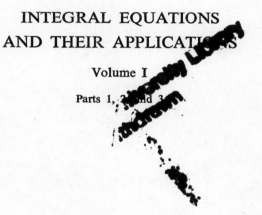

INTEGRAL EQUATIONS
and their Applications

VOLUME I

by

W. POGORZELSKI

PERGAMON PRESS
OXFORD · LONDON · EDINBURGH · NEW YORK
TORONTO · PARIS · FRANKFURT

PWN – POLISH SCIENTIFIC PUBLISHERS
WARSZAWA

Pergamon Press Ltd., Headington Hill Hall, Oxford
4 & 5 Fitzroy Square, London W.1
Pergamon Press (Scotland) Ltd., 2 & 3 Teviot Place, Edinburgh 1
Pergamon Press Inc., 44–01 21st Street, Long Island City, New York 11101
Pergamon of Canada, Ltd., 6 Adelaide Street East, Toronto, Ontario
Pergamon Press S.A.R.L., 24 rue des Écoles, Paris 5e
Pergamon Press GmbH, Kaiserstrasse 75, Frankfurt-am-Main

First edition 1966

Library of Congress Catalog Card No. 64-18247

This translation has been made from *Równania całkowe i ich zastosowania*, Vols. 1–3, published in 1953–1960 by Polish Scientific Publishers, Warszawa

PRINTED IN POLAND

(1699/66)

CONTENTS

PART 2

Systems of Linear Integral Equations. Non-linear Integral Equations. Applications of Integral Equations in the Theory of Differential Equations

FROM THE EDITORS

This volume appears after the untimely death of the author, which occurred while the book was in the press. The author had succeeded, however, in finishing the manuscript, and the second volume will contain chapters on polyharmonic equations, generalized analytic functions, multidimensional singular integral equations, applications to boundary problems of partial differential equations of second order and some physical and technological applications.

LIST OF SYMBOLS

$N(x, y)$	kernel of equation 8
$N_n(x, y)$	iterated kernel 10
$\mathfrak{N}(x, y, \lambda)$	resolvent kernel 11
$N\begin{pmatrix} x_1, x_2, \ldots, x_n \\ y_1, y_2, \ldots, y_n \end{pmatrix}$	Fredholm determinant 33
$D(\lambda)$	sum of first Fredholm series 34
$D(x, y, \lambda)$	sum of second Fredholm series 44
$D_n\left(\begin{matrix} x_1, x_2, \ldots, x_n \\ y_1, y_2, \ldots, y_n \end{matrix}\middle\vert \lambda\right)$	Fredholm minor 51
(f, φ)	scalar product of functions 63
$a+bN$	Fredholm operator 86
$\|f(x)\|$	norm of a function 97
$\delta(f, \varphi)$	distance between two points in function space 115
$\det \lvert b_{\alpha\beta} \rvert$	determinant of matrix with elements $b_{\alpha\beta}$ 133
$\delta_{\alpha\beta}$	Kronecker delta 133

PART 1

The General Properties of Fredholm's and Volterra's Equations

Translated by

JACQUES J. SCHORR-CON

INTRODUCTION

AN INTEGRAL EQUATION is an equation in which the unknown function appears under the integral sign.

The theory of integral equations is one of the most important branches of mathematical analysis, mainly on account of its importance in boundary value problems in the theory of partial differential equations. Integral equations are also connected with the theory of orthogonal systems, with the theory of analytic functions, and with the theory of quadratic forms of infinitely many variables; they also bear an essential connection with the modern field of mathematics called *functional analysis*.

Integral equations arise in many problems of physics and technology. In most recent investigations a particularly important rôle in problems in the theory of elasticity and the theory of aircraft wing, is played by singular integral equations (with Cauchy type kernels).

Integral equations have been encountered in mathematics for a number of years, originally in the theory of Fourier integrals. An integral equation was also obtained in *Abel's problem* of finding the trajectory along which a material point should slide to make the time of descent an initially given function of the altitude. One then obtains an integral equation of the form

$$\int_0^x \frac{\varphi(y)\,dy}{\sqrt{x-y}} = f(x),$$

where $f(x)$ is the given function, and $\varphi(y)$ is the unknown function. The actual development of the theory of integral equations began, however, only at the end of the nineteenth century due to the works of the Italian mathematician V. Volterra, and principally to the year 1900, in which the Swedish mathematician

I. Fredholm published his famous work on a new method of solution for the Dirichlet problem. *

From then on, up to the present moment, integral equations have been the subject of uninterrupted research of numerous mathematicians, since they continuously supply interesting new problems.

An integral equation is called *linear* if linear operations are performed in it upon the unknown function, that is, if it has the form

$$A(x)\varphi(x)+B(x)+\int_{\Omega} N(x,y)\varphi(y)\,dy=0, \tag{1}$$

where $\varphi(x)$ is the unknown function, $A(x), B(x), N(x, y)$ are given functions, and the integration extends over the domain Ω of the variable y. Because of the great importance of linear integral equations in mathematics the greater part of this book is devoted to these equations.

Linear integral equations are divided into two basic types:

(1) *Volterra integral equations,* in which the upper limit of integration is variable;

(2) *Fredholm integral equations,* with a fixed domain of integration.

The theory of these two types of equations differs in principle. The theory of Volterra's equations is much easier, whereas the theory of Fredholm equations is more difficult but also more interesting.

The left-hand side of the integral equation (1) (as of every integral equation), which we shall denote by the symbol

$$\psi=\hat{N}\varphi=A(x)\varphi(x)+B(x)+\int_{\Omega} N(x,y)\varphi(y)\,dy,$$

for given functions A, B, N describes a correspondence by which every function φ integrable in the set Ω assigns some function $\psi(x)$ integrable in that set. ** This correspondence is a certain

* Sur une nouvelle méthode pour la résolution du problème de Dirichlet. *Ofr. Forh. Akad.* Stockholm, 1900. Sur une classe d'équations fonctionnelles, *C. R. Acad. Sci.*, Paris, 1902.

** The kind of integrability will be described later.

functional operation. A symbol of a functional operation is called an *operator*. In the above example it is the letter $\hat{N}$.

The solution of integral equation (1) consists in finding a function φ such that

$$\hat{N}[\varphi(x)] = 0.$$

Before proceeding to the exposition of the theory of integral equations we shall give two simple but fundamental examples of problems leading to integral equations.

Let us first consider a *boundary value problem* from the theory of ordinary differential equations, which consists in finding the solution of a second order differential equation

$$\frac{d^2 y}{dx^2} = p(x)\,y + q(x), \tag{2}$$

vanishing at the end-points of the closed interval $[a, b]$:

$$y(a) = 0, \quad y(b) = 0. \tag{3}$$

The functions $p(x)$ and $q(x)$ are defined and continuous in the closed interval $[a, b]$. Now let us consider the equation

$$\frac{d^2 y}{dx^2} = F(x), \tag{2'}$$

where $F(x)$ is a given function, continuous in the interval $[a, b]$. The general solution of this equation is of the form

$$y = \int_a^x \Big[\int_a^z F(t)\,dt\Big]\,dz + C_1 x + C_2 = \int_a^x (x-t)\,F(t)\,dt + C_1 x + C_2,$$

where C_1 and C_2 are arbitrary constants. Choosing the arbitrary constants C_1 and C_2 in such a way that the boundary condition (3) is satisfied, we obtain the solution of the equation (2) in the form

$$y(x) = \int_a^b G(x, t)\,F(t)\,dt, \tag{4}$$

where the function $G(x, t)$ is defined by the relations

$$G(x, t) = \frac{(x-a)(t-b)}{b-a}, \quad \text{when } x \leqq t,$$
$$G(x, t) = \frac{(x-b)(t-a)}{b-a}, \quad \text{when } x \geqq t. \tag{5}$$

Hence we conclude directly that the function $y(x)$, which is a solution of the differential equation (2) with boundary conditions (3), satisfies the equation

$$y(x) = \int_a^b G(x, t)\, p(t)\, y(t)\, dt + \int_a^b G(x, t)\, q(t)\, dt. \tag{6}$$

Conversely, the solution y of equation (6) satisfies the given equation (2) and the boundary conditions (3). Thus we see that the solution of the problem is reduced to the solution of the integral equation (6), in which the unknown function appears under the integral sign with fixed limits. Such an equation is called a *Fredholm integral equation of the second kind.* The problem considered may be also applied in the theory of deformation of an elastic rod supported at two points.

The other example, taken from the field of electrostatics, is the following fundamental problem: what should be the distribution of electricity on the surface of a conductor for the electric charge to remain in equilibrium? Now, this occurs when the interior boundary value of the normal component of field intensity is equal to zero at every point of the closed boundary S of the conductor. It is known* that the interior boundary value of the normal component of field intensity at a point P of a surface S is less by $2\pi\, \mu(P)$ than the normal component at the same point P given by the surface integral

$$\int_S \frac{\cos\varphi}{r_{PQ}^2}\, \mu(Q)\, d\sigma_Q,$$

---

* See vol. IV of *Analiza matematyczna* (*Mathematical Analysis*) by the present author, Warszawa, 1951, p. 164.

where $\mu(P)$ denotes the charge density at the point P, φ is the angle between the vector QP and the outward drawn normal to the surface S at the point P, and r_{PQ} is the distance between the points P and Q. Thus, the condition of equilibrium reduces to the equation

$$\int_S \frac{\cos\varphi}{r_{PQ}^2}\,\mu(Q)\,d\sigma_Q - 2\pi\mu(P) = 0, \tag{7}$$

which is a Fredholm integral equation with the unknown function μ. We shall undertake a discussion of this equation in **Part 2.**

CHAPTER I

VOLTERRA'S INTEGRAL EQUATIONS

§ 1. Volterra's equation of the second kind

A *Volterra equation of the second kind* is a linear integral equation of the form

$$\varphi(x) = f(x) + \lambda \int_a^x N(x, y)\,\varphi(y)\,dy, \tag{1}$$

where $\varphi(x)$ is the unknown function, $f(x)$ and $N(x, y)$ are given functions, and λ is a constant. The principal feature of this equation is the fact that the limit of integration x is a variable.

The function $f(x)$ is defined and bounded in the closed interval

$$a \leqq x \leqq b, \tag{2}$$

and the function of two variables $N(x, y)$ is defined and bounded in the triangle

$$a \leqq y \leqq x, \quad a \leqq x \leqq b. \tag{3}$$

We assume that the function $f(x)$ is Riemann-integrable in the interval $[a, b]$. Thereupon we assume the existence of the Riemann integrals

$$\int_a^x N(x, y)\,dy, \quad \int_y^b N(x, y)\,dx,$$

the first for every fixed value of x in the interval $[a, b]$, and the second for every value of y in that interval. The given function of two variables $N(x, y)$ under the integral sign is called the *kernel* of a Volterra integral equation.

Let $M(x, y)$ be a given function defined and bounded in the rectangle

$$a \leqq x \leqq b, \quad p \leqq y \leqq q.$$

If we assume the existence of the Riemann integrals

$$\int_a^b M(x, y)\,dx, \qquad \int_p^q M(x, y)\,dy,$$

the first for every fixed y in the interval $[p, q]$, *the second for every fixed x in the interval* $[a, b]$, *then follows the existence and equality of the two iterated integrals*

$$\int_p^q \Big[\int_a^b M(x, y)\,dx\Big]\,dy = \int_a^b \Big[\int_p^q M(x, y)\,dy\Big]\,dx.$$

This property, well known for continuous functions, has been proved for Riemann-integrable functions with the aid of a certain lemma of ARZÉLA.*

Let us now take the square

$$a \leqq s \leqq x, \qquad a \leqq y \leqq x,$$

where x has an arbitrary value, fixed within the interval $[a, b]$, and in that square let us define a function $M_x(s, y)$ by the equality

$$M_x(s, y) = N(x, y)\,N(y, s)\,\varphi(s),$$

when the point (s, y) lies in the triangle

$$a \leqq y \leqq x, \qquad a \leqq s \leqq y,$$

and by the equality

$$M_x(s, y) = 0,$$

when the point (s, y) lies in the remaining portion of the square, i.e. when

$$a \leqq y \leqq x, \qquad y < s \leqq x,$$

and $\varphi(s)$ is an arbitrary Riemann-integrable function in the interval $[a, b]$.

Applying the above theorem on iterated integrals to the

---

* The proof of this proposition may be found by the reader in vol. II of the work of M. FICHTENGOL'TS *Course of Differential and Integral Calculus* (in Russian), Moscow 1951, p. 172.

function $M_x(s, y)$, we have

$$\int_a^x \left[\int_a^x M_x(s, y)\, ds\right] dy = \int_a^x \left[\int_a^x M_x(s, y)\, dy\right] ds,$$

and hence follows the existence and equality of the two iterated integrals

$$\int_a^x \left[\int_a^y N(x, y) N(y, s) \varphi(s)\, ds\right] dy$$

$$= \int_a^x \left[\int_s^x N(x, y) N(y, s)\, dy\right] \varphi(s)\, ds,$$

valid for every value of x within the interval $[a, b]$. This relation is called the *Dirichlet transformation.*

We now proceed to the solution of the Volterra equation (1). Accordingly, note that, if there exists an integrable function $\varphi(x)$ satisfying equation (1), then this function also satisfies the so called *iterated equation* obtained from equation (1) by substituting under the integral sign instead of $\varphi(y)$ the entire right-hand side of that equation, i.e. the equation

$$\varphi(x) = f(x) + \lambda \int_a^x N(x, y)\left[f(y) + \lambda \int_a^y N(y, s)\varphi(s)\, ds\right] dy. \quad (4)$$

Applying the Dirichlet transformation to the kernel $N(x, y)$, which, on the basis of the assumptions made, is possible, we obtain the iterated equation in the equivalent form

$$\varphi(x) = f(x) + \lambda \int_a^x N(x, y) f(y)\, dy + \lambda^2 \int_a^x N_1(x, y)\varphi(y)\, dy, \quad (5)$$

where the function

$$N_1(x, y) = \int_y^x N(x, s) N(s, y)\, ds \quad (6)$$

is called the *iterated kernel* of the kernel $N(x, y)$.

This kernel is defined and bounded in the triangle (3). We shall prove, just as for the given kernel $N(x, y)$, that for the iterated kernel (6), the integrals

$$\int_a^x N_1(x, y)\, dy, \quad \int_y^b N_1(x, y)\, dx$$

exist, the first for a value of x fixed in the interval $[a, b]$, the second for a value of y fixed in that interval. The existence of the first integral follows directly from the preceding considerations by the substitution $\varphi = 1$. In order to prove the existence of the second integral, let us consider the auxiliary function $P_y(x, s)$ defined in the square

$$y \leqq x \leqq b, \quad y \leqq s \leqq b$$

(for a value of y fixed in the interval $[a, b]$) in the following way:

$$P_y(x, s) = N(x, s)\, N(s, y)$$

in the triangle

$$y \leqq x \leqq b, \quad y \leqq s \leqq x,$$

and

$$P_y(x, s) = 0$$

in the remaining portion of the square, i.e. when

$$y \leqq x \leqq b, \quad x < s \leqq b.$$

From the assumptions relating to the kernel N, it follows that the integrals

$$\int_y^b P_y(x, s)\, ds, \quad \int_y^b \Big[\int_y^b P_y(x, s)\, ds\Big] dx,$$

exist, and since

$$\int_y^b P_y(x, s)\, ds = \int_y^x N(x, s)\, N(s, y)\, ds = N_1(x, y),$$

so also does the integral

$$\int_y^b N_1(x, y)\, dx .$$

Repeating the above transformation we obtain a *two-fold iterated equation* of the form

$$\varphi(x) = f(x) + \lambda \int_a^x N(x, y) f(y)\, dy +$$

$$+ \lambda^2 \int_a^x N_1(x, y) f(y)\, dy + \lambda^3 \int_a^x N_2(x, y)\, \varphi(y)\, dy ,$$

where

$$N_2(x, y) = \int_y^x N(x, s)\, N_1(s, y)\, ds . \tag{7}$$

We call the function $N_2(x, y)$ a *two-fold iterated kernel.*

After the n-th repetition of the above transformation we find that the function $\varphi(x)$ satisfying equation (1) also satisfies an *n-fold iterated equation* of the form

$$\varphi(x) = f(x) + \lambda \int_a^x [N(x, y) + \lambda N_1(x, y) + \lambda^2 N_2(x, y) +$$

$$+ \ldots + \lambda^{n-1} N_{n-1}(x, y)] f(y)\, dy + \lambda^{n+1} \int_a^x N_n(x, y)\, \varphi(y)\, dy , \tag{8}$$

where the iterated kernels $N_1, N_2, \ldots, N_n$ are defined inductively by the relation

$$N_n(x, y) = \int_y^x N(x, s)\, N_{n-1}(s, y)\, ds \qquad (N_0 = N) . \tag{9}$$

Basing ourselves upon the assumptions adopted for the kernel N and repeating an argument analogous to that applied to the kernel $N_1(x, y)$, we shall prove by induction the existence of the iterated kernels $N_n(x, y)$ and their integrability with respect to the variables x and y separately, just as for the kernel N.

Let M be the upper bound of the absolute value of the kernel $N(x, y)$ in domain (3). Then, in view of equality (9), we have successively

$$|N_1(x, y)| < M^2 |x-y|,$$

$$|N_2(x, y)| < M^3 \frac{|x-y|^2}{1.2},$$

$$\cdots\cdots\cdots\cdots\cdots\cdots \tag{10}$$

$$|N_n(x, y)| < M^{n+1} \frac{|x-y|^n}{1.2.3\ldots n}$$

for every n. Now if m is the upper bound of the absolute value of the function $\varphi(x)$ in the interval $[a, b]$, then the following inequality holds:

$$\left|\lambda^{n+1} \int_a^x N_n(x, y)\varphi(y)\,dy\right| < m \frac{[M|\lambda|.|x-a|]^{n+1}}{(n+1)!}. \tag{11}$$

The right-hand side of this inequality is the $(n+1)$th term of the following series which is absolutely and uniformly convergent for all values of $|x-a|$:

$$e^{M|\lambda(x-a)|} = \sum_{n=0}^{\infty} \frac{[M|\lambda|.|x-a|]^n}{n!}.$$

Consequently the last integral in formula (8) tends to zero as $n \to \infty$.

From the iterated equation (8) we conclude that if there exists an integrable function $\varphi(x)$ satisfying the given Volterra integral equation (1), then it is unique and given by the formula

$$\varphi(x) = f(x) + \lambda \int_a^x \mathfrak{R}(x, y, \lambda) f(y)\,dy, \tag{12}$$

where the function under the integral sign is the sum of a series which converges absolutely and uniformly in domain (3):

$$\mathfrak{R}(x, y, \lambda) = N(x, y) + \sum_{n=1}^{\infty} \lambda^n N_n(x, y). \tag{13}$$

This function is called the *resolvent kernel* of the integral equation (1). On the basis of inequality (10) series (13) converges for every value of λ, and therefore the resolvent kernel is an entire function of the parameter λ. The ease of investigation and solution of the Volterra integral equation is due primarily to the inequalities (10).

It still has to be proved that function (12) does indeed satisfy Volterra equation (1). With this in view, in the right-hand side of equation (1) let us substitute for $\varphi(y)$ the expression defined by formula (12); we then have

$$\varphi(y) = f(y) + \lambda \int_a^y \mathfrak{N}(y, s, \lambda) f(s)\, ds.$$

The right-hand side of equation (1) then takes the following value:

$$f(x) + \lambda \int_a^x N(x, y) \left[f(y) + \lambda \int_a^y \mathfrak{N}(y, s, \lambda) f(s)\, ds \right] dy,$$

i.e.

$$f(x) + \lambda \int_a^x N(x, y) f(y)\, dy + \lambda^2 \int_a^x \left[\int_s^x N(x, y) \mathfrak{N}(y, s, \lambda)\, dy \right] f(s)\, ds,$$

or, upon transposing the variables y and s:

$$f(x) + \lambda \int_a^x \left[N(x, y) + \lambda \int_y^x N(x, s) \mathfrak{N}(s, y, \lambda)\, ds \right] f(y)\, dy. \tag{14}$$

Let us now turn our attention to the series (8) and the recurrence relation (9). We immediately see that

$$N(x, y) + \lambda \int_y^x N(x, s) \mathfrak{N}(s, y, \lambda)\, ds$$
$$= N(x, y) + \sum_{n=1}^{\infty} \lambda^n N_n(x, y) = \mathfrak{N}(x, y, \lambda),$$

and therefore the value (14) of the right-hand side of equation (1), upon the substitution of expression (12) for $\varphi(y)$, is equal to

$$f(x) + \lambda \int_a^x \mathfrak{N}(x, y, \lambda) f(y)\, dy,$$

i.e. to the expression (12). Consequently, the function defined by formula (12) is indeed the solution of Volterra equation (1).

Thus we have:

THEOREM. *A Volterra equation of the second kind*

$$\varphi(x) = f(x) + \lambda \int_a^x N(x, y)\varphi(y)\,dy$$

has one and only one bounded solution, given by the formula

$$\varphi(x) = f(x) + \lambda \int_a^x \mathfrak{R}(x, y, \lambda) f(y)\,dy,$$

where the resolvent kernel $\mathfrak{R}$ *is the sum of the series*

$$\mathfrak{R}(x, y, \lambda) = N(x, y) + \sum_{n=1}^{\infty} \lambda^n N_n(x, y)$$

convergent for all values of λ. *It is assumed that the function* $f(x)$ *is integrable in the interval* $[a, b]$, *and the function* $N(x, y)$ *is integrable in the triangle*

$$a \leqq x \leqq b, \quad a \leqq y \leqq x.$$

The method previously set forth may be applied analogously to the case of an unknown function of several variables and therefore, for example, to an equation of the form

$$\varphi(x, y) = f(x, y) + \lambda \int_a^x \int_a^y N(x, y; s, t)\varphi(s, t)\,ds\,dt,$$

where f and N are the given functions and $\varphi(x, y)$ is the unknown function.

§ 2. Volterra's equation of the first kind

A *Volterra equation of the first kind* is an equation of the form

$$\int_a^x N(x, y)\varphi(y)\,dy = f(x), \tag{15}$$

in which the unknown function φ appears only under the integral sign. The kernel $N(x, y)$ and the function $f(x)$ are given functions, defined and continuous in the domain

$$a \leqq x \leqq b, \quad 0 \leqq y \leqq x. \tag{16}$$

Let us assume that the functions $f(x)$ and $N(x, y)$ have continuous derivatives with respect to the variable x in the interval (16); moreover, we have to assume that the given function $f(x)$ satisfies the condition

$$f(a) = 0. \tag{17}$$

It is now easy to reduce equation (15) to a Volterra equation of the second kind. If we differentiate both sides of equation (15) with respect to x, then from the theorem on differentiating an integral as a function of a parameter, it follows that the function $\varphi(y)$ satisfying equation (15) also satisfies the following equation:

$$N(x, x)\varphi(x) + \int_a^x N'_x(x, y)\varphi(y)\,dy = f'(x). \tag{18}$$

Conversely, owing to assumption (17) we may assert that the function $\varphi(x)$ satisfying equation (18) also satisfies equation (15). If we assume that $N(x, x) \neq 0$ in the interval (a, b), then by dividing both members of equation (18) by $N(x, x)$ we reduce it to the equation investigated in the preceding section, and obtain a solution in the form (12).

If $N(x, x) = 0$ in the interval (a, b), then equation (18) would again be of the first kind, and assuming the existence of the second derivatives of the kernel we could reduce it to a Volterra equation of the second kind by differentiating both sides twice.

§ 3. Volterra's singular equation

We call a Volterra equation *singular* if the kernel $N(x, y)$ of that equation is unbounded. We shall solve a Volterra singular equation of the first kind having the form:

$$\int_a^x \frac{K(x, y)}{(x-y)^\alpha}\varphi(y)\,dy = f(x), \tag{19}$$

where the exponent α is a positive number less than one,

$$0 < \alpha < 1,$$

and $K(x, y)$ is a given function, bounded and integrable in the triangle (16), where $K(x, x) \neq 0$. We point out that the assumption $f(a) = 0$ is no longer required.

We solve equation (19) by reducing it to an equation of the first kind with a bounded kernel. We do this by multiplying both sides of equation (19) by the function

$$\frac{1}{(z-x)^{1-\alpha}}$$

and integrating with respect to x from a to z we obtain the equation

$$\int_a^z \frac{1}{(z-x)^{1-\alpha}} \left[\int_a^x \frac{K(x, y)}{(x-y)^\alpha} \varphi(y) \, dy \right] dx = \int_a^z \frac{f(x) \, dx}{(z-x)^{1-\alpha}}, \tag{20}$$

or, upon application of the Dirichlet transformation the equation

$$\int_a^z \left[\int_y^z \frac{K(x, y) \, dx}{(z-x)^{1-\alpha}(x-y)^\alpha} \right] \varphi(y) \, dy = f_1(z). \tag{21}$$

This is already a Volterra equation of the first kind with a bounded kernel

$$N(z, y) = \int_y^z \frac{K(x, y) \, dx}{(z-x)^{1-\alpha}(x-y)^\alpha}, \tag{22}$$

where the known function $f_1(z)$ is

$$f_1(z) = \int_a^z \frac{f(x) \, dx}{(z-x)^{1-\alpha}}. \tag{23}$$

The solution φ of the given equation (19) obviously satisfies the transformed equation (21). We shall now show that the converse is also true: the solution of equation (21) satisfies the given equation (19).

We solve equation (21) according to the method indicated in the preceding section. To do this we assume that the functions $K(x, y)$ and $f(x)$ have continuous derivatives with respect to x, and with these assumptions we shall first show that the functions $N(z, y)$ and $f(z)$ have derivatives continuous with respect to the variable z. Since the theorem on differentiating under the integral sign cannot be directly applied to the improper integral (22), we carry out a substitution of the variable of integration

$$x = y+(z-y)t.$$

By reducing the limits of integration (y, z) with respect to the variable x to the limits of integration (0,1) with respect to the variable t, we obtain

$$N(z, y) = \int_0^1 \frac{K[y+(z-y)t, y]\,dt}{(1-t)^{1-\alpha}t^{\alpha}}. \tag{24}$$

Hence the existence of the continuous derivative $N_z'(z, y)$ is evident.

In order to prove the existence of the derivative of function (23), we transform that integral by the method of integration by parts, whence we obtain

$$f_1(z) = -\int_a^z f(x)\,d\left[\frac{1}{\alpha}(z-x)^{\alpha}\right]$$

$$= \left[-\frac{1}{\alpha}(z-x)^{\alpha}f(x)\right]_a^z + \frac{1}{\alpha}\int_a^z (z-x)^{\alpha}f'(x)\,dx$$

$$= \frac{1}{\alpha}(z-a)^{\alpha}f(a) + \frac{1}{\alpha}\int_a^z (z-x)^{\alpha}f'(x)\,dx.$$

This implies the following expression for the derivative of function (23):

$$f_1'(z) = \frac{f(a)}{(z-a)^{1-\alpha}} + \int_a^z \frac{f'(x)\,dx}{(z-x)^{1-\alpha}}. \tag{25}$$

By differentiating both sides we may then reduce equation (21) to a Volterra equation of the second kind

$$N(z,z)\varphi(z) + \int_a^z N_z'(z,y)\varphi(y)\,dy = f_1'(z), \tag{26}$$

where, in accordance with formula (24) and the known formula for Euler's integral (the *Beta* function) $B(\alpha, \beta)$, when $\beta = 1-\alpha$, we have

$$N(z,z) = \lim_{y \to z} N(z,y)$$

$$= K(z,z)\int_0^1 \frac{dt}{(1-t)^{1-\alpha}t^{\alpha}} = K(z,z)\frac{\pi}{\sin \alpha\pi}. \tag{27}$$

The solution of equation (26) also satisfies equations (21) and (20), since $f(a) = 0$.

It still remains to show that the solution of equation (20) satisfies the given equation (19). Now, denoting by $h(x)$ the difference between the left-hand and the right-hand sides of equation (19), in which φ is the solution of equation (20), we have

$$\int_a^z \frac{h(x)\,dx}{(z-x)^{1-\alpha}} = 0. \tag{28}$$

To determine $h(x)$, note that equation (28) implies the equation

$$\int_a^y \frac{1}{(y-z)^{\alpha}}\left[\int_a^z \frac{h(x)\,dx}{(z-x)^{1-\alpha}}\right]dz = 0,$$

and hence the equation

$$\int_a^y \left[\int_x^y \frac{dz}{(y-z)^\alpha (z-x)^{1-\alpha}} \right] h(x)\, dx = 0;$$

however, since

$$\int_x^y \frac{dz}{(y-z)^\alpha (z-x)^{1-\alpha}} = \int_0^1 \frac{dt}{t^{1-\alpha}(1-t)^\alpha} = \frac{\pi}{\sin \alpha\pi},$$

it follows that for every y in the interval (a, b)

$$\int_a^y h(x)\, dx = 0 \quad \text{and} \quad h(x) = 0 .$$

The solution φ of equation (20) is thus the only solution of equation (19).

§ 4. Abel's integral equation

The Abel integral equation

$$\int_0^x \frac{\varphi(y)\, dy}{(x-y)^\alpha} = f(x) \tag{29}$$

is a particular case of the integral equation (19) when $K \equiv 1$.

This equation may be solved explicitly in the following way: when $K \equiv 1$ the kernel of the transformed equation (21) has the constant value

$$\int_y^z \frac{dx}{(z-x)^{1-\alpha}(x-y)^\alpha} = \int_0^1 \frac{dt}{(1-t)^{1-\alpha} t^\alpha} = \frac{\pi}{\sin \alpha\pi}$$

and the equation takes the simple form

$$\frac{\pi}{\sin \alpha\pi} \int_0^z \varphi(y)\, dy = f_1(z) .$$

Hence it follows that the solution of equation (29) can be written in the form

$$\varphi(z) = \frac{\sin \alpha\pi}{\pi} f_1'(z) = \frac{\sin \alpha\pi}{\pi} \left[\frac{f(0)}{z^{1-\alpha}} + \int_0^z \frac{f'(x)\,dx}{(z-x)^{1-\alpha}} \right]. \tag{30}$$

The following problem in mechanics can be reduced to the solution of Abel's integral equation; the problem consists in finding a line in the vertical plane such that the time T taken by a material point to slide along that line (without initial velocity) from the level $z = h$ to the level $z = 0$ be a predetermined function of the altitude h:

$$T = f(h).$$

We assume that the axis Oz is directed vertically upward, and that the axis Ox is horizontal. Now, from the theorem on work, † we have for every t

$$\frac{1}{2} m \left(\frac{dl}{dt} \right)^2 = mg(h-z),$$

where l is the length of the arc traversed from the initial moment to the moment t. Hence

$$T = \int_0^h \frac{dl}{\sqrt{2g(h-z)}}.$$

Taking

$$\frac{dl}{dz} = \varphi(z)$$

as the unknown function, we obtain the integral equation

$$\int_0^h \frac{\varphi(z)\,dz}{\sqrt{2g(h-z)}} = f(h), \tag{32}$$

which is a special case of the Abel integral equation (29) with $\alpha = 1/2$. According to (30) the solution of equation (32) has the form

$$\varphi(z) = \sqrt{2g}\,\frac{f(0)}{\pi\sqrt{z}} + \frac{\sqrt{2g}}{\pi}\int_0^z \frac{f'(s)\,ds}{\sqrt{z-s}}\,. \tag{33}$$

Hence we see that, if $f(0) \neq 0$, then $\varphi(z) \to \infty$ as $z \to 0$. This means that the line approaches the final level $z = 0$ tangentially. Having found function (33) we obtain the equation for the trajectory from the differential equation (31), namely

$$\sqrt{1+\left(\frac{dx}{dz}\right)^2} = \varphi(z),$$

whence

$$x+C = \int_0^z \sqrt{\varphi^2(u)-1}\,du\,. \tag{34}$$

As an example, let us find such a trajectory of a point that the time T be a constant:

$$T = f(h) = \text{const.}$$

Then from formula (33) we have

$$\varphi(z) = \sqrt{2g}\,\frac{T}{\pi\sqrt{z}}$$

and

$$x+C = \int_0^z \sqrt{\frac{2g\,T^2}{\pi^2 u} - 1}\,du\,. \tag{35}$$

The line obtained is a *cycloid*, tangential to the horizontal axis Ox at its lowest point $z = 0$. The time of motion along the cycloid, and only along that line, is independent of the deflection. This is a well-known property of the cycloid, called a *tautochrone*.*

---

* Tautochrone—from the Greek ταυτωχρόνω = in the same time.

CHAPTER II

FREDHOLM'S INTEGRAL EQUATION OF THE SECOND KIND

§ 1. General considerations

A *Fredholm integral equation of the second kind* is an equation of the form

$$\varphi(x)=f(x)+\lambda\int_{\Omega} N(x,y)\,\varphi(y)\,dy, \tag{1}$$

where $f(x)$ is a given function, defined at every point x of the bounded set Ω, $N(x, y)$ is a given function, defined for every pair of points x and y of the set Ω, and $\varphi(x)$ is an unknown function in the set Ω.

The set Ω may be a bounded interval or the sum of a finite number of such intervals having no common points. More generally: Ω may be a multidimensional domain or the sum of a finite number of such domains having no points in common. In the latter case x and y are variable points of the domain Ω, and dy is a volume element. Finally, Ω may be a bounded surface, and then dy is an element of area.

Just as for the Volterra equation, we call the given function $N(x, y)$ the *kernel* of the Fredholm equation.

We assume that the function $f(x)$ is Riemann-integrable in the set Ω. We further assume that the function $N(x, y)$ is bounded and that the Riemann integrals

$$\int_{\Omega} N(x,y)\,dy \quad \text{and} \quad \int_{\Omega} N(x,y)\,dx$$

exist, the first for every fixed value of x in the set Ω, the second for every fixed value of y in the set Ω. Without essential changes in the subsequent argument it is also possible to assume the Lebesgue integrability of the above functions (summability).

The coefficient λ in equation (1) is a parameter. We introduce it because of its primary rôle in the solution of the equation.

A *Fredholm equation of the first kind* is an equation of the form

$$\int_{\Omega} N(x, y)\,\varphi(y)\,dy = f(x), \tag{2}$$

where the unknown function appears only under the integral sign.

The theory of this equation will be given later, as it is more difficult, and is partly based on the theory of the equation of the second kind.

In order to solve equation (1) we shall first apply the method of expansion in powers of the parameter λ, analogous to the method of solution of the Volterra equation presented in Chapter I, § 1.

Note then that, if the integrable function $\varphi(x)$ satisfies the integral equation (1), then it also satisfies the equation obtained by substituting the expression

$$\varphi(y) = f(y) + \lambda \int_{\Omega} N(y, s)\,\varphi(s)\,ds$$

for $\varphi(y)$ under the integral sign. Such an equation has the form

$$\varphi(x) = f(x) + \lambda \int_{\Omega} N(x, y)\Big[f(y) + \lambda \int_{\Omega} N(y, s)\,\varphi(s)\,ds\Big]\,dy. \tag{3}$$

From the assumed property of the kernel $N(x, y)$ it follows that the function

$$N(x, y)\,N(y, s)\,\varphi(s)$$

is bounded and Riemann-integrable with respect to s for fixed points x and y in the set Ω and Riemann-integrable with respect to y for fixed points x and s in the set Ω. Hence, in view of the property of iterated Riemann integrals (see footnote on p. 7), the iterated integrals

$$\int_{\Omega}\Big[\int_{\Omega} N(x, y)\,N(y, s)\,\varphi(s)\,ds\Big]\,dy = \int_{\Omega}\Big[\int_{\Omega} N(x, y)\,N(y, s)\,dy\Big]\,\varphi(s)\,ds$$

exist and are equal, where φ is an arbitrary function integrable in the set Ω. In view of the above, we may write down equation

(3) in the equivalent form

$$\varphi(x) = f(x) + \lambda \int_{\Omega} N(x, y) f(y)\, dy +$$
$$+ \lambda^2 \int_{\Omega} \Big[\int_{\Omega} N(x, y) N(y, s)\, dy \Big] \varphi(s)\, ds \qquad (3')$$

and finally

$$\varphi(x) = f(x) + \lambda \int_{\Omega} N(x, y) f(y)\, dy + \lambda^2 \int_{\Omega} N_2(x, y) \varphi(y)\, dy, \qquad (3'')$$

where

$$N_2(x, y) = \int_{\Omega} N(x, s) N(s, y)\, ds. \qquad (4)$$

We call function (4) an *iterated kernel* of the kernel $N(x, y)$. Since the function $N(x, s)\, N(s, y)$ is integrable with respect to x for fixed points s and y, and integrable with respect to y for fixed points s and x, the iterated kernel $N_2(x, y)$ is Riemann-integrable with respect to x for a fixed point y and Riemann-integrable with respect to y for a fixed point x.

By repeating the above transformations we may establish that the function $\varphi(x)$ satisfying equation (1) also satisfies the equation

$$\varphi(x) = f(x) + \lambda \int_{\Omega} N(x, y) f(y)\, dy +$$
$$+ \lambda^2 \int_{\Omega} N_2(x, y) f(y)\, dy + \lambda^3 \int_{\Omega} N_3(x, y) \varphi(y)\, dy. \qquad (5)$$

The function

$$N_3(x, y) = \int_{\Omega} N_2(x, s) N(s, y)\, ds \qquad (6)$$

is called a *two-fold iterated kernel* of the kernel $N(x, y)$.

By repeating the above transformation n times, we find that the function $\varphi(x)$ satisfying the integral equation (1) also satisfies the *n-fold iterated equation*

$$\varphi(x) = f(x) + \lambda \int_{\Omega} N(x, y) f(y)\, dy + \lambda^2 \int_{\Omega} N_1(x, y) f(y)\, dy + \ldots +$$
$$+ \lambda^n \int_{\Omega} N_n(x, y) f(y)\, dy + \lambda^{n+1} \int_{\Omega} N_{n+1}(x, y) \varphi(y)\, dy. \qquad (7)$$

The *n-fold iterated kernel* $N_{n+1}(x, y)$ is defined by the recursive formula

$$N_{n+1}(x, y) = \int_{\Omega} N_n(x, s) N(s, y) ds, \tag{8}$$

holding for $n = 1, 2, 3, \ldots$, if we assume that $N_1 = N$. Repeating the above argument we conclude by induction that each iterated kernel $N_n(x, y)$ is Riemann-integrable with respect to the variable y for a fixed point x.

If M is the upper bound of the absolute value of the function $N(x, y)$ in the domain Ω, i.e.

$$|N(x, y)| \leqq M,$$

then from equality (8) we have

$$|N_{n+1}(x, y)| \leqq M^{n+1} V^n, \tag{9}$$

where V denotes the volume of the domain Ω (more generally: the measure of the set Ω). Thus if m is the greater of the upper bounds of the functions $|f(x)|$ and $|\varphi(x)|$ in the domain Ω, then the two last integrals of the sum (7) satisfy the inequalities

$$|\lambda^n \int_{\Omega} N_n(x, y) f(y) dy| \leqq |\lambda M V|^n m. \tag{10}$$

Hence, and on the basis of equality (7), with the assumption that $n \to \infty$, we conclude that if there exists a solution $\varphi(x)$ of the integral equation (1), and moreover, the inequality

$$|\lambda M V| < 1 \tag{11}$$

is satisfied, then the integrable solution $\varphi(x)$ is unique and is equal to the sum of the absolutely and uniformly convergent series

$$\varphi(x) = f(x) + \sum_{n=1}^{\infty} \lambda^n \int_{\Omega} N_n(x, y) f(y) dy, \tag{12}$$

where

$$N_1 = N.$$

We may write this solution in the form

$$\varphi(x) = f(x) + \lambda \int_{\Omega} \mathfrak{N}(x, y, \lambda) f(y)\, dy, \tag{13}$$

where the function $\mathfrak{N}$ is the sum of a series convergent absolutely and uniformly, provided that λ satisfies condition (11), namely

$$\mathfrak{N}(x, y, \lambda) = \sum_{n=1}^{\infty} \lambda^{n-1} N_n(x, y). \tag{14}$$

We call the function (14), dependent only on N, the *resolvent kernel* of equation (1).

It now has to be shown that the function defined by formula (13) is indeed a solution of Fredholm integral equation (1). To this end let us note that, according to the recursive relation (8), we have

$$N_{n+1}(x, y) = \underbrace{\int_{\Omega}\int_{\Omega} \ldots \int_{\Omega}}_{(n\ \text{times})} N(x, s_1) N(s_1, s_2) \ldots$$

$$\ldots N(s_n, y)\, ds_1\, ds_2 \ldots ds_n = \int_{\Omega} N(x, s) N_n(s, y)\, ds$$

and, in general,

$$N_{n+p}(x, y) = \int_{\Omega} N_n(x, s) N_p(s, y)\, ds \tag{15}$$

for every pair of integers n and p if we assume that $N_1 = N$. Hence, in view of (14), it follows that the resolvent kernel $\mathfrak{N}$ satisfies the integral equation

$$\mathfrak{N}(x, y, \lambda) = N(x, y) + \lambda \int_{\Omega} N(x, s) \mathfrak{N}(s, y, \lambda)\, ds \tag{16}$$

and the equation

$$\mathfrak{N}(x, y, \lambda) = N(x, y) + \lambda \int_{\Omega} \mathfrak{N}(x, s, \lambda) N(s, y)\, ds. \tag{17}$$

We shall now show that, conversely, if the resolvent kernel $\mathfrak{N}$ satisfies equation (16), then function (13) satisfies Fredholm equation (1). Substituting expression (13) for $\varphi(x)$ in equation (1) we obtain on the left-hand side

$$f(x) + \lambda \int_{\Omega} \mathfrak{N}(x, y, \lambda) f(y)\, dy,$$

and on the right

$$f(x)+\lambda\int_{\Omega} N(x, y)\left[f(y)+\lambda\int_{\Omega} \mathfrak{N}(y, s, \lambda) f(s)\, ds\right] dy$$

$$=f(x)+\lambda\int_{\Omega}\left[N(x, y)+\lambda\int_{\Omega} N(x, s)\,\mathfrak{N}(s, y, \lambda)\, ds\right] f(y)\, dy;$$

we obtain the last expression by transposing y and s in the second integral.

Taking equation (16) into account we see directly that the expression in the right-hand side reduces to the expression in the left-hand side and that function (13) is indeed the unique solution of equation (1) when the absolute value of the parameter λ is sufficiently small, namely satisfying inequality (11), or equivalently

$$|\lambda| < \frac{1}{MV}. \tag{18}$$

In the above argument we assumed that the functions appearing in the equation were Riemann-integrable. The above argument may be generalized by assuming Lebesgue-integrability. Then it is not essential that the functions appearing in the equation be bounded.

For, let us assume that the real function $f(x)$ is integrable together with its square in the domain Ω, i.e. that the integral (denoted by A)

$$\int_{\Omega}[f(x)]^2\, dx = A > 0 \tag{19}$$

exists. We further assume that the real kernel is integrable together with its square, i.e. that the integral

$$\int_{\Omega}\int_{\Omega} N^2(x, y)\, dx\, dy = B > 0 \tag{20}$$

exists. Moreover, we assume that the integral of the square of the kernel $N(x, y)$ with respect to the variable y is bounded; thus there exists a positive constant C such that the inequality

$$\int_{\Omega} N^2(x, y)\, dy \leq C \tag{21}$$

is satisfied for every point x of the domain Ω.

Basing ourselves on assumptions (19), (20), (21) we shall prove the absolute and uniform convergence of series (12) when the value of $|\lambda|$ is sufficiently small. In order to estimate the decrease of the iterated kernel $N(x, y)$ let us first consider the equality

$$N_n(x, y) = \int_\Omega N_{n-1}(x, s)\, N(s, y)\, ds,$$

which, on the basis of the Buniakovski–Schwarz inequality, * implies

$$N_n^2(x, y) \leqq \int_\Omega N_{n-1}^2(x, s)\, ds \cdot \int_\Omega N^2(s, y)\, ds. \tag{22}$$

Integrating both sides of this inequality with respect to y we obtain, in view of asumption (20), the inequality

$$\int_\Omega N_n^2(x, y)\, dy \leqq B \int_\Omega N_{n-1}^2(x, s)\, ds. \tag{23}$$

Now, if we denote by C_n the upper bound of the integral

$$\int_\Omega N_n^2(x, y)\, dy$$

in the domain Ω, then inequality (23) yields

$$C_n \leqq B C_{n-1}$$

for every positive integer n. Hence, on account of inequality (21), we obtain by induction

$$C_n \leqq B^{n-1} C \tag{24}$$

---

* If $f(x)$ and $\varphi(x)$ are two real functions, integrable together with their squares in the domain Ω, then we may write the inequality

$$\int_\Omega [f(x)+\lambda\varphi(x)]^2\, dx = \int_\Omega f^2(x)\, dx + 2\lambda \int_\Omega f(x)\varphi(x)\, dx + \lambda^2 \int_\Omega \varphi^2(x)\, dx \geqslant 0$$

for every real value λ. Hence it follows that

$$\left[\int_\Omega f(x)\varphi(x)\, dx\right]^2 \leqslant \int_\Omega f^2(x)\, dx \cdot \int_\Omega \varphi^2(x)\, dx.$$

This is just the *Buniakovski–Schwarz inequality*.

which is the estimate of the integral of the squared kernel for every n. On the basis of the Buniakovski–Schwarz inequality we obtain for the terms of series (12) the inequality

$$\Big[\int_\Omega N_n(x, y)f(y)\,dy\Big]^2 \leqq \int_\Omega N_n^2(x, y)\,dy \cdot \int_\Omega f^2(y)\,dy.$$

From inequality (24) and assumption (19) it follows that the terms of series (12) satisfy the following inequality for every n:

$$\Big|\lambda^n \int_\Omega N_n(x, y)f(y)\,dy\Big| \leqq |\lambda|^n(\sqrt{B})^{n-1}\sqrt{AC}. \qquad (25)$$

Series (12) without the term f converges absolutely and uniformly in the domain Ω if the parameter λ satisfies the inequality

$$|\lambda| < \frac{1}{\sqrt{B}}. \qquad (26)$$

An inequality analogous to (25) is satisfied also by the last integral in equality (7) when the function φ is integrable together with its square, and hence that integral tends to zero when $|\lambda| < 1/\sqrt{B}$. Hence we may now assert that if the solution $\varphi(x)$ of the given equation integrable together with its square exists, then it is the sum of series (12) under assumption (26).

Just as above, function (12) may be expressed in form (13), where the resolvent kernel $\mathfrak{N}$ is the sum of series (14). If we introduce the additional assumption of the boundedness of the integral

$$\int_\Omega N^2(s, y)\,ds \leqq D, \qquad (27)$$

then, on account of inequalities (22) and (24), we may write

$$N_n^2(x, y) \leqq B^{n-2}CD$$

and

$$|\lambda^{n-1}N_n(x, y)| \leqq |\lambda\sqrt{B}|^{n-2}|\lambda|\sqrt{CD} \quad (n > 1). \qquad (28)$$

Series (14) without the first term is indeed absolutely and uniformly convergent if

$$|\lambda| < \frac{1}{\sqrt{B}}.$$

The proof that function (13), for $|\lambda\sqrt{B}| < 1$, is the unique solution of equation (1), integrable together with its square, does not differ from the proof of the analogous theorem with the stronger assumptions (p. 26).

It is not difficult to generalize the above considerations to functions taking complex values. It is merely sufficient to replace everywhere the squares of the functions by the squares of their moduli.

§ 2. Fredholm's First Theorem

In the preceding section we obtained the solution of the Fredholm equation

$$\varphi(x) = f(x) + \lambda \int_{\Omega} N(x, y)\varphi(y)\,dy \tag{29}$$

as a power series in the parameter λ uniformly convergent for $|\lambda|$ sufficiently small.

The first person to give the solution of equation (29) in the general form for all values of the parameter λ was the Swedish mathematician IVAR FREDHOLM. The results of Fredholm's investigations, published at the beginning of the present century, are contained in three theorems, which are among the most important and beautiful mathematical discoveries.

The method used by Fredholm consisted in replacing the integral in the integral equation (29) by a sum, the reduction of this equation to a system of linear equations and letting the number of terms of the sum tend to infinity. This bold idea of Fredholm was crowned with success, since it led precisely to the discoveries which we shall give in his three theorems.

Fredholm's theory applies to every domain Ω, the number of its dimensions in no way complicates the argument.

To begin with, in order to fix our ideas, we shall consider the Fredholm equation

$$\varphi(x) = f(x) + \lambda \int_{a}^{b} N(x, y)\varphi(y)\,dy \tag{30}$$

with a Riemann integral in a given interval (a, b). In accordance with Fredholm's method we take the partition of the interval

(a, b) into n equal parts by the points

$$a, x_1, x_2, \ldots, x_{n-1}, x_n = b, \quad h = x_{\nu+1} - x_\nu = \frac{b-a}{n}$$

and replace equation (30) by the following equation:

$$\varphi(x) = f(x) + \lambda h \sum_{\nu=1}^{n} N(x, x_\nu)\varphi(x_\nu). \tag{31}$$

Requiring that this equation be satisfied at the n points of division $x_1, x_2, \ldots, x_n$, we obtain a set of n linear equations

$$\begin{aligned}
\varphi(x_1) &= f(x_1) + \lambda h \sum_{\nu=1}^{n} N(x_1, x_\nu)\varphi(x_\nu),\\
\varphi(x_2) &= f(x_2) + \lambda h \sum_{\nu=1}^{n} N(x_2, x_\nu)\varphi(x_\nu),\\
&\cdots\cdots\cdots\cdots\cdots\cdots\\
\varphi(x_n) &= f(x_n) + \lambda h \sum_{\nu=1}^{n} N(x_n, x_\nu)\varphi(x_\nu)
\end{aligned} \tag{32}$$

with n unknown values of the functions $\varphi(x_\nu)$. Letting

$$\varphi(x_\nu) = \varphi_\nu, \quad N(x_\mu, x_\nu) = N_{\mu\nu}$$

and transferring the expressions containing the series over to the left-hand side, we may write the system of equations (32) in the following form:

$$\begin{aligned}
&(1-\lambda h N_{11})\varphi_1 - \lambda h N_{12}\,\varphi_2 - \lambda h N_{13}\,\varphi_3 - \ldots\\
&\qquad\qquad \ldots - \lambda h N_{1n}\varphi_n = f(x_1),\\
&-\lambda h N_{21}\,\varphi_1 + (1-\lambda h N_{22})\varphi_2 - \lambda h N_{23}\,\varphi_3 - \ldots\\
&\qquad\qquad \ldots - \lambda h N_{2n}\varphi_n = f(x_2),\\
&-\lambda h N_{31}\,\varphi_1 - \lambda h N_{32}\,\varphi_2 + (1-\lambda h N_{33})\varphi_3 - \ldots\\
&\qquad\qquad \ldots - \lambda h N_{3n}\varphi_n = f(x_3),\\
&\cdots\cdots\cdots\cdots\cdots\cdots\cdots\cdots\\
&-\lambda h N_{n1}\,\varphi_1 - \lambda h N_{n2}\,\varphi_2 - \lambda h N_{n3}\,\varphi_3 - \ldots\\
&\qquad\qquad \ldots + (1-\lambda h N_{nn})\varphi_n = f(x_n).
\end{aligned} \tag{33}$$

The solutions $\varphi_1, \varphi_2, \ldots, \varphi_n$ of the above system of equations will be expressed in the form of ratios of certain determinants by the common characteristic determinant

$$D_n(\lambda) = \begin{vmatrix} 1-\lambda h N_{11} & -\lambda h N_{12} & -\lambda h N_{13} & \dots & -\lambda h N_{1n} \\ -\lambda h N_{21} & 1-\lambda h N_{22} & -\lambda h N_{23} & \dots & -\lambda h N_{2n} \\ -\lambda h N_{31} & -\lambda h N_{32} & 1-\lambda h N_{33} & \dots & -\lambda h N_{3n} \\ \dots & \dots & \dots & \dots & \dots \\ -\lambda h N_{n1} & -\lambda h N_{n2} & -\lambda h N_{n3} & \dots & 1-\lambda h N_{nn} \end{vmatrix}, \quad (34)$$

provided that this determinant is not equal to zero. Let us expand determinant (34) in powers of the factor $-\lambda h$. Now the first term not containing this factor is obviously equal to unity. The term containing $-\lambda h$ in the first power is the sum of all the determinants containing only one column with that factor, i.e. is the sum of determinants of the form

$$\begin{vmatrix} 1 & 0 & \dots & 0 & -\lambda h N_{1\nu} & 0 & \dots & 0 \\ 0 & 1 & \dots & 0 & -\lambda h N_{2\nu} & 0 & \dots & 0 \\ \dots & \dots & \dots & \dots & \dots & \dots & \dots & \dots \\ 0 & 0 & \dots & 0 & -\lambda h N_{\nu\nu} & 0 & \dots & 0 \\ \dots & \dots & \dots & \dots & \dots & \dots & \dots & \dots \\ 0 & 0 & \dots & 0 & -\lambda h N_{n\nu} & 0 & \dots & 1 \end{vmatrix} = -\lambda h N_{\nu\nu}, \quad (35)$$

where $\nu = 1, 2, 3, \dots, n$.

The factor containing the factor $-\lambda h$ to the second power is the sum of all the determinants containing two columns with that factor, i.e. is the sum of determinants of the form

$$\begin{vmatrix} 1 & 0 & \dots & -\lambda h N_{1p} & \dots & -\lambda h N_{1q} & \dots & 0 \\ 0 & 1 & \dots & -\lambda h N_{2p} & \dots & -\lambda h N_{2q} & \dots & 0 \\ \dots & \dots & \dots & \dots & \dots & \dots & \dots & \dots \\ 0 & 0 & \dots & -\lambda h N_{pp} & \dots & -\lambda h N_{pq} & \dots & 0 \\ \dots & \dots & \dots & \dots & \dots & \dots & \dots & \dots \\ 0 & 0 & \dots & -\lambda h N_{qp} & \dots & -\lambda h N_{qq} & \dots & 0 \\ \dots & \dots & \dots & \dots & \dots & \dots & \dots & \dots \\ 0 & 0 & \dots & -\lambda h N_{np} & \dots & -\lambda h N_{nq} & \dots & 1 \end{vmatrix}$$

$$= (-\lambda h)^2 \begin{vmatrix} N_{pp} & N_{pq} \\ N_{qp} & N_{qq} \end{vmatrix}, \quad (36)$$

where (p, q) is an arbitrary pair of integers taken from the sequence $1, 2, 3, \dots, n$ with $p < q$.

In the same way we conclude that the term containing the factor $-\lambda h$ to the third power is the sum of determinants of the form

$$(-\lambda h)^3 \begin{vmatrix} N_{pp} & N_{pq} & N_{pr} \\ N_{qp} & N_{qq} & N_{qr} \\ N_{rp} & N_{rq} & N_{rr} \end{vmatrix}, \tag{37}$$

where (p, q, r) is an arbitrary triple of integers selected from the sequence $1, 2, 3, \ldots, n$ with $p < q < r$. The remaining terms are obtained in a similar manner.

From the above considerations we conclude that the required expansion of determinant (34) may be expressed in the form

$$D_n(\lambda) = 1 - \lambda h \sum_{\nu=1}^{n} N_{\nu\nu} + \frac{(-\lambda h)^2}{2!} \sum_{p,q=1}^{n} \begin{vmatrix} N_{pp} & N_{pq} \\ N_{qp} & N_{qq} \end{vmatrix} +$$

$$+ \frac{(-\lambda h)^3}{3!} \sum_{p,q,r=1}^{n} \begin{vmatrix} N_{pp} & N_{pq} & N_{pr} \\ N_{qp} & N_{qq} & N_{qr} \\ N_{rp} & N_{rq} & N_{rr} \end{vmatrix} + \ldots +$$

$$+ \frac{(-\lambda h)^n}{n!} \sum_{p_1, p_2, \ldots, p_n=1}^{n} \begin{vmatrix} N_{p_1p_1} & N_{p_1p_2} & \ldots & N_{p_1p_n} \\ N_{p_2p_1} & N_{p_2p_2} & \ldots & N_{p_2p_n} \\ \cdot & \cdot & \cdot & \cdot \\ N_{p_np_1} & N_{p_np_2} & \ldots & N_{p_np_n} \end{vmatrix} \tag{38}$$

where it is agreed that the sums are taken over all the permutations of pairs (p, q), triples (p, q, r) and so on. This convention gives a basis for dividing each of the above sums by the number of permutations, i.e. by the numbers $2!, 3!, \ldots, n!$, respectively. Indeed, in determinants (36), (37) etc., the numbers (p, q), (p, q, r) etc., occurred in order of increasing size, whence in sums (38) the determinants are repeated $2!$ times, $3!$ times, $\ldots$, $n!$ times respectively and therefore the division of each of the sums by $2!, 3!, \ldots, n!$, respectively, yields the values of the terms of determinant (34) referred to in considering determinants (36), (37), and so on.

For the sake of simplicity Fredholm introduced the following symbol for a determinant formed from the values of the kernel:

$$\begin{vmatrix} N(x_1, y_1) & N(x_1, y_2) & \dots & N(x_1, y_n) \\ N(x_2, y_1) & N(x_2, y_2) & \dots & N(x_2, y_n) \\ \dots & \dots & \dots & \dots \\ N(x_n, y_1) & N(x_n, y_2) & \dots & N(x_n, y_n) \end{vmatrix} = N\begin{pmatrix} x_1, x_2, \dots, x_n \\ y_1, y_2, \dots, y_n \end{pmatrix}. \qquad (39)$$

This determinant is called *Fredholm's determinant*, and the above symbol is taken for every kernel $N(x, y)$ also in a multi-dimensional domain.

The fundamental property of Fredholm's determinant is that, *if any pair of arguments in the upper or the lower sequence is transposed, the value of the determinant changes the sign.*

Indeed, the transposition of two arguments in the upper sequence corresponds to the transposition of two rows of the determinant, and the transposition of two arguments in the lower sequence corresponds to the transposition of two columns.

Using the symbol (39) we may write the expansion of the determinant $D_n(\lambda)$ in the form

$$D_n(\lambda) = 1 - \lambda h \sum_{p=1}^{n} N(x_p, x_p) + \frac{(-\lambda h)^2}{2!} \sum_{p,q=1}^{n} N\begin{pmatrix} x_p, x_q \\ x_p, x_q \end{pmatrix} + \frac{(-\lambda h)^3}{3!} \sum_{p,q,r=1}^{n} N\begin{pmatrix} x_p, x_q, x_r \\ x_p, x_q, x_r \end{pmatrix} + \dots \qquad (40)$$

If we now suppose that $h \to 0$ and $n \to \infty$, then each of the terms of sum (40) tends to some single, double, triple integral, etc. Thus arises the series

$$D(\lambda) = 1 - \lambda \int_a^b N(s, s)\, ds + \frac{\lambda^2}{2!} \int_a^b \int_a^b N\begin{pmatrix} s_1, s_2 \\ s_1, s_2 \end{pmatrix} ds_1\, ds_2 - \frac{\lambda^3}{3!} \int_a^b \int_a^b \int_a^b N\begin{pmatrix} s_1, s_2, s_3 \\ s_1, s_2, s_3 \end{pmatrix} ds_1\, ds_2\, ds_3 + \dots, \qquad (41)$$

whose convergence for every value of λ was demonstrated by Fredholm on the basis of a certain theorem of Hadamard. In what follows we shall call the function $D(\lambda)$ *Fredholm's function* $D(\lambda)$.

It is possible to prove rigorously that the sum $D(\lambda)$ of the series (41) is the limit of the sequence $D_n(\lambda)$ as $n \to \infty$. Such a proof was given by HILBERT. We do not give it here as it is not required for the solution of the integral equation.

The solution of the system of equations (33) is expressed in the form of ratios of certain determinants by determinant (38), whence Fredholm supposed that the solutions $\varphi(x)$ of the integral equation (30) (which had been obtained before in the form of a series convergent for small $|\lambda|$) are to be sought for arbitrary λ in the form of a ratio of two power series in the parameter λ, where the divisor would be the series found in form (41). This supposition turned out to be correct and led to the beautiful discovery expressed in Fredholm's First Theorem.

Since Fredholm's reasoning applies to every domain Ω, we shall now return to Fredholm's equation (29) in an arbitrary domain and investigate the power series analogous to the series of form (41), namely

$$D(\lambda) = 1 + \sum_{p=1}^{\infty} \frac{(-\lambda)^p}{p!} \int\limits_{\Omega} \dots \int\limits_{\Omega} N\begin{pmatrix} s_1, s_2, \dots, s_p \\ s_1, s_2, \dots, s_p \end{pmatrix} ds_1\, ds_2 \dots ds_p. \tag{42}$$

We call it *Fredholm's first series*, retaining symbol (39) for the determinants under the integral sign and treating the expressions as iterated integrals formed of integrals in the domain Ω.

HADAMARD'S LEMMA. *If the elements of the determinant*

$$\Delta = \begin{vmatrix} a_{11} & a_{12} & \dots & a_{1n} \\ a_{21} & a_{22} & \dots & a_{2n} \\ \cdot & \cdot & \cdot & \cdot \\ a_{n1} & a_{n2} & \dots & a_{nn} \end{vmatrix} \tag{43}$$

are real and decreasing in such a way that sum of the squares of the elements of each row is constant,

$$a_{\nu 1}^2 + a_{\nu 2}^2 + a_{\nu 3}^2 + \dots + a_{\nu n}^2 = k_\nu \,(\text{const}) \qquad (\nu = 1, 2, 3, \dots, n), \tag{44}$$

then the determinant Δ on reaching an extremum becomes orthogonal.

Let us assume, in fact, that only the elements of the ν-th row change in such a way that the sum of their squares is constant. Expanding the determinant Δ in terms of the ν-th row, we then have

$$\Delta = D_{\nu 1} a_{\nu 1} + D_{\nu 2} a_{\nu 2} + \ldots + D_{\nu n} a_{\nu n} .$$

Writing the necessary condition for an extremum in the form of two equalities

$$D_{\nu 1} da_{\nu 1} + D_{\nu 2} da_{\nu 2} + \ldots + D_{\nu n} da_{\nu n} = 0 ,$$
$$a_{\nu 1} da_{\nu 1} + a_{\nu 2} da_{\nu 2} + \ldots + a_{\nu n} da_{\nu n} = 0 ,$$

we conclude that

$$\frac{a_{\nu 1}}{D_{\nu 1}} = \frac{a_{\nu 2}}{D_{\nu 2}} = \ldots = \frac{a_{\nu n}}{D_{\nu n}} .$$

For every determinant Δ we have

$$D_{\nu 1} a_{\mu 1} + D_{\nu 2} a_{\mu 2} + \ldots + D_{\nu n} a_{\mu n} = 0 ,$$

when $\nu \neq \mu$, and hence, if the determinant attains an extremum, then

$$a_{\nu 1} a_{\mu 1} + a_{\nu 2} a_{\mu 2} + \ldots + a_{\nu n} a_{\mu n} = 0 , \tag{45}$$

when $\nu \neq \mu$. We obtain an analogous result by interchanging the elements of every row. Hence it follows that if the determinant reaches a maximum then it is orthogonal.

The above result makes it possible to calculate the upper bound of the absolute value of the determinant Δ on assumption (44). For, according to the theorem on multiplication of determinants, the square of the determinant Δ is a determinant of the form

$$\Delta^2 = \begin{vmatrix} c_{11} & c_{12} & \ldots & c_{1n} \\ c_{21} & c_{22} & \ldots & c_{2n} \\ \cdot & \cdot & \cdot & \cdot \\ c_{n1} & c_{n2} & \ldots & c_{nn} \end{vmatrix} ,$$

where

$$c_{\mu\nu} = \sum_{i=1}^{n} a_{\mu i} a_{\nu i}.$$

If the maximum absolute value of the determinant Δ is $|\Delta_0|$, which on assumption (44) is attained, then

$$\Delta_0^2 = \begin{vmatrix} k_1 & 0 & \dots & 0 \\ 0 & k_2 & \dots & 0 \\ \cdot & \cdot & \cdot & \cdot \\ 0 & 0 & \dots & k_n \end{vmatrix} = k_1 k_2 \dots k_n,$$

in accordance with result (45). We thus have for the absolute value of the determinant the inequality

$$|\Delta|^2 \leqq \prod_{\nu=1}^{n} (a_{\nu 1}^2 + a_{\nu 2}^2 + \dots + a_{\nu n}^2), \tag{46}$$

given by HADAMARD.

The above theorem has a simple geometric interpretation. Namely, if the elements of the same rows

$$a_{\nu 1}, a_{\nu 2}, \dots, a_{\nu n}$$

are treated as rectangular components of n vectors with squared lengths $k_1, k_2, \dots, k_n$ in an n-dimensional space, then in accordance with Hadamard's lemma the volume of the n-dimensional parallelepiped constructed on these vectors is greatest when the vectors are mutually perpendicular.

If M is the upper bound of the absolute values of all the elements of a determinant (43), i.e. if we have

$$|a_{ik}| \leqq M,$$

then on the basis of inequality (46) the absolute value of the determinant Δ satisfies the inequality

$$|\Delta| \leqq n^{n/2} M^n. \tag{47}$$

This estimate is better than the estimate

$$|\Delta| \leqq n! M^n,$$

which follows from the fact that the determinant is the sum of $n!$ products each of which has an absolute value not greater than M^n.

Hadamard's lemma may be generalized to a determinant with complex elements by replacing the squares of the elements by the squares of their moduli. Thus, suppose we are given a determinant of the n-th order

$$\Delta = \begin{vmatrix} a_{11} & a_{12} & \dots & a_{1n} \\ a_{21} & a_{22} & \dots & a_{2n} \\ \cdot & \cdot & \cdot & \cdot \\ a_{n1} & a_{n2} & \dots & a_{nn} \end{vmatrix}$$

with complex elements of the form

$$a_{\alpha\beta} = a'_{\alpha\beta} + i a''_{\alpha\beta}.$$

Let us determine the maximum of $|\Delta|^2$ as a function of the real variables $a'_{\alpha\beta}$, $a''_{\alpha\beta}$ under the assumption that the sum of the squares of the moduli of the elements of each row is constant:

$$\sum_{\beta=1}^{n} |a_{\alpha\beta}|^2 = \sum_{\beta=1}^{n} (a'^2_{\alpha\beta} + a''^2_{\alpha\beta}) = k_\alpha \qquad (\alpha = 1, 2, 3, \dots, n),$$

where $k_1, k_2, \dots, k_n$ are positive constants. This maximum obviously exists. Note that the square of the modulus of the determinant $|\Delta|^2$ is equal to the product of the determinant Δ by its complex conjugate $\bar{\Delta}$,

$$|\Delta|^2 = \Delta\bar{\Delta},$$

and the conjugate value $\bar{\Delta}$ is equal to the determinant of the conjugate elements

$$\bar{a}_{\alpha\beta} = a'_{\alpha\beta} - i a''_{\alpha\beta},$$

i.e.

$$\bar{\Delta} = \begin{vmatrix} \bar{a}_{11} & \bar{a}_{12} & \dots & \bar{a}_{1n} \\ \bar{a}_{21} & \bar{a}_{22} & \dots & \bar{a}_{2n} \\ \cdot & \cdot & \cdot & \cdot \\ \bar{a}_{n1} & \bar{a}_{n2} & \dots & \bar{a}_{nn} \end{vmatrix}.$$

Applying the theorem on multiplication of determinants, we thus have

$$|\Delta|^2 = \Delta\bar{\Delta} = \begin{vmatrix} b_{11} & b_{12} & \dots & b_{1n} \\ b_{21} & b_{22} & \dots & b_{2n} \\ \dots & \dots & \dots & \dots \\ b_{n1} & b_{n2} & \dots & b_{nn} \end{vmatrix},$$

where

$$b_{\alpha\beta} = \sum_{\nu=1}^{n} a_{\alpha\nu}\,\bar{a}_{\beta\nu}\,.$$

To determine the maximum of the function $|\Delta|^2$ under the assumption that the sums

$$\sum_{\beta=1}^{n} |a_{\alpha\beta}|^2 = k_\alpha \qquad (\alpha = 1, 2, \dots, n)$$

are constant, we apply the method of Lagrange multipliers. In other words, we find the condition for an extremum of the auxiliary function

$$\Phi = \Delta\bar{\Delta} + \lambda_1 \sum_{\nu=1}^{n} |a_{1\nu}|^2 + \lambda_2 \sum_{\nu=1}^{n} |a_{2\nu}|^2 + \dots + \lambda_n \sum_{\nu=1}^{n} |a_{n\nu}|^2,$$

where $\lambda_1, \lambda_3, \dots, \lambda_n$ are constants which will be determined from the conditions of the problem. Now the condition for an extremum is expressed by the equalities

$$\left.\begin{aligned} \frac{\partial\Phi}{\partial a'_{\alpha\nu}} &= \bar{\Delta}\frac{\partial\Delta}{\partial a'_{\alpha\nu}} + \Delta\frac{\partial\bar{\Delta}}{\partial a'_{\alpha\nu}} + 2\lambda_\alpha a'_{\alpha\nu} = 0, \\ \frac{\partial\Phi}{\partial a''_{\alpha\nu}} &= \bar{\Delta}\frac{\partial\Delta}{\partial a''_{\alpha\nu}} + \Delta\frac{\partial\bar{\Delta}}{\partial a''_{\alpha\nu}} + 2\lambda_\alpha a''_{\alpha\nu} = 0, \end{aligned}\right\} \quad (\alpha, \nu = 1, 2, \dots, n). \quad (45)$$

However, since

$$\Delta = \sum_{\beta=1}^{n} a_{\alpha\beta}\,\Delta_{\alpha\beta}, \qquad \bar{\Delta} = \sum_{\beta=1}^{n} \bar{a}_{\alpha\beta}\,\bar{\Delta}_{\alpha\beta}$$

where $\Delta_{\alpha\beta}$ is the cofactor of the element $a_{\alpha\beta}$, we have

$$\frac{\partial\Phi}{\partial a'_{\alpha\nu}} = \bar{\Delta}\Delta_{\alpha\nu} + \Delta\bar{\Delta}_{\alpha\nu} + 2\lambda_\alpha a'_{\alpha\nu} = 0,$$

$$\frac{\partial\Phi}{\partial a''_{\alpha\nu}} = i\bar{\Delta}\Delta_{\alpha\nu} - i\Delta\bar{\Delta}_{\alpha\nu} + 2\lambda_\alpha a''_{\alpha\nu} = 0.$$

Hence we obtain the equalities

$$\Delta\bar{\Delta}_{\alpha\nu} + \lambda_\alpha a_{\alpha\nu} = 0 \quad (\alpha, \nu = 1, 2, \ldots, n),$$

which are satisfied in the case of a maximum of $|\Delta|^2$. Multiplying both sides of these equalities by $\bar{a}_{\beta\nu}$ and summing over ν, we have

$$\Delta \cdot \sum_{\nu=1}^{n} \bar{a}_{\beta\nu}\bar{\Delta}_{\alpha\nu} + \lambda_\alpha \sum_{\nu=1}^{n} a_{\alpha\nu}\bar{a}_{\beta\nu} = 0.$$

But

$$\sum_{\nu=1}^{n} \bar{a}_{\beta\nu}\bar{\Delta}_{\alpha\nu} = 0 \quad (\alpha \neq \beta),$$

and

$$\sum_{\nu=1}^{n} \bar{a}_{\alpha\nu}\bar{\Delta}_{\alpha\nu} = \bar{\Delta},$$

whence

$$\lambda_\alpha b_{\alpha\beta} = 0, \quad \text{when} \quad \alpha \neq \beta,$$

$$\Delta\bar{\Delta} + \lambda_\alpha b_{\alpha\alpha} = 0.$$

But

$$b_{\alpha\alpha} = k_\alpha > 0, \quad \max \Delta\bar{\Delta} > 0,$$

whence $\lambda_\alpha \neq 0$, and in the case of a maximum we have

$$b_{\alpha\beta} = 0 \quad (\alpha \neq \beta).$$

Finally we obtain

$$\max |\Delta|^2 = k_1 k_2 \ldots k_n,$$

or, explicitly

$$|\Delta|^2 \leq \prod_{\alpha=1}^{n} \sum_{\beta=1}^{n} |a_{\alpha\beta}|^2,$$

which is just the content of Hadamard's lemma for a determinant with complex elements.

CONCLUSION. *Fredholm's first series* (42) *converges for all values of the parameter* λ *provided that the kernel* $N(x, y)$ *is bounded and integrable.*

Indeed, if M is the upper bound of the modulus of kerne $N(x, y)$,

$$|N(x, y)| \leqq M,$$

then according to Hadamard's estimate (47) we have

$$\left| N\begin{pmatrix} s_1, s_2, \dots, s_p \\ s_1, s_2, \dots, s_p \end{pmatrix} \right| \leqq p^{p/2} M^p.$$

Hence the absolute values of the terms of the series (42) decrease faster than the terms of the series

$$\sum_{p=1}^{\infty} \frac{|\lambda|^p}{p!} p^{p/2} (MV)^p, \tag{48}$$

where V denotes the volume of the domain Ω. In accordance with D'Alembert's criterion let us consider the ratio of two consecutive terms of series (48):

$$\frac{\dfrac{|\lambda|^{p+1}}{(p+1)!} (p+1)^{(p+1)/2} (MV)^{p+1}}{\dfrac{|\lambda|^p}{p!} p^{p/2} (MV)^p} = \frac{|\lambda| MV}{\sqrt{p+1}} \sqrt{\left(1+\frac{1}{p}\right)^p}. \tag{49}$$

Since

$$\lim_{p\to\infty} \left(1+\frac{1}{p}\right)^p = e,$$

ratio (49) tends to zero as $p \to \infty$. Hence series (48) and consequently, also Fredholm's series (42) are convergent for all values of λ. Hadamard's estimate and the above conclusion hold also for the kernel $N(x, y)$ with complex values if M denotes the upper bound of the modulus of the kernel in the domain Ω.

Hence the sum $D(\lambda)$ of Fredholm's series is defined by this series in the entire plane of the complex variable λ, and is therefore an *entire function of the parameter* λ.

We shall now proceed to determine the solution of the *Fredholm equation of the second kind*

$$\varphi(x) = f(x) + \lambda \int_{\Omega} N(x, y)\varphi(y)\,dy. \tag{50}$$

We have already mentioned that we seek the solutions in the form of a quotient of the sums of two power series in the parameter λ, where the series $D(\lambda)$ just investigated is to be the divisor. In view of solution (13) on p. 25 for small λ we seek solutions of the form

$$\varphi(x) = f(x) + \lambda \int_{\Omega} \mathfrak{R}(x, y, \lambda) f(y)\,dy, \tag{51}$$

and the function $\mathfrak{R}(x, y, \lambda)$, called the *resolvent kernel*, is to be the product

$$\mathfrak{R}(x, y, \lambda) = \frac{D(x, y, \lambda)}{D(\lambda)}, \tag{52}$$

where $D(\lambda)$ is the sum of Fredholm's first series (42) assumed to be different from zero, while $D(x, y, \lambda)$ is the sum of certain functional series to be determined.

On p. 25 we have already shown that expression (51) is a solution of the integral equation (50) if the resolvent kernel $\mathfrak{R}$ satisfies the equation

$$\mathfrak{R}(x, y, \lambda) = N(x, y) + \lambda \int_{\Omega} N(x, s)\mathfrak{R}(s, y, \lambda)\,ds. \tag{53}$$

We emphasize that — as follows from the proof — this property holds for every function $\mathfrak{R}$ satisfying equation (53), and not only for a particular form of kernel (14) on p. 25. In view of form (52) of the resolvent kernel the numerator $D(x, y, \lambda)$ should satisfy the integral equation

$$D(x, y, \lambda) = N(x, y)D(\lambda) + \lambda \int_{\Omega} N(x, s) D(s, y, \lambda)\,ds. \tag{54}$$

We seek the solution of that equation in the form of a power series in the parameter λ,

$$D(x, y, \lambda) = C_0(x, y) + \sum_{p=1}^{\infty} \frac{(-\lambda)^p}{p!} C_p(x, y), \tag{55}$$

knowing that $D(\lambda)$ is the sum of the numerical series

$$D(\lambda) = 1 + \sum_{p=1}^{\infty} \frac{(-\lambda)^p}{p!} c_p, \tag{56}$$

where

$$c_p = \int_\Omega \cdots \int_\Omega N\begin{pmatrix} s_1, s_2, \ldots, s_p \\ s_1, s_2, \ldots, s_p \end{pmatrix} ds_1 \ldots ds_p. \tag{57}$$

Substituting $\lambda = 0$ in formula (54) we see that

$$D(x, y, 0) = N(x, y),$$

and hence

$$C_0(x, y) = N(x, y).$$

To determine the further coefficients $C_p(x, y)$, note that by comparing the coefficients of the same powers of the parameter λ on the left-hand and the right-hand sides of equality (54), we obtain the following recursive relation between the consecutive functions C_p and C_{p-1}:

$$C_p(x, y) = c_p N(x, y) - p \int_\Omega N(x, s) C_{p-1}(s, y) \, ds. \tag{58}$$

Hence we have

$$C_1(x, y) = c_1 N(x, y) - \int_\Omega N(x, s) C_0(s, y) \, ds$$

$$= N(x, y) \int_\Omega N(s, s) \, ds - \int_\Omega N(x, s) N(s, y) \, ds$$

$$= \int_\Omega N\begin{pmatrix} x, s \\ y, s \end{pmatrix} ds. \tag{59}$$

We shall prove that, in general,

$$C_p(x, y) = \int_\Omega \dots \int_\Omega N\begin{pmatrix} x, s_1, s_2, \dots, s_p \\ y, s_1, s_2, \dots, s_p \end{pmatrix} ds_1\, ds_2 \dots ds_p, \quad (60)$$

where $s_1, s_2, \dots, s_p$ are the variables of integration.

With this aim let us expand the determinant in (60) under the integral sign with respect to the elements of the first row, transposing in turn the first column one place to the right. Then we have

$$N\begin{pmatrix} x, s_1, s_2, \dots, s_p \\ y, s_1, s_2, \dots, s_p \end{pmatrix} = \begin{vmatrix} N(x, y) & N(x, s_1) & N(x, s_2) & \dots & N(x, s_p) \\ N(s_1, y) & N(s_1, s_1) & N(s_1, s_2) & \dots & N(s_1, s_p) \\ N(s_2, y) & N(s_2, s_1) & N(s_2, s_2) & \dots & N(s_2, s_p) \\ \dots & \dots & \dots & \dots & \dots \\ N(s_p, y) & N(s_p, s_1) & N(s_p, s_2) & \dots & N(s_p, s_p) \end{vmatrix}$$

$$= N(x, y) N\begin{pmatrix} s_1, s_2, \dots, s_p \\ s_1, s_2, \dots, s_p \end{pmatrix} - N(x, s_1) N\begin{pmatrix} s_1, s_2, \dots, s_p \\ y, s_2, \dots, s_p \end{pmatrix} -$$

$$- N(x, s_2) N\begin{pmatrix} s_1, s_2, \dots, s_p \\ s_1, y, \dots, s_p \end{pmatrix} - N(x, s_3) N\begin{pmatrix} s_1, s_2, s_3, \dots, s_p \\ s_1, s_2, y, \dots, s_p \end{pmatrix} -$$

$$- \dots - N(x, s_p) N\begin{pmatrix} s_1, s_2, \dots, s_p \\ s_1, s_2, \dots, y \end{pmatrix}.$$

Now let us integrate both sides of the above equality n times with respect to the variables $s_1, s_2, \dots, s_p$ and note that the integrals of all the terms on the right, beginning with the second, are equal, since each of the pairs $\binom{s_2}{y}, \binom{s_3}{y}, \dots, \binom{s_p}{y}$ may in each case be transposed to the first place without a change of sign, and the symbols of the variables of integration may be replaced by others. In accordance with this remark and notation (57) we obtain the following equality:

$$\int_\Omega \dots \int_\Omega N\begin{pmatrix} x, s_1, s_2, \dots, s_p \\ y, s_1, s_2, \dots, s_p \end{pmatrix} ds_1\, ds_2 \dots ds_p = c_p N(x, y) -$$

$$- p \int_\Omega N(x, s) \left[\int_\Omega N\begin{pmatrix} s, s_1, s_2, \dots, s_{p-1} \\ y, s_1, s_2, \dots, s_{p-1} \end{pmatrix} ds_1 \dots ds_{p-1} \right] ds. \quad (61)$$

This equality says that the same recursive relation (58) holds between consecutive integrals of the form (60) as between the coefficients $C_p(x, y)$. According to equality (59), formula (60) holds for $p = 1$, and hence we conclude by induction that it holds for all p.

The required series (55), which we call *Fredholm's second series*, has, therefore, the following form:

$$D(x, y, \lambda) = N(x, y) + \\ + \sum_{p=1}^{\infty} \frac{(-\lambda)^p}{p!} \int\limits_{\Omega} \dots \int\limits_{\Omega} N\begin{pmatrix} x, s_1, s_2, \dots, s_p \\ y, s_1, s_2, \dots, s_p \end{pmatrix} ds_1\, ds_2 \dots ds_p. \quad (62)$$

We see the similarity between the construction of this functional series and the first numerical Fredholm series $D(\lambda)$, defined by formula (41). Here the determinants under the integral sign in series (62) are obtained by adjoining a row with the variable x and a column with the variable y to the analogous determinants under the integral sign in series (41).

In view of the complete similarity of construction, series (62) just as series (41), *converges for all values of the parameter* λ, and is therefore an entire function of that parameter.

This result is of fundamental importance, since it in no way restricts the applicability of expression (62).

Finally, we have thus proved in the assumption $D(\lambda) \neq 0$, the existence of a solution of the integral equation of form (51), where the resolvent kernel $N(x, y, \lambda)$ is the ratio (52) of two entire functions of the parameter λ defined by the power series (41) and (62).

According to the theory of analytic functions, the resolvent kernel $\mathfrak{N}(x, y, \lambda)$ is a *meromorphic function* of the parameter λ, i.e. an analytic function whose singularities may only be the *poles*, i.e. they can only be the *zeros of the divisor* $D(\lambda)$.

We have already proved that the solution of form (51) is unique for $|\lambda|$ sufficiently small. Now, in order to prove that Fredholm's solution

$$\varphi(x) = f(x) + \lambda \int\limits_{\Omega} \frac{D(x, y, \lambda)}{D(\lambda)} f(y)\, dy$$

is *unique* for any λ provided that $D(\lambda) \neq 0$, we shall base ourselves on the equality

$$\mathfrak{R}(x, y, \lambda) = N(x, y) + \lambda \int_{\Omega} \mathfrak{R}(x, s, \lambda) N(s, y)\, ds, \tag{63}$$

which, as already shown, satisfies that solving kernel when $|\lambda|$ is sufficiently small. We shall show that equality (63) is satisfied by the resolvent kernel in Fredholm's form

$$\mathfrak{R}(x, y, \lambda) = \frac{D(x, y, \lambda)}{D(\lambda)}$$

for every λ such that $D(\lambda) \neq 0$.

This follows directly from the remark that both sides of equality (63) are meromorphic functions of the parameter λ, and hence if they are equal in a region in which $|\lambda|$ is sufficiently small then they are equal for all λ, provided that $D(\lambda) \neq 0$. At any rate we can verify this property directly proceeding from the formula

$$D(x, y, \lambda) = N(x, y) + \\ + \sum_{p=1}^{\infty} \frac{(-\lambda)^p}{p!} \int_{\Omega} \cdots \int_{\Omega} N\begin{pmatrix} x, s_1, s_2, \ldots, s_p \\ y, s_1, s_2, \ldots, s_p \end{pmatrix} ds_1 \ldots ds_p .$$

Expanding the determinant under the integral sign with respect to the elements of the first column, we have

$$N\begin{pmatrix} x, s_1, s_2, \ldots, s_p \\ y, s_1, s_2, \ldots, s_p \end{pmatrix} = N(x, y) N\begin{pmatrix} s_1, \ldots, s_p \\ s_1, \ldots, s_p \end{pmatrix} + \\ + \sum_{h=1}^{p} (-1)^{h+2} N(s_h, y) N\begin{pmatrix} x, s_1, \ldots, s_{h-1}, s_{h+1}, \ldots, s_p \\ s_1, s_2, \ldots, s_h, \ldots\ldots\ldots, s_p \end{pmatrix}.$$

Thereupon, transposing s_h to the first place, let us note that the integral with respect to s_h of each of the components of the above sum has the same value

$$\int_{\Omega} (-1)^{h+2} N(s_h, y) N\begin{pmatrix} x, s_1, \ldots, s_{h-1}, s_{h+1}, \ldots, s_p \\ s_1, s_2, \ldots, s_h, \quad s_{h+1}, \ldots, s_p \end{pmatrix} ds_h \\ = (-1)^{2h+1} \int_{\Omega} N(s, y) N\begin{pmatrix} x, s_1, \ldots, s_{h-1}, s_{h+1}, \ldots, s_p \\ s, s_1, \ldots, s_{h-1}, s_{h+1}, \ldots, s_p \end{pmatrix} ds,$$

consequently we have

$$\frac{(-\lambda)^p}{p!}\int_{\Omega}\cdots\int_{\Omega} N\begin{pmatrix} x, s_1, \dots, s_p \\ y, s_1, \dots, s_p \end{pmatrix} ds_1 \dots ds_p$$

$$= N(x, y)\frac{(-\lambda)^p}{p!}\int_{\Omega}\cdots\int_{\Omega} N\begin{pmatrix} s_1, s_2, \dots, s_p \\ s_1, s_2, \dots, s_p \end{pmatrix} ds_1 \dots ds_p +$$

$$+\lambda\int_{\Omega}\Bigg[\frac{(-\lambda)^{p-1}}{(p-1)!}\times$$

$$\times\int_{\Omega}\cdots\int_{\Omega} N\begin{pmatrix} x, s_1, \dots, s_{p-1} \\ s, s_1, \dots, s_{p-1} \end{pmatrix} ds_1 \dots ds_{p-1}\Bigg] N(s, y)\, ds.$$

Hence, upon summing the terms of the second Fredholm series we obtain

$$D(x, y, \lambda) = N(x, y) D(\lambda) + \lambda \int_{\Omega} D(x, s, \lambda) N(s, y)\, ds, \tag{64}$$

and then, after dividing both sides by $D(\lambda) \neq 0$, we obtain the required equality (63).

Now in order to prove that the solution in the form obtained by Fredholm is unique, let us assume that $\varphi(x)$ is the given integrable solution of the Fredholm equation

$$\varphi(s) = f(s) + \lambda \int_{\Omega} N(s, y)\varphi(y)\, dy \tag{65}$$

in the case $D(\lambda) \neq 0$. Multiplying both sides of this equation by the resolvent kernel $\mathfrak{R}(x, y, \lambda)$ in Fredholm's form and integrating both sides with respect to s, we have

$$\int_{\Omega} \mathfrak{R}(x, s, \lambda)\varphi(s)\, ds$$

$$= \int_{\Omega} \mathfrak{R}(x, s, \lambda) f(s)\, ds + \lambda \int_{\Omega}\Big[\int_{\Omega} \mathfrak{R}(x, s, \lambda) N(s, y)\, ds\Big]\varphi(y)\, dy\,.$$

Using the property of kernel (65) we thus obtain

$$\int_{\Omega} N(x, y)\varphi(y)\, dy = \int_{\Omega} \mathfrak{R}(x, s, \lambda) f(s)\, ds,$$

and, since φ is the given solution of equation (65), the last equality implies that

$$\varphi(x) = f(x) + \lambda \int_{\Omega} \mathfrak{N}(x, s, \lambda) f(s)\, ds,$$

whence Fredholm's solution is unique for all λ provided that $D(\lambda) \neq 0$, which is what we set out to prove. We may now state the following theorem which is one of the most beautiful theorems in mathematics:

FREDHOLM'S FIRST THEOREM. *Fredholm's equation of the second kind*

$$\varphi(x) = f(x) + \lambda \int_{\Omega} N(x, y)\, \varphi(y)\, dy$$

under the assumption that the functions $f(x)$ and $N(x, y)$ are integrable has in the case $D(\lambda) \neq 0$ a unique solution, which is of the form

$$\varphi(x) = f(x) + \lambda \int_{\Omega} \mathfrak{N}(x, y, \lambda) f(y)\, dy, \tag{66}$$

where the resolvent kernel $\mathfrak{N}$ is a meromorphic function of the parameter λ, being the ratio of two entire functions of the parameter λ

$$\mathfrak{N}(x, y, \lambda) = \frac{D(x, y, \lambda)}{D(\lambda)}, \tag{67}$$

defined by Fredholm's series of the form

$$D(\lambda) = 1 + \sum_{p=1}^{\infty} \frac{(-\lambda)^p}{p!} \int_{\Omega} \cdots \int_{\Omega} N\begin{pmatrix} s_1, s_2, \dots, s_p \\ s_1, s_2, \dots, s_p \end{pmatrix} ds_1\, ds_2 \dots ds_p,$$

$$D(x, y, \lambda) = N(x, y) + \sum_{p=1}^{\infty} \frac{(-\lambda)^p}{p!} \int_{\Omega} \cdots \int_{\Omega} N\begin{pmatrix} x, s_1, s_2, \dots, s_p \\ y, s_1, s_2, \dots, s_p \end{pmatrix} ds_1\, ds_2 \dots ds_p. \tag{68}$$

These series converge for all values of λ.

Fredholm's First Theorem refers to the case where λ is not a zero of the function $D(\lambda)$. The case where λ is a zero of the entire function $D(\lambda)$ has to be investigated separately; the Second and the Third Theorems of Fredholm are devoted to it.

We shall first consider the fundamental property of the zeros of the function $D(\lambda)$.

THEOREM. *Every zero of Fredholm's function $D(\lambda)$ is a pole of the resolvent kernel*

$$\mathfrak{N}(x, y, \lambda) = \frac{D(x, y, \lambda)}{D(\lambda)}.$$

The order of this pole is at most equal to the order of the zero of the denominator $D(\lambda)$.

To prove this theorem, note that from the first Fredholm series, upon interchanging the indices of the variables of integration, the following equality is obtained:

$$D'(\lambda) = -\int_\Omega N(s, s)\, ds - \sum_{p=2}^{\infty} \frac{(-\lambda)^{p-1}}{(p-1)!} \times$$

$$\times \int_\Omega \left[\int_\Omega \dots \int_\Omega N\begin{pmatrix} s, s_1, s_2, \dots, s_{p-1} \\ s, s_1, s_2, \dots, s_{p-1} \end{pmatrix} ds_1 \dots ds_{p-1} \right] ds.$$

Hence we have the fundamental relation

$$D'(\lambda) = -\int_\Omega D(s, s, \lambda)\, ds. \tag{69}$$

The theorem follows directly from this relation. For, if λ_0 is a zero of order k of the function $D(\lambda)$, then it is a zero of the order $k-1$ of its derivative $D'(\lambda)$, and consequently the point λ_0 may be a zero of the order at most $k-1$ of the entire function $D(x, y, \lambda)$. This point is therefore the pole of ratio (67) of order at most k. In the special case when λ_0 is a single zero we have

$$D(\lambda_0) = 0, \quad D'(\lambda_0) \neq 0,$$

and hence, in view of relation (69), λ_0 cannot be zero of the function $D(x, y, \lambda)$ and is a single pole of the resolvent kernel.

The zeros of the function $D(\lambda)$ are called the *eigenvalues of the kernel* $N(x, y)$. This is a fundamental concept in theory of integral equations. Note that $D(0) = 1$, and hence zero is never an eigenvalue.

The set of all the eigenvalues of the kernel is called the *spectrum* of the integral equation.

THEOREM. *If a real kernel $N(x, y)$ has a complex eigenvalue $\lambda_0 = \alpha+\beta i$, then it also has the eigenvalue $\lambda_0 = \alpha-\beta i$, conjugate to λ_0.*

In fact, if the kernel $N(x, y)$ is real, then the entire function $D(\lambda)$ also takes real values on the real axis and therefore, according to *Schwarz's principle of reflection*, the values of the function $D(\lambda)$ at points symmetrical with respect to the real axis are complex conjugates. Hence it follows that if

$$D(\alpha+\beta i) = 0,$$

then also

$$D(\alpha-\beta i) = 0,$$

which was to be proved.

From relation (69) it follows that

$$\frac{D'(\lambda)}{D(\lambda)} = -\int_{\Omega} \frac{D(s, s, \lambda)}{D(\lambda)} ds,$$

$$\frac{d}{d\lambda} \log D(\lambda) = -\int_{\Omega} \mathfrak{N}(s, s, \lambda)\, ds, \qquad D(\lambda) \neq 0.$$

Consequently, if $|\lambda|$ is sufficiently small, we may write the equality

$$\frac{d}{d\lambda} \log D(\lambda) = -\int_{\Omega} \sum_{n=0}^{\infty} \lambda^n N_{n+1}(s, s)\, ds,$$

where the series on the right is convergent. Hence

$$\log D(\lambda) = -\sum_{n=0}^{\infty} \frac{\lambda^{n+1}}{n+1} \int_{\Omega} N_{n+1}(s, s)\, ds, \tag{70}$$

since $D(0) = 1$. The integrals of the iterated kernels

$$\int_{\Omega} N_{n+1}(s, s)\, ds$$

are called the *traces* of the kernel $N(x, y)$.

The radius of convergence of series (70) is equal to the smallest modulus of the eigenvalues. *If a kernel possesses no eigenvalues, then series* (70) *is convergent for every value of* λ.

Remark. The Volterra integral equation of the second kind

$$\varphi(x) = f(x) + \lambda \int_a^x N(x, y)\varphi(y)\,dy$$

may be considered as a special case of the Fredholm equation of the second kind

$$\varphi(x) = f(x) + \lambda \int_a^b K(x, y)\varphi(y)\,dy,$$

whose kernel is defined by the equalities

$$K(x, y) = N(x, y), \quad a \leqq x \leqq b,\ a \leqq y \leqq x,$$

$$K(x, y) = 0, \quad a \leqq x \leqq b,\ x < y \leqq b.$$

In view of the convergence of the resolvent kernel for all values of the parameter λ, we conclude that the Volterra equation possesses no eigenvalues.

§ 3. Fredholm's Second Theorem

An equation of the form

$$\varphi(x) = \lambda \int_\Omega N(x, y)\varphi(y)\,dy \tag{71}$$

is called *Fredholm's homogeneous equation.*

From form (66) of the solution given by Fredholm's First Theorem, upon substituting $f(x) = 0$, it follows that if $D(\lambda) \neq 0$ then the homogeneous Fredholm equation possesses only zero solutions $\varphi(x) = 0$ in the domain Ω.

Now Fredholm's Second Theorem concerns precisely the existence of *non-zero* solutions of equation (71) where $\lambda = \lambda_0$ is an eigenvalue of the kernel $N(x, y)$, i.e. a zero of the entire function $D(\lambda)$:

$$D(\lambda_0) = 0.$$

Let us first consider the case where λ_0 is a *simple* zero of the function $D(\lambda)$, i.e. where

$$D(\lambda_0) = 0, \qquad D'(\lambda_0) \neq 0. \tag{72}$$

Relation (69) then implies that the function $D(x, y, \lambda_0)$ is not identically equal to zero.

Let us now turn our attention to equation (54)

$$D(x, y, \lambda) = N(x, y) D(\lambda) + \lambda \int_\Omega N(x, s) D(s, y, \lambda)\, ds,$$

satisfied by Fredholm entire functions for all λ. Assuming that $\lambda \to \lambda_0$, we obtain the equation

$$D(x, y, \lambda_0) = \lambda_0 \int_\Omega N(x, s) D(s, y, \lambda_0)\, ds, \tag{73}$$

whence, upon substituting for y a particular value y_1 such that the function $D(x, y_1, \lambda_0)$ be non-zero, we conclude that in case (72) Fredholm homogeneous equation (71) possesses a non-zero solution

$$\varphi(x) = D(x, y_1, \lambda_0). \tag{74}$$

Multiplying function (74) by an arbitrary constant C we obtain the function

$$CD(x, y_1, \lambda_0), \tag{75}$$

which is obviously also a solution of the homogeneous equation (71). From general considerations, given below, it follows that in case (72) every solution of equation (71) has form (75).

Let us now consider the general case, where λ_0 is a zero of arbitrary multiplicity q, i.e. when

$$D(\lambda_0) = 0, \qquad D^{(\nu)}(\lambda_0) = 0, \qquad D^{(q)}(\lambda_0) \neq 0$$
$$(\nu = 1, 2, \ldots, q-1). \tag{76}$$

In order to prove in this case the existence of non-zero solutions of the homogeneous equation, Fredholm introduced following idea called by him minors. A *Fredholm minor of order n relative to the kernel* $N(x, y)$, denoted by the symbol

$$D_n\left(\begin{matrix} x_1, x_2, \ldots, x_n \\ y_1, y_2, \ldots, y_n \end{matrix}\middle|\, \lambda\right),$$

is the sum of the following power series in the parameter λ,

$$D_n\left(\begin{matrix}x_1, x_2, \dots, x_n\\ y_1, y_2, \dots, y_n\end{matrix}\middle|\lambda\right) = N\begin{pmatrix}x_1, x_2, \dots, x_n\\ y_1, y_2, \dots, y_n\end{pmatrix} + \sum_{p=1}^{\infty}\frac{(-\lambda)^p}{p!}\times$$

$$\times\int_\Omega\dots\int_\Omega N\begin{pmatrix}x_1, \dots, x_n, s_1, \dots, s_p\\ y_1, \dots, y_n, s_1, \dots, s_p\end{pmatrix} ds_1\dots ds_p, \qquad (77)$$

where $x_1, x_2, \dots, x_n$ and $y_1, y_2, \dots, y_n$ are two sequences of arbitrary variables.

Series (77) *converges for all values of the parameter* λ, as can be proved by means of Hadamard's theorem, just as we did previously for Fredholm's series $D(\lambda)$ and $D(x, y, \lambda)$.

Differentiating the first of Fredholm's series (68) n times, we have

$$\frac{d^n D(\lambda)}{d\lambda^n} = (-1)^n\int_\Omega\dots\int_\Omega N\begin{pmatrix}s_1, \dots, s_n\\ s_1, \dots. s_n\end{pmatrix} ds_1\dots ds_n +$$

$$+(-1)^n\sum_{p=1}^{\infty}\frac{(-\lambda)^p}{p!}\times$$

$$\times\int_\Omega\dots\int_\Omega N\begin{pmatrix}s_1, \dots, s_n, s_{n+1}, \dots, s_{n+p}\\ s_1, \dots, s_n, s_{n+1}, \dots, s_{n+p}\end{pmatrix} ds_1\dots ds_{n+p}.$$

Hence by comparing with series (77) we obtain the important relation

$$\frac{d^n D(\lambda)}{d\lambda^n} = (-1)^n\int_\Omega\dots\int_\Omega D_n\left(\begin{matrix}x_1, \dots, x_n\\ x_1, \dots, x_n\end{matrix}\middle|\lambda\right) dx_1\dots dx_n, \qquad (78)$$

between the n-th derivative of Fredholm's function $D(\lambda)$ and Fredholm's minor of order n (n is an arbitrary positive integer).

From relation (78) we see directly that if λ_0 is a zero of order q of the function $D(\lambda)$, then the minor of order q

$$D_q\left(\begin{matrix}x_1, x_2, \dots, x_n\\ y_1, y_2, \dots, y_n\end{matrix}\middle|\lambda_0\right)$$

for that value of λ_0 *is not identically equal to zero*, since then

$$D^{(q)}(\lambda_0) \neq 0.$$

Obviously equality (78) does not exclude the possibility that minors of lower order than q may also have this property.

We shall now find the integral equation analogous to equation (54), which satisfies Fredholm's minor (77). To this end, let us consider Fredholm's determinant under the integral sign in formula (77):

$$N\begin{pmatrix} x_1, \dots, x_n, s_1, \dots, s_p \\ y_1, \dots, y_n, s_1, \dots, s_p \end{pmatrix}$$

$$= \begin{vmatrix} N(x_1, y_1) & N(x_1, y_2) & \dots & N(x_1, y_n) & N(x_1, s_1) & \dots & N(x_1, s_p) \\ N(x_2, y_1) & N(x_2, y_2) & \dots & N(x_2, y_n) & N(x_2, s_1) & \dots & N(x_2, s_p) \\ \dots & \dots & \dots & \dots & \dots & \dots & \dots \\ N(x_n, y_1) & N(x_n, y_2) & \dots & N(x_n, y_n) & N(x_n, s_1) & \dots & N(x_n, s_p) \\ N(s_1, y_1) & N(s_1, y_2) & \dots & N(s_1, y_n) & N(s_1, s_1) & \dots & N(s_1, s_p) \\ \dots & \dots & \dots & \dots & \dots & \dots & \dots \\ N(s_p, y_1) & N(s_p, y_2) & \dots & N(s_p, y_n) & N(s_p, s_1) & \dots & N(s_p, s_p) \end{vmatrix}. \quad (79)$$

Expanding that determinant with respect to the elements of the first row and integrating p times with respect to $s_1, s_2, \dots, s_p$ for $p \geqq 1$ we obtain the equality

$$\int\limits_{\Omega} \dots \int\limits_{\Omega} N\begin{pmatrix} x_1, \dots, x_n, s_1, \dots, s_p \\ y_1, \dots, y_n, s_1, \dots, s_p \end{pmatrix} ds_1 \dots ds_p$$

$$= \sum_{h=1}^{n} (-1)^{h+1} N(x_1, y_h) \times$$

$$\times \int\limits_{\Omega} \dots \int\limits_{\Omega} N\begin{pmatrix} x_2, \dots \dots \dots \dots \dots, x_n, s_1, \dots, s_p \\ y_1, \dots, y_{h-1}, y_{h+1}, \dots, y_n, s_1, \dots, s_p \end{pmatrix} ds_1 \dots ds_p +$$

$$+ \sum_{h=1}^{p} (-1)^{h+n+1} \int\limits_{\Omega} \dots \int\limits_{\Omega} N(x_1, s_h) \times$$

$$\times N\begin{pmatrix} x_2, \dots, x_n, s_1, s_2, \dots \dots, s_h, \dots \dots \dots, s_p \\ y_1, \dots, y_{n-1}, y_n, s_1, \dots, s_{h-1}, s_{h+1}, \dots, s_p \end{pmatrix} ds_1 \dots ds_p, \quad (80)$$

where the symbols for the determinants N occurring on the right-hand side of formula (80) do not contain the variable x_1 in the upper sequence, and the variable y_h or s_h in the lower. Now note that all the terms of the latter of the above sums have the same value. In fact, by transposing the variable s_h in the upper sequence to the first place (by means of $h+n-2$ transpositions) and omitting the index h we may write each of the terms of the second sum in the form

$$-\int_\Omega N(x_1, s)\times$$
$$\times\left[\int_\Omega \dots \int_\Omega N\begin{pmatrix} s, & x_2, \dots, x_n, s_1, \dots, s_{p-1} \\ y_1, & y_2, \dots, y_n, s_1, \dots, s_{p-1}\end{pmatrix} ds_1 \dots ds_{p-1}\right] ds,$$

since, after $h+n-2$ changes of sign of the determinant the factor in front of each of the integrals is

$$(-1)^{(h+n+1)+(h+n-2)} = (-1)^{2(h+n)-1} = -1.$$

Consequently we may write equality (80) in the form

$$\int_\Omega \dots \int_\Omega N\begin{pmatrix} x_1, \dots, x_n, s_1, \dots, s_p \\ y_1, \dots, y_n, s_1, \dots, s_p\end{pmatrix} ds_1 \dots ds_p$$
$$= \sum_{h=1}^{n} (-1)^{h+1} N(x_1, y_h)\times$$
$$\times \int_\Omega \dots \int_\Omega N\begin{pmatrix} x_2, \dots\dots\dots\dots\dots\dots, x_n, s_1, \dots, s_p \\ y_1, \dots, y_{h-1}, y_{h+1}, \dots, y_n, s_1, \dots, s_p\end{pmatrix} ds_1 \dots ds_p -$$
$$-p\int_\Omega N(x_1, s)\times$$
$$\times\left[\int_\Omega \dots \int_\Omega N\begin{pmatrix} s, & x_2, \dots, x_n, s_1, \dots, s_{p-1} \\ y_1, & y_2, \dots, y_n, s_1, \dots, s_{p-1}\end{pmatrix} ds_1 \dots ds_{p-1}\right] ds. \quad (81)$$

Substituting the above expressions, holding for all p, in equation (77), we obtain for the Fredholm minor the integral equation

$$D_n\left(\begin{matrix} x_1, \ldots, x_n \\ y_1, \ldots, y_n \end{matrix}\middle| \lambda\right)$$

$$= \sum_{h=1}^{n} (-1)^{h+1} N(x_1, y_h) D_{n-1}\left(\begin{matrix} x_2, \ldots\ldots\ldots\ldots\ldots, x_n \\ y_1, \ldots, y_{h-1}, y_{h+1}, \ldots, y_n \end{matrix}\middle| \lambda\right) +$$

$$+\lambda \int_{\Omega} N(x_1, s) D_n\left(\begin{matrix} s, & x_2, \ldots, x_n \\ y_1, & y_2, \ldots, y_n \end{matrix}\middle| \lambda\right) ds, \quad (82)$$

having taken into account the fact that

$$\frac{(-\lambda)^p}{p!}(-p) = \lambda \frac{(-\lambda)^{p-1}}{(p-1)!}.$$

The above argument may be carried out in a similar fashion, by expanding determinant (79) with respect to an arbitrary i-th row, where $1 \leqq i \leqq n$. We then obtain the following integral equation for the minor D_n:

$$D_n\left(\begin{matrix} x_1, \ldots, x_n \\ y_1, \ldots, y_n \end{matrix}\middle| \lambda\right)$$

$$= \sum_{h=1}^{n} (-1)^{h+i} N(x_i, y_h) D_{n-1}\left(\begin{matrix} x_1, x_2, \ldots, x_{i-1}, x_{i+1}, \ldots, x_n \\ y_1, y_2, \ldots, y_{h-1}, y_{h+1}, \ldots, y_n \end{matrix}\middle| \lambda\right) +$$

$$+\lambda \int_{\Omega} N(x_i, s) D_n\left(\begin{matrix} x_1, \ldots, x_{i-1}, s, x_{i+1}, \ldots, x_n \\ y_1, \ldots\ldots\ldots\ldots\ldots\ldots\ldots, y_n \end{matrix}\middle| \lambda\right) ds. \quad (83)$$

Similarly, expanding determinant (79) with respect to the i-th column ($i = 1, 2, \ldots, n$) and integrating, we obtain the following equation:

$$D_n\left(\begin{matrix} x_1, \ldots, x_n \\ y_1, \ldots, y_n \end{matrix}\middle| \lambda\right)$$

$$= \sum_{h=1}^{n} (-1)^{h+i} N(x_h, y_i) D_{n-1}\left(\begin{matrix} x_1, \ldots, x_{h-1}, x_{h+1}, \ldots, x_n \\ y_1, \ldots, y_{i-1}, y_{i+1}, \ldots, y_n \end{matrix}\middle| \lambda\right) +$$

$$+\lambda \int_{\Omega} N(s, y_i) D_n\left(\begin{matrix} x_1, \ldots\ldots\ldots\ldots\ldots\ldots\ldots, x_n \\ y_1, \ldots, y_{i-1}, s, y_{i+1}, \ldots, y_n \end{matrix}\middle| \lambda\right) ds. \quad (84)$$

Relation (83) obtained, holding for all values of λ, makes it possible to find the non-zero solution of the homogeneous equation (71) in the case where $\lambda = \lambda_0$ is an eigenvalue of the kernel.

Let us thus suppose that $\lambda = \lambda_0$ is a zero of order q of the function $D(\lambda)$. Then, as we have already established on the basis of equality (78), the minor D_q is not identically equal to zero, and the minors $D_1, D_2, \ldots, D_{q-1}$ need not be identically equal to zero. Consequently, let the minor D_ν be the first minor in the sequence $D_1, D_2, \ldots, D_{q-1}$ which is not identically equal to zero, i.e. all the preceding minors $D_1, D_2, \ldots, D_{\nu-1}$ are equal to zero.

The number ν is equal at least to unity and is at most the order q of the zero λ_0. We call this number the *rank* of the eigenvalue λ_0. Now, if ν is the rank of the eigenvalue λ_0 then $D_{\nu-1} = 0$ and relation (83) implies that the minor D_ν satisfies the homogeneous integral equation

$$D_\nu\left(\begin{matrix} x_1, \ldots, x_i, \ldots, x_\nu \\ y_1, \ldots\ldots\ldots\ldots, y_\nu \end{matrix}\middle|\, \lambda_0\right)$$

$$= \lambda_0 \int_\Omega N(x_i, s)\, D_\nu\left(\begin{matrix} x_1, \ldots, x_{i-1}, s, x_{i+1}, \ldots, x_\nu \\ y_1, \ldots\ldots\ldots\ldots\ldots\ldots\ldots\ldots, y_\nu \end{matrix}\middle|\, \lambda_0\right) ds, \qquad (85)$$

where $i = 1, 2, 3, \ldots, \nu$. The equation obtained indicates directly that the function

$$\varphi_i(x) = D_\nu\left(\begin{matrix} x_1, \ldots, x_{i-1}, x, x_{i+1}, \ldots, x_\nu \\ y_1, \ldots\ldots\ldots\ldots\ldots\ldots\ldots\ldots, y_\nu \end{matrix}\middle|\, \lambda_0\right) \qquad (86)$$

is a solution of the homogeneous equation (71) not identically equal to zero for selected fixed values of the remaining variables $x_1, \ldots, x_\nu$ and $y_1, \ldots, y_\nu$.

Substituting x for x_i at ν different points in the minor (86) we obtain ν solutions (i.e. as many as the value of the rank),

$$\varphi_1(x), \quad \varphi_2(x), \quad \ldots, \quad \varphi_\nu(x)$$

of the homogeneous equation (71), not identically equal to zero.

Usually, for the sake of symmetry, it is more convenient to give the solutions of the homogeneous equation in the form

$$\Phi_i(x) = \frac{D_\nu\left(\begin{matrix} x_1, \dots, x_{i-1}, x, x_{i+1}, \dots, x_n \\ y_1, \dots\dots\dots\dots\dots\dots\dots, y_n \end{matrix}\middle| \lambda_0\right)}{D_\nu\left(\begin{matrix} x_1, \dots, x_{i-1}, x_i, x_{i+1}, \dots, x_n \\ y_1, \dots\dots\dots\dots\dots\dots\dots, y_n \end{matrix}\middle| \lambda_0\right)}$$

$$(i = 1, 2, \dots, \nu) \qquad (87)$$

where the numbers $x_1, \dots, x_n$ and $y_1, \dots, y_n$ are chosen so that the denominator does not vanish (which is possible in accordance with the definition of the rank ν).

We shall now show that the solutions (86) or (87) obtained are *linearly independent*, i.e., if there exist constants $C_1, C_2, \dots, C_\nu$ such that

$$C_1 \Phi_1(x) + C_2 \Phi_2(x) + \dots + C_\nu \Phi_\nu(x) = 0, \qquad (88)$$

then $C_1 = C_2 = \dots = C_\nu = 0$.

In fact, if relation (88) were to hold with not all $C_i = 0$, then by substituting in it in turn $x = x_1, x = x_2, \dots, x = x_\nu$ we would obtain

$$C_1 \Phi_1(x_1) = 0, \quad C_2 \Phi_2(x_2) = 0, \quad \dots, \quad C_\nu \Phi_\nu(x_\nu) = 0,$$

since, as is known from the theory of determinants, we have

$$\Phi_i(x_k) = \begin{cases} 0 & \text{for} \quad i \neq k, \\ 1 & \text{for} \quad i = k, \end{cases}$$

and this would imply

$$C_1 = C_2 = \dots = C_\nu = 0,$$

contrary to the hypothesis.

The solution of the homogeneous equation (71), not identically equal to zero, is called the *characteristic solution* of that equation corresponding to a given eigenvalue λ_0, or an *eigenfunction* of the kernel N.

Formula (86) or (87) thus represents a system of ν characteristic solutions of the homogeneous equation which are linearly independent and correspond to a given eigenvalue λ_0. We shall call this system the *fundamental system* of characteristic solutions. Of course, any linear combination of solutions (87) of the form

$$\varphi(x) = A_1 \Phi_1(x) + A_2 \Phi_2(x) + \ldots + A_\nu \Phi_\nu(x), \tag{89}$$

where $A_1, A_2, \ldots, A_\nu$ are constants, is also a solution of the homogeneous equation (71).

We shall show that the converse is also true: *every solution* $\varphi(x)$ *of equation* (71) *is some linear combination of characteristic solutions* $\Phi_1(x), \Phi_2(x), \ldots, \Phi_\nu(x)$.

With this aim in view we shall introduce the following *auxiliary function* H of two variables:

$$H(x, y) = \frac{D_{\nu+1}\left(\begin{matrix} x, x_1, \ldots, x_\nu \\ y, y_1, \ldots, y_\nu \end{matrix}\middle| \lambda_0\right)}{D_\nu\left(\begin{matrix} x_1, \ldots, x_\nu \\ y_1, \ldots, y_\nu \end{matrix}\middle| \lambda_0\right)}. \tag{90}$$

Multiplying both sides of equation (71) by this function, under the assumption that φ is the unknown function, and integrating, we obtain the equation

$$\int_\Omega H(x, y)\varphi(y)\,dy = \lambda_0 \int_\Omega \Big[\int_\Omega N(s, y) H(x, s)\,ds\Big] \varphi(y)\,dy. \tag{91}$$

Let us now multiply both sides of this equality by λ_0 and add term by term to the equality

$$\varphi(x) = \lambda_0 \int_\Omega N(x, y)\varphi(y)\,dy.$$

Thus we obtain the equation

$$\varphi(x) = \lambda_0 \int_\Omega K(x, y)\varphi(y)\,dy \tag{92}$$

(also satisfied by the given function), where the new kernel has the form

$$K(x, y) = N(x, y) - H(x, y) + \lambda_0 \int_\Omega N(s, y) H(x, s)\,ds. \tag{93}$$

To transform this kernel, let us expand the minor $D_{\nu+1}$ according to formula (84):

$$D_{\nu+1}\begin{pmatrix} x, x_1, \ldots, x_\nu \\ y, y_1, \ldots, y_\nu \end{pmatrix}\lambda_0\Bigg) = N(x, y) D_\nu\begin{pmatrix} x_1, \ldots, x_\nu \\ y_1, \ldots, y_\nu \end{pmatrix}\lambda_0\Bigg) +$$

$$+ \sum_{h=1}^{\nu} (-1)^h N(x_h, y) D_\nu\begin{pmatrix} x, & x_1, \ldots, x_{h-1}, x_{h+1}, \ldots, x_\nu \\ y_1, & y_2, \ldots\ldots\ldots\ldots, y_\nu \end{pmatrix}\lambda_0\Bigg) +$$

$$+ \lambda_0 \int_\Omega N(s, y) D_{\nu+1}\begin{pmatrix} x, x_1, \ldots, x_\nu \\ s, y_1, \ldots, y_\nu \end{pmatrix}\lambda_0\Bigg) ds. \tag{94}$$

Now, in every minor D_ν if we transpose the variable x from the first place to between the variables x_{h-1} and x_{h+1} and divide both sides of equality (94) by the constant

$$D_\nu\begin{pmatrix} x_1, \ldots, x_\nu \\ y_1, \ldots, y_\nu \end{pmatrix}\lambda_0\Bigg) \neq 0.$$

we obtain

$$H(x, y) = N(x, y) + \sum_{h=1}^{\nu} N(x_h, y) \Phi_h(x) + \\ + \lambda_0 \int_\Omega N(s, y) H(x, s) ds. \tag{95}$$

Substituting this expression in formula (93), we have

$$K(x, y) = -\sum_{h=1}^{\nu} N(x_h, y) \Phi_h(x), \tag{96}$$

and hence equation (92) takes on the form

$$\varphi(x) = -\lambda_0 \sum_{h=1}^{\nu} \int_\Omega N(x_h, y) \Phi_h(x) \varphi(y) dy. \tag{97}$$

Now if we extract the function $\Phi_h(x)$ from under the integral sign, we see that in each term on the right-hand side the function $\varphi(x)$ indeed has the form

$$\varphi(x) = C_1 \Phi_1(x) + C_2 \Phi_2(x) + \ldots + C_\nu \Phi_\nu(x),$$

where $C_1, C_2, \ldots, C_\nu$ are certain constants, i.e. the function $\varphi(x)$ is a linear combination of characteristic solutions $\Phi_i(x)$.

Expression (89), *in which* $A_1, A_2, \ldots, A_\nu$ *are arbitrary constants, thus represents all the solutions of the homogeneous equation* (71).

Obviously every solution of (89) may also be expressed as a linear combination of some other basic system of linearly independent solutions

$$\overline{\Phi}_1(x), \quad \overline{\Phi}_2(x), \quad \ldots, \quad \overline{\Phi}_\nu(x),$$

which are properly chosen linear combinations of solutions

$$\Phi_1(x), \quad \Phi_2(x), \quad \ldots, \quad \Phi_\nu(x).$$

If a zero λ_0 is of the first order, then the rank $\nu = 1$ and the homogeneous equation possesses only one characteristic solution,

$$\Phi(x) = D(x, y, \lambda_0),$$

where we have neglected the arbitrary constant factor. We may therefore enunciate the following theorem:

FREDHOLM'S SECOND THEOREM. *If* λ_0 *is a zero of multiplicity* q *of the function* $D(\lambda)$, *then the homogeneous equation*

$$\varphi(x) = \lambda_0 \int_\Omega N(x, y)\varphi(y)\,dy$$

possesses at least one, and at most q, *linearly independent solutions*

$$\varphi_i(x) = D_\nu\left(\begin{matrix} x_1, x_2, \ldots, x_{i-1}, x, x_{i+1}, \ldots, x_\nu \\ y_1, \ldots\ldots\ldots\ldots\ldots\ldots\ldots\ldots, y_\nu \end{matrix}\middle| \lambda_0\right)$$

$$(i = 1, 2, \ldots, \nu;\ 1 \leqq \nu \leqq q),$$

not identically zero, and any other solution of this equation is a linear combination of these solutions.

§ 4. Fredholm's associated equation

Consider the Fredholm equation of the second kind

$$\varphi(x) = f(x) + \lambda \int_\Omega N(x, y)\varphi(y)\,dy. \tag{98}$$

We call the corresponding equation of the form

$$\psi(x) = g(x) + \lambda \int_\Omega N(y, x)\psi(y)\,dy \tag{99}$$

Fredholm's *associated* equation, whose kernel is obtained by the permutation of the variables x, y in the kernel of the given equation (ψ is the unknown function, g is the given function). The relation between equations (98) and (99) is symmetric, since, conversely, equation (98) is associated with equation (99).

Formula (68) on p. 47 for the first and the second Fredholm series implies directly that if $D(\lambda)$ and $D(x, y, \lambda)$ are the Fredholm series of a given equation (98), then $D(\lambda)$ and $D(y, x, \lambda)$ are the Fredholm series of the associated equation (99). The first Fredholm series $D(\lambda)$ is common to both associated equations, and hence the *kernels of these equations have the same eigenvalues* as the zeros of the function $D(\lambda)$. Thus if

$$\mathfrak{R}(x, y, \lambda) = \frac{D(x, y, \lambda)}{D(\lambda)}$$

is a resolvent kernel of equation (98), then

$$\mathfrak{R}(y, x, \lambda) = \frac{D(y, x, \lambda)}{D(\lambda)}$$

is a resolvent kernel of the associated equation and the solution of that equation, according to Fredholm's First Theorem, has the form

$$\psi(x) = g(x) + \lambda \int_{\Omega} \frac{D(y, x, \lambda)}{D(\lambda)} g(y)\, dy \tag{100}$$

assuming that λ is not an eigenvalue, i.e. that $D(\lambda) \neq 0$.

From formula (77) on p. 52 we conclude that, if

$$D_n\left(\begin{matrix} x_1, \ldots, x_n \\ y_1, \ldots, y_n \end{matrix} \middle| \lambda \right)$$

is a minor of order n of the given equation (98), then

$$D_n\left(\begin{matrix} y_1, \ldots, y_n \\ x_1, \ldots, x_n \end{matrix} \middle| \lambda \right)$$

is a minor of the associated equation (99). Hence, on account of equality (78) on p. 52 we conclude that not only has the kernel of equation (97) the same eigenvalues as equation (98) but also the rank ν of each eigenvalue is the same. From relation (84) on p. 55, satisfied by the minors, according to the definition of the rank ν of the eigenvalue λ_0 we conclude that the following relation is satisfied:

$$D_\nu\left(\begin{matrix} x_1, \dots\dots\dots\dots\dots\dots, x_n \\ y_1, \dots, y_{i-1}, x, y_{i+1}, \dots, y_n \end{matrix}\middle| \lambda_0\right)$$

$$= \lambda_0 \int_\Omega N(s, x) D_\nu\left(\begin{matrix} x_1, \dots\dots\dots\dots\dots\dots, x_n \\ y_1, \dots, y_{i-1}, s, y_{i+1}, \dots, y_n \end{matrix}\middle| \lambda_0\right) ds.$$

Hence (for fixed $x_1, x_2, \dots, x_n$ and $y_1, y_2, \dots, y_n$) the function

$$\psi_i(x) = D_\nu\left(\begin{matrix} x_1, \dots\dots\dots\dots\dots\dots, x_n \\ y_1, \dots, y_{i-1}, x, y_{i+1}, \dots, y_n \end{matrix}\middle| \lambda_0\right) \tag{101}$$

is a *characteristic solution* (i.e. not identically equal to zero) *of the homogeneous associated equation*

$$\psi(x) = \int_\Omega N(s, x)\psi(s)\, ds. \tag{99'}$$

Substituting $i = 1, 2, \dots, \nu$ in expression (101) we obtain ν characteristic solutions

$$\psi_1(x), \ \psi_2(x), \ \dots, \ \psi_\nu(x)$$

of the associated equation, corresponding to the eigenvalue λ_0. In a manner analogously to formula (87) on p. 57, the characteristic solutions of the associated equation (99′) are written in the form

$$\Psi_i(x) = \frac{D_\nu\left(\begin{matrix} x_1, \dots\dots\dots\dots\dots\dots, x_n \\ y_1, \dots, y_{i-1}, x, y_{i+1}, \dots, y_n \end{matrix}\middle| \lambda_0\right)}{D_\nu\left(\begin{matrix} x_1, \dots\dots\dots\dots\dots\dots, x_n \\ y_1, \dots, y_{i-1}, y_i, y_{i+1}, \dots, y_n \end{matrix}\middle| \lambda_0\right)}, \tag{102}$$

where the values of $x_1, \dots, x_n$, and $y_1, \dots, y_n$ are chosen so that the denominator is different from zero.

Substituting x in ν different places in the lower sequence of formula (102) we obtain the fundamental system of ν characteristic solutions

$$\Psi_1(x), \quad \Psi_2(x), \quad \ldots, \quad \Psi_\nu(x) \tag{103}$$

of the associated equation. Their number is equal to the number of solutions of the equation given.

In the same way as for solutions (87) one proves that the characteristic solutions (103) are linearly independent and that every solution of the associated homogeneous equation is a linear combination of solutions (103).

Thus there is a close connection between the Fredholm equation of the second kind and its associated equation, expressed by the similarity of the formulae for their solution.

We define the *scalar product* (f, φ) of two functions $f(x)$ and $\varphi(x)$ defined on the set Ω by

$$(f, \varphi) = \int_\Omega f(x)\varphi(x)\,dx.$$

DEFINITION. Two functions f and φ are called *orthogonal* in the domain Ω if their scalar product is equal to zero:

$$(f, \varphi) = \int_\Omega f(x)\varphi(x)\,dx = 0;$$

the term orthogonal is based on considerations regarding a function space which we shall give in Chapter IV.

THEOREM. *Characteristic solutions, corresponding to distinct eigenvalues of Fredholm's integral equation and its associate equation, are orthogonal.*

In fact, let $\varphi(x)$ be a characteristic solution of the given equation

$$\varphi(x) = \lambda \int_\Omega N(x, y)\varphi(y)\,dy,$$

corresponding to an eigenvalue λ_0 and let $\Psi(x)$ be a characteristic solution of the associated equation corresponding to some other eigenvalue λ_1 $(\lambda_0 \neq \lambda_1)$. We then have

$$\Phi(x) = \lambda_0 \int_\Omega N(x, y)\Phi(y)\,dy, \qquad \Psi(x) = \lambda_1 \int_\Omega N(y, x)\Psi(y)\,dy.$$

Multiplying both sides of the first equation by $\lambda_1 \Psi(x)$, and those of the second by $\lambda_0 \Phi(x)$, integrating and then subtracting the resulting equations, we obtain

$$(\lambda_1-\lambda_0)\int_\Omega \Phi(x)\Psi(x)\,dx = \lambda_0\lambda_1\int_\Omega\int_\Omega N(x,y)\Psi(x)\Phi(y)\,dy\,dx - \\ -\lambda_1\lambda_0\int_\Omega\int_\Omega N(y,x)\Psi(y)\Phi(x)\,dy\,dx = 0,$$

since the second integral, upon interchanging x and y, is identical to the first. Since we have assumed that $\lambda_1 \neq \lambda_0$, the above implies the equality

$$\int_\Omega \Phi(x)\Psi(x)\,dx = 0,$$

i.e. the *orthogonality* of the characteristic solutions Φ and Ψ.

§ 5. Fredholm's Third Theorem

Fredholm's third theorem concerns the solution of the *non-homogeneous* equation

$$\varphi(x) = f(x) + \lambda_0 \int_\Omega N(x,y)\varphi(y)\,dy \tag{104}$$

in the case when λ_0 is an eigenvalue, i.e. when $D(\lambda_0) = 0$, and hence when Fredholm's formula (67) on p. 47 cannot be applied.

We shall first find a *necessary* condition which has to be satisfied by the given function $f(x)$ in equation (104) in order that a solution exist. Suppose that equation (104) has a solution $\varphi(x)$. Let $\Psi(x)$ be any characteristic solution of the associated equation corresponding to the eigenvalue λ_0. Then we have

$$\Psi(x) = \lambda_0 \int_\Omega N(y,x)\Psi(y)\,dy.$$

Multiplying both sides of equation (104) by $\Psi(x)$ and integrating, we obtain

$$\int_\Omega \Psi(x)\varphi(x)\,dx = \int_\Omega f(x)\Psi(x)\,dx + \lambda_0\int_\Omega\int_\Omega N(x,y)\Psi(x)\varphi(y)\,dx\,dy.$$

Interchanging the variables x and y in the last integral, we obtain

$$\int_\Omega f(x)\Psi(x)\,dx = \int_\Omega \Big[\Psi(x) - \lambda_0\int_\Omega N(y,x)\Psi(y)\,dy\Big]\varphi(x)\,dx = 0.$$

Hence we see that equation (104) does not always have a solution in the case when $D(\lambda_0) = 0$, but that *a necessary condition for the existence of a solution is the orthogonality of the given function* $f(x)$ *to all the characteristic solutions* $\Psi(x)$ *of the associated equation*:

$$\int_{\Omega} f(x)\Psi(x)\,dx = 0. \tag{105}$$

Since every characteristic solution of the integral equation is a linear combination of the basic solutions defined by formula (102) on p. 62, a necessary condition for the existence of a solution of the non-homogeneous equation (104) in the case when $D(\lambda_0) = 0$ is the orthogonality of the given function $f(x)$ to ν fundamental solutions of the associated equation:

$$\int_{\Omega} f(x)\Psi_i(x)\,dx = 0 \qquad (i = 1, 2, \dots, \nu) \tag{106}$$

corresponding to the same eigenvalue λ_0.

If condition (106) is not satisfied then the non-homogeneous equation has no solutions.

We shall now prove that condition (106) is also *sufficient* for the existence of a solution of the nonhomogeneous equation (104), and we shall find that solution.

Now, just as in § 3, we introduce the auxiliary function H of two variables, which is the ratio of two minors,

$$H(x, y) = \frac{D_{\nu+1}\left(\begin{matrix} x, x_1, \dots, x_\nu \\ y, y_1, \dots, y_\nu \end{matrix}\middle| \lambda_0\right)}{D_\nu\left(\begin{matrix} x_1, \dots, x_\nu \\ y_1, \dots, y_\nu \end{matrix}\middle| \lambda_0\right)}, \tag{107}$$

where the minor D_ν is not equal to zero, in accordance with the assumption that ν is the rank of the eigenvalue λ_0.

We multiply both sides of equation (104) by H, under the assumption that it has a solution φ, and then we integrate. We obtain

$$\int_{\Omega} H(x, y)\varphi(y)\,dy$$
$$= \int_{\Omega} H(x, y)f(y)\,dy + \lambda_0 \int_{\Omega}\Big[\int_{\Omega} H(x, s)N(s, y)\,ds\Big]\varphi(y)\,dy. \tag{108}$$

Now multiplying both sides of equation (108) by λ_0 and adding to equation (104), we see upon transformation that the function $\varphi(x)$ also satisfies an integral equation of the form

$$\varphi(x) = f(x) + \lambda_0 \int_\Omega H(x, y) f(y)\, dy + \lambda_0 \int_\Omega K(x, y)\, \varphi(y)\, dy, \quad (109)$$

where, just as in § 3, we use the notation

$$K(x, y) = N(x, y) - H(x, y) + \lambda_0 \int_\Omega H(x, s) N(s, y)\, ds. \quad (110)$$

We already know that by expanding the minor $D_{\nu+1}$ according to formula (94) on p. 59 we obtain

$$K(x, y) = -\sum_{h=1}^{\nu} N(x_h, y)\, \Phi_h(x). \quad (110')$$

Substituting this expression in equality (109), we conclude that *if a solution of the nonhomogeneous equation* (104) *exists, then it has the following form*:

$$\varphi(x) = f(x) + \lambda_0 \int_\Omega \frac{D_{\nu+1}\begin{pmatrix} x, x_1, \ldots, x_\nu \\ y, y_1, \ldots, y_\nu \end{pmatrix}\!\lambda_0}{D_\nu\begin{pmatrix} x_1, \ldots, x_\nu \\ y_1, \ldots, y_\nu \end{pmatrix}\!\lambda_0} f(y)\, dy + \sum_{h=1}^{\nu} C_h \Phi_h(x), \quad (111)$$

where the C_h are constants.

We shall show that function (111) is indeed a solution of equation (104) when the orthogonality conditions (106) are satisfied.

Obviously it is sufficient to establish that the sum of the first two terms of expression (111) is a solution, since the third term, being a linear combination of the fundamental solutions $\Phi_h(x)$, is a solution of the homogeneous equation, and, when added to the solution of a nonhomogeneous equation, also yields a solution of that equation. Let us then substitute the expression

$$\varphi(x) = f(x) + \lambda_0 \int_\Omega H(x, y) f(y)\, dy$$

in equation (104) and denote by R the difference between the right-hand and left-hand side,

$$R = f(x) + \lambda_0 \int_\Omega N(x, y) f(y)\, dy + \\ + \lambda_0^2 \int_\Omega \Big[\int_\Omega N(x, s) H(s, y)\, ds\Big] f(y)\, dy - \\ - \Big[f(x) + \lambda_0 \int_\Omega H(x, y) f(y)\, dy\Big]. \quad (112)$$

It is possible to derive the following expression for $H(x, y)$ in the same way as (95) on p. 59 was derived from equation (94) and from equation (83) on p. 55:

$$H(x, y) = N(x, y) + \sum_{h=1}^{\nu} N(x, y_h) \Psi_h(y) + \\ + \lambda_0 \int_\Omega N(x, s) H(s, y)\, ds. \quad (113)$$

Hence it follows that

$$R = -\lambda_0 \sum_{h=1}^{\nu} N(x, y_h) \int_\Omega \Psi_h(y) f(y)\, dy = 0,$$

in accordance with equality (106). *Function* (111) *is therefore indeed a solution of equation* (104), assuming that conditions (106) are satisfied. Consequently, we may state the following theorem:

FREDHOLM'S THIRD THEOREM. *For the nonhomogeneous equation*

$$\varphi(x) = f(x) + \lambda_0 \int_\Omega N(x, y) \varphi(y)\, dy$$

to possess a solution in the case $D(\lambda_0) = 0$ *it is necessary and sufficient that the given function* $f(x)$ *be orthogonal to all the characteristic solutions* $\Psi_i(x)$ $(i = 1, 2, \ldots, \nu)$ *of the associated homogeneous equation corresponding to the eigenvalue* λ_0, *and forming the fundamental system. The general solution then has form* (111) *where* $C_1, C_2, \ldots, C_\nu$ *are arbitrary constants.*

§ 6. Remark on the integral equation with complex functions

The above three theorems of Fredholm also hold when the given functions $N(x, y)$ and $f(x)$ have complex values provided we define the integral of the function $f(x) = f_1(x) + i f_2(x)$ with complex values, as follows:

$$\int_{\Omega} [f_1(x)+if_2(x)]\,dx = \int_{\Omega} f_1(x)\,dx + i\int_{\Omega} f_2(x)\,dx. \qquad (114)$$

In considering orthogonal systems of complex functions and function spaces it is more usual to adopt another definition for the scalar product of two functions, and hence also another definition of orthogonality:

DEFINITION. *The scalar product* (f, φ) *of two complex functions*

$$f(x) = f_1(x) + if_2(x) \quad \text{and} \quad \varphi(x) = \varphi_1(x) + i\varphi_2(x),$$

defined on the set Ω, is defined to be

$$(f, \varphi) = \int_{\Omega} f(x)\overline{\varphi(x)}\,dx = \int_{\Omega} (f_1 + if_2)(\varphi_1 - i\varphi_2)\,dx, \qquad (115)$$

where $\overline{\varphi(x)} = \varphi_1(x) - i\varphi_2(x)$ denotes the function conjugate to the complex function $\varphi(x) = \varphi_1(x) + i\varphi_2(x)$.

The above definition is in accordance with the previous definition for real functions:

$$(f, \varphi) = \int_{\Omega} f(x)\varphi(x)\,dx.$$

Formula (115) implies that the scalar product of the permuted pair φ, f is the complex conjugate of the scalar product of the pair f, φ:

$$(\varphi, f) = \overline{(f, \varphi)}. \qquad (116)$$

We call two complex functions *orthogonal* if their scalar product is zero, i.e., according to formula (115), if

$$(f, \varphi) = \int_{\Omega} f(x)\overline{\varphi(x)}\,dx = 0. \qquad (117)$$

The orthogonality of a pair of complex functions is independent of their order in the scalar product, since if equality (117) holds, then according to formula (116) the equality

$$(\varphi, f) = \int_{\Omega} \overline{f(x)}\varphi(x)\,dx = 0 \qquad (118)$$

also holds. The definition of the scalar product of two complex functions, expressed by formula (117), has the advantage that a scalar product of a complex function by itself has a non-negative real value, equal to the integral of the square of the modulus of the function

$$(f,f)=\int_{\Omega} f(x)\overline{f(x)}\,dx=\int_{\Omega}[f_1^2(x)+f_2^2(x)]\,dx=\int_{\Omega}|f(x)|^2\,dx. \quad (119)$$

The positive square root $\sqrt{(f,f)}$ of the above number is called the *norm* of the complex function f. The norm of a complex number is a non-negative number which is equal to zero if and only if the function is equal to zero *almost everywhere*, i.e. if the set of all x for which the function $f(x)$ is different from zero has Lebesgue measure zero.

In connection with the new definition of orthogonal functions expressed by formula (117), we change the definition of the Fredholm associated equation. Thus, we now give the term equation *associated* with the Fredholm equation of the second kind

$$\varphi(x)=f(x)+\lambda\int_{\Omega} N(x,y)\,\varphi(y)\,dy \quad (120)$$

to an equation of the form

$$\psi(x)=g(x)+\bar{\lambda}\int_{\Omega}\overline{N(y,x)}\,\psi(y)\,dy, \quad (121)$$

whose kernel is *conjugate* to the kernel $N(y,x)$ obtained by interchanging the variables x and y in the kernel $N(x,y)$ of the given equation.

Hence, it follows that, if

$$D(\lambda)=\sum_{\nu=0}^{\infty}A_\nu\lambda^\nu \quad (122)$$

is the sum of the first Fredholm series for equation (120), then the first Fredholm series for the associated equation (121) has the form

$$\sum_{\nu=0}^{\infty}\overline{A_\nu}\,\bar{\lambda}^\nu,$$

and hence its sum $\overline{D(\lambda)}$ is the complex conjugate of sum (122).

Thus, if $\lambda_0 = \alpha + \beta i$ is an eigenvalue of the given equation (120), then the number $\bar{\lambda}_0 = \alpha - \beta i$ is an eigenvalue of the associated equation with the same rank ν. Hence the *spectrum* of the associated equation is formed from complex values, conjugate to the values forming the spectrum of the equation given.

With each eigenvalue λ_0 of the given equation are connected ν fundamental characteristic solutions

$$\Phi_1(x), \quad \Phi_2(x), \quad \ldots, \quad \Phi_\nu(x)$$

of the homogeneous equation

$$\varphi(x) = \lambda_0 \int_\Omega N(x, y)\varphi(y)\,dy$$

and ν fundamental characteristic solutions

$$\Psi_1(x), \quad \Psi_2(x), \quad \ldots, \quad \Psi_\nu(x)$$

of the homogeneous associated equation

$$\psi(x) = \bar{\lambda}_0 \int_\Omega \overline{N(y, x)}\psi(y)\,dy.$$

The definition of orthogonality and of the associated equation leaves unchanged the text of the theorem on p. 63 on orthogonality of the characteristic solutions. For it is easy to show, as on page 64, that *every characteristic solution $\Phi(x)$ of the homogeneous equation*

$$\Phi(x) = \lambda_1 \int_\Omega N(x, y)\Phi(y)\,dy,$$

corresponding to an eigenvalue λ_1, is orthogonal to every characteristic solution of the associated equation

$$\Psi(x) = \lambda_2 \int \overline{N(y, x)}\Psi(y)\,dy,$$

corresponding to an eigenvalue λ_2 not conjugate to the eigenvalue λ_1.

Thus we have

$$\int_\Omega \Phi(x)\overline{\Psi(x)}\,dx = 0,$$

where $\lambda_2 \neq \bar{\lambda}_1$.

Fredholm's Third Theorem is also analogous to the previous form:

The Fredholm non-homogeneous equation

$$\varphi(x) = f(x) + \lambda_0 \int_\Omega N(x, y)\varphi(y)\,dy$$

in the case $D(\lambda_0) = 0$, *has a solution* φ *if and only if the given function* $f(x)$ *is orthogonal to all the fundamental characteristic solutions* $\psi_i(x)$ *of the associated equation corresponding to the eigenvalue* $\bar{\lambda}_0$ *conjugate to the given eigenvalue* λ_0, *i.e. if and only if*

$$\int_\Omega f(x)\overline{\Psi_i(x)}\,dx = 0 \quad (i = 1, 2, \dots, \nu).$$

§ 7. Fredholm's equation with degenerate kernel

We call the kernel $N(x, y)$ of a Fredholm equation of the second kind

$$\varphi(x) = f(x) + \lambda \int_\Omega N(x, y)\varphi(y)\,dy \tag{123}$$

degenerate if it is the sum of products of functions of one variable

$$N(x, y) = \sum_{\nu=1}^{n} K_\nu(x) L_\nu(y). \tag{124}$$

The Fredholm equation with degenerate kernel plays an important rôle in the theory and applications of integral equations, since it can easily be solved by a finite number of integrations.

Assume that the given functions K_ν, L_ν are integrable. Substituting expression (124) in formula (123) we notice immediately that if equation (123) has a solution then it is the sum of the function $f(x)$ and of a certain linear combination of the functions $K_\nu(x)$:

$$\varphi(x) = f(x) + \sum_{\nu=1}^{n} A_\nu K_\nu(x), \tag{125}$$

where A_ν are constants. In order to determine the constants A_1, $\dots, A_n$, we substitute expression (125) in equation (123). We then obtain an equation which has to be satisfied identically:

$$\sum_{\nu=1}^{n} A_\nu K_\nu(x) = \lambda \sum_{\nu=1}^{n} K_\nu(x) \int_\Omega L_\nu(y) [f(y) + A_1 K_1(y) + \\ + A_2 K_2(y) + \ldots + A_n K_n(y)] \, dy . \tag{126}$$

Without loss of generality we may always assume that the functions $K_1, K_2, \ldots, K_n$ form a linearly independent system, since in the contrary case we could reduce the kernel $\sum_{\nu=1}^{n} K_\nu(x) L_\nu(y)$ to a sum of a smaller number of products. Hence, in order that identity (126) be satisfied it is necessary and sufficient that, for each $\nu = 1, 2, \ldots, n$, the coefficients of the function $K_\nu(x)$ be equal.

Hence we obtain the following system of linear equations:

$$\begin{gathered}
(1-\lambda a_{11})A_1 - \lambda a_{12} A_2 - \ldots - \lambda a_{1n} A_n = \lambda \int_\Omega L_1(y) f(y) \, dy , \\
-\lambda a_{21} A_1 + (1-\lambda a_{22}) A_2 - \ldots - \lambda a_{2n} A_n = \lambda \int_\Omega L_2(y) f(y) \, dy , \\
\cdots\cdots\cdots\cdots\cdots\cdots\cdots\cdots\cdots\cdots \\
-\lambda a_{n1} A_1 - \lambda a_{n2} A_2 - \ldots + (1-\lambda a_{nn}) A_n = \lambda \int_\Omega L_n(y) f(y) \, dy ,
\end{gathered} \tag{127}$$

where the coefficients $a_{\mu\nu}$ have the values

$$a_{\mu\nu} = \int_\Omega L_\mu(y) K_\nu(y) \, dy . \tag{128}$$

The system of equations (127) has a unique solution $A_1, A_2, \ldots, A_n$ if the determinant

$$D_n(\lambda) = \begin{vmatrix} 1-\lambda a_{11} & -\lambda a_{12} & \ldots & -\lambda a_{1n} \\ -\lambda a_{21} & 1-\lambda a_{22} & \ldots & -\lambda a_{2n} \\ \cdots & \cdots & \cdots & \cdots \\ -\lambda a_{n1} & -\lambda a_{n2} & \ldots & 1-\lambda a_{nn} \end{vmatrix} \tag{129}$$

is not equal to zero. This determinant is a polynomial of degree n in the parameter λ. The coefficients $A_1, A_2, \ldots, A_n$ are thus expressed in the form of products of determinants with a common divisor (129). Hence we conclude that equation (123) with degenerate kernel (124) has, in the case $D_n(\lambda) \neq 0$, a unique solution of the form

$$\varphi(x) = f(x) + \lambda \int_{\Omega} \frac{D_n(x, y, \lambda)}{D_n(\lambda)} f(y)\, dy, \tag{130}$$

where the notation

$$D_n(x, y, \lambda) = \begin{vmatrix} 0 & K_1(x) & K_2(x) & \dots & K_n(x) \\ L_1(y) & 1-\lambda a_{11} & -\lambda a_{21} & \dots & -\lambda a_{n1} \\ L_2(y) & -\lambda a_{12} & 1-\lambda a_{22} & \dots & -\lambda a_{n2} \\ \dots & \dots & \dots & \dots & \dots \\ L_n(y) & -\lambda a_{1n} & -\lambda a_{2n} & \dots & 1-\lambda a_{nn} \end{vmatrix} \tag{131}$$

has been introduced. Thus, in this case the resolvent kernel is a ratio of two polynomials of degree n in the parameter λ. These polynomials are special cases of the first and the second Fredholm series. *The eigenvalues of a degenerate kernel are the roots of the algebraic equation* $D_n(\lambda) = 0$, and hence there are at most n of them. We determine the corresponding characteristic solutions from the set of equations (127) which is then homogeneous ($f = 0$) and in the case $D_n(\lambda) = 0$ possesses non-zero solutions.

EXAMPLE. Suppose we are given an integral equation

$$\varphi(x) = f(x) + \lambda \int_0^1 (x+y)\, \varphi(y)\, dy.$$

The solution should have the form

$$\varphi(x) = f(x) + A_1 x + A_2,$$

whence we have the identity

$$f(x) + A_1 x + A_2 \equiv f(x) + \lambda \int_0^1 (x+y) [f(y) + A_1 y + A_2]\, dy$$

and the system of equations

$$A_1 (1 - \tfrac{1}{2}\lambda) - A_2 \lambda = \lambda \int_0^1 f(y)\, dy,$$

$$-\tfrac{1}{3} A_1 \lambda + A_2 (1 - \tfrac{1}{2}\lambda) = \lambda \int_0^1 y f(y)\, dy.$$

Hence we obtain A_1 and A_2 and the solution of the given integral equation in the form

$$\varphi(x) = f(x) + 2\lambda \int_0^1 \frac{6\lambda xy + 3(2-\lambda)(x+1) + 2\lambda}{12 - 12\lambda - \lambda^2} f(y)\,dy$$

if the parameter λ is not one of the eigenvalues. The eigenvalues are roots of the equation

$$12 - 12\lambda - \lambda^2 = 0$$

and hence

$$\lambda_1 = -6 + 4\sqrt{3}, \quad \lambda_2 = -6 - 4\sqrt{3}.$$

The corresponding characteristic solutions are

$$\varphi_1(x) = C(\lambda_1 x + 1 - \tfrac{1}{2}\lambda_1), \quad \varphi_2(x) = C(\lambda_2 x + 1 - \tfrac{1}{2}\lambda_2)$$

where C is an arbitrary constant.

§ 8. A limit theorem. Approximate solution of an integral equation

Given a sequence of bounded continuous kernels

$$N_1(x, y),\ N_2(x, y),\ \ldots,\ N_\nu(x, y),\ \ldots,$$

converging uniformly to the function $N(x, y)$,

$$N_\nu(x, y) \to N(x, y),$$

for x *and* y *lying in the domain* Ω, *then the sequence of solutions*

$$\varphi_1(x),\ \varphi_2(x),\ \ldots,\ \varphi_\nu(x),\ \ldots$$

of Fredholm integral equations of the second kind

$$\varphi_\nu(x) = f(x) + \lambda \int_\Omega N_\nu(x, y)\,\varphi_\nu(y)\,dy \tag{132}$$

tends uniformly to the solution $\psi(x)$ *of the integral equation with limit kernel*

$$\psi(x) = f(x) + \lambda \int_\Omega N(x, y)\,\psi(y)\,dy \tag{133}$$

where we assume that λ *is not an eigenvalue of any of the kernels* $N_\nu(x, y)$ *and* $N(x, y)$.

Now, the solutions of equation (132) are of the form

$$\varphi_\nu(x) = f(x) + \lambda \int_\Omega \frac{D_\nu(x, y, \lambda)}{D_\nu(\lambda)} f(y)\, dy, \tag{134}$$

where $D_\nu(\lambda)$ and $D_\nu(x, y, \lambda)$ are the sums of the Fredholm series of the kernel $N_\nu(x, y)$. We have

$$D_\nu(\lambda) = \sum_{n=0}^{\infty} C_n^{(\nu)} \lambda^n. \tag{135}$$

Let

$$D(\lambda) = \sum_{n=0}^{\infty} C_n \lambda^n \tag{136}$$

be the first Fredholm series for the limit kernel $N(x, y)$. Each coefficient of series (135) obviously tend to the corresponding coefficient of series (126), i.e.

$$C_n^{(\nu)} \to C_n,$$

as $\nu \to \infty$. Moreover, by hypothesis there exists a positive number M such that the kernels $N_\nu(x, y)$ and $N(x, y)$ are bounded above by M in the domain Ω, and hence, according to Hadamard's estimate for Fredholm's determinant, there exists a convergent series

$$\sum_{n=0}^{\infty} k_n \lambda^n, \tag{137}$$

whose coefficients k^n are greater than the absolute values of the corresponding coefficients of the series (135) and (136):

$$k_n > |C_n^{(\nu)}|, \quad k_n > |C_n| \quad (n = 0, 1, 2, \ldots).$$

Now, for any positive number ε we choose an index n_0 such that

$$\sum_{n=n_0}^{\infty} k_n |\lambda|^n < \tfrac{1}{3}\varepsilon, \tag{138}$$

and split the sums $D_\nu(\lambda)$, $D(\lambda)$ into two parts

$$D_\nu(\lambda) = S_{n_0}^{(\nu)} + R_{n_0}^{(\nu)}, \quad D(\lambda) = S_{n_0} + R_{n_0},$$

where $S_{n_0}^{(\nu)}$ and S_{n_0} are the partial sums of series (135) and (136). Then we have

$$|D_\nu(\lambda)-D(\lambda)| \leqq |S_{n_0}^{(\nu)}-S_{n_0}|+|R_{n_0}^{(\nu)}|+|R_{n_0}|. \qquad (139)$$

But according to inequality (138) we have

$$|R_{n_0}^{(\nu)}| < \tfrac{1}{3}\varepsilon, \quad |R_{n_0}| < \tfrac{1}{3}\varepsilon$$

or all ν. Since $C_n^{(\nu)} \to C_n$ as $\nu \to \infty$, then, keeping n_0 fixed we may choose a ν_ε such that

$$|S_{n_0}^{(\nu)}-S_{n_0}| < \tfrac{1}{3}\varepsilon$$

for $\nu < \nu_\varepsilon$. Hence

$$|D_\nu(\lambda)-D(\lambda)| \leqq \varepsilon \qquad (140)$$

for $\nu > \nu_\varepsilon$, i.e. $D_\nu(\lambda) \to D(\lambda)$ as $\nu \to \infty$.

In the same way we prove that the sequence of Fredholm functions $D_\nu(x, y, \lambda)$ tends uniformly to the Fredholm function $D(x, y, \lambda)$:

$$D_\nu(x, y, \lambda) \to D(x, y, \lambda),$$

as $\nu \to \infty$. Hence, it follows that the sequence of solutions (134) of Fredholm equations (132) tends to the limit function

$$\lim_{\nu\to\infty} \varphi_\nu(x) = f(x)+\lambda \int_\Omega \frac{D(x, y, \lambda)}{D(\lambda)} f(y)\, dy. \qquad (141)$$

This function is precisely the solution $\psi(x)$ *of Fredholm equation* (133) *with the limit kernel* $N(x, y)$.

The above theorem is of practical value for the *approximate solution* of the integral equation. For if the given kernel $N(x, y)$ is the limit of the sequence of kernels $N_\nu(x, y)$ for which the solution of the Fredholm equation may be more easily obtained, then as the approximate solution of the equation with kernel $N(x, y)$ we may take the solution of the equation with the kernel $N_\nu(x, y)$. For the kernel $N_\nu(x, y)$, it is, of course, best to use the degenerate kernel of the form (124) on p. 71. We may do this in infinitely many ways. For example, on the basis of the Weierstrass theorem on approximating a function by polynomials, it is possible to take as the approximate kernel $N_\nu(x, y)$ a properly chosen polynomial of the coordinates of the points x and y. Such a kernel will have the form of a degenerate kernel, and the determination of the approximate solution of the integral equation will reduce to a simple algebraic calculation.

§ 9. Remark on unbounded kernels

Fredholm's three theorems were previously proved under the assumption that the kernel was bounded.

D. HILBERT* was the first to show that if an unbounded kernel has the form

$$N(x, y) = \frac{K(x, y)}{|x-y|^{\alpha}},$$

where K is a bounded function, then for the case $\alpha < 1/2$ it is possible to apply Fredholm's formulae provided that in Fredholm's determinants one substitutes $N(x, x) = 0$.

T. CARLEMAN** proved, more generally, that if the kernel is integrable, together with its square, i.e. if the integral

$$\int_\Omega \int_\Omega |N(x, y)|^2 \, dx \, dy$$

exists, then the sums of both Fredholm series are entire functions of the parameter λ and three theorems of Fredholm may be applied directly. Another proof of the above theorem was recently given by S. Mikhlin. ***

For integral equations with unbounded kernels which are not integrable with their square, there exists a method of solution based on the properties of iterated kernels, which will be given in the next chapter.

---

* *Göttinger Nachrichten*, 1904.

** *Mathematische Zeitschrift*, 1921.

*** *Dokl. Akad. Nauk SSSR*, Vol. XLII, No 9, 1944.

§ 10. Remark on continuous and differentiable kernels

Consider an integral equation

$$\varphi(x) = f(x) + \lambda \int_{\Omega} N(x, y)\, \varphi(y)\, dy \tag{142}$$

and the integral equation of the resolvent kernel

$$\begin{aligned} \mathfrak{N}(x, y, \lambda) &= N(x, y) + \lambda \int_{\Omega} N(x, s)\, \mathfrak{N}(s, y, \lambda)\, ds \\ &= N(x, y) + \lambda \int_{\Omega} \mathfrak{N}(x, s, \lambda)\, N(s, y)\, ds . \end{aligned} \tag{143}$$

From these equations two conclusions follow directly:

1. *If the kernel $N(x, y)$ and the function $f(x)$ are continuous in the domain Ω, then the solution φ of equation* (142) *and the resolvent kernel* (143) *are also continuous in Ω.*

2. *If the kernel $N(x, y)$ and the function $f(x)$ have continuous derivatives with respect to x and y in the domain Ω, then the solution φ and the resolvent kernel $\mathfrak{N}$ also have continuous derivatives with respect to x and y.*

Now assume that the function $f(x)$ and the kernel $N(x, y)$ satisfy *Hölder's condition in the domain Ω*, i.e. that

$$\begin{aligned} |f(x_1) - f(x_2)| &\leqq k_1 |x_1 x_2|^{\mu}, \\ |N(x_1, y_1) - N(x_2, y_2)| &\leqq k_2 [|x_1 x_2|^{\mu} + |y_1 y_2|^{\mu}] \end{aligned} \tag{144}$$

($0 < \mu \leqq 1$), where $|x_1 x_2|$ and $|y_1 y_2|$ denote the distances between two points of the domain Ω. We then conclude from equations (142) and (143) that *the solution φ and the resolvent kernel $\mathfrak{N}$ also satisfy Hölder's condition with the same exponent μ.*

For example, we have

$$\begin{aligned} &|\varphi(x_1) - \varphi(x_2)| \\ &\qquad \leqq |f(x_1) - f(x_2)| + \lambda \int_{\Omega} |N(x_1, y) - N(x_2, y)|\, |\varphi(y)|\, dy \\ &\qquad \leqq \text{const}. |x_1 x_2|^{\mu} . \end{aligned}$$

CHAPTER III

WEAKLY SINGULAR FREDHOLM EQUATIONS

§ 1. General considerations

A Fredholm equation of the second kind is called *singular* if its kernel is unbounded or if its domain of integration is unbounded.

We have already said that if a kernel is unbounded but the integral of the square of its modulus exists, then the equation may be solved directly by means of Fredholm's formulae. We call such an equation *weakly singular.*

Similarly, we give the name *weakly singular* to the Fredholm equation of the form

$$\varphi(x) = f(x) + \lambda \int_{\Omega} \frac{K(x, y)}{|xy|^{\alpha}} \varphi(y)\, dy, \tag{1}$$

where Ω denotes a domain in n-dimensional space, $K(x, y)$ a given bounded function of two variables in the domain Ω, $|xy|$ the distance between two points x and y of that domain, α — a positive real number less than the number of dimensions:

$$\alpha < n .$$

This condition implies that the integral in the right-hand side of equation (1) is an improper integral which converges absolutely, i.e. the limit

$$\int_{\Omega} \frac{|K(x, y)|}{|xy|^{\alpha}} |\varphi|\, dy = \lim_{r_\gamma \to 0} \int_{\Omega-\gamma} \frac{|K(x, y)|}{|xy|^{\alpha}} |\varphi|\, dy, \tag{2}$$

where r_γ is the diameter of an arbitrary domain γ containing the point x (on the assumption that the functions K and φ are bounded and integrable).

Singular equations of form (1) are frequently encountered in many applications. If $\alpha < n/2$ then the kernel is integrable together with its square and the equation may be solved directly by using Fredholm's formulae. On the other hand, in every case when $\alpha < n$, as we shall show, the equation may be reduced to an *iterated* equation with a bounded kernel, which will be equivalent to the equation given.

If α is equal to the number of dimensions n, then the improper integral (1) exists only in the case when certain special conditions are satisfied, and equation (1) is called *strongly singular* (*singular integral equation with Cauchy type kernel*). The investigation of such equations requires the application of methods other than those required in the investigation of singular equations mentioned previously. On account of their great importance in certain branches of mathematics and in engineering applications, singular equations with Cauchy type kernels have been the subject of numerous recent investigations, which will be discussed in greater detail in the following chapters of this book.

In the special case when $n = 1$, the singular equation (1) takes the form

$$\varphi(x) = f(x) + \lambda \int_a^b \frac{K(x, y)}{|x-y|^\alpha} \varphi(y)\, dy,$$

when $\alpha < 1$, and the singular equation with Cauchy type kernel takes the form

$$\varphi(x) = f(x) + \lambda \int_a^b \frac{K(x, y)}{x-y} \varphi(y)\, dy.$$

We also mention that if the kernel is *unbounded logarithmically*, i.e. if it has the form

$$N(x, y) = K(x, y) \log|xy| + K'(x, y),$$

where K and K' are bounded, then the equation may be solved by Fredholm series, since the product

$$|xy|^\alpha \log|xy|$$

is bounded for arbitrarily small α, as $|xy| \to 0$.

§ 2. Iteration of the singular equation

We already know that the function φ satisfying the Fredholm integral equation of the second kind

$$\varphi(x) = f(x) + \lambda \int_{\Omega} N(x, y)\varphi(y)\,dy, \tag{3}$$

also satisfies the $(p-1)$-fold iterated equation

$$\varphi(x) = f_p(x) + \lambda^p \int_{\Omega} N_p(x, y)\varphi(y)\,dy, \tag{4}$$

where the iterated kernel is defined by the recursive formula

$$N_p(x, y) = \int_{\Omega} N_{p-1}(x, s)N(s, y)\,ds \quad (N_1 = N), \tag{5}$$

and the given function f_p is as follows (cf. Chapter II, § 1):

$$f_p(x) = f(x) + \sum_{\nu=1}^{p-1} \lambda^\nu \int_{\Omega} N_\nu(x, y) f(y)\,dy \quad (f_1 = f). \tag{6}$$

Now we shall show that *if the singular kernel has the form*

$$N(x, y) = \frac{K(x, y)}{|xy|^\alpha}, \tag{7}$$

where K is bounded and integrable, then there always exists p_0 dependent on α such that for $p > p_0$ the iterated kernels $N_p(x, y)$ are bounded.

To this end we shall first prove that there exist constants C, C_1, and C_2, for which the inequality

$$\int_{\Omega} \frac{ds}{|xs|^\alpha |ys|^\beta} < \begin{cases} \dfrac{C}{|xy|^{\alpha+\beta-n}}, & \text{when} \quad \alpha+\beta > n, \\ C_1 \log|xy| + C_2, & \text{when} \quad \alpha+\beta = n \end{cases} \tag{8}$$

holds, where $|xs|$, $|ys|$, $|xy|$ are the distances between three points x, y, s of the n-dimensional domain Ω, $x \neq y$, α and β are two given real numbers such that

$$0 < \alpha < n, \quad 0 < \beta < n.$$

We shall first prove inequality (8) for $n = 1$. Then, substituting $s = x+(y-x)t$, we have

$$\int_a^b \frac{ds}{|x-s|^\alpha |y-s|^\beta} = \frac{1}{|y-x|^{\alpha+\beta-1}} \int_{\frac{a-x}{y-x}}^{\frac{b-x}{y-x}} \frac{dt}{t^\alpha(1-t)^\beta}, \tag{9}$$

whence inequality (8) follows directly.

In order to prove inequality (8) in the case $n > 1$, we shall make use of an ingenious method given by J. HADAMARD. Consider an n-dimensional sphere Π of radius $R = 2|xy|$, centered at the point x, and split the integral in the left-hand side of inequality (8) into two parts extending over the interior of the sphere Π and the exterior $\Omega-\Pi$:

$$\int_\Omega \frac{ds}{|xs|^\alpha |ys|^\beta} = \int_\Pi \frac{ds}{|xs|^\alpha |ys|^\beta} + \int_{\Omega-\Pi} \frac{ds}{|xs|^\alpha |ys|^\beta}. \tag{10}$$

To the interior portion extending over the sphere Π we apply the conformal transformation of the point x with the ratio $1/2|xy|$ which reduces the sphere Π to the sphere Π' with unit radius. Then we have directly

$$\int_\Pi \frac{ds}{|xs|^\alpha |ys|^\beta} = \frac{1}{2^{\alpha+\beta-n}|xy|^{\alpha+\beta-n}} \int_{\Pi'} \frac{ds'}{|xs'|^\alpha |y's'|^\beta}; \tag{11}$$

since $ds = 2^n |xy|^n ds'$. The integral obtained is bounded, since

$$|xy'| = \tfrac{1}{2}.$$

In order to estimate the second component of (10), note that for every point outside the sphere Π the inequality

$$\frac{1}{2} < \frac{|ys|}{|xs|} < \frac{3}{2}$$

holds, and hence

$$\int_{\Omega-\Pi} \frac{ds}{|xs|^\alpha |ys|^\beta} < 2^\beta \int_{\Omega-\Pi} \frac{ds}{|xs|^{\alpha+\beta}} < 2^\beta \omega_n \int_{2|xy|}^{L} \frac{r^{n-1}\,dr}{r^{\alpha+\beta}}, \tag{12}$$

where L is the diameter of the domain Ω, and

$$\omega_n = \frac{2(\sqrt{\pi})^n}{\Gamma(\frac{1}{2}n)}$$

is the surface area of an n-dimensional sphere of unit radius. Expressions (11) and (12) imply inequality (8) for $\alpha+\beta > n$. In the case where $\alpha+\beta = n$ integral (11) is unbounded, while the integral on the right-hand side of inequality (12) increases as $\log|xy|$ when $|xy| \to 0$, and thus inequality (8) also holds in this case.

In addition, if $\alpha+\beta < n$, then integral (8) is bounded as $|xy| \to 0$.

Inequality (8) implies that if the kernel of the integral equation has the form

$$N(x, y) = \frac{K(x, y)}{|xy|^\alpha} \qquad (\alpha < n),$$

then the first iterated kernel satisfies the inequality

$$|N_2(x, y)| \leqq \int_\Omega \frac{|K(x, s)|}{|xs|^\alpha} \frac{|K(s, y)|}{|sy|^\alpha} ds < \frac{M^2 C}{|xy|^{2\alpha-n}} \qquad (2\alpha > n),$$

and the second iterated kernel satisfies the inequality

$$|N_3(x, y)| = \int_\Omega \frac{M^2 C}{|xs|^{2\alpha-n}} \frac{M}{|sy|^\alpha} ds < \frac{M^3 C^2}{|xy|^{3\alpha-2n}} \qquad (3\alpha > 2n).$$

In general, we conclude by induction that for $p\alpha > (p-1)n$ the $(p-1)$-fold iterated kernel satisfies the inequality

$$|N_p(x, y)| < \frac{M^p C^{p-1}}{|xy|^{p\alpha-(p-1)n}}, \tag{13}$$

where M is the upper bound of the function $|K(x, y)|$. In inequality (13), we see that each iteration lowers the exponent of the distance $|xy|$ in the denominator by the number $n-\alpha$.

Let p_0 be the greatest positive integer for which

$$p\alpha-(p-1)n \geqq 0;$$

we obviously have

$$p_0 = \mathrm{E}\left(\frac{n}{n-\alpha}\right).$$

The number p_0 increases as the difference $n-\alpha$ decreases. From the relation

$$N_{p+1}(x, y) = \int_{\Omega} N_p(x, s) N_1(s, y)\, ds \tag{14}$$

we then conclude that the kernel N_{p_0+1} and all the subsequent kernels will be bounded, since for $p > p_0$

$$p\alpha-(p-1)n+\alpha < n$$

and we know that the integral

$$\int_{\Omega} \frac{ds}{|xs|^{\alpha}|sy|^{\beta}}$$

is bounded for $\alpha+\beta < n$.

The problem of solving the integral equation with singular kernel (7) can thus be reduced to the solution by Fredholm's method of the iterated equation with *bounded* kernel.

§ 3. Equivalence of the Fredholm equation and the iterated equation

Now we have to investigate the principal question, whether or not the converse is true, i.e. whether or not all the solutions of the iterated equation (4) satisfy the given equation (3).

The problem is simple if λ^p is not an eigenvalue of the iterated kernel $N_p(x, y)$. For if we assume that the function $\psi(x)$ is the unique solution of the iterated equation (4) we form a sequence of operations starting with the function ψ:

$$\begin{aligned}
\varphi_1(x) &= f(x)+\lambda \int_{\Omega} N(x, y)\psi(y)\, dy, \\
\varphi_2(x) &= f(x)+\lambda \int_{\Omega} N(x, y)\varphi_1(y)\, dy, \\
&\ldots\ldots\ldots\ldots\ldots\ldots\ldots\ldots \\
\varphi_{p-1}(x) &= f(x)+\lambda \int_{\Omega} N(x, y)\varphi_{p-2}(y)\, dy, \\
\psi(x) &= f(x)+\lambda \int_{\Omega} N(x, y)\varphi_{p-1}(y)\, dy
\end{aligned} \tag{15}$$

and arriving, in accordance with the hypothesis, back at the function ψ as the solution of the $(p-1)$-fold iterated equation. Adding equalities (15), we obtain the equality

$$\frac{\varphi_1+\varphi_2+\ldots+\varphi_{p-1}+\psi}{p} = f(x)+\lambda \int_\Omega N(x,y) \frac{\psi+\varphi_1+\varphi_2+\ldots+\varphi_{p-1}}{p}\, dy$$

stating that the function

$$\varphi_0(x) = \frac{\varphi_1(x)+\varphi_2(x)+\ldots+\varphi_{p-1}(x)+\psi(x)}{p} \tag{16}$$

is a solution of the given equation (3). Function (16), however, must also satisfy the iterated equation

$$\varphi_0(x) = f_p(x)+\lambda^p \int_\Omega N_p(x,y)\, \varphi_0(y)\, dy,$$

and if we then assume that λ^p is not an eigenvalue of the kernel $N_p(x, y)$ then function (16) must be identical with the function $\psi(x)$:

$$\varphi_0(x) = \psi(x),$$

as the unique solution of that equation.

The problem is more difficult when λ_0^p is an eigenvalue of the iterated kernel $N_p(x, y)$. Although function (16) is then also a solution of the original equation (3) when ψ satisfies equation (4), we may not assert that it is identical with the solution $\psi(x)$ of the iterated equation, which, if it exists, is then not unique. Therefore we do not know whether the converse is true, i.e. whether every solution of the iterated equation satisfies the given equation (3). In fact, in that case not every iterated equation is completely equivalent to the given equation, since it is not always true that solutions of the iterated equation are solutions of the original equation, if only the reason being that the characteristic solutions of the iterated equation with an eigenvalue

μ may be characteristic solutions of the original equation with various eigenvalues λ_0' and λ_0'' such that

$$\lambda_0'^p = \lambda_0''^p = \mu .$$

In order to analyse exactly the problem of equivalence of the given equation and the iterated equation, we shall first give the properties of a certain linear operation called Fredholm's operation.

Fredholm's operation on an integrable function φ is the operation defined by

$$(a_1+b_1\hat{N})\varphi = a_1\varphi(x)+b_1\int_\Omega N(x, y)\varphi(y)\,dy . \tag{17}$$

We call its symbol $a_1+b_1\hat{N}$ a *Fredholm operator*; a_1 and b_1 are certain constants. The kernel of the operation $N(x, y)$ may be regular or singular.

Suppose we are given another operator

$$(a_2+b_2\hat{N})\psi = a_2\psi(x)+b_2\int_\Omega N(x, y)\psi(y)\,dy \tag{18}$$

with constant coefficients a_2 and b_2 not necessarily the same as above. If the function, which is the result of operation (17) carried out upon the function φ, is subjected to operation (18), we obtain the following result:

$$\begin{aligned}
&(a_2+b_2\hat{N})[(a_1+b_1\hat{N})\varphi] \\
&= a_2\Big[a_1\varphi+b_1\int_\Omega N\varphi\,dy\Big]+ \\
&\quad +b_2\int_\Omega N(x, y)\Big[a_1\varphi(y)+b_1\int_\Omega N(y, s)\varphi(s)\,ds\Big]dy \\
&= a_1a_2\varphi(x)+ \\
&\quad +(a_1b_2+a_2b_1)\int_\Omega N(x, y)\varphi(y)\,dy+b_1b_2\int_\Omega N_2(x, y)\varphi(y)\,dy .
\end{aligned}$$

We denote this symbolically by

$$\begin{aligned}
&(a_2+b_2\hat{N})[(a_1+b_1\hat{N})\varphi] \\
&\qquad = [a_1a_2+(a_1b_2+a_2b_1)\hat{N}+b_1b_2\hat{N}^2]\varphi .
\end{aligned} \tag{19}$$

Thus, the formal product of two Fredholm operations satisfies the usual *distributive law*; furthermore, such a product is commutative, i.e.

$$(a_1+b_1\hat{N})[(a_2+b_2\hat{N})\varphi] = (a_2+b_2\hat{N})[(a_1+b_1\hat{N})\varphi]. \quad (20)$$

In general: *A Fredholm polynomial operator of degree p is an operator defined by the relation*

$$\begin{aligned}&(A_0+A_1\hat{N}+A_2\hat{N}^2+\ldots+A_p\hat{N}^p)\varphi(x)\\ &= A_0\varphi(x)+A_1\int_\Omega N_1(x,y)\varphi(y)\,dy+A_2\int_\Omega N_2(x,y)\varphi(y)\,dy+\\ &\quad+\ldots+A_p\int_\Omega N_p(x,y)\varphi(y)\,dy,\end{aligned} \quad (21)$$

where $A_0, A_1, \ldots, A_p$ are constants.

Suppose we are given p Fredholm operators

$$a_1+b_1\hat{N}, \quad a_2+b_2\hat{N}, \quad a_3+b_3\hat{N}, \quad \ldots, \quad a_p+b_p\hat{N}. \quad (22)$$

On the basis of equalities (21) and (19), it is easy to prove by induction that the result of p consecutive operations (22) on an arbitrary integrable function φ is the operation defined by the polynomial operator

$$\begin{aligned}&(a_p+b_p\hat{N})\ldots(a_2+b_2\hat{N})(a_1+b_1\hat{N})\varphi(x)\\ &\quad= (A_0+A_1\hat{N}+A_2\hat{N}^2+\ldots+A_{p-1}\hat{N}^{p-1}+A_p\hat{N}^p)\varphi(x),\end{aligned} \quad (23)$$

which is the formal product of operators (22) in accordance with algebraic principles concerning the multiplication of polynomials. The result of operations (23) is therefore independent of the order of operations.

We shall now investigate the problem of equivalence of the Fredholm homogeneous equation

$$\varphi(x)-\lambda_0\int_\Omega N(x,y)\varphi(y)\,dy = 0 \quad (24)$$

and its iterated equation

$$\psi(x)-\lambda_0^p\int_\Omega N_p(x,y)\psi(y)\,dy = 0 \quad (25)$$

with a regular kernel.

In order that these considerations also hold for a singular kernel we shall generalize the definition of the eigenvalue of a kernel: an *eigenvalue of a singular or regular kernel* $N(x, y)$ is a number λ_0 such that equation (24) possesses a solution $\varphi(x)$ called a *characteristic solution*, which is not equal to zero almost everywhere, and hence has a positive norm. Since the solution of equation (24) is also a solution of the iterated equation (25), λ_0^p is an eigenvalue of the iterated equation (25). If p is sufficiently large so that the kernel N_p is bounded, then the set of eigenvalues of the kernel of equation (25) is separated, and the number of linearly independent characteristic solutions corresponding to each eigenvalue (i.e. the rank of the eigenvalue) is finite. Consequently, the eigenvalues of a singular kernel of the form

$$N(x, y) = \frac{K(x, y)}{|xy|^\alpha}$$

are also discrete, and the number of linearly independent characteristic solutions of equation (24) corresponding to each eigenvalue λ_0 is finite, and does not exceed the rank of the corresponding eigenvalue λ_0 of the iterated equation.

In order to establish whether, conversely, every solution ψ of the iterated equation (25) satisfies equation (24), let us write equation (24), making use of the Fredholm operator (17), in the form

$$(1-\lambda_0 \hat{N})\varphi = 0, \tag{26}$$

and the iterated equation in the form

$$(1-\lambda_0^p \hat{N}^p)\psi = 0. \tag{27}$$

Now note that operator (27) may be formally factorized in the following manner:

$$1-\lambda_0^p \hat{N}^p = (1-\lambda_0 \omega_p \hat{N})(1-\lambda_0 \omega_p^2 \hat{N})\ldots$$
$$\ldots(1-\lambda_0 \omega_p^{p-1} \hat{N})(1-\lambda_0 \omega_p^p \hat{N}), \tag{28}$$

where

$$\omega_p = e^{2\pi i/p}, \quad \omega_p^p = 1.$$

Using the property of Fredholm operators expressed by equation (23) the left-hand side of the iterated equation (25) may be considered as the result of the following p successive Fredholm operations:

$$(1-\lambda_0\,\omega_p\,\hat{N})(1-\lambda_0\,\omega_p^2\,\hat{N})\ldots(1-\lambda_0\,\omega_p^{p-1}\,\hat{N})(1-\lambda_0\,\hat{N})\,\psi=0\,. \qquad (29)$$

Assuming that λ_0 is an eigenvalue of the kernel $N(x, y)$ and λ_0^p is an eigenvalue of the iterated kernel $N_p(x, y)$, we note that there always exists an integer p sufficiently great, so that none of the points

$$\lambda_0\,\omega_p\,,\ \lambda_0\,\omega_p^2\,,\ \lambda_0\,\omega_p^3\,,\ \ldots,\ \lambda_0\,\omega_p^{p-1} \qquad (30)$$

is an eigenvalue of the kernel $N(x, y)$. In fact, if such a p did not exist, then the set of eigenvalues with modulus $|\lambda_0|$ would be infinite, which contradicts Fredholm's theory, that these points are separated, as poles of the resolvent kernel.

Thus let p be so large that the kernel N_p is bounded, and none of the points (30) is an eigenvalue of the kernel. We shall prove that in this case every solution ψ of the iterated equation (29) or (27) also satisfies the given equation (26). For this purpose, let us foım the sequence of functions $\varphi_1, \varphi_2, \ldots, \varphi_{p-1}$ by means of the following successive operations:

$$\begin{aligned}
\varphi_1 &= (1-\lambda_0\,\hat{N})\,\psi\,,\\
\varphi_2 &= (1-\lambda_0\,\omega_p^{p-1}\,\hat{N})\,\varphi_1\,,\\
\varphi_3 &= (1-\lambda_0\,\omega_p^{p-2}\,\hat{N})\,\varphi_2\,, \qquad (31)\\
&\ldots\ldots\ldots\ldots\ldots\ldots\\
\varphi_{p-1} &= (1-\lambda_0\,\omega_p^2\,N)\,\varphi_{p-2}\,.
\end{aligned}$$

Now, in accordance with equation (29), the next operation $1-\lambda_0\omega_p\hat{N}$ upon the function φ_{p-1} yields zero, since it is just the solution of equation (27) or (29). We therefore have

$$(1-\lambda_0\,\omega_p\,\hat{N})\,\varphi_{p-1}=0\,,$$

or, explicitly,

$$\varphi_{p-1}(x)-\lambda_0\,\omega_p\int_\Omega N(x, y)\,\varphi_{p-1}(y)\,dy=0\,. \qquad (32)$$

But by hypothesis $\lambda_0 \omega_p$ is not an eigenvalue of the kernel $N(x, y)$, and hence equation (32) has only the zero solution:

$$\varphi_{p-1} = 0.$$

Consequently, according to the last equation (31) the function φ_{p-2} satisfies the Fredholm equation

$$(1 - \lambda_0 \omega_p^2 \hat{N}) \varphi_{p-2} = 0,$$

and since $\lambda_0 \omega_p^2$ is also not an eigenvalue, $\varphi_{p-2} = 0$. Proceeding in this manner, we obtain in turn:

$$\varphi_{p-3} = 0, \ \varphi_{p-4} = 0, \ \ldots, \ \varphi_3 = 0, \ \varphi_2 = 0, \ \varphi_1 = 0.$$

The last equality expresses that

$$(1 - \lambda_0 \hat{N}) \psi = \psi(x) - \lambda_0 \int_\Omega N(x, y) \psi(y) \, dy = 0, \tag{32'}$$

and thus an arbitrary solution $\psi(x)$ of the iterated equation (25) satisfies the original equation (24). Equations (24) and (25) are therefore completely equivalent, provided that none of the numbers (30) is an eigenvalue of the kernel N.

We shall also mention that with the above choice of the integer p, equations (24) and (25) have the same number of linearly independent characteristic solutions, i.e. *the eigenvalues* λ_0 *and* λ_p *of the kernels N and* N_p *are of the same rank.*

We shall use an analogous method to investigate the equivalence of the non-homogeneous Fredholm equation

$$\varphi(x) = f'(x) + \lambda_0 \int_\Omega N(x, y) \varphi(y) \, dy \tag{33}$$

and its iterated equation

$$\psi(x) = f_p(x) + \lambda_0^p \int_\Omega N_p(x, y) \psi(y) \, dy \tag{34}$$

in the case where λ_0 is an eigenvalue of the kernel $N(x, y)$.

The given equation (33) may be written in the form

$$(1 - \lambda_0 \hat{N}) \varphi - f = 0. \tag{33'}$$

On the basis of expansion (28) we have

$$(1-\lambda_0\,\omega_p\,\hat{N})(1-\lambda_0\,\omega_p^2\,\hat{N})\ldots(1-\lambda_0\,\omega_p^{p-1}\,\hat{N})f = \frac{1-\lambda_0^p\,\hat{N}^p}{1-\lambda_0\,\hat{N}}\,f$$

$$= (1+\lambda_0\,\hat{N}+\lambda_0^2\,\hat{N}^2+\ldots+\lambda_0^{p-1}\,\hat{N}^{p-1})f = f_p(x)\,, \qquad (35)$$

according to expression (6) on p. 81 we may also write the iterated equation (34) in the form

$$(1-\lambda_0\,\omega_p\,\hat{N})(1-\lambda_0\,\omega_p^2\,\hat{N})\ldots$$
$$\ldots(1-\lambda_0\,\omega_p^{p-1}\,\hat{N})[(1-\lambda_0\,\hat{N})\psi-f] = 0\,. \qquad (34')$$

Assuming that $\psi(x)$ is a solution of the iterated equation (34′) and that none of the points

$$\lambda_0\,\omega_p\,,\ \lambda_0\,\omega_p^2\,,\ \ldots,\ \lambda_0\,\omega_p^{p-1}$$

is an eigenvalue of the kernel $N(x, y)$, we now form the sequence of functions

$$\begin{aligned} \varphi_1(x) &= (1-\lambda_0\,\hat{N})\psi-f\,,\\ \varphi_2(x) &= (1-\lambda_0\,\omega_p^{p-1}\,\hat{N})\,\varphi_1\,,\\ \varphi_3(x) &= (1-\lambda_0\,\omega_p^{p-2}\,\hat{N})\,\varphi_2\,, \qquad (36)\\ &\ldots\ldots\ldots\ldots\ldots\\ \varphi_{p-1}(x) &= (1-\lambda_0\,\omega_p^2\,\hat{N})\,\varphi_{p-2} \end{aligned}$$

and arrive at the equality

$$(1-\lambda_0\,\omega_p\,\hat{N})\,\varphi_{p-1} = 0\,, \qquad (37)$$

since the result of the sequence of operations (36) is just the left-hand side of the iterated equation (34′).

But, by hypothesis, $\lambda_0\,\omega_p$ is not an eigenvalue and therefore equation (37) has only the solution $\varphi_{p-1} = 0$. Further, from the equation obtained,

$$\varphi_{p-1} = (1-\lambda_0\,\omega_p^2\,\hat{N})\,\varphi_{p-2} = 0\,,$$

we conclude that $\varphi_{p-2} = 0$, then $\varphi_{p-3} = 0$, and so on. Finally we arrive at $\varphi_1 = 0$, i.e. at the equality

$$(1-\lambda_0\,\hat{N})\psi-f = 0\,,$$

or explicitly,

$$\psi(x)-\lambda_0 \int_\Omega N(x, y)\psi(y)\,dy - f(x) = 0.$$

This relation states that the solution $\psi(x)$ of equation (34) is also a solution of the original non-homogeneous equation (33). Thus every Fredholm singular equation may be reduced by a suitable choice of p to an iterated equation with a bounded kernel N_p which will be completely equivalent to the given equation, even in the case where λ_0 is an eigenvalue of the given kernel N. Thus, the conditions of solvability of the given equation (33) are the same as for the iterated equation (34): *Also, in the case of an eigenvalue λ_0, the solution in the known form exists if, and only if, the given function $f_p(x)$ is orthogonal to all the characteristic solutions of the associated equation*

$$\Psi(x) = \bar{\lambda}_0^p \int_\Omega \overline{N_p(y, x)}\, \Psi(y)\,dy, \tag{38}$$

corresponding to the eigenvalue $\bar{\lambda}_0^p$ conjugate to the eigenvalue λ_0^p i.e. if, and only if, the function $f_p(x)$ satisfies the equation

$$\int_\Omega f_p(x)\,\overline{\Psi(x)}\,dx = 0. \tag{39}$$

If the equation associated with the original equation has the form

$$(1-\bar{\lambda}_0 N^*)\Psi = \Psi(x) - \bar{\lambda}_0 \int_\Omega \overline{N(y, x)}\,\Psi(y)\,dy = 0, \tag{40}$$

then its iterated equation (27) is of the form

$$(1-\bar{\lambda}_0^p N^{*p})\Psi = (1-\bar{\lambda}_0 \bar{\omega}_p N^*)(1-\bar{\lambda}_0 \bar{\omega}_p^2 N^*)\ldots$$
$$\ldots(1-\bar{\lambda}_0 \bar{\omega}_p^{p-1} N^*)(1-\bar{\lambda}_0 N^*)\Psi = 0. \tag{41}$$

Hence we conclude, just as above, that it is completely equivalent to the original associated equation (40) since none of the numbers

$$\bar{\lambda}_0 \bar{\omega}_p,\ \bar{\lambda}_0 \bar{\omega}_p^2,\ \ldots,\ \bar{\lambda}_0 \bar{\omega}_p^{p-1}$$

is an eigenvalue of the kernel N^* of the associated equation for the values (30) conjugate to them are not eigenvalues of the given kernel N. All the characteristic solutions $\Psi(x)$ of the iterated equation (41), and only these, are at the same time solutions of equation (40) associated with equation (33).

The condition expressed by equation (39) may be replaced by the necessary and sufficient condition for orthogonality of the given function $f(x)$ to all the characteristic solutions $\Psi(x)$ of the associated equation (40).

We have already said that if λ_0 is an eigenvalue of the kernel $N(x, y)$, then λ_0^p is an eigenvalue of the iterated kernel N_p. It remains to decide the question whether, conversely, if $\lambda_0^p = \mu$ is an eigenvalue of the iterated kernel then λ_0 is an eigenvalue of the original kernel N. The answer is contained in the following theorem:

THEOREM. *If a number μ is an eigenvalue of the iterated kernel $N_p(x, y)$, then at least one of the distinct numbers*

$$h_1, h_2, h_3, \ldots, h_p, \tag{42}$$

which are the roots of the equation $h^p = \mu$, is an eigenvalue of the kernel $N(x, y)$.

Let $\psi(x)$ be an arbitrary characteristic solution of the iterated equation, which we shall write in the form

$$(1-\mu\hat{N}^p)\psi = 0, \tag{43}$$

where μ is a given eigenvalue of that equation. Let us now consider the p functions obtained by means of the following operation carried out upon the function ψ:

$$\varphi_\nu(x) = (1+h_\nu\hat{N}+h_\nu^2\hat{N}^2+\ldots+h_\nu^{p-1}N^{p-1})\psi$$
$$(\nu = 1, 2, \ldots, p). \tag{44}$$

Each of these functions is a solution of the original equation, since, according to the properties of Fredholm's operator, we have

$$(1-h_\nu\hat{N})\varphi_\nu = (1-h_\nu\hat{N})(1+h_\nu\hat{N}+\ldots+h_\nu^{p-1}\hat{N}^{p-1})\psi$$
$$= (1-h_\nu^p\hat{N})\psi = 0, \tag{45}$$

i.e.

$$\varphi_\nu(x)-h_\nu\int_\Omega N(x, y)\varphi_\nu(y)\,dy = 0. \tag{46}$$

Now adding the p functions (44) and taking into account the obvious equalities

$$\sum_{\nu=1}^{p} h_\nu = 0, \quad \sum_{\nu=1}^{p} h_\nu^2 = 0, \quad \ldots, \quad \sum_{\nu=1}^{p} h_\nu^{p-1} = 0,$$

we obtain

$$\varphi_1(x)+\varphi_2(x)+\ldots+\varphi_p(x) = p\psi(x). \tag{47}$$

Since $\psi(x)$ is a characteristic solution of the iterated equation corresponding to the eigenvalue μ, equality (47) implies that at least one of the p functions $\varphi_\nu(x)$ satisfying the original equation (46) is non-zero almost everywhere, and hence is the characteristic solution corresponding to the eigenvalue h_ν. Consequently, at least one of the numbers $h_1, h_2, \ldots, h_p$ is an eigenvalue of the kernel N.

COROLLARY 1. *If*

$$\lambda_1, \lambda_2, \lambda_3, \ldots, \lambda_n, \ldots$$

is a sequence of all the eigenvalues of the kernel $N(x, y)$, then

$$\lambda_1^p, \lambda_2^p, \lambda_3^p, \ldots, \lambda_n^p, \ldots$$

is a sequence of all the eigenvalues of the iterated kernel N_p, and only such.

COROLLARY 2. *Every linear combination of characteristic solutions of the original equations* (46), *where h_ν are the roots of the equation $h^p = \mu$, and only such a combination, is a characteristic solution of the* $(p-1)$*-fold iterated equation corresponding to the eigenvalue μ.*

This corollary follows directly from the remark that characteristic solutions of equations (46) are at the same time characteristic solutions of the iterated equation for the eigenvalue μ and, conversely, according to equation (47) every characteristic solution $\psi(x)$ of the iterated equation is the sum of certain characteristic solutions of equations (46). We also see that the rank of the eigenvalue μ is not less than the greatest of the ranks of the eigenvalues chosen from the sequence $h_1, h_2, \ldots, h_\nu$.

§ 4. Integral equations in an infinite interval

Integral equations in an infinite interval have the following characteristic property: Their eigenvalues may form a set which exhaust some interval. This property is demonstrated for example, by the following integral equation, given by E. PICARD:

$$\varphi(x)-\lambda\int_0^\infty e^{-|x-s|}\varphi(s)\,ds=0. \tag{48}$$

This equation may be reduced to a differential equation; for by writing it in the form

$$\varphi(x)-\lambda\int_0^x e^{-(x-s)}\varphi(s)\,ds-\lambda\int_x^\infty e^{-(s-x)}\varphi(s)\,ds=0 \tag{49}$$

and differentiating both sides twice, we obtain

$$\varphi'(x)+\lambda e^{-x}\int_0^x e^s\varphi(s)\,ds-\lambda e^x\int_x^\infty e^{-s}\varphi(s)\,ds=0 \tag{50}$$

and

$$\varphi''(x)+(2\lambda-1)\varphi(x)=0. \tag{51}$$

The general solution of equation (51) has the form

$$\varphi(x)=C_1e^{x\sqrt{1-2\lambda}}+C_2e^{-x\sqrt{1-2\lambda}}. \tag{52}$$

In order that this solution satisfy the given equation (48) it is required that the conditions

$$\varphi'(0)-\lambda\int_0^\infty e^{-s}\varphi(s)\,ds=0,\quad \varphi(0)-\lambda\int_0^\infty e^{-s}\varphi(s)\,ds=0, \tag{53}$$

following from equations (49) and (50), be satisfied. Now, in the case where $1-2\lambda<0$, i.e. $\lambda>1/2$, the condition $\varphi(0)=\varphi'(0)$ is satisfied provided solution (52) has the form

$$\varphi(x)=C[\sin(\sqrt{2\lambda-1}\,x)+\sqrt{2\lambda-1}\cos(\sqrt{2\lambda-1}\,x)], \tag{54}$$

where C is an arbitrary constant. It may be verified directly that function (54) satisfies equation (48), and since it is a homogeneous equation, all the values of the parameter λ in the infinite interval $(1/2, \infty)$ are eigenvalues, since to each value in this interval there correspond *non-zero* solutions of form (54). If $1-2\lambda > 0$, then a function of the form (52) may satisfy conditions (53) only when $0 < \lambda < 1/2$, since otherwise the integrals occurring in those conditions would be divergent. If λ satisfies the above inequality then the solution of the integral equation (48) has the form

$$\varphi(x) = C[\sinh(\sqrt{1-2\lambda}\,x)+\cosh(\sqrt{1-2\lambda}\,x)]. \qquad (55)$$

Finally, we see that the singular equation (48) possesses a non-zero solution for all λ in the interval $(0, \infty)$, i.e. that *a singular equation may possess a continuous spectrum*, whereas, as we have seen, the spectrum of a regular equation always consists of separated points.

CHAPTER IV

SYSTEMS OF ORTHOGONAL FUNCTIONS

§ 1. Definition of an orthogonal system of functions

Systems of orthogonal functions play an important rôle in the theory of integral equations and in their application. In order that the arguments possess the greatest generality we shall conduct them from the start for functions which, together with the square of their moduli, are Lebesgue integrable. These arguments also apply to real functions as a special case.

We recall that two complex functions $f(x)$ and $\varphi(x)$ defined in the domain Ω are called *orthogonal* if their scalar product is equal to zero:

$$\int_{\Omega} f(x)\,\overline{\varphi(x)}\,dx = \int_{\Omega} \overline{f(x)}\,\varphi(x)\,dx = 0, \tag{1}$$

where the bar denotes the complex conjugate. The *norm* of a complex function is the positive square root of the scalar product of the function by itself, i.e. of the integral of the square of its modulus. Denoting the norm of a function $f(x)$ by the symbol $\|f\|$ we have

$$\|f\| = \sqrt{(f,f)} = \sqrt{\int_{\Omega} |f(x)|^2\,dx}\,. \tag{2}$$

We shall give some properties of the norm which are important in later considerations. Applying the Buniakovski–Schwarz inequality to the scalar product of two complex functions

$$(\varphi, \psi) = \int_{\Omega} \varphi(x)\,\overline{\psi(x)}\,dx$$

we have

$$|(\varphi, \psi)|^2 \leqq \Big[\int_{\Omega} |\varphi(x)| \,.\, |\psi(x)|\,dx\Big]^2 \leqq \int_{\Omega} |\varphi(x)|^2\,dx \,.\int_{\Omega} |\psi(x)|^2\,dx\,,$$

and hence

$$|(\varphi, \psi)| \leqq \|\varphi\| \cdot \|\psi\|, \tag{3}$$

which is the first result.

We shall obtain the second property by using the equality

$$\|\varphi+\psi\|^2 = (\varphi+\psi, \varphi+\psi) = (\varphi, \varphi)+(\varphi, \psi)+(\psi, \varphi)+(\psi, \psi).$$

Applying inequality (3) to the second and third term we obtain

$$\|\varphi+\psi\|^2 \leqq \|\varphi\|^2+2\|\varphi\| \cdot \|\psi\|+\|\psi\|^2,$$

from which it follows that

$$\|\varphi+\psi\| \leqq \|\varphi\|+\|\psi\|. \tag{4}$$

This property of the norm just derived is called the *triangle inequality*, on account of its interpretation in the function space, which will be given further on.

DEFINITION. *A sequence (finite or infinite) of functions*

$$\varphi_1(x), \varphi_2(x), \ldots, \varphi_n(x), \ldots,$$

defined and integrable together with the square of their moduli in the domain Ω, *is called an orthogonal system of functions if every pair of functions from this system is orthogonal, i.e. if*

$$\int_\Omega \varphi_\mu(x)\overline{\varphi_\nu(x)}\,dx = 0 \qquad (\mu \neq \nu).$$

Moreover, a system of functions is called *normalized,* if the norm of every function is equal to unity:

$$\int_\Omega |\varphi_\mu(x)|^2\,dx = 1.$$

If an orthogonal system is not normalized, then we can normalize it directly by dividing every function by its norm, provided this is non-zero.

The most important, well-known example of an orthogonal system in the interval $(0, 2\pi)$ is the sequence of trigonometric functions

$$\cos x, \sin x, \cos 2x, \sin 2x, \ldots, \cos nx, \sin nx, \ldots$$

Other examples of orthogonal systems in the interval $(-1, 1)$ are the sequence $P_n(x)$ of Legendre polynomials, defined by the formula

$$P_n(x) = \frac{1}{2^n n!} \frac{d^n}{dx^n} [(x^2-1)^n]$$

and the sequence of spherical functions of consecutive orders.

THEOREM. *A finite sequence of orthogonal functions with positive norms*

$$\varphi_1(x), \varphi_2(x), \ldots, \varphi_n(x)$$

forms a system of linearly independent functions.

In fact, if there exists a linear relation

$$A_1 \varphi_1(x) + A_2 \varphi_2(x) + \ldots + A_n \varphi_n(x) = 0,$$

where not all the constants $A_1, A_2, \ldots, A_n$ are zero, then by multiplying both sides of this relation by $\overline{\varphi_\nu(x)}$ (where ν is an arbitrary number from the sequence $1, 2, \ldots, n$) and integrating, we obtain, in accordance with the assumed orthogonality

$$A_\nu \int_\Omega |\varphi_\nu(x)|^2 dx = 0,$$

thus $A_\nu = 0$ for all $\nu = 1, 2, \ldots, n$ — contrary to the hypothesis.

Every sequence of linearly independent functions

$$\varphi_1(x), \varphi_2(x), \ldots, \varphi_n(x),$$

which are integrable, together with the square of their moduli, in the domain Ω, may be *orthogonalized*, i.e. it is possible to form from it a sequence of orthogonal functions each of which is a linear combination of the functions given. Suppose that the norms of all the functions given differ from zero:

$$\int_\Omega |\varphi_\nu(x)|^2 dx \neq 0 \quad (\nu = 1, 2, \ldots, n).$$

We take $\Phi_1(x) = \varphi_1(x)$, and seek the next function in the form

$$\Phi_2(x) = \varphi_2(x) + C_1 \varphi_1(x),$$

choosing the constant C_1 so that

$$\int_{\Omega} \Phi_1(x)\overline{\Phi_2(x)}\,dx = \int_{\Omega} \overline{\varphi_1(x)}\,\varphi_2(x)\,dx + C_1 \int_{\Omega} |\varphi_1(x)|^2\,dx = 0\,.$$

Having $\Phi_1(x)$ and $\Phi_2(x)$, we seek the third function in the form of a linear combination

$$\Phi_3(x) = \varphi_3(x) + C_1' \Phi_1(x) + C_2' \Phi_2(x)\,,$$

requiring that

$$\int_{\Omega} \Phi_3(x)\overline{\Phi_1(x)}\,dx = \int_{\Omega} \varphi_3 \overline{\Phi_1}\,dx + C_1' \int_{\Omega} |\Phi_1|^2\,dx = 0\,,$$
$$\int_{\Omega} \Phi_3(x)\overline{\Phi_2(x)}\,dx = \int_{\Omega} \varphi_3 \overline{\Phi_2}\,dx + C_2' \int_{\Omega} |\Phi_2|^2\,dx = 0;$$

whence the constants C_1' and C_2' are uniquely determined, since by assumption the moduli $|\Phi_1|$ and $|\Phi_2|$ are non-zero almost everywhere.

Having Φ_1, Φ_2, Φ_3, we seek the fourth function in the form

$$\Phi_4(x) = \varphi_4(x) + C_1'' \Phi_1(x) + C_2'' \Phi_2(x) + C_3'' \Phi_3(x);$$

requiring that that function be orthogonal to the three preceding ones; we obtain the constants C_1'', C_2'', C_3''. Proceeding in this manner in succession, we obtain a sequence of functions

$$\Phi_1(x),\ \Phi_2(x),\ \Phi_3(x),\ \ldots,\ \Phi_n(x),$$

forming an orthogonal system. The norms of these functions differ from zero, and hence by dividing each of the functions obtained by its norm we shall obtain a normalized orthogonal (orthonormal) system.

§ 2. Generalized Fourier series

Suppose we are given an orthonormal system of functions $\{\varphi_n(x)\}$, defined in the domain Ω and a function $f(x)$ defined and integrable together with the square of its modulus in that domain. If we assume that there exist constants $c_1, c_2, \ldots, c_n, \ldots$, such that the given function is the sum of the series

$$f(x) = \sum_{\nu=1}^{\infty} c_\nu \varphi_\nu(x),$$

convergent uniformly in the domain Ω, then, by multiplying both sides of the equation by an arbitrary function $\overline{\varphi_n(x)}$ and integrating, on account of orthogonality we would find that all the c_n should have the values as follows:

$$c_n = \int_\Omega f(x)\overline{\varphi_n(x)}\,dx\,.$$

On the basis of the above we introduce the following definition:

DEFINITION. *If a function $f(x)$ is defined and integrable (together with the square of its modulus) on the domain Ω, then the generalized Fourier series of $f(x)$, with respect to an orthogonal system $\{\varphi_\nu(x)\}$, is a series of the form*

$$\sum_{\nu=1}^{\infty} c_\nu \varphi_\nu(x)\,, \tag{5}$$

whose coefficients are defined by the formulae

$$c_\nu = \int_\Omega f(x)\overline{\varphi_\nu(x)}\,dx \qquad (\nu = 1, 2, 3, \ldots) \tag{6}$$

and are called the generalized Fourier coefficients of the function $f(x)$ with respect to the system $\{\varphi_\nu(x)\}$.

Every function $f(x)$ satisfying the above conditions has a Fourier series with respect to the given orthonormal system $\{\varphi_\nu(x)\}$, but obviously, *it is impossible to assert a priori either that its Fourier series converges or that it is its sum.*

The ordinary Fourier trigonometric series

$$\sum_{n=0}^{\infty} (a_n \cos nx + b_n \sin nx)$$

of the function $f(x)$ in the interval $(-\pi, \pi)$ is a special case of a generalized Fourier series (5) where the orthogonal system $\{\varphi_\nu(x)\}$ is a sequence of trigonometric functions:

$$\frac{1}{\sqrt{2}},\ \cos x,\ \sin x,\ \cos 2x,\ \sin 2x,\ \ldots,\ \cos nx,\ \sin nx,\ \ldots,$$

normalized by dividing by $\sqrt{\pi}$

The Fourier coefficients of an arbitrary function $f(x)$ have an interesting property, expressed by the *Bessel inequality.* We have *

$$\int_\Omega |f(x)-\sum_{\nu=1}^{n} c_\nu \varphi_\nu(x)|^2\,dx$$

$$= \int_\Omega |f(x)|^2\,dx + \sum_{\nu=1}^{n} \int_\Omega |c_\nu|^2 |\varphi_\nu(x)|^2\,dx -$$

$$- \sum_{\nu=1}^{n} \int_\Omega \overline{f(x)}\, c_\nu \varphi_\nu(x)\,dx - \sum_{\nu=1}^{n} \int_\Omega f(x)\, \bar{c}_\nu \overline{\varphi_\nu(x)}\,dx,$$

and since

$$\int_\Omega |\varphi_\nu(x)|^2\,dx = 1,$$

$$\int_\Omega f(x)\,\overline{\varphi_\nu(x)}\,dx = c_\nu,$$

$$\int_\Omega \overline{f(x)}\,\varphi_\nu(x)\,dx = \bar{c}_\nu,$$

we have

$$\int_\Omega |f(x)-\sum_{\nu=1}^{n} c_\nu \varphi_\nu(x)|^2\,dx = \int_\Omega |f(x)|^2\,dx - \sum_{\nu=1}^{n} |c_\nu|^2. \tag{7}$$

Integral (7) has a non-negative value, and hence for every n we have the following inequality;

$$\sum_{\nu=1}^{n} |c_\nu|^2 \leqq \int_\Omega |f(x)|^2\,dx = \|f\|^2. \tag{8}$$

Hence we conclude that the series $\sum_{\nu=1}^{\infty} |c_\nu|^2$ is always convergent and that its sum satisfies the inequality

$$\sum_{\nu=1}^{\infty} |c_\nu|^2 \leqq \int_\Omega |f(x)|^2\,dx = \|f\|^2. \tag{9}$$

The inequality (9) involving the Fourier coefficients is called *Bessel's inequality.*

---

* We are using the identity

$$|a+b|^2 = (a+b)(\bar{a}+\bar{b}) = a\bar{a}+b\bar{b}+a\bar{b}+\bar{a}b.$$

If the left-hand side of (7) tends to zero as $n \to \infty$, then the Fourier coefficients satisfy the following relation:

$$\sum_{\nu=1}^{\infty} |c_\nu|^2 = \|f\|^2, \tag{10}$$

called *Parseval's equation*. This property is possessed, for example, by the coefficients of a simple trigonometric Fourier series.

THEOREM. *The integral*

$$\int_\Omega |f(x) - \sum_{\nu=1}^{n} h_\nu \varphi_\nu(x)|^2 \, dx$$

with variable parameters h_ν attains its minimum value when the parameters h_ν are equal to the Fourier coefficients of the function $f(x)$ with respect to the orthogonal system $\{\varphi_\nu(x)\}$.

In fact, proceeding in a manner similar to the above, we have

$$\int_\Omega |f(x) - \sum_{\nu=1}^{n} h_\nu \varphi_\nu(x)|^2 \, dx$$

$$= \int_\Omega |f(x)|^2 \, dx + \sum_{\nu=1}^{n} |h_\nu|^2 - \sum_{\nu=1}^{n} h_\nu \bar{c}_\nu - \sum_{\nu=1}^{n} \bar{h}_\nu c_\nu$$

$$= \int_\Omega |f(x)|^2 \, dx - \sum_{\nu=1}^{n} |c_\nu|^2 + \sum_{\nu=1}^{n} |h_\nu - c_\nu|^2 .$$

Hence it is immediately apparent that the given integral is minimal when $h_\nu = c_\nu$.

§ 3. Complete orthogonal systems

DEFINITION. *An orthonormal system of functions $\{\varphi_\nu(x)\}$ is called complete if there exists no function with positive norm which is orthogonal to all the functions of that system.*

It may be shown, that the sequence of trigonometric functions

$$\frac{\cos nx}{\sqrt{\pi}}, \quad \frac{\sin nx}{\sqrt{\pi}} \qquad (n = 0, 1, 2, \ldots)$$

is such a system in the interval $(-\pi, \pi)$.

If from this system we were to eliminate the first term $1/\sqrt{\pi}$ corresponding to $n = 0$, then the remaining system would no longer be complete. Obviously, every complete orthogonal system must be infinite.

THEOREM. *If an orthonormal system of functions* $\{\varphi_\nu(x)\}$ *is complete and the Fourier series* $\sum_{\nu=1}^{\infty} c_\nu \varphi_\nu(x)$ *of a given function* $f(x)$ *with respect to the given system converges uniformly, then the sum of that series is equal to the given function* $f(x)$ *almost everywhere* *.

In fact, if we let

$$\omega(x) = \sum_{\nu=1}^{\infty} c_\nu \varphi_\nu(x) - f(x),$$

we see that the function $\omega(x)$ is orthogonal to all the functions $\varphi_\nu(x)$ of the given system, since the hypothesis implies that it is possible to integrate the Fourier series term by term, and consequently

$$(\omega, \varphi_n) = \sum_{\nu=1}^{\infty} c_\nu (\varphi_\nu, \varphi_n) - (f, \varphi_n) = c_n - c_n = 0$$

for all integers n. By hypothesis, the system $\{\varphi_n\}$ is complete and hence $\omega = 0$ almost everywhere, which was to be shown.

THEOREM. *If the Fourier coefficients of every function (integrable with the square of its modulus) satisfy Parseval's equation with respect to a given system of functions, then this system is complete.*

In fact, if the given system of functions were not complete then there would exist a function $f(x)$ with positive norm, orthogonal to all the functions $\varphi_\nu(x)$. Then all the Fourier coefficients of that function with respect to the system $\{\varphi_\nu(x)\}$ would be zero,

$$c_\nu = \int_\Omega f(x) \overline{\varphi_\nu(x)}\, dx = 0,$$

and hence could not satisfy Parseval's equation which contradicts the original assumption.

---

* The expression *almost everywhere* means everywhere with the exception of a set of points with Lebesgue measure zero.

The last two theorems show that the completeness of a system of functions is closely connected with Parseval's equation. In § 5 we shall show that if a system of functions $\{\varphi_\nu(x)\}$ is complete then the Fourier coefficients with respect to that system of every function (integrable with the square of its modulus) satisfy Parseval's equation.

§ 4. Sequences and series convergent in the mean

DEFINITION. *A sequence of functions $\{u_n(x)\}$ which are defined and integrable (together with the square of their moduli) on the set Ω, is called convergent in the mean in that set to the function $f(x)$ (integrable together with the square of its modulus) if*

$$\|f-u_n\| \to 0, \qquad as \qquad n\to\infty, \tag{11}$$

or explicitly,

$$\int_\Omega |f(x)-u_n(x)|^2\,dx \to 0, \qquad as \qquad n\to\infty.$$

Convergence in the mean is similar to ordinary convergence if instead of the modulus of the difference we take the norm of the difference.

Obviously, if a sequence of functions is uniformly convergent to a function in a given set then it is also convergent in the mean, but not conversely.

We shall show that *if a sequence of functions $\{u_n(x)\}$ is convergent in the mean to the function $f(x)$ then this function is unique in the class of functions which are integrable, together with the square of their moduli, if we neglect functions which differ from it only on a set of measure zero.*

In fact, if there exist two functions $f(x)$ and $\varphi(x)$ to which the sequence of functions $\{u_n(x)\}$ converges in the mean, then we would have

$$\|f-u_n\|\to 0, \quad \|\varphi-u_n\|\to 0, \quad \text{as} \quad n\to\infty.$$

But according to the triangle inequality (p. 98) we have

$$\|f-\varphi\| \leqq \|f-u_n\|+\|\varphi-u_n\|$$

for all n. Hence it follows that

$$\|f-\varphi\| = 0,$$

and thus

$$f(x) = \varphi(x)$$

almost everywhere.

For convergence in the mean we have the following theorem, analogous to Cauchy's theorem for ordinary convergence of sequences:

THEOREM. *For a sequence of functions* $\{u_n(x)\}$ *to be convergent in the mean to some function it is necessary and sufficient that for any arbitrary positive number* ε *there exists an integer* N_ε *such that*

$$\|u_n - u_p\| < \varepsilon, \quad n > N_\varepsilon,\ p > N_\varepsilon. \tag{12}$$

This condition is of course *necessary*. For, if a sequence of functions $\{u_n(x)\}$ converges in the mean to the function $f(x)$, then there exists an N such that

$$\|u_n - f\| < \tfrac{1}{2}\varepsilon, \quad n > N,$$

and hence

$$\begin{aligned} \|u_p - u_n\| &= \|u_p - f - (u_n - f)\| \\ &\leqq \|u_p - f\| + \|u_n - f\| < \varepsilon, \end{aligned} \tag{13}$$

for $n > N$, $p > N$.

The proof that condition (12) is *sufficient* is to be found in the book by S. SAKS: *Teoria calki* (*Theory of the Integral*), Warszawa 1930.

We shall also prove the following theorem which will be required in the theory of equations with symmetric kernel:

THEOREM. *If a sequence of functions* $\{u_n(x)\}$ *which, together with the squares of their moduli, are integrable in the set* Ω, *is convergent in the mean to the function* $f(x)$, *and* $\varphi(x)$ *is an arbitrary function integrable together with the square of its modulus on the set* Ω, *then*

$$\lim_{n\to\infty} \int_\Omega u_n(x)\varphi(x)\,dx = \int_\Omega f(x)\varphi(x)\,dx. \tag{14}$$

Indeed, applying the Buniakovski-Schwarz inequality we have

$$\left|\int_\Omega [u_n(x)-f(x)]\,\varphi(x)\,dx\right|^2$$
$$\leqq \int_\Omega |u_n(x)-f(x)|^2\,dx \int_\Omega |\varphi(x)|^2\,dx\,, \qquad (15)$$

and since, by hypothesis, the integral

$$\int_\Omega |u_n(x)-f(x)|^2\,dx$$

tends to zero as $n\to\infty$, the theorem is proved.

DEFINITION. *A functional series* $\sum_{\nu=1}^{\infty} u_\nu(x)$ *with terms integrable together with the square of the modulus is called convergent in the mean to the function* $f(x)$ *in the set* Ω, *if the sequence of partial sums of that sequence is convergent in the mean to the function* $f(x)$, *i.e. if*

$$\|f-\sum_{\nu=1}^{n} u_\nu\| \to 0\,, \qquad n\to\infty.$$

From this follow properties which are analogous to the results obtained above for sequences.

§ 5. Riesz–Fischer Theorem*

This important theorem is stated as follows:

If $\{u_\nu(x)\}$ *is a given orthonormal system of functions defined and integrable together with the squares of their moduli in the domain* Ω, *and* $\{h_\nu\}$ *is a given sequence such that the series*

$$\sum_{\nu=1}^{\infty} |h_\nu|^2 \qquad (16)$$

converges, then there exists a unique function $f(x)$, *integrable together with the square of its modulus for which the numbers*

---

* This theorem was proved by the outstanding Hungarian mathematician F. RIESZ (*Comptes Rendus de l'Ac. des Sc.*, Paris 1907) and simultaneously by E. FISCHER (*Comptes Rendus de l'Ac. des Sc.*, Paris 1908).

h_ν are the Fourier coefficients with respect to the system $\{u_\nu(x)\}$ and to which the Fourier series converges in the mean.

In order to prove this theorem, let us consider the sequence of partial sums

$$s_n(x) = \sum_{\nu=1}^{n} h_\nu u_\nu(x) . \tag{17}$$

We have

$$\int_\Omega |s_{n+p}(x) - s_n(x)|^2 \, dx = |h_{n+1}|^2 + |h_{n+2}|^2 + \ldots + |h_{n+p}|^2 .$$

Since, by assumption, sequence (16) is convergent, for every $\varepsilon > 0$ there exists N_ε such that

$$\|s_{n+p} - s_n\| < \varepsilon, \quad n > N, \ p - \text{arbitrary}.$$

Hence it follows that, in accordance with the theorem of the last section on convergence in the mean, there exists a unique function $f(x)$, integrable in the domain Ω together with the square of its modulus to which sequence (17) converges in the mean, and consequently

$$\|f - \sum_{\nu=1}^{n} h_\nu u_\nu\| \to 0, \quad n \to \infty . \tag{18}$$

We shall show that the numbers h_ν are precisely the Fourier coefficients of the function $f(x)$ with respect to the system $\{u_\nu(x)\}$.

In fact, on the basis of formula (18) we have *

$$\|f - \sum_{\nu=1}^{n} h_\nu u_\nu\|^2$$

$$= \|f\|^2 - \sum_{\nu=1}^{n} |c_\nu|^2 + \sum_{\nu=1}^{n} |h_\nu - c_\nu|^2 \to 0, \quad n \to \infty , \tag{19}$$

and thus, according to Bessel inequality, must hold

$$h_\nu = c_\nu = \int_\Omega f(x) \overline{u_\nu(x)} \, dx \tag{20}$$

---

* See the theorem on p. 103.

and the Fourier series $\sum_{\nu=1}^{\infty} c_\nu u_\nu(x)$ of the function $f(x)$ with respect to the system $\{u_\nu(x)\}$ is convergent in the mean to that function:

$$\|f - \sum_{\nu=1}^{n} c_\nu u_\nu\| \to 0, \quad n \to \infty. \tag{21}$$

At the same time, from formula (19) we conclude that with respect to the system $\{u_\nu(x)\}$, the Fourier coefficients c_ν of the function $f(x)$ obtained satisfy Parseval's equation

$$\sum_{\nu=1}^{\infty} |c_\nu|^2 = \|f\|^2, \tag{22}$$

which, at any rate, agrees with the remark on p. 104.

The Riesz–Fischer Theorem implies the following important corollary:

COROLLARY. *The generalized Fourier series*

$$\sum_{\nu=1}^{\infty} c_\nu u_\nu(x)$$

of an arbitrary function $f(x)$ (integrable together with its modulus in the domain Ω) with respect to a complete orthonormal system $\{u_\nu(x)\}$, is convergent in the mean to that function $f(x)$ and its Fourier coefficients satisfy Parseval's equation.

Now by hypothesis we have

$$c_\nu = \int_\Omega f(x) \overline{u_\nu(x)}\, dx \tag{23}$$

and the series $\sum_{\nu=1}^{\infty} |c_\nu|^2$ is convergent, and hence, in accordance with the Riesz–Fischer Theorem, there exists a function $F(x)$ for which the c_ν are also Fourier coefficients:

$$c_\nu = \int_\Omega F(x) \overline{u_\nu(x)}\, dx \tag{24}$$

and to which the series $\sum_{\nu=1}^{\infty} c_\nu u_\nu(x)$ is convergent in the mean:

$$\|F - \sum_{\nu=1}^{n} c_\nu u_\nu\| \to 0, \quad n \to \infty. \tag{25}$$

Equalities (23) and (24) imply that

$$\int_{\Omega} [F(x) - f(x)] \overline{u_\nu(x)}\, dx = 0, \tag{26}$$

i.e. the difference of the functions $F(x)$ and $f(x)$ is orthogonal to all the functions of the given system $\{u_\nu(x)\}$.

Now if the given system $\{u_\nu(x)\}$ were not complete, then the functions $F(x)$ and $f(x)$ with the same Fourier series might be different (on a set of points having a positive measure). In the given case, however, in view of the assumed *completeness* of the system $\{u_\nu(x)\}$, equality (26) implies that

$$F(x) - f(x) = 0$$

almost everywhere in Ω. Thus, according to formula (25) we have

$$\left\| f - \sum_{\nu=1}^{n} c_\nu u_\nu \right\| \to 0, \quad n \to \infty, \tag{27}$$

i.e.

The Fourier series $\sum_{\nu=1}^{\infty} c_\nu u_\nu(x)$ *of an arbitrary function* $f(x)$ *with respect to a complete orthonormal system is convergent to it in the mean.*

Moreover, it is evident from the Riesz–Fischer Theorem that the Fourier coefficients c_ν of that function satisfy the Parseval equality.

§ 6. Generalized orthogonal systems

The definition and properties of orthogonal systems given earlier may be generalized to sequences of functions of two variables x and y in the domain Ω. This generalization is important in the theory of integral equations.

Consider the sequence

$$\{u_{\mu\nu}(x, y)\} \tag{28}$$

formed from complex functions of pairs of points (x, y) of the domain Ω. We assume that for every function of that sequence there exist iterated integrals

$$\int_\Omega \int_\Omega u_{\mu\nu}(x, y)\, dx\, dy, \qquad \int_\Omega \int_\Omega |u_{\mu\nu}(x, y)|^2\, dx\, dy \neq 0.$$

We call the sequence of functions (28) an *orthogonal system* if

$$\int_\Omega \int_\Omega u_{\mu\nu}(x, y)\, \overline{u_{\alpha\beta}(x, y)}\, dx\, dy = 0 \tag{29}$$

when $(\mu, \nu) \neq (\alpha, \beta)$; it is called *normalized* if the norm of every function is equal to unity

$$\|u_{\mu\nu}(x, y)\|^2 = \int_\Omega \int_\Omega |u_{\mu\nu}(x, y)|^2\, dx\, dy = 1.$$

As before, we call an orthogonal system $\{u_{\mu\nu}(x, y)\}$ *complete* if there exists no function $f(x, y)$ with positive norm orthogonal to all the functions $u_{\mu\nu}(x, y)$. All the theorems and corollaries given before for the system $u_\mu(x)$ may be proved in a similar manner for the system $\{u_{\mu\nu}(x, y)\}$, and therefore we shall not repeat them.

If $\{u_\mu(x)\}$ and $\{v_\nu(x)\}$ are two orthonormal systems, then the double sequence of products $\{u_\mu(x)\, v_\nu(y)\}$ is also an orthonormal system. In fact, we then have

$$\int_\Omega \int_\Omega u_\mu(x)\, v_\nu(y)\, \overline{u_\alpha(x)}\, \overline{v_\beta(y)}\, dx\, dy$$

$$= \int_\Omega u_\mu(x)\, \overline{u_\alpha(x)}\, dx \,.\, \int_\Omega v_\nu(y)\, \overline{v_\beta(y)}\, dy = \begin{cases} 1, & \mu = \alpha,\ \nu = \beta, \\ 0, & \mu \neq \alpha,\ \nu \neq \beta. \end{cases} \tag{30}$$

If both systems $\{u_\nu\}$ and $\{v_\nu\}$ are complete, then so also is the system $\{u_\mu(x)\, v_\nu(y)\}$. In fact, if $\{u_\mu(x)\, v_\nu(y)\}$ were not complete, then there would exist a function $f(x, y)$ with positive norm such that

$$\int_\Omega \int_\Omega f(x, y)\, \overline{u_\mu(x)}\, \overline{v_\nu(y)}\, dx\, dy = 0$$

for all ν. But then, on account of the completeness of the system $\{v_\nu\}$, this would imply that

$$\int_\Omega f(x, y)\, \overline{u_\mu(x)}\, dx = 0 \tag{31}$$

true almost everywhere with respect to y, i.e. when $y \in \Omega - \Omega'$, where Ω' is the set of points of Ω with measure zero. But then in view of the completeness of system $\{u_\mu\}$, we would have

$$f(x, y) = 0$$

almost everywhere with respect to x when $y \in \Omega - \Omega'$. Hence we conclude that

$$\int_\Omega \int_\Omega |f(x, y)|^2 \, dx \, dy = 0$$

contrary to the assumption, and hence the system $\{u_\mu(x) \, v_\nu(y)\}$ is complete.

The above property is very useful in its applications to integral equations. For, if $N(x, y)$ is a kernel of an integral equation for which the integrals

$$\int_\Omega \int_\Omega N(x, y) \, dx \, dy, \qquad \int_\Omega \int_\Omega |N(x, y)|^2 \, dx \, dy \tag{32}$$

exist, then the double Fourier series of the kernel $N(x, y)$

$$\sum_{\mu, \nu = 1}^{\infty} c_{\mu\nu} u_\mu(x) v_\nu(y), \qquad c_{\mu\nu} = \int_\Omega \int_\Omega N(x, y) \overline{u_\mu(x)} \, \overline{v_\nu(y)} \, dx \, dy \tag{33}$$

converges to it in the mean, i.e. we have

$$\left\| N(x, y) - \sum_{\nu=1}^{\beta} \sum_{\mu=1}^{\alpha} c_{\mu\nu} u_\mu(x) v_\nu(y) \right\| < \varepsilon \tag{34}$$

when $\alpha > L_\varepsilon$, $\beta > L_\varepsilon$, where L_ε depends on an arbitrary positive ε, of course on the assumption that the systems $\{u_\nu\}$ and $\{v_\nu\}$ are complete.

Property (34) makes it possible to approximate the kernel $N(x, y)$ integrable together with the square of its modulus according to the norm by a sum of products of functions of a point.

§ 7. Application to the solution of an integral equation

Suppose we are given an integral equation

$$\varphi(x) = f(x) + \lambda \int_\Omega N(x, y) \varphi(y) \, dy. \tag{35}$$

From formulae (33) and (34) we see that if the kernel $N(x, y)$ is integrable together with the square of its modulus, then it is possible to select a sum of products of functions of one variable such that the norm of the difference between that function and the kernel is less than an arbitrarily small number.

In this connection, we shall give a new *direct* method of solving the integral equation (35) without making use of Fredholm's formulae. We shall show that the solution of equation (35) with a kernel integrable together with the square of its modulus may be reduced (in the presence of certain additional assumptions) to the solution of an equation with a *degenerate* kernel.

We use the notation

$$N(x, y) - \sum_{\nu=1}^{p} K_\nu(x) L_\nu(y) = M(x, y). \tag{36}$$

As we have seen, the degenerate kernel $\sum_\nu K_\nu L_\nu$ may be chosen so that the square of the norm

$$\int_\Omega \int_\Omega |M(x, y)|^2 \, dx \, dy = B \tag{37}$$

be less than an arbitrarily small number. With the notation (36) we shall write the integral equation (35) in the form

$$\varphi(x) = f(x) + f_1(x) + \lambda \int_\Omega M(x, y) \varphi(y) \, dy, \tag{38}$$

where

$$f_1(x) = \lambda \int_\Omega \sum_{\nu=1}^{p} K_\nu(x) L_\nu(y) \varphi(y) \, dy. \tag{39}$$

Now let us temporarily treat the function $f_1(x)$ as known and solve equation (38) by the method of expansion in power series of a parameter, given in § 1 of Chapter II. The solution of equation (38) is then expressed in the form

$$\varphi(x) = f(x) + f_1(x) + \lambda \int_\Omega \mathfrak{M}(x, y, \lambda) [f(y) + f_1(y)] \, dy, \tag{40}$$

where the resolvent kernel $\mathfrak{M}$ of the kernel M is the sum of the series

$$\mathfrak{M}(x, y, \lambda) = \sum_{n=1}^{\infty} \lambda^{n-1} M_n(x, y), \tag{41}$$

convergent for sufficiently small $|\lambda|$. The M_n denote the iterated kernels of the kernel M. Now, according to inequality (28) on p. 110, the terms of the series (41) satisfy the inequalities

$$|\lambda^{n-1} M_n(x, y)| \leqq |\lambda \sqrt{B}|^{n-2} |\lambda| \sqrt{CD}, \tag{42}$$

where B is as in (37), and C and D are the upper bounds of the integrals

$$\int_\Omega |M(x, y)|^2 \, dy \leqq C, \qquad \int_\Omega |M(x, y)|^2 \, dx \leqq D \tag{43}$$

assuming that these integrals are bounded. Inequality (42) implies that series (41) converges if

$$|\lambda| \sqrt{B} < 1. \tag{44}$$

Since for every λ it is possible to choose a degenerate kernel $\sum_\nu K_\nu L_\nu$ such that the norm $\sqrt{B}$ be arbitrarily small, the inequality (44) can always be satisfied, and series (41) converges for any λ and suitably chosen p. The above property is essential in the method under consideration.

Since in equation (40) the function $f_1(x)$ is not known, but contains an unknown function, this equation is a new integral equation equivalent to the given equation (35).

Now, it is fundamental that the kernel of the new equation (40) is degenerate, for it is easily shown that this equation is expressible in the form

$$\varphi(x) = F(x) + \lambda \int_\Omega \sum_{\nu=1}^{n} K_\nu^*(x) L_\nu(y) \varphi(y) \, dy, \tag{45}$$

where the known functions F and K^* are expressed as follows:

$$\begin{aligned} F(x) &= f(x) + \lambda \int_\Omega \mathfrak{M}(x, y, \lambda) f(y) \, dy, \\ K_\nu^*(x) &= K_\nu(x) + \lambda \int_\Omega \mathfrak{M}(x, s, \lambda) K_\nu(s) \, ds. \end{aligned} \tag{46}$$

We solve equation (45) by the well-know algebraic method.

Thus, we can always reduce the integral equation (45) with an arbitrary kernel N (satisfying the very general integrability conditions mentioned above) to an integral equation with a degenerate kernel, which avoids the application of Fredholm's formulae. The above considerations indicate a method of approximate solution of the integral equation. For, if by the choice of a degenerate kernel $\sum_{\nu} K_\nu L_\nu$ we make the third term of sum (38) sufficiently small relative to the given function $f(x)$, then as the approximate solution of the given equation (35) we can take the solution of the equation

$$\varphi(x) = f(x) + \lambda \int_{\Omega} \sum_{\nu=1}^{p} K_\nu(x) L_\nu(y) \varphi(y) \, dy$$

with a degenerate kernel.

§ 8. Interpretation of generalized orthogonal sequences in Hilbert space and in function space

In modern mathematics every set of elements for which axioms of a geometrical nature have been postulated is called a *space*. Elements of the space are called its *points*. A space is called *linear* if the sum of every pair of elements and the product of every element by a real number is defined, where these operations obey the ordinary laws of algebra.

A space is called a *metric* space if to every pair a, b of its points there corresponds a non-negative number $\rho(a, b)$, called the *distance* between these points, satisfying the following conditions:

$$\begin{aligned} &\rho(a, b) = 0, \quad \text{only when } a = b, \\ &\rho(b, a) = \rho(a, b), \\ &\rho(a, b) + \rho(b, c) \geqq \rho(a, c). \end{aligned} \tag{47}$$

A space is called a *function space* if its elements are functions defined in the same set.

Hilbert space and the *space of functions which are integrable together with the squares of their moduli* bear a close relation to orthogonal systems. Let us consider these spaces in greater detail.

A *Hilbert space* is a space of sequences $\{a_n\}$, such that the series $\sum_{n=1}^{\infty} |a_n|^2$ is convergent, and for which the following definitions have been adopted:

I. The *sum* of two points $a = \{a_n\}$, $b = \{b_n\}$ of a Hilbert space is is defined to be the point $a+b = \{a_n+b_n\}$.

II. The *product* of a point $a = \{a_n\}$ by a real or complex number λ is the point $\lambda a = \{\lambda a_n\}$.

III. The *distance* $\rho(a, b)$ between two points $a = \{a_n\}$ and $b = \{b_n\}$ of a Hilbert space is the non-negative number

$$\rho(a, b) = \sqrt{\sum_{n=1}^{\infty} |a_n - b_n|^2}. \tag{48}$$

This number, as can easily be shown, satisfies conditions (47). Thus, a Hilbert space is a linear metric space.

The *zero* of a Hilbert space is the element $\{u_n\}$ defined by the zero sequence $u_n = 0$ $(n = 1, 2, 3, \ldots)$.

The distance of a point $a = \{a_n\}$ from zero is expressed by the formula

$$\rho(a, 0) = \sqrt{\sum_{n=1}^{\infty} |a_n|^2}.$$

This number is also called the *norm* of the point a.

We call a Hilbert space *real* if its elements $\{a_n\}$ are sequences of real numbers, and hence the scalar field must be real.

The *scalar product* of two points $a = \{a_n\}$ and $b = \{b_n\}$ of a Hilbert space is the sum of the following convergent series:

$$(a, b) = \sum_{n=1}^{\infty} a_n \bar{b}_n. \tag{49}$$

If a Hilbert space is real, then

$$(a, b) = (b, a).$$

Two points a and b in a Hilbert space are called *orthogonal* if their scalar product is zero.

The Hilbert space is closely related to the space L^2 of functions integrable with the squares of the moduli.

The *space* $L^2(\Omega)$ *is the space whose elements are all functions* f, *real or complex, and which are integrable together with the squares of their moduli in the same set* Ω.

For this space we adopt as the definition of distance $\delta(f, \varphi)$ between two of its elements $f(x)$ and $\varphi(x)$ the norm of the difference of these functions

$$\delta(f, \varphi) = \|f-\varphi\|. \tag{50}$$

This definition satisfies conditions (47), and hence the above function space is a metric space.

We also adopt the usual definition of the *sum* of two functions and *product by a real or complex number*, i.e. the above space is *linear*. In particular, the *distance of a point* $f(x)$ *from zero is equal to the norm of the function* $f(x)$:

$$\delta(f, 0) = \|f\|.$$

Suppose we are given an arbitrary complete orthonormal system $\{u_n(x)\}$, composed of functions defined in the same set Ω as the elements of a given function space. We know then that every function $f \in L^2(\Omega)$ has, with respect to the system $\{u_n(x)\}$, a Fourier series $\sum_{n=1}^{\infty} c_n u_n(x)$, whose coefficients satisfy Parseval's equation

$$\sum_{n=1}^{\infty} |c_n|^2 = \|f\|^2. \tag{51}$$

Thus, to every point f of a function space $L^2(\Omega)$ there corresponds a point $\{c_n\}$ of a Hilbert space which is the sequence of Fourier coefficients of the function $f(x)$ with respect to the system $\{u_n(x)\}$. Conversely, according to the Riesz–Fischer theorem, to every point $\{c_n\}$ of the Hilbert space there corresponds a unique element $f(x)$ of the space $L^2(\Omega)$ for which the numbers c_n are the Fourier coefficients with respect to the system $\{u_n(x)\}$.

In the above correspondence the results of linear operations on elements of a Hilbert space correspond to the results of linear operations on the corresponding elements of the function space $L^2(\Omega)$. Parseval's equation (51) expresses the fact that the distances of the corresponding elements $f(x)$ and $c = \{c_n\}$ from the zero element in the function space and in the Hilbert space are equal:

$$\delta(f, 0) = \rho(c, 0).$$

We shall now calculate the distance $\delta(a, b)$ between two points $a = \{a_n\}$ and $b = \{b_n\}$ of the Hilbert space corresponding in the above way to two points $f(x)$ and $\varphi(x)$ in the space $L^2(\Omega)$. Thus, we have

$$a_n = \int_\Omega f(x)\overline{u_n(x)}\,dx, \qquad b_n = \int_\Omega \varphi(x)\overline{u_n(x)}\,dx \tag{52}$$

and

$$\sum_{n=1}^{\infty} |a_n|^2 = \|f\|^2, \qquad \sum_{n=1}^{\infty} |b_n|^2 = \|\varphi\|^2. \tag{53}$$

Now, note that the differences $a_n - b_n$ are the Fourier coefficients of the function $f(x) - \varphi(x)$, i.e.

$$a_n - b_n = \int_\Omega [f(x) - \varphi(x)]\overline{u_n(x)}\,dx,$$

and hence, according to Parseval's equation, we have

$$\sum_{n=1}^{\infty} |a_n - b_n|^2 = \int_\Omega |f(x) - \varphi(x)|^2\,dx = \|f - \varphi\|^2. \tag{54}$$

In other words,

$$\rho(a, b) = \delta(f, \varphi),$$

i.e. *the distance between two points of function space is equal to the distance between the two corresponding points of a Hilbert space.*

The *scalar product* of two points $f(x)$ and $\varphi(x)$ of a function space $L^2(\Omega)$, is the same as that introduced previously:

$$(f, \varphi) = \int_\Omega f(x)\overline{\varphi(x)}\,dx. \tag{55}$$

We shall show that this scalar product is equal to the scalar product of the two corresponding points a and b in a Hilbert space.

In fact, for any arbitrary value of the parameter λ the numbers $a_n+\lambda b_n$ are the Fourier coefficients of the function $f(x)+\lambda\varphi(x)$, and so we have,

$$\sum_{n=1}^{\infty} |a_n+\lambda b_n|^2 = \int_{\Omega} |f(x)+\lambda\varphi(x)|^2\, dx \tag{56}$$

or

$$\sum_{n=1}^{\infty} (a_n+\lambda b_n)(\overline{a}_n+\overline{\lambda b}_n) = \int_{\Omega} (f+\lambda\varphi)(\overline{f}+\overline{\lambda\varphi})\, dx.$$

Hence, on the basis of equality (53), it follows that

$$\overline{\lambda}\sum_{n=1}^{\infty} a_n\overline{b}_n+\lambda\sum_{n=1}^{\infty}\overline{a}_n b_n = \overline{\lambda}\int_{\Omega} f\overline{\varphi}\, dx+\lambda\int_{\Omega}\overline{f}\varphi\, dx,$$

or

$$\overline{\lambda}(a, b)+\lambda\overline{(a, b)} = \overline{\lambda}(f, \varphi)+\lambda\overline{(f, \varphi)}.$$

Choosing $\lambda = 1$ and $\lambda = -i$ we obtain the two equalities

$$(a, b)+\overline{(a, b)} = (f, \varphi)+\overline{(f, \varphi)},$$

$$(a, b)-\overline{(a, b)} = (f, \varphi)-\overline{(f, \varphi)},$$

from which we conclude that

$$(a, b) = (f, \varphi).$$

If the functions f and φ are orthogonal, i.e. $(f, \varphi) = 0$, then the corresponding points of the Hilbert space are also orthogonal.

From the above considerations we see that *the space of functions $L^2(\Omega)$ is isometric to Hilbert space.* We shall further add that an orthonormal system $\{\varphi_\nu(x)\}$ in the function space $L^2(\Omega)$ is analogous to an orthogonal system of unit vectors in an n-dimensional space, and that the theorem on convergence in the mean of the Fourier series to the function $f(x)$,

$$\left\| f-\sum_{\nu=1}^{n} c_\nu\varphi_\nu \right\| \to 0,$$

is analogous to expressing an arbitrary vector in an n-dimensional space as a linear combination of unit vectors.

In modern mathematics Hilbert space is defined in a more general way. * A special case of such a space is just the previously considered space of sequence $\{u_n\}$ and the space of functions L^2.

* See R. Sikorski, *Funkcie rzeczywiste* (*Real Functions*), Vol. II, p. 106.

CHAPTER V

FREDHOLM'S EQUATION WITH SYMMETRIC KERNEL

§ 1. Properties of a symmetric kernel. Hilbert's Theorem

The kernel of a Fredholm integral equation of the second kind

$$\varphi(x) = f(x) + \lambda \int_{\Omega} N(x, y)\, \varphi(y)\, dy \tag{1}$$

is called *symmetric* if it is identical to the kernel of the associated equation, i.e. if

$$N(x, y) = \overline{N(y, x)}. \tag{2}$$

In the case of a *real* kernel the symmetry condition reduces to the equality

$$N(x, y) = N(y, x). \tag{3}$$

On account of their properties, integral equations with symmetric kernels play a very important rôle in the theory of integral equations and its applications. The investigation of the most important properties of equations with symmetric kernels is due to D. HILBERT and E. SCHMIDT.

First we shall show that *all iterated kernels of a symmetric kernel are also symmetric.*

Indeed from the recursive relations

$$N_{n+1}(x, y) = \int_{\Omega} N(x, s)\, N_n(s, y)\, ds = \int_{\Omega} N_n(x, s)\, N(s, y)\, ds,$$

under the assumption that the kernels N_n and N are symmetric, it follows that

$$\begin{aligned} \overline{N_{n+1}(y, x)} &= \int_{\Omega} \overline{N(y, s)}\, \overline{N_n(s, x)}\, ds \\ &= \int_{\Omega} N(s, y)\, N_n(x, s)\, ds = N_{n+1}(x, y), \end{aligned}$$

and hence the kernel N_{n+1} is also symmetric. Thus by induction we conclude that every iterated kernel of a symmetric kernel is symmetric.

The above equality implies that $\overline{N_n(x, x)} = N_n(x, x)$, and therefore the functions $N_n(x, x)$ are real.

Consequently, *all the traces of a symmetric kernel*

$$a_n = \int_{\Omega} N_n(x, x)\, dx$$

are also real.

THEOREM. *The eigenvalues of a symmetric kernel are real.*

In fact, suppose that the complex number $\lambda_0 = \alpha + i\beta$ $(\beta \neq 0)$ is an eigenvalue of the symmetric kernel $N(x, y)$, and $\varphi = \varphi_1 + i\varphi_2$ is the corresponding eigenfunction.

On the basis of definition (2) we then have

$$\varphi_1(x) + i\varphi_2(x) = (\alpha + i\beta) \int_{\Omega} N(x, y)[\varphi_1(y) + i\varphi_2(y)]\, dy,$$

$$\varphi_1(x) + i\varphi_2(x) = (\alpha + i\beta) \int_{\Omega} \overline{N(y, x)}[\varphi_1(y) + i\varphi_2(y)]\, dy.$$

But we know (see p. 70) that the eigenfunction of an integral equation is orthogonal to the eigenfunction of the associated equation corresponding to an eigenvalue *non-conjugate* to the given one, and hence (since $\beta \neq 0$)

$$\int_{\Omega} (\varphi_1 + i\varphi_2)\overline{(\varphi_1 + i\varphi_2)}\, dx = \int_{\Omega} (\varphi_1^2 + \varphi_2^2)\, dx = 0.$$

Thus $\varphi_1 = 0$, $\varphi_2 = 0$ almost everywhere, contrary to the hypothesis. Therefore λ_0, if it exists, must be a real number.

HILBERT'S THEOREM. *Every symmetric kernel with a norm not equal to zero has at least one eigenvalue.*

We know that the solution of the given integral equation (1) may be represented as a power series in the parameter λ:

$$\varphi(x) = f(x) + \sum_{n=1}^{\infty} \lambda^n \int_{\Omega} N_n(x, y) f(y)\, dy. \tag{4}$$

This series converges when $|\lambda|$ is sufficiently small. It then converges uniformly with respect to x and y in the set Ω (compare Chapt. II, § 2). On account of the form of Fredholm's solution the radius of convergence of series (4) is equal to the smallest of the moduli $|\lambda_0|$ of the zeros of the Fredholm function $D(\lambda)$. Now, if the kernel $N(x, y)$ had no eigenvalues, then series (4) would be convergent for all values of the parameter λ (as, for example, the solution of the Volterra equation).

Thus, it is sufficient to show that, *for a symmetric kernel with a norm not equal to zero series* (4) *is not convergent for all* λ (with the exception of some special functions f), in order to infer the existence of at least one eigenvalue, in accordance with Hilbert's theorem.

Multiplying both sides of equality (4) by $\overline{f(x)}$ and integrating, we obtain the sequence

$$\int_\Omega \varphi(x)\overline{f(x)}\,dx = \sum_{n=0}^{\infty} A_n \lambda^n, \tag{5}$$

where we use the notation

$$A_n = \int_\Omega \int_\Omega N_n(x, y)\overline{f(x)}f(y)\,dx\,dy \qquad (N_0 = 1,\ N_1 = N). \tag{6}$$

On the basis of the recursive relation for iterated kernels

$$N_{n+p}(x, y) = \int_\Omega N_n(x, s) N_p(s, y)\,ds \tag{7}$$

we may write

$$N_{2n}(x, y) = \int_\Omega N_n(x, s) N_n(s, y)\,ds,$$

and since $N_n(s, y) = \overline{N_n(y, s)}$ on account of the assumed symmetry of the kernel, we have

$$A_{2n} = \int_\Omega \Big[\int_\Omega N_n(x, s)\overline{f(x)}\,dx\Big]\cdot\Big[\int_\Omega \overline{N_n(y, s)}f(y)\,dy\Big]\,ds$$

$$= \int_\Omega \Big|\int_\Omega N_n(x, s)\overline{f(x)}\,dx\Big|^2\,ds. \tag{8}$$

Hence all the coefficients of series (5) with even subscripts are non-negative real numbers:

$$A_{2n} \geqq 0.$$

Using the recursive relation (7) and notation (6), we also have

$$A_{2n} = \int_\Omega \Big[\int_\Omega N_{n-1}(x, s)\overline{f(x)}\,dx\Big] . \Big[\overline{\int_\Omega N_{n+1}(y, s) f(y)\,dy}\Big]\,ds .$$

Hence, by the Schwarz inequality, we conclude that

$$A_{2n}^2 \leqq \int_\Omega \Big|\int_\Omega N_{n-1}(x, s)\overline{f(x)}\,dx\Big|^2 ds . \int_\Omega \Big|\int_\Omega N_{n+1}(x, s)\overline{f(x)}\,dx\Big|^2 ds ,$$

and thus, according to equality (8), the following inequalities

$$A_{2n}^2 \leqq A_{2n-2} A_{2n+2} \tag{9}$$

hold for every $n \geqq 2$.

Let us now note the equalities

$$\begin{aligned} A_2 &= \int_\Omega \int_\Omega N_2(x, y)\overline{f(x)} f(y)\,dx\,dy = \int_\Omega \Big|\int_\Omega N(x, s)\overline{f(x)}\,dx\Big|^2 ds ,\\ A_4 &= \int_\Omega \int_\Omega N_4(x, y)\overline{f(x)} f(y)\,dx\,dy = \int_\Omega \Big|\int_\Omega N_2(x, y)\overline{f(x)}\,dx\Big|^2 dy . \end{aligned} \tag{10}$$

Since we have assumed that the given kernel $N(x, s)$ has a non-zero norm, there exists a function $f \in L^2(\Omega)$ such that $A_2 > 0$.

We shall now show that $A_4 > 0$. For if $A_4 = 0$ then the second of the formulae (10) would imply that

$$\int_\Omega N_2(x, y)\overline{f(x)}\,dx = 0$$

almost everywhere with respect to y in the set Ω, and then from the first of the formulae (10) it would follow that $A_2 = 0$, contrary to the hypothesis; consequently $A_4 > 0$.

This implies, on the basis of inequality (9), that all the coefficients $A_6, A_8, A_{10}, \ldots, A_{2n}, \ldots$ with even indices are positive and satisfy the inequality

$$\frac{A_{2n+2}}{A_{2n}} \geqq \frac{A_{2n}}{A_{2n-2}} , \tag{9'}$$

i.e. they form a non-decreasing sequence. The series $\sum_{n=0}^{\infty} A_n \lambda^n$ therefore cannot converge for all λ. Hence we conclude that series (4) is not convergent for all λ and that the kernel $N(x, y)$ has at least one eigenvalue.

The above proof makes it possible at the same time to determine the interval in which at least one eigenvalue λ_0 of the kernel $N(x, y)$ is contained.

Indeed, in view of inequality (9′) the terms of the series $\sum_{n=0}^{\infty} A_n \lambda^n$ satisfy the inequalities

$$\frac{A_{2n+2}\lambda^{2n+2}}{A_{2n}\lambda^{2n}} \geqq \frac{A_1}{A_2}\lambda^2,$$

and therefore the series diverges when

$$\frac{A_4}{A_2}|\lambda|^2 > 1, \quad |\lambda| > \sqrt{\frac{A_2}{A_4}},$$

and consequently, at least one eigenvalue of the kernel $N(x, y)$ is contained in the interval

$$\left(-\sqrt{\frac{A_2}{A_4}}, \sqrt{\frac{A_2}{A_4}}\right)$$

since, as we know, they are real.

The above theorem may also be proved by inspecting the series (see p. 47)

$$-\frac{D'(\lambda)}{D(\lambda)} = \sum_{n=0}^{\infty} a_{n+1}\lambda^n, \tag{11}$$

where the terms

$$a_{n+1} = \int_{\Omega} N_{n+1}(x, x)\, dx \quad (N_1 = N)$$

are called the *traces* of the kernel N. We have already mentioned (p. 122) that the traces of a symmetric kernel are real. Proceeding in a manner similar to the above, we have

$$a_{2n} = \int_{\Omega} N_{2n}(x, x)\, dx = \int_{\Omega}\left[\int_{\Omega} N_n(x, s)\, N_n(s, x)\, ds\right] dx$$

$$= \int_{\Omega}\int_{\Omega} |N_n(x, s)|^2\, ds\, dx,$$

and in particular

$$a_2 = \int_{\Omega}\int_{\Omega} |N(x, s)|^2\, ds\, dx, \quad a_4 = \int_{\Omega}\int_{\Omega} |N_2(x, s)|^2\, ds\, dx.$$

According to the assumed property of the kernel we have $a_2 > 0$. We shall prove that also $a_4 > 0$. Indeed, if $a_4 = 0$ then $N_2(x, s) = 0$ almost everywhere in the set Ω. We shall show that this would imply $N(x, s) = 0$ almost everywhere, contrary to the hypothesis. For, let us multiply both sides of the equality

$$N_2(x, s) = \int_\Omega N(x, t) N(t, s)\, dt$$

by $u(x)\overline{u(s)}$, where u is an arbitrary function in $L^2(\Omega)$, and integrate twice with respect to the variables x and s. We obtain

$$\int_\Omega \int_\Omega N_2(x, s) u(x) \overline{u(s)}\, ds\, dx = \int_\Omega \Big| \int_\Omega N(x, t) u(x)\, dx \Big|^2 dt = 0,$$

if $N_2 = 0$ almost everywhere. This implies that

$$\int_\Omega N(x, t) u(x)\, dx = 0$$

almost everywhere, and consequently

$$\int_\Omega \int_\Omega N(x, t) u(x) v(t)\, dx\, dt = 0, \tag{12}$$

where v is also an arbitrary function in $L^2(\Omega)$. Let us now note that, according to the chapter on orthogonal systems (p. 111), there exists a series $\sum_{\nu=1}^{\infty} c_\nu u_\nu(x) v_\nu(t)$, formed from functions in $L^2(\Omega)$, and which is convergent in the mean to the kernel $\overline{N(x, t)}$. This means that

$$\lim_{n\to\infty} \Big\| \overline{N(x, t)} - \sum_{\nu=1}^{n} c_\nu u_\nu(x) v_\nu(t) \Big\| = 0.$$

Thus, on the basis of equality (12) and in view of the theorem on sequences convergent in the mean (p. 107), we have

$$\int_\Omega \int_\Omega |N(x, t)|^2\, dx\, dt = \lim_{n\to\infty} \sum_{\nu=1}^{n} \int_\Omega \int_\Omega N(x, t) c_\nu u_\nu(x) v_\nu(t)\, dx\, dt = 0,$$

contrary to the hypothesis, and hence

$$a_4 > 0.$$

We shall show that all the subsequent traces with even indices $a_6, a_8, a_{10}, \ldots$ are also positive. For this purpose we shall apply the Buniakovski–Schwarz inequality to the integral

$$a_{2n} = \int_\Omega \int_\Omega N_{n-1}(x, s) N_{n+1}(s, x)\, ds\, dx.$$

We then obtain

$$a_{2n}^2 \leqq \int_\Omega \int_\Omega |N_{n-1}(x, s)|^2\, dx\, ds \,.\, \int_\Omega \int_\Omega |N_{n+1}(x, s)|^2\, dx\, ds,$$

and hence

$$a_{2n}^2 \leqq a_{2n-2}\, a_{2n+2}.$$

Since $a_2 > 0$, $a_4 > 0$, it follows from the above inequality that all the traces with even indices are positive. Further, we see that

$$\frac{a_{2n+2}}{a_{2n}} \geqq \frac{a_{2n}}{a_{2n-2}},$$

and hence the sequence of coefficients $\{a_{2n}\}$ is non-decreasing and *series* (11) *is not convergent for every* λ. This implies the existence of λ_0 such that $D(\lambda_0) = 0$, i.e. the validity of Hilbert's Theorem.

With the aid of the traces of the kernel a_{2n} it is possible to determine the eigenvalue λ_0 with the smallest modulus. Let us note that the sequence $\{a_{2n}\}$ is the sequence of all the traces of the iterated kernel $N_2(x, y)$ the smallest eigenvalue of which is equal to the square λ_0^2 of the eigenvalue λ_0 of the kernel $N(x, y)$ with the smallest absolute value. On the other hand, for the Fredholm series $D_2(\lambda^2)$ of the iterated kernel N_2 we have the equality

$$-\frac{D_2'(\lambda^2)}{D_2(\lambda^2)} = \sum_{n=0}^{\infty} a_{2n+2}\, \lambda^{2n},$$

and since the coefficients satisfy the inequalities

$$0 < \frac{a_{2n}}{a_{2n+2}} \leqq \frac{a_{2n-2}}{a_{2n}} \leqq \frac{a_2}{a_4},$$

the following limit exists:

$$\lim_{n\to\infty} \frac{a_{2n}}{a_{2n+2}}.$$

This limit is equal to the radius of convergence of the series $\sum_{n=0}^{\infty} a_{2n+2}\,\lambda^{2n}$, and therefore to the square λ_0^2 of the eigenvalue λ_0 of the kernel $N(x, y)$. The required eigenvalue λ_0 is therefore equal to one of the two numbers

$$\lambda_0 = \pm\sqrt{\lim_{n\to\infty} \frac{a_{2n}}{a_{2n+2}}}$$

or else both are eigenvalues.

§ 2. Expansion of a symmetric kernel in eigenfunctions

Let $N(x, y)$ be a symmetric kernel (with non-zero norm) *which has an infinite number of eigenvalues.* We order these eigenvalues (always real, and non-zero) in a sequence

$$\lambda_1, \lambda_2, \lambda_3, \ldots, \lambda_n, \ldots \tag{13}$$

in such a way *that each eigenvalue is repeated as many times as the ordinal number of its rank,* or the number of linearly independent eigenfunctions.

We may always assume that

$$0 < |\lambda_1| \leqq |\lambda_2| \leqq |\lambda_3| \leqq \ldots \leqq |\lambda_n| \leqq |\lambda_{n+1}| \leqq \ldots$$

Evidently $|\lambda_n| \to \infty$ as $n \to \infty$, since otherwise there would exist a boundary point which would be a singular point of the resolvent kernel without being a pole which contradicts the fact that the kernel is a meromorphic function of the parameter λ. Let

$$\varphi_1(x), \varphi_2(x), \varphi_3(x), \ldots, \varphi_n(x), \ldots \tag{13'}$$

be a sequence of eigenfunctions corresponding to eigenvalues (13), where these functions are no longer repeated and are linearly independent in each group corresponding to the same eigenvalue. Since a symmetric kernel is identical to the kernel of the associated equation and its eigenvalues are real, according to the theorem on p. 70 *two functions of sequence* (13′) *corresponding to two different eigenvalues are orthogonal.* Moreover, eigenfunctions corresponding to the same eigenvalue may always be replaced by an orthogonal system of the same number of eigenfunctions. We may therefore always assume that the sequence of eigenfunctions (13′) of a given symmetric kernel $N(x, y)$ is an *orthonormal* system, i.e.

$$\int_{\Omega} \varphi_{\alpha}(x) \overline{\varphi_{\beta}(x)}\, dx = \begin{cases} 0, & \alpha \neq \beta, \\ 1, & \alpha = \beta. \end{cases} \tag{14}$$

Let us now determine the Fourier series $\sum_{n=1}^{\infty} c_n \varphi_n(x)$ of the kernel $N(x, y)$ with respect to the orthogonal system $\{\varphi_n(x)\}$ of its eigenfunctions, treating y as a constant. The coefficients of that series are

$$c_n(y) = \int_{\Omega} N(x, y) \overline{\varphi_n(x)}\, dx .$$

But the function $\varphi_n(x)$, being an eigenfunction, also satisfies the homogeneous Fredholm equation

$$\varphi_n(y) = \lambda_n \int_{\Omega} N(y, x) \varphi_n(x)\, dx , \tag{15}$$

and thus

$$\overline{\varphi_n(y)} = \lambda_n \int_{\Omega} \overline{N(y, x)}\, \overline{\varphi_n(x)}\, dx = \lambda_n \int_{\Omega} N(x, y) \overline{\varphi_n(x)}\, dx . \tag{15'}$$

Hence

$$c_n(y) = \frac{\overline{\varphi_n(y)}}{\lambda_n} \tag{16}$$

and the Fourier series of the given kernel $N(x, y)$ with respect to the orthonormal system $\{\varphi_n(x)\}$ of its eigenvalues has the basic form

$$\sum_{n=1}^{\infty} \frac{\varphi_n(x)\overline{\varphi_n(y)}}{\lambda_n}. \tag{17}$$

Obviously there is no *a priori* reason for asserting that series (17) converges nor that its sum is the kernel $N(x, y)$.

THEOREM. *If the Fourier series of a symmetric kernel $N(x, y)$ converges uniformly with respect to each of the variables in the domain Ω, then its sum is almost everywhere equal to that kernel, i.e.*

$$N(x, y) = \sum_{n=1}^{\infty} \frac{\varphi_n(x)\overline{\varphi_n(y)}}{\lambda_n}$$

almost everywhere.

To prove the above theorem, assume that it is not the case, i.e. that the difference

$$Q(x, y) = N(x, y) - \sum_{n=1}^{\infty} \frac{\varphi_n(x)\overline{\varphi_n(y)}}{\lambda_n} \tag{18}$$

is not almost everywhere equal to zero, i.e. that

$$\int_\Omega \int_\Omega |Q(x, y)|^2 \, dx \, dy > 0. \tag{19}$$

Since the kernel of the integral equation

$$\psi(x) = c \int_\Omega Q(x, y) \psi(y) \, dy \tag{20}$$

is symmetric and satisfies inequality (19), there exists a number c such that equation (20) has a solution $\psi(x)$ not almost everywhere equal to zero. We shall show that this solution $\psi(x)$ is orthogonal to all the eigenfunctions $\varphi_p(x)$ of the kernel $N(x, y)$. For, according to equalities (18), (20) and the assumed uniform convergence for any p, we have

$$\int_\Omega \psi(x)\overline{\varphi_p(x)}\, dx = c \int_\Omega \int_\Omega N(x, y)\overline{\varphi_p(x)}\psi(y)\, dx\, dy -$$

$$- \sum_{n=1}^{\infty} c \int_\Omega \int_\Omega \frac{\overline{\varphi_p(x)}\varphi_n(x)\overline{\varphi_n(y)}}{\lambda_n} \psi(y)\, dx\, dy.$$

Hence, from equalities (14) and (15), we obtain

$$\int_\Omega \psi(x)\overline{\varphi_p(x)}\,dx$$

$$= c\int_\Omega\int_\Omega N(x,y)\overline{\varphi_p(x)}\psi(y)\,dx\,dy - c\int_\Omega \frac{\overline{\varphi_p(y)}}{\lambda_p}\psi(y)\,dy$$

$$= c\int_\Omega\left[\int_\Omega N(x,y)\overline{\varphi_p(x)}\,dx - \frac{\overline{\varphi_p(y)}}{\lambda_p}\right]\psi(y)\,dy = 0. \qquad (21)$$

Substituting expression (18) into equation (20) we have, according to formula (21)

$$\psi(x) = c\int_\Omega N(x,y)\psi(y)\,dy - \sum_{n=1}^{\infty} c\varphi_n(x)\int_\Omega \frac{\overline{\varphi_n(y)}\psi(y)}{\lambda_n}\,dy$$

$$= c\int N(x,y)\psi(y)\,dy. \qquad (22)$$

The function $\psi(x)$ is also an eigenfunction of the kernel $N(x, y)$, and so it must be a linear combination of certain eigenfunctions of the sequence $\{\varphi_n(x)\}$ corresponding to the eigenvalue c,

$$\psi(x) = A_1\varphi_{n_1}(x) + A_2\varphi_{n_2}(x) + \ldots + A_q\varphi_{n_q}(x), \qquad (23)$$

where q is the rank of that eigenvalue c. However, since we have proved that the function $\psi(x)$ is orthogonal to all the functions $\varphi_n(x)$, upon multiplying both sides of equality (23) by $\varphi_{n\nu}(x)$ and integrating we obtain

$$\int_\Omega \psi(x)\varphi_{n_\nu}(x)\,dx = A_\nu = 0 \quad (\nu = 1, 2, \ldots, q).$$

Thus, we have identically $\psi(x) = 0$, contrary to the hypothesis. Consequently, inequality (19) cannot be true and the equality

$$N(x,y) = \sum_{n=1}^{\infty} \frac{\varphi_n(x)\overline{\varphi_n(y)}}{\lambda_n} \qquad (24)$$

holds almost everywhere. If the kernel $N(x, y)$ is continuous, equality (24) holds everywhere.

Now assume that the symmetric kernel $N(x, y)$ has a finite number of eigenvalues. Let us order them as before:

$$\lambda_1, \lambda_2, \ldots, \lambda_n, \tag{25}$$

repeating each as many times as the number of its rank. Let

$$\varphi_1(x), \varphi_2(x), \ldots, \varphi_n(x) \tag{26}$$

be a finite sequence of the respective eigenfunctions. We may always assume that sequence (26) is a finite orthonormal set. We then have the following important and interesting theorem:

THEOREM. *Every symmetric kernel with a finite number of eigenvalues* $\lambda_1, \lambda_2, \ldots, \lambda_n$ *can be expressed in the form*

$$N(x, y) = \sum_{\nu=1}^{n} \frac{\varphi_\nu(x)\overline{\varphi_\nu(y)}}{\lambda_\nu}, \tag{27}$$

if we neglect the term with norm equal to zero, where $\varphi_\nu(x)$ *is the eigenfunction corresponding to* λ_ν.

The proof of this theorem is analogous to the preceding, but instead of the convergent series (24) we substitute the finite sum (27). The symmetric kernel with a finite number of eigenvalues is therefore degenerate.

Conversely, if a symmetric kernel is degenerate, i.e. has the form of a sum of products

$$N(x, y) = \sum_{\nu=1}^{n} A_\nu(x)\overline{A_\nu(y)}, \tag{28}$$

then, as we know from the section on degenerate kernels (p. 71), its eigenvalues are the roots of an algebraic equation and their number is finite. Thus, we have the following important corollary:

COROLLARY. *A symmetric kernel has an infinite number of eigenvalues if and only if it is non-degenerate.*

From formula (16) for the Fourier coefficients $c_n(y)$ of the kernel $N(x, y)$ with respect to a system of eigenfunctions $\{\varphi_n(x)\}$, and from Bessel's inequality, we conclude that

$$\sum_{n=1}^{\infty} \left| \frac{\varphi_n(y)}{\lambda_n} \right|^2 \leq \int_{\Omega} |N(x, y)|^2 \, dx. \tag{29}$$

On account of the normalization of the system, by integrating, we thus obtain

$$\sum_{n=1}^{\infty} \frac{1}{|\lambda_n|^2} \leq \int_{\Omega} \int_{\Omega} |N(x, y)|^2 \, dx \, dy. \tag{30}$$

From this inequality follows the important result that the *series*

$$\sum_{n=1}^{\infty} \frac{1}{\lambda_n^p} \tag{31}$$

where λ_i $(i = 1, 2, \ldots)$ *are eigenvalues of a symmetric kernel, is absolutely convergent for* $p \geqq 2$.

We also mention that if an orthogonal system $\{\varphi_\nu(x)\}$ is treated as an orthogonal system of unit vectors in a function space, analogous to a system of n unit vectors in an n-dimensional space, then the expression for the symmetric kernel in the form of a sum

$$N(x, y) = \sum_{\nu=1}^{\infty} \frac{\varphi_\nu(x) \overline{\varphi_\nu(y)}}{\lambda_\nu}$$

will be analogous to the expression for a Hermitian form in its canonical form

$$\sum_{\alpha, \beta=1}^{n} a_{\alpha\beta} x_\alpha \overline{x_\beta} = \sum_{\nu=1}^{n} \frac{\xi_\nu \overline{\xi_\nu}}{\lambda_\nu} \qquad (a_{\alpha\beta} = \overline{a}_{\alpha\beta})$$

by referring to the principal directions.

The real numbers λ_ν are roots of the equation*

$$\det |\delta_{\alpha\beta} - \lambda a_{\alpha\beta}| = 0,$$

analogous to equation $D(\lambda) = 0$, defining the eigenvalues λ_ν of the kernel $N(x, y)$.

---

* The symbol $\det |b_{\alpha\beta}|$ denotes the determinant of the matrix whose elements are $b_{\alpha\beta}$. The *Kronecker delta* $\delta_{\alpha\beta}$ is defined as follows:

$$\delta_{\alpha\beta} = \begin{cases} 0, & \text{when } \alpha \neq \beta, \\ 1, & \text{when } \alpha = \beta. \end{cases}$$

THEOREM. *If $\varphi_n(x)$ is an orthogonal system of all eigenfunctions of the symmetric kernel $N(x, y)$ corresponding to the eigenvalues λ_n, then the symmetric kernel*

$$K(x, y) = N(x, y) - \sum_{n=1}^{p} \frac{\varphi_n(x)\overline{\varphi_n(y)}}{\lambda_n} \tag{32}$$

has the eigenvalues $\lambda_{p+1}, \lambda_{p+2}, \ldots$, and only these eigenvalues (p is any positive integer).

We see immediately that, on account of orthogonality, we have

$$\int_\Omega K(x, y)\varphi_{p+\alpha}(y)\,dy$$

$$= \int_\Omega N(x, y)\varphi_{p+\alpha}(y)\,dy = \frac{\varphi_{p+\alpha}(x)}{\lambda_{p+\alpha}} \qquad (\alpha = 1, 2, 3, \ldots),$$

and thus the functions of the sequence $\varphi_{p+1}, \varphi_{p+2}, \ldots$ are eigenfunctions of the kernel K with eigenvalues $\lambda_{p+1}, \lambda_{p+2}, \ldots$

We shall show that no other value of $\lambda_0 \neq \lambda_{p+\alpha}$ is an eigenvalue of the kernel K.

In order to prove this, assume that λ_0 is an eigenvalue of the kernel K and $\varphi_0(x)$ is the corresponding eigenfunction. We then have

$$\varphi_0(x) - \lambda_0 \int_\Omega N(x, y)\varphi_0(y)\,dy +$$

$$+ \lambda_0 \sum_{n=1}^{p} \frac{\varphi_n(x)}{\lambda_n} \int_\Omega \overline{\varphi_n(y)}\varphi_0(y)\,dy = 0. \tag{33}$$

Multiplying by $\overline{\varphi_\nu(x)}$, where $\nu \leqq p$, and integrating, we obtain

$$\int_\Omega \varphi_0(x)\overline{\varphi_\nu(x)}\,dx - \lambda_0 \int_\Omega \int_\Omega N(x, y)\overline{\varphi_\nu(x)}\varphi_0(y)\,dy\,dx +$$

$$+ \frac{\lambda_0}{\lambda_\nu} \int_\Omega \overline{\varphi_\nu(y)}\varphi_0(y)\,dy = 0.$$

The sum of the last two terms is equal to zero, and hence

$$\int_\Omega \varphi_0(x)\overline{\varphi_\nu(x)}\,dx = 0. \tag{33'}$$

Since v may be any of the numbers $1, 2, \ldots, p$, equation (33) implies

$$\varphi_0(x) - \lambda_0 \int_\Omega N(x, y)\varphi_0(y)\,dy = 0.$$

Consequently, λ_0 is also an eigenvalue of the kernel N and must be equal to at least one of the values $\lambda_1, \lambda_2, \ldots, \lambda_p$, and in that case the corresponding eigenfunction $\varphi_0(x)$ must be a linear combination

$$\varphi_0(x) = C_0\varphi_\alpha(x) + C_1\varphi_{\alpha+1}(x) + \ldots + C_\beta\varphi_{\alpha+\beta}(x)$$

of some functions selected from the sequence $\varphi_1, \varphi_2, \ldots, \varphi_p$. But then, in view of the orthogonality of (33′), it would follow that $C_0 = 0$, $C_1 = 0, \ldots, C_\beta = 0$, and $\varphi_0(x) = 0$, contrary to the hypothesis. Therefore the kernel K has no eigenvalues other than $\lambda_{p+1}, \lambda_{p+2}, \ldots$

Previously we have given a method of determining the first eigenvalue λ_1 as the radius of convergence of a certain series. Now, the above theorem gives a method of determining the subsequent eigenvalues. In general, if one knows the eigenvalues

$$\lambda_1, \lambda_2, \ldots, \lambda_p,$$

ordered according to ascending values of the modulus, then according to the preceding theorem, the subsequent eigenvalue will be the first eigenvalue of kernel (32), and we shall determine it as the radius of convergence of a certain series in the manner given above.

§ 3. Expansions of iterated kernels

Suppose we are given a sequence of all the eigenvalues of a symmetric non-degenerate kernel $N(x, y)$ (always real and non-zero):

$$\lambda_1, \lambda_2, \ldots, \lambda_n, \ldots, \tag{34}$$

repeated as many times as the number of the rank. We then know (p. 94), that the sequence of the p-th powers

$$\lambda_1^p, \lambda_2^p, \ldots, \lambda_n^p, \ldots \tag{35}$$

contains all the eigenvalues of the iterated kernel $N_p(x, y)$ and only these. Since the kernel is symmetric, eigenvalues (34) are real numbers. If p is an odd integer then the value λ_n^p of sequence (35) is repeated the same number of times as the value λ_n is repeated in sequence (34); if p is even, then the value λ_n^p is repeated in sequence (35) the same number of times as λ_n or $-\lambda_n$ is repeated in sequence (34). The fact that the eigenvalues of a symmetric kernel are real, implies, on the basis of the considerations on p. 89, that the equation iterated an odd number of times is completely equivalent to the original equation with a symmetric kernel, even in the case of an eigenvalue.

If

$$\varphi_1(x),\ \varphi_2(x),\ \ldots,\ \varphi_n(x),\ \ldots \tag{36}$$

is an orthonormal system of eigenfunctions of the original equation corresponding to values (34), such that every other eigenfunction is a linear combination of them, then functions (36) are also the eigenfunctions of the iterated equation with kernel N_p, corresponding to the values $\{\lambda_n^p\}$, where all other eigenfunctions of the iterated equations are linear combinations of the functions (36), in accordance with the corollary of p. 94.

Hence it follows that the Fourier series of the iterated kernel $N_p(x, y)$ with respect to an orthonormal system of its eigenfunctions $\{\varphi_n(x)\}$ has the form

$$\sum_{n=1}^{\infty} \frac{\varphi_n(x)\overline{\varphi_n(y)}}{\lambda_n^p} \qquad (p \geqq 2). \tag{37}$$

To prove the convergence of this series, note that from the inequality

$$\Big[\sum_{\nu=n_1}^{n_2} |A_\nu| \cdot |B_\nu|\Big]^2 \leqq \sum_{\nu=n_1}^{n_2} |A_\nu|^2 \sum_{\nu=n_1}^{n_2} |B_\nu|^2$$

we have

$$\left[\sum_{\nu=n_1}^{n_2} \left| \frac{\varphi_n(x)\overline{\varphi_n(y)}}{\lambda_n^p} \right| \right]^2 \leqq \sum_{\nu=n_1}^{n_2} \left| \frac{\varphi_n(x)}{\lambda_n^{p/2}} \right|^2 \sum_{\nu=n_1}^{n_2} \left| \frac{\varphi_n(y)}{\lambda_n^{p/2}} \right|^2 . \tag{38}$$

Thus, if we assume

$$\int_{\Omega} |N(x, y)|^2 \, dx \leqq \text{const}, \tag{39}$$

then on the basis of inequality (29) on p. 132 we conclude that the first of the two sums on the right-hand side of inequality (38) for fixed x is less than an arbitrary positive number ε when n_1 is sufficiently large, and $n_2 > n_1$ is arbitrary, while the second sum is bounded with respect to the variable y for any indices n_1, n_2. Conversely, for fixed y, the second of the two sums on the right-hand side of inequality (38) is less than an arbitrary number ε if n_1 is sufficiently large, and the first of these sums is bounded with respect to the variable x. Hence we conclude that series (37) is *absolutely and uniformly convergent* with respect to the variable x in the domain Ω for fixed y and also with respect to the variable y for fixed x. Using the theorem on p. 130, we may draw an important conclusion that *every iterated kernel* $N_p(x, y)$ $(p \geqq 2)$ *of a symmetric kernel is almost everywhere equal to the sum of its Fourier series*:

$$N_p(x, y) = \sum_{n=1}^{\infty} \frac{\varphi_n(x)\overline{\varphi_n(y)}}{\lambda_n^p} \qquad (p \geqq 2). \tag{40}$$

In the case of continuity, equality (40) holds everywhere.

We recall that this theorem is based on the assumption that the non-degenerate symmetric kernel is integrable together with the square of its modulus, with respect to the pair of points (x, y), that its norm is non-zero, and that integral (39) is bounded.

Note also that

$$|\varphi_n(x)\varphi_n(y)| \leqq \tfrac{1}{2}|\varphi_n(x)|^2 + \tfrac{1}{2}|\varphi_n(y)|^2 \tag{41}$$

and

$$N_p(x, x) = \sum_{n=1}^{\infty} \frac{|\varphi_n(x)|^2}{\lambda_n^p} \qquad (p \geqq 2). \tag{42}$$

If we assume that the kernel $N(x, y)$ is continuous, then the functions $N_p(x, y)$ and $\varphi_n(x)$ are continuous, and on the basis of a theorem of DINI: *If the sum of a series of positive continuous functions is a continuous function, then the convergence is uniform,* we conclude that series (42) is uniformly convergent. In view of inequality (41), this implies that series (40) *converges uniformly with respect to the pair of variables* (x, y) *on the assumption that the kernel* $N(x, y)$ *is continuous.*

From the property of Fourier series of iterated kernels it is possible to derive the following theorem on the symmetric kernel:

THEOREM. *The Fourier series of every continuous symmetric kernel with non-zero norm converges in the mean to that kernel when one of the variables is fixed.*

Indeed, consider the integral

$$\int_{\Omega} \left| N(x, y) - \sum_{\nu=1}^{n} \frac{\varphi_\nu(x)\overline{\varphi_\nu(y)}}{\lambda_\nu} \right|^2 dx$$

$$= \int_{\Omega} \left| N(x, y) \right|^2 dx - \sum_{\nu=1}^{n} \left| \frac{\varphi_\nu(y)}{\lambda_\nu} \right|^2 .$$

However, we know that

$$N_2(x, y) = \sum_{\nu=1}^{\infty} \frac{\varphi_\nu(x)\overline{\varphi_\nu(y)}}{\lambda_\nu^2}$$

everywhere, and hence

$$N_2(x, x) = \sum_{\nu=1}^{\infty} \frac{|\varphi_\nu(x)|^2}{\lambda_\nu^2} .$$

From this it follows that

$$\int_{\Omega} N(x, s) N(s, x)\, ds = \int_{\Omega} |N(x, s)|^2\, ds = \sum_{\nu=1}^{\infty} \left| \frac{\varphi_\nu(x)}{\lambda_\nu} \right|^2 ,$$

and so

$$N_4(x, y) = \sum_{n=1}^{\infty} \frac{\varphi_n(x)\overline{\varphi_n(y)}}{\lambda_n^4} ,$$

for fixed y. This completes the proof.

Evidently, this theorem does not imply that the system $\{\varphi(x)\}$ is complete.

§ 4. Hilbert–Schmidt Theorem

DEFINITION. *We say that a function $h(x)$ is orthogonal to a symmetric kernel $N(x, y)$, if*

$$\int_\Omega N(x, y)\, h(y)\, dy = 0. \tag{43}$$

This then implies that

$$\int_\Omega N(y, x)\, \overline{h(y)}\, dy = 0. \tag{43'}$$

LEMMA. *For a function $h \in L^2(\Omega)$ to be orthogonal to a symmetric kernel $N(x, y)$ it is necessary and sufficient that it be orthogonal to all the eigenfunctions of the kernel.*

The condition is *necessary*: for if equality (43′) holds, then

$$\int_\Omega \int_\Omega N(y, x)\, \varphi_n(x)\, \overline{h(y)}\, dy\, dx = 0 \quad (n = 1, 2, \ldots), \tag{44}$$

where $\{\varphi_n(x)\}$ is an orthonormal system of eigenfunctions of the kernel $N(x, y)$. Since

$$\lambda_n \int_\Omega N(y, x)\, \varphi_n(x)\, dx = \varphi_n(y),$$

(44) yields

$$\int_\Omega \varphi_n(y)\, \overline{h(y)}\, dy = 0, \tag{45}$$

which expresses the fact that the function h is orthogonal to every eigenfunction $\varphi_n(x)$.

In order to prove that the condition expressed by equation (45) is *sufficient* we note that the iterated kernel N_4 is the sum of a series convergent uniformly with respect to x and y,

$$N_4(x, y) = \sum_{n=1}^{\infty} \frac{\varphi_n(x)\, \overline{\varphi_n(y)}}{\lambda_n^4}, \tag{46}$$

provided that inequality (39) on p. 137 is satisfied. Hence, upon integration, it follows that

$$\int_\Omega \int_\Omega N_4(x, y)\, \overline{h(x)}\, h(y)\, dx\, dy$$

$$= \sum_{n=1}^{\infty} \int_\Omega \frac{\varphi_n(x)\, \overline{h(x)}}{\lambda_n^2}\, dx \cdot \int_\Omega \frac{\overline{\varphi_n(y)}\, h(y)}{\lambda_n^2}\, dy = 0, \tag{47}$$

according to assumption (45) for the function $h \in L^2(\Omega)$. Since

$$N_4(x, y) = \int_\Omega N_2(x, s) N_2(s, y)\, ds,$$

substituting this expression in formula (47) we obtain

$$\int_\Omega \Big[\int_\Omega N_2(x, s) \overline{h(x)}\, dx\Big]\Big[\int_\Omega \overline{N_2(y, s)}\, h(y)\, dy\Big]\, ds$$
$$= \int_\Omega \Big|\int_\Omega N_2(x, s) \overline{h(x)}\, dx\Big|^2 ds = 0.$$

This implies that

$$\int_\Omega N_2(x, s) \overline{h(x)}\, dx = 0 \tag{48}$$

almost everywhere. Multiplying both sides by $h(s)$ and integrating, we have

$$\int_\Omega \int_\Omega N_2(x, s) \overline{h(x)}\, h(s)\, dx\, ds = 0,$$

and since

$$N_2(x, s) = \int_\Omega N(x, t) N(t, s)\, dt,$$

we obtain

$$\int_\Omega \Big|\int_\Omega N(x, t) \overline{h(x)}\, dx\Big|^2 dt = 0.$$

Thus

$$\int_\Omega N(x, t) \overline{h(x)}\, dx = 0.$$

Hence almost everywhere the condition expressed by equation (45) is also sufficient for the orthogonality of the function h with respect to the kernel N.

HILBERT–SCHMIDT THEOREM. *Every function $f(x)$ of the form*

$$f(x) = \int_\Omega N(x, y)\, h(y)\, dy \tag{49}$$

is almost everywhere the sum of its Fourier series with respect to the orthonormal system $\varphi_n(x)$ of eigenfunctions of the symmetric kernel N. It is assumed that the kernel N is integrable together with the square of its modulus with respect to both of its variables, that the integral $\int |N(x, y)|^2\, dx$ is bounded, and that $h \in L^2(\Omega)$.

We have to prove that

$$f(x) = \sum_{n=1}^{\infty} f_n \varphi_n(x), \tag{50}$$

where the coefficients f_n are the Fourier coefficients of the function $f(x)$ with respect to the system $\{\varphi_n(x)\}$, i.e.

$$f_n = \int_\Omega f(x) \overline{\varphi_n(x)}\, dx. \tag{51}$$

It is to be shown that:

1) *the Fourier series on the right-hand side of equation* (50) *converges;*

2) *its sum is the function $f(x)$ given.*

To prove the first part of the theorem, let us substitute expression (49) in formula (51). We obtain

$$f_n = \int_\Omega \int_\Omega N(x, y) \overline{\varphi_n(x)}\, h(y)\, dx\, dy.$$

But, by hypothesis, we have

$$\int_\Omega N(x, y) \overline{\varphi_n(x)}\, dx = \int_\Omega \overline{N(y, x) \varphi_n(x)}\, dx = \frac{1}{\lambda_n} \overline{\varphi_n(y)};$$

thus

$$f_n = \int_\Omega \frac{1}{\lambda_n} \overline{\varphi_n(y)}\, h(y)\, dy = \frac{h_n}{\lambda_n}, \tag{52}$$

where the h_n are the Fourier coefficients of the given function h with respect to the system $\{\varphi_n(x)\}$:

$$h_n = \int_\Omega h(x) \overline{\varphi_n(x)}\, dx. \tag{53}$$

We may therefore write

$$\sum_{n=1}^{\infty} f_n \varphi_n(x) = \sum_{n=1}^{\infty} \frac{h_n}{\lambda_n} \varphi_n(x). \tag{54}$$

In order to prove that this series is convergent, note that

$$\left[\sum_{n=n_1}^{n_2} \left| \frac{h_n}{\lambda_n} \varphi_n(x) \right| \right]^2 \leq \sum_{n=n_1}^{n_2} |h_n|^2 \sum_{n=n_1}^{n_2} \left| \frac{\varphi_n(x)}{\lambda_n} \right|^2 \tag{55}$$

for all n_1 and n_2. Now, on account of the convergence of the series $\sum_n |h_n|^2$, according to Bessel's inequality, the first of the two sums on the right-hand side is less than any arbitrarily chosen positive number ε provided n_1 is sufficiently large, and $n_2 > n_1$ is arbitrary, while the second sum is bounded on account of the assumption that $\int_\Omega |N(x, y)|^2 dx$ is bounded. Consequently, *the Fourier series* (54) *of the function $f(x)$ with respect to the system $\{\varphi_n(x)\}$ is absolutely and uniformly convergent in the domain Ω.*

It now has to be shown that the sum of the series (54), i.e.

$$S(x) = \sum_{n=1}^{\infty} \frac{h_n}{\lambda_n} \varphi_n(x), \tag{56}$$

is equal to the function $f(x)$. Let

$$R(x) = f(x) - S(x)$$

and note that the functions $f(x)$ and $S(x)$ have the same Fourier coefficients with respect to the system $\{\varphi_n(x)\}$. Consequently, multiplying $R(x)$ by $\overline{\varphi_n(x)}$ and integrating, we have

$$\int_\Omega R(x) \overline{\varphi_n(x)} \, dx = 0, \tag{57}$$

which means that $R(x)$ is orthogonal to all the eigenfunctions $\varphi_n(x)$ of the kernel $N(x, y)$. But by the previous lemma this implies that $R(x)$ is orthogonal to the kernel N:

$$\int_\Omega N(y, x) \overline{R(y)} \, dy = 0. \tag{58}$$

Multiplying both sides by $h(x)$ and integrating, we obtain

$$\int_\Omega \int_\Omega N(y, x) \overline{R(y)} h(x) \, dx \, dy = 0, \tag{59}$$

and consequently, in view of (49), we have

$$\int_\Omega \overline{R(y)} f(y) \, dy = 0. \tag{60}$$

The function f is therefore orthogonal to R.

On the other hand, we have

$$\int_{\Omega} |R(x)|^2\,dx = \int_{\Omega} \overline{R(x)}\,[f(x)-S(x)]\,dx$$

$$= -\int_{\Omega} \overline{R(x)}\,S(x)\,dx = -\sum_{n=1}^{\infty} \frac{h_n}{\lambda_n} \int_{\Omega} \varphi_n(x)\,\overline{R(x)}\,dx = 0,$$

on the basis of equality (57). Consequently, $R(x) = 0$ almost everywhere, i.e. *the function $f(x)$ is almost everywhere equal to the sum of its absolutely and uniformly convergent Fourier series*:

$$f(x) = \sum_{n=1}^{\infty} \frac{h_n}{\lambda_n}\,\varphi_n(x). \tag{61}$$

§ 5. Application of the Hilbert–Schmidt Theorem

Using the Hilbert–Schmidt Theorem, it is possible to obtain a series expansion of the solution $\varphi(x)$ of the integral equation

$$\varphi(x) = f(x) + \lambda \int_{\Omega} N(x, y)\,\varphi(y)\,dy \tag{62}$$

with respect to the system of eigenfunctions $\{\varphi_n(x)\}$ of a symmetric kernel $N(x, y)$. For the given functions N and f we adopt the same assumptions as before. Assuming that λ is not equal to any of the eigenvalues, $\lambda \neq \lambda_n$, there exists a unique solution $\varphi(x) \in L^2(\Omega)$ of equation (62). Equation (62) may be written in the form

$$\frac{\varphi(x) - f(x)}{\lambda} = \int_{\Omega} N(x, y)\,\varphi(y)\,dy. \tag{63}$$

But, according to the Hilbert–Schmidt Theorem, the right-hand side of equation (63) may be expanded as an absolutely and uniformly convergent series of eigenfunctions $\{\varphi_n(x)\}$.

Consequently,

$$\frac{\varphi(x) - f(x)}{\lambda} = \sum_{n=1}^{\infty} c_n\,\varphi_n(x). \tag{64}$$

In order to calculate the coefficients c_n, we substitute expression (64) in equality (63). We then obtain

$$\sum_{n=1}^{\infty} c_n \varphi_n(x) = \int_{\Omega} N(x, y) f(y)\, dy + \lambda \int_{\Omega} N(x, y) \sum_{n=1}^{\infty} c_n \varphi_n(y)\, dy. \quad (65)$$

Series (64), being uniformly convergent, may be integrated term by term to give

$$\int_{\Omega} N(x, y)\, \varphi_n(y)\, dy = \frac{\varphi_n(x)}{\lambda_n},$$

and hence equality (65) implies that

$$\sum_{n=1}^{\infty} c_n \left(1 - \frac{\lambda}{\lambda_n}\right) \varphi_n(x) = \int_{\Omega} N(x, y) f(y)\, dy. \quad (66)$$

But, according to the Hilbert–Schmidt Theorem, we have again

$$\int_{\Omega} N(x, y) f(y)\, dy = \sum_{n=1}^{\infty} \frac{f_n}{\lambda_n} \varphi_n(x), \quad (67)$$

where the f_n are the Fourier coefficients of the function $f(x)$, i.e.

$$f_n = \int_{\Omega} f(x)\, \overline{\varphi_n(x)}\, dx, \quad (68)$$

and where the series on the right-hand side is absolutely and uniformly convergent. From equalities (66) and (67) it follows that

$$\sum_{n=1}^{\infty} \left[c_n \left(1 - \frac{\lambda}{\lambda_n}\right) - \frac{f_n}{\lambda_n} \right] \varphi_n(x) = 0. \quad (69)$$

Multiplying both sides in turn by $\varphi_1, \varphi_2, \varphi_3, \ldots$ and integrating, because of the orthogonality we obtain

$$c_n \left(1 - \frac{\lambda}{\lambda_n}\right) - \frac{f_n}{\lambda_n} = 0 \quad (70)$$

for every n. Consequently

$$c_n = \frac{f_n}{\lambda_n - \lambda}.$$

Substituting these values in series (64), we obtain the required expansion of the solution of equation (62) as an absolutely and uniformly convergent series in terms of eigenfunctions of the kernel:

$$\varphi(x)=f(x)-\lambda\sum_{n=1}^{\infty}\frac{f_n}{\lambda-\lambda_n}\varphi_n(x)\qquad(\lambda\neq\lambda_n). \tag{71}$$

Expansion (71) is in accordance with the Mittag–Leffler Theorem on the expansion of a meromorphic function.

From equality (71) we see that the function $\varphi(x)$ is a meromorphic function of the parameter λ with *simple* poles λ_n. The fact that the poles are simple is a characteristic of a symmetric kernel and may be shown directly. Evidently, *this does not imply that the rank and the order of the zeros of the function $D(\lambda)$ is equal to unity.*

If λ were equal to one of the eigenvalues $\lambda=\lambda_p=\lambda_{p+1}=$ $=\lambda_{p+2}=\dots=\lambda_{p+q-1}$ with rank q, then equation (70) for $n=p,p+1,p+2,\dots,p+q-1$ would be satisfied if and only if

$$f_{p+\nu}=\int_{\Omega}f(x)\overline{\varphi_{p+\nu}(x)}\,dx=0\qquad(\nu=0,1,2,\dots,q-1), \tag{72}$$

and $c_{p+\nu}$ were arbitrary. Condition (72) is in accordance with the condition studied in Fredholm's Third Theorem and it has to be extended to all the eigenfunctions corresponding to the value λ_p which, as we know, is repeated in the above series as many times as the number of its rank. In that case the solution of the equation takes the form

$$\varphi(x)=f(x)-\lambda\sum_{n=1}^{\infty}{}'\frac{f_n}{\lambda-\lambda_n}\varphi_n(x)+$$

$$+C_1\varphi_p(x)+C_2\varphi_{p+1}(x)+\dots+C_q\varphi_{p+q-1}(x), \tag{73}$$

where $\sum'$ denotes that in the summation we have excluded all the values of n equal to $p,p+1,\dots,p+q-1$ for which

$$\lambda_p=\lambda_{p+1}=\lambda_{p+2}=\dots=\lambda_{p+q-1},$$

where q is the rank of that eigenvalue; $C_1,C_2,\dots,C_q$ are arbitrary constants.

By a similar method we may find the expansion of the resolvent kernel $\mathfrak{N}$ as a series of eigenfunctions $\{\varphi_n(x)\}$. We use the integral equation satisfied by the resolvent kernel

$$\mathfrak{N}(x, y, \lambda) = N(x, y) + \lambda \int_{\Omega} N(x, s)\, \mathfrak{N}(s, y, \lambda)\, ds, \tag{74}$$

and hence, on the basis of the Hilbert–Schmidt Theorem, we conclude that there must exist an absolutely and uniformly convergent expansion

$$\frac{\mathfrak{N}(x, y, \lambda) - N(x, y)}{\lambda} = \int_{\Omega} N(x, s)\, \mathfrak{N}(s, y, \lambda)\, ds = \sum_{n=1}^{\infty} b_n(y)\, \varphi_n(x), \tag{75}$$

when λ is not an eigenvalue. Therefore we have

$$\sum_{n=1}^{\infty} b_n(y)\, \varphi_n(x) = \int_{\Omega} N(x, s)\, N(s, y)\, ds + \lambda \sum_{n=1}^{\infty} \int_{\Omega} b_n(y)\, N(x, s)\, \varphi_n(s)\, ds,$$

and further

$$\sum_{n=1}^{\infty} b_n(y) \left(1 - \frac{\lambda}{\lambda_n}\right) \varphi_n(x) = \int_{\Omega} N(x, s)\, N(s, y)\, ds. \tag{76}$$

Applying the Hilbert–Schmidt Theorem again, we obtain

$$\int_{\Omega} N(x, s)\, N(s, y)\, ds = \sum_{n=1}^{\infty} \frac{F_n(y)}{\lambda_n}\, \varphi_n(x), \tag{77}$$

where

$$F_n(y) = \int_{\Omega} N(s, y)\, \overline{\varphi_n(x)}\, ds = \frac{\overline{\varphi_n(y)}}{\lambda_n}.$$

Substituting expansion (77) in equality (76), we obtain

$$\sum_{n=1}^{\infty} \left[b_n(y) \left(1 - \frac{\lambda}{\lambda_n}\right) - \frac{\overline{\varphi_n(y)}}{\lambda_n^2} \right] \varphi_n(x) = 0,$$

whence, as before, on account of the orthogonality of the system $\{\varphi_n(x)\}$, it follows that

$$b_n(y) = \frac{\overline{\varphi_n(y)}}{\lambda_n(\lambda_n - \lambda)} .$$

The required expansion of the resolvent kernel is therefore obtained in the form

$$\mathfrak{R}(x, y, \lambda) = N(x, y) - \lambda \sum_{n=1}^{\infty} \frac{\varphi_n(x)\overline{\varphi_n(y)}}{\lambda_n(\lambda - \lambda_n)} \quad (\lambda \neq \lambda_n), \qquad (78)$$

from which it may be seen that the eigenvalues λ_n are the first order poles of a meromorphic function of the parameter λ. The result (78) accords with the Mittag-Leffler Theorem on the expansion of a meromorphic function in partial fractions. The absolute and uniform convergence of series (78) with respect to x and y is evident in view of the similar convergence of the series

$$\sum_{n=1}^{\infty} \frac{\varphi_n(x)\overline{\varphi_n(y)}}{\lambda_n^2} .$$

Expansions (71) and (78) obtained are clearer and more convenient to apply than Fredholm's formulae.

Expansion (78) implies an interesting theorem on the rank of an eigenvalue, which, so far, we know is at least equal to unity and at most to the order of the zero of the Fredholm function $D(\lambda)$:

THEOREM. *The rank of an eigenvalue of a symmetric kernel is equal to the order of that value as a zero of the Fredholm function* $D(\lambda)$.

We know that

$$\frac{D'(\lambda)}{D(\lambda)} = -\int_{\Omega} \mathfrak{R}(s, s, \lambda)\, ds ,$$

whence, according to expansion (78), we obtain

$$\frac{D'(\lambda)}{D(\lambda)} = -\int_{\Omega} N(s, s)\, ds + \lambda \sum_{n=1}^{\infty} \frac{1}{\lambda_n(\lambda - \lambda_n)} , \qquad (79)$$

since the functions $\varphi_n(s)$ are normalized. Now, if λ_p is an eigenvalue with rank q, i.e. if

$$\lambda_{p-1} \neq \lambda_p = \lambda_{p+1} = \lambda_{p+2} = \ldots = \lambda_{p+q-1} \neq \lambda_{p+q},$$

then the corresponding principal part of product (79) is:

$$\frac{\lambda}{\lambda_p} \frac{q}{\lambda-\lambda_p} = \frac{q}{\lambda-\lambda_p} + \frac{q}{\lambda_p}. \tag{80}$$

On the other hand, if α is the order of a zero of the function $D(\lambda)$, i.e.

$$D(\lambda) = (\lambda-\lambda_p)^\alpha \Phi(\lambda),$$

where $\Phi(\lambda_p) \neq 0$, then we have

$$\frac{D'(\lambda)}{D(\lambda)} = \frac{\alpha}{\lambda-\lambda_p} + \frac{\Phi'(\lambda)}{\Phi(\lambda)}.$$

Hence it follows, by comparison with equality (80) that $\alpha \neq q$, and thus *the rank of an eigenvalue is equal to the order of that value as a zero of the function* $D(\lambda)$. This proves the theorem.

§ 6. Particular symmetric kernels

DEFINITION 1. *We call a symmetric kernel* $N(x, y)$ *closed if there exists no function* $h(x)$ *with a non-zero norm satisfying the equation*

$$\int_\Omega N(x, y) h(y) dy = 0. \tag{81}$$

The lemma of p. 139 implies that *a symmetric kernel is closed if and only if the orthogonal system* $\{\varphi_n(x)\}$ *of all its eigenfunctions is complete.*

Indeed, from the above lemma we know that a necessary and sufficient condition for the solvability of the equation

$$\int_\Omega N(x, y) \varphi(y) dy = 0$$

is the orthogonality of the function φ to all the functions of the system of eigenfunctions $\{\varphi_n(x)\}$, i.e.

$$\int_\Omega \varphi_n(x) \overline{\varphi(y)} dy = 0.$$

Hence it follows that *a closed kernel must have an infinite number of eigenvalues.*

DEFINITION 2. *We call a symmetric kernel definite if there exists no function $h(x)$ with a non-zero norm for which*

$$\int_\Omega \int_\Omega N(x, y) \overline{h(x)} h(y) \, dx \, dy = 0. \tag{82}$$

A definite kernel is always closed, for, if

$$\int_\Omega N(x, y) h(y) \, dy = 0$$

for a function h with a positive norm, then the equality (82) would hold, contrary to the hypothesis.

We shall now show that *all the eigenvalues of a definite kernel have the same algebraic sign.* Indeed, if two eigenvalues λ_m and λ_n had different signs, then the function

$$h(x) = \sqrt{|\lambda_m|} \cdot \varphi_m(x) + \sqrt{|\lambda_n|} \cdot \varphi_n(x)$$

would satisfy the equation

$$\int_\Omega N(x, y) h(y) \, dy = \frac{\sqrt{|\lambda_m|}}{\lambda_m} \varphi_m(x) + \frac{\sqrt{|\lambda_n|}}{\lambda_n} \varphi_n(x),$$

from which it would follow that

$$\int_\Omega \int_\Omega N(x, y) h(x) h(y) \, dy \, dx = \frac{|\lambda_m|}{\lambda_m} + \frac{|\lambda_n|}{\lambda_n} = 0,$$

contradicting the hypothesis.

It is easy to show that *the iterated kernel of a closed kernel is definite.* Indeed, if

$$N_2(x, y) = \int_\Omega N(x, s) N(s, y) \, ds,$$

then it is impossible that

$$\int_\Omega \int_\Omega N_2(x, y) \overline{h(x)} h(y) \, dx \, dy = 0$$

for any function $h(x)$ with positive norm, since this would imply that

$$\int_\Omega \left| \int_\Omega N(x, s)\overline{h(x)}\, dx \right|^2 ds = 0,$$

whence

$$\int_\Omega N(x, s)\overline{h(x)}\, dx = 0$$

for almost all s, contradicting the hypothesis.

DEFINITION 3. *We call a symmetric kernel* $N(x, y)$ *positive if for every function* $h \in L^2(\Omega)$ *we have*

$$\int_\Omega \int_\Omega N(x, y)\overline{h(x)}\, h(y)\, dx\, dy \geqq 0. \tag{83}$$

We shall show that *all the eigenvalues of a positive kernel are positive.* Indeed, taking $h(x) = \varphi_n(x)$ we obtain

$$\int_\Omega \int_\Omega N(x, y)\overline{\varphi_n(x)}\,\varphi_n(y)\, dx\, dy = \int_\Omega \frac{|\varphi_n(x)|^2}{\lambda_n}\, dx = \frac{1}{\lambda_n},$$

and it follows therefore that $\lambda_n > 0$.

Conversely, *if all the eigenvalues of a kernel are positive then the kernel is positive.* In fact, the Hilbert–Schmidt Theorem implies the equality

$$\int_\Omega N(x, y)\, h(y)\, dy = \sum_{n=1}^{\infty} \frac{h_n}{\lambda_n}\, \varphi_n(x), \tag{84}$$

where the h_n are the Fourier coefficients of the function $h(x)$ with respect to the system $\{\varphi_n(x)\}$. Hence we have

$$\int_\Omega \int_\Omega N(x, y)\overline{h(x)}\, h(y)\, dx\, dy = \sum_{n=1}^{\infty} \frac{|h_n|^2}{\lambda_n} > 0.$$

MERCER'S THEOREM. *A symmetric kernel* $N(x, y)$ *positive, continuous, and such that the integral* $\int_\Omega |N(x, y)|^2\, dx$ *is bounded in the set* Ω, *is the sum of its Fourier series which is absolutely and uniformly convergent with respect to the pair o variables* x, y:

$$N(x, y) = \sum_{n=1}^{\infty} \frac{\varphi_n(x)\overline{\varphi_n(y)}}{\lambda_n}. \tag{85}$$

We already know that for a symmetric kernel the function $N(x, x)$ is real. We shall prove that *for a positive kernel we must always have* $N(x, x) \geqq 0$.

Indeed, if it is assumed that the function $N(x, x)$ is *negative* at a point x_0, then because of the continuity of the function $N(x, y)$ there would exist a neighbourhood D_ε of the point x_0 with diameter ε sufficiently small, in which the real part of the function $N(x, y)$ would also be negative for both points x, y lying in the domain D_ε.

Suppose we are given a function $h(x)$ positive in the domain D_ε and equal to zero outside it. We then have

$$\operatorname{re} \int_\Omega \int_\Omega N(x, y)\, h(x)\, h(y)\, dx\, dy$$

$$= \operatorname{re} \int_{D_\varepsilon} \int_{D_\varepsilon} N(x, y)\, h(x)\, h(y)\, dx\, dy < 0,$$

contradicting the hypothesis that the given kernel N is positive.

Now consider the difference

$$N(x, y) - \sum_{n=1}^{p} \frac{\varphi_n(x)\overline{\varphi_n(y)}}{\lambda_n}. \tag{86}$$

This function is a positive symmetric kernel, since according to the theorem on p. 134 its eigenvalues $\lambda_{p+1}, \lambda_{p+2}, \ldots$ are positive by hypothesis. Hence it follows, on the basis of the property just shown, that

$$N(x, x) - \sum_{n=1}^{p} \frac{|\varphi_n(x)|^2}{\lambda_n} \geqq 0. \tag{87}$$

Since inequality (87) holds for all p, the sequence

$$\sum_{n=1}^{\infty} \frac{|\varphi_n(x)|^2}{\lambda_n}$$

converges for all x. Hence, by the already familiar method, on the basis of the Buniakovski–Schwarz inequality

$$\left[\sum_{v=0}^{m} \frac{\varphi_{n+v}(x)\,\varphi_{n+v}(y)}{\sqrt{\lambda_{n+v}}\,\sqrt{\lambda_{n+v}}}\right]^2 \leqq \sum_{v=0}^{m} \frac{|\varphi_{n+v}(x)|^2}{\lambda_{n+v}} \sum_{v=0}^{m} \frac{|\varphi_{n+v}(y)|^2}{\lambda_{n+v}}$$

for any n and m, and inequality (29) on p. 132, we prove that the series

$$\sum_{n=1}^{\infty} \frac{\varphi_n(x)\,\overline{\varphi_n(y)}}{\lambda_n} \tag{88}$$

converges absolutely and uniformly with respect to each of the variables x and y separately. On the basis of the theorem of p. 130 we conclude that the sum of the series is the given positive kernel $N(x, y)$, which was to be shown.

We mention that using the argument of pp. 137–8, *series* (88) *also converges uniformly with respect to the pair of variables* (x, y).

To conclude this section we shall also show that the equation with a kernel of the form

$$N(x, y)\,p(y),$$

where $N(x, y)$ is symmetric, may be reduced to an equation with a symmetric kernel. This equation had been considered by E. SCHMIDT.

Consider the equation

$$\varphi(x) = f(x) + \lambda \int_{\Omega} N(x, y)\,p(y)\,\varphi(y)\,dy,$$

where $N(x, y)$ is a symmetric kernel, and $p(y)$ is a positive function. By substituting

$$\psi(x) = \varphi(x)\sqrt{p(x)}$$

this equation is reduced to the equation

$$\psi(x) = f(x)\sqrt{p(x)} + \lambda \int_{\Omega} N(x, y)\sqrt{p(x)\,p(y)}\,\psi(y)\,dy \tag{89}$$

with a symmetric kernel $N(x, y)\,\sqrt{p(x)\,p(y)}$.

The argument may be generalized to an equation of the form

$$\varphi(x) = f(x) + \lambda \int N(x, y)\,p(x)\,q(y)\,\varphi(y)\,dy, \tag{90}$$

where $N(x, y)$ is a symmetric kernel, while the quotient $q(x)/p(x)$ is positive and bounded. For, by substituting

$$\psi(x) = \sqrt{\frac{q(x)}{p(x)}}\,\varphi(x)$$

we obtain the integral equation

$$\psi(x) = \sqrt{\frac{q(x)}{p(x)}}\,f(x) + \lambda \int_{\Omega} N(x, y) \sqrt{p(x)\,p(y)\,q(x)\,q(y)}\,\psi(y)\,dy$$

with a symmetric kernel.

CHAPTER VI

FREDHOLM'S EQUATION OF THE FIRST KIND

§ 1. General remarks

We know that a *Fredholm equation of the first kind* is an equation of the form

$$\int_{\Omega} N(x, y)\varphi(y)\,dy = f(x), \tag{1}$$

where the functions N and f are given, and φ is the unknown function. The solution of equation (1) offers difficulties differing in principle from those involved in an equation of the second kind.

First of all it is easy to see that equation (1) does not always have a solution. If, for example, the kernel $N(x, y)$ is the sum of products of functions of a single variable

$$N(x, y) = \sum_{\nu=1}^{n} A_\nu(x) B_\nu(y),$$

but the function $f(x)$ is not a linear combination of the functions $A_\nu(x)$, then equation (1) has no solution.

In the subsequent investigations of the Fredholm equation of the first kind we always assume that the integral is defined in the sense of Lebesgue. This assumption is of primary importance for the Fredholm equation of the first kind, since it extends the class of functions among which a solution exists.

§ 2. Equation with symmetric kernel

We shall first give the solution of the Fredholm integral equation of the first kind with *closed symmetric* kernel $N(x, y)$, since in this case it is obtained relatively easily on the basis of the theorems given in Chapter V, concerning the equations with symmetric kernels. We have the following theorem, constituting a special case of Picard's theorem, which will be given later on:

THEOREM. *The Fredholm integral equation of the first kind with a closed symmetric kernel possesses a unique solution in* $L^2(\Omega)$ *if and only if the series*

$$\sum_{n=1}^{\infty} |\lambda_n f_n|^2 \tag{2}$$

converges, where λ_n *is the sequence of eigenvalues of the kernel* $N(x, y)$ *and the* f_n *are the Fourier coefficients of the given function* $f(x)$ *with respect to the orthonormal system* $\{\varphi_n(x)\}$ *of all eigenfunctions of the kernel* $N(x, y)$:

$$f_n = \int_{\Omega} f(x)\overline{\varphi_n(x)}\,dx. \tag{3}$$

First of all, we shall note that because of the assumption that the kernel $N(x, y)$ is closed the orthogonal system $\{\varphi_n(x)\}$ is complete.

Let us first show that condition (2) is *necessary*. It there exists a function $\varphi \in L^2(\Omega)$, which is a solution of equation (1), then it satisfies the equation

$$\int_{\Omega}\int_{\Omega} N(x, y)\overline{\varphi_n(x)}\varphi(y)\,dx\,dy = \int_{\Omega} f(x)\overline{\varphi_n(x)}\,dx = f_n,$$

and since

$$\int_{\Omega} N(x, y)\overline{\varphi_n(x)}\,dx = \int_{\Omega} \overline{N(y, x)\varphi_n(x)}\,dx = \frac{\overline{\varphi_n(y)}}{\lambda_n},$$

it follows that

$$\int_{\Omega} \overline{\varphi_n(y)}\varphi(y)\,dy = \lambda_n f_n. \tag{4}$$

Thus, the numbers $\lambda_n f_n$ are the Fourier coefficients of the function $\varphi(y)$ with respect to the system $\{\varphi_n\}$, and in this case the series

$$\sum_{n=1}^{\infty} |\lambda_n f_n|^2$$

is convergent.

We shall now show that the condition for the convergence of series (2) is at the same time *sufficient*. Indeed, if series (2) converges, then the Riesz–Fischer Theorem implies that *there exists a unique function* $\psi \in L^2(\Omega)$ *such that its Fourier coefficients with respect to the system* $\{\varphi_n(x)\}$ *are just the numbers* $\lambda_n f_n$, i.e.

$$\lambda_n f_n = \int_\Omega \psi(x)\overline{\varphi_n(x)}\,dx, \tag{5}$$

and to which the Fourier series

$$\sum_{n=1}^{\infty} \lambda_n f_n \varphi_n(x)$$

converges in the mean. The function $\psi(x)$ is precisely the solution of the integral equation (1).

Indeed, note that the function

$$F(x) = \int_\Omega N(x, y)\psi(y)\,dy$$

and the function $f(x)$ have the same Fourier coefficients with respect to the system $\{\varphi_n\}$, since

$$\int_\Omega F(x)\overline{\varphi_n(x)}\,dx = \int_\Omega\int_\Omega N(x, y)\overline{\varphi_n(x)}\psi(y)\,dx\,dy$$

$$= \int_\Omega \frac{\overline{\varphi_n(y)}}{\lambda_n}\psi(y)\,dy = f_n.$$

Hence it follows that the difference $F(x)-f(x)$ is orthogonal to all the functions $\{\varphi_n(x)\}$, i.e.

$$\int_\Omega [F(x)-f(x)]\overline{\varphi_n(x)}\,dx = 0,$$

and since the system $\{\varphi_n(x)\}$ is complete, it follows that $F(x)-f(x) = 0$ almost everywhere and the function $\psi(x)$ satisfies the equation

$$\int_\Omega N(x, y)\psi(y)\,dy = f(x)$$

almost everywhere.

This solution is unique in $L^2(\Omega)$; for if the function $\psi_1(x)$ were the second solution then

$$\int_{\Omega} N(x, y)[\psi(y) - \psi_1(y)]\, dy = 0,$$

contrary to the assumption that the kernel N is closed. Hence it follows that $\psi = \psi_1$ almost everywhere.

We shall also mention that closure of the kernel is essential not only for the uniqueness of the solution but also for its existence. For, if the kernel $N(x, y)$ were not closed, then the system $\{\varphi_n(x)\}$ would not be complete and the difference

$$\int_{\Omega} N(x, y)\psi(y)\, dy - f(x)$$

would not necessarily be almost everywhere equal to zero.

§ 3. Schmidt's Theorem on the non-symmetric kernel

The Hilbert–Schmidt Theorem for the symmetric kernel was generalized by E. Schmidt to the non-symmetric kernel.

Suppose we are given a kernel $N(x, y)$, not necessarily symmetric, which is integrable together with the square of its modulus. With this kernel Schmidt associated the following kernels:

$$\begin{aligned} N^*(x, y) &= \int_{\Omega} N(s, x)\overline{N(s, y)}\, ds, \\ N_*(x, y) &= \int_{\Omega} N(x, s)\overline{N(y, s)}\, ds, \end{aligned} \tag{6}$$

which are symmetric since

$$\begin{aligned} N^*(y, x) &= \overline{N^*(x, y)}, \\ N_*(y, x) &= \overline{N_*(x, y)}. \end{aligned}$$

These kernels are *positive* since for any function $h \in L^2(\Omega)$ we have

$$\int_{\Omega}\int_{\Omega} N^*(x, y) h(x)\overline{h(y)}\, dx\, dy = \int_{\Omega}\left|\int_{\Omega} N(s, x) h(x)\, dx\right|^2 ds \geqq 0$$

and the same inequality for $N_*(x, y)$.

Thus, *the kernels N^* and N_* have positive eigenvalues.* We shall show that *they are common to both kernels.* In fact, let us denote by λ_n^2 the eigenvalue of the kernel N^*, and by $\varphi_n(x)$ its corresponding eigenfunction. We then have

$$\varphi_n(x) = \lambda_n^2 \int_\Omega N^*(x, y)\, \varphi_n(y)\, dy . \tag{7}$$

If we now introduce the function

$$\psi_n(x) = \lambda_n \int_\Omega N(x, y)\, \varphi_n(y)\, dy \tag{8}$$

(assuming that $\lambda_n > 0$) then, in view of expressions (6), we shall have, conversely,

$$\varphi_n(x) = \lambda_n \int_\Omega \overline{N(y, x)}\, \psi_n(y)\, dy . \tag{9}$$

This equality shows that the function $\psi_n(x)$ is not almost everywhere equal to zero. Now substituting expression (9) for the function φ_n in the right-hand side of equality (8) we obtain

$$\psi_n(x) = \lambda_n^2 \int_\Omega N_*(x, y)\, \psi_n(y)\, dy , \tag{10}$$

and hence λ_n^2 is also an eigenvalue of the kernel $N_*(x, y)$, and $\psi(x)$ is its corresponding eigenfunction.

Conversely, it may be shown that if λ_n^2 is an eigenvalue of the kernel $N_*(x, y)$ then it is also an eigenvalue of the kernel $N^*(x, y)$. The corresponding eigenfunctions are also connected by relations (9) and (8).

We shall now prove that *an eigenvalue λ_n^2 has the same rank relative to the kernel N^* and relative to the kernel N_**. To this end we consider two arbitrary eigenfunctions $\varphi_n^{(1)}$, $\varphi_n^{(2)}$ of the kernel N^*, corresponding to the eigenvalue λ_n^2. Let $\psi_n^{(1)}$ and $\psi_n^{(2)}$ denote the corresponding eigenfunctions of the kernel N_* obtained from relation (8), i.e.

$$\psi_n^{(1)}(x) = \lambda_n \int_\Omega N(x, y)\, \varphi_n^{(1)}(y)\, dy ,$$

$$\psi_n^{(2)}(x) = \lambda_n \int_\Omega N(x, y)\, \varphi_n^{(2)}(y)\, dy .$$

We then have

$$\int_{\Omega} \psi_n^{(1)}(x)\overline{\psi_n^{(2)}(x)}\,dx = \lambda_n \int_{\Omega}\int_{\Omega} N(x, y)\,\varphi_n^{(1)}(y)\overline{\psi_n^{(2)}(x)}\,dx\,dy$$

and

$$\int_{\Omega} \varphi_n^{(1)}(x)\overline{\varphi_n^{(2)}(x)}\,dx = \lambda_n \int_{\Omega}\int_{\Omega} N(y, x)\,\varphi_n^{(1)}(x)\overline{\psi_n^{(2)}(y)}\,dx\,dy,$$

and hence the scalar products of the functions $\varphi_n^{(1)}$, $\varphi_n^{(2)}$ and $\psi_n^{(1)}$, $\psi_n^{(2)}$ are equal:

$$\int_{\Omega} \psi_n^{(1)}(x)\overline{\psi_n^{(2)}(x)}\,dx = \int_{\Omega} \varphi_n^{(1)}(x)\overline{\varphi_n^{(2)}(x)}\,dx.$$

In particular, when $\varphi_n^{(1)} = \varphi_n^{(2)}$, we obtain

$$\int_{\Omega} |\psi_n^{(1)}(x)|^2\,dx = \int_{\Omega} |\varphi_n^{(1)}(x)|^2\,dx,$$

and hence the norms of corresponding functions φ_n and ψ_n are equal. From the foregoing we conclude that for every orthonormal system of eigenfunctions φ_n of the kernel N^* corresponding to an eigenvalue λ_n^2, the system of eigenfunctions ψ_n obtained from formula (10) is also orthonormal, and therefore linearly independent. Hence it follows that the rank of the eigenvalue λ_n^2 relative to the kernel N_* cannot be less than the rank of that eigenvalue relative to the kernel N^*. Similarly, making use of the reciprocity of the above relations we shall show that to two orthogonal eigenfunctions $\psi_n^{(1)}$, $\psi_n^{(2)}$ of the kernel N_* (for the eigenvalue λ_n^2) there correspond two orthogonal eigenfunctions $\varphi_n^{(1)}$ and $\varphi_n^{(2)}$ of the kernel N^* calculated from formula (10). Hence it follows that the rank of the eigenvalue λ_n^2 relative to the kernel N^* cannot be smaller than the rank of that eigenvalue relative to the kernel N_*. Consequently the eigenvalue λ_n^2 has the same rank relative to the kernel N^* and relative to the kernel N_*, which was to be proved.

Thus if $\{\lambda_n^2\}$ is a sequence of the common eigenvalues of positive kernels N_* and N^*, repeated the same number of times as the number of their rank, then the corresponding orthonormal systems of eigenfunctions of these kernels

$$\{\varphi_n(x)\} \quad \text{and} \quad \{\psi_n(x)\}$$

are connected by relations (8) and (9). We also mention that the completeness of one of these systems does not necessarily imply the completeness of the other one.

On the properties of the kernels N^* and N_* we base the following theorem:

SCHMIDT'S THEOREM. *Every function $f(x)$ having one of the two forms*

$$f(x) = \int_\Omega N(x, y)\, h(y)\, dy \quad \textit{and} \quad f(x) = \int_\Omega \overline{N(y, x)}\, h(y)\, dy \tag{11}$$

is the sum of its Fourier series with respect to the system $\psi_n(x)$ in the case of the first form and with respect to the system $\varphi_n(x)$ in the case of the second form. It is assumed that the kernel $N(x, y)$ and the function $h(x)$ are integrable together with the square of their moduli and that the integrals

$$\int_\Omega |N(x, y)|^2\, dx, \qquad \int_\Omega |N(x, y)|^2\, dy$$

are bounded.

We shall prove this theorem only in the case of the first of the forms (11). Now, the Fourier coefficients of the first of the functions (11) with respect to the system $\{\psi_n(x)\}$ are, according to equality (9), the numbers

$$f_n = \int_\Omega \ (x)\overline{\psi_n(x)}\, dx = \int_\Omega \int_\Omega N(x, y)\, \overline{\psi_n(x)}\, h(y)\, dx\, dy$$

$$= \frac{1}{\lambda_n} \int_\Omega h(y)\, \overline{\varphi_n(y)}\, dy = \frac{h_n}{\lambda_n},$$

where h_n denote the Fourier coefficients of the function h with respect to the system $\{\varphi_n(x)\}$. Hence the Fourier series of the first of the functions (11) has the form

$$S(x) = \sum_{n=1}^{\infty} \frac{h_n}{\lambda_n}\, \psi_n(x). \tag{12}$$

Similarly as before in the Hilbert–Schmidt Theorem, it can be proved that series (12) converges absolutely and uniformly. Since the sum $S(x)$ of series (12) has the same Fourier coefficients as the function $f(x)$, then, repeating the same proof as for the Hilbert–Schmidt Theorem, we conclude that $S(x) = f(x)$ almost everywhere. Thus, the theorem is proved.

§ 4. Picard's Theorem

E. PICARD has given the following theorem on the solution of the Fredholm integral equation of the first kind in the general case when the kernel $N(x, y)$ is not necessarily symmetric, under the assumption that the symmetric kernel $N_*(x, y)$ corresponding to it is closed:

PICARD'S THEOREM. *Assuming that the kernel N_* is closed, the Fredholm integral equation of the first kind,*

$$\int_\Omega N(x, y)\varphi(y)\,dy = f(x), \tag{13}$$

possesses a solution in $L^2(\Omega)$ if, and only if, the series

$$\sum_{n=1}^{\infty} |\lambda_n f_n|^2, \tag{14}$$

converges, where $\{\lambda_n^2\}$ is the sequence of eigenvalues of the kernel $N_*(x, y)$ and the numbers f_n are the Fourier coefficients of the given function $f(x)$ with respect to the system of eigenfunctions $\{\psi_n(x)\}$ of the kernel N_*.

The proof is similar to that for the symmetric kernel. To begin with the condition is *necessary*, since if we assume that there exists a solution φ, then according to the Schmidt Theorem, the function $f(x)$ is the sum of the series

$$f = \sum_{n=1}^{\infty} f_n \psi_n(x),$$

where the f_n are the Fourier coefficients of the function $f(x)$:

$$\begin{aligned} f_n &= \int_\Omega f(x)\overline{\psi_n(x)}\,dx \\ &= \int_\Omega\int_\Omega N(x, y)\varphi(y)\overline{\psi_n(x)}\,dx\,dy = \frac{1}{\lambda_n}\int_\Omega \overline{\varphi_n(y)}\varphi(y)\,dy. \end{aligned}$$

Therefore the numbers

$$\lambda_n f_n = \int_\Omega \overline{\varphi_n(y)}\,\varphi(y)\,dy$$

are the Fourier coefficients of the function $\varphi(y)$ *with respect to the system* $\{\varphi_n(x)\}$ and sequence (14) converges. Condition (14) is also *sufficient*, since when it is satisfied, by the Riesz–Fischer Theorem there exists a function $\varphi(x)$ for which the numbers $\lambda_n f_n$ are the Fourier coefficients with respect to the system $\{\varphi_n(x)\}$:

$$\lambda_n f_n = \int_\Omega \varphi(x)\,\overline{\varphi_n(x)}\,dx$$

and to which this series converges in the mean, i.e.

$$\lim_{n\to\infty} \left\|\varphi - \sum_{\nu=1}^{n} \lambda_\nu f_\nu \varphi_\nu\right\| = 0 .$$

The function $\varphi(x)$ just found satisfies the given integral equation (13). Indeed, the functions

$$\int_\Omega N(x, y)\,\varphi(y)\,dy, \quad f(x)$$

have the same Fourier coefficients with respect to $\psi_n(x)$, and consequently we have the equality

$$\int_\Omega \Big[\int_\Omega N(x, y)\,\varphi(y)\,dy - f(x)\Big]\,\overline{\psi_n(x)}\,dx = 0 \tag{15}$$

for every function ψ_n. Since the kernel N_* is closed, the system $\{\psi_n(x)\}$ is complete, and thus we have almost everywhere

$$\int_\Omega N(x, y)\,\varphi(y)\,dy - f(x) = 0 .$$

$\varphi(y)$ is therefore a solution of equation (13).

If we also assume that the kernel N^* is closed, then the *solution obtained is unique in the set* $L^2(\Omega)$. In fact, if $\varphi(y)$ and $\varphi_1(y)$ were two solutions, then their difference $h(y) = \varphi(y) - \varphi_1(y)$ would satisfy the equations

$$\int_\Omega N(x, y)\,h(y)\,dy = 0 \quad \text{and} \quad \int_\Omega \overline{N(x, y)}\,\overline{h(y)}\,dy = 0 .$$

Multiplying both sides by $N(x, s)$ and integrating with respect to x we obtain

$$\int_\Omega \Big[\int_\Omega N(x, s)\overline{N(x, y)}\, dx\Big]\overline{h(y)}\, dy = 0,$$

i.e.

$$\int_\Omega N^*(s, y)\overline{h(y)}\, dy = 0.$$

Hence, if the kernel N^* is closed, it follows that $h = \varphi - \varphi_1 = 0$ almost everywhere.

CHAPTER VII

DETAILED INVESTIGATION OF THE RESOLVENT KERNEL

§ 1. Integral equation of the resolvent kernels

In this last chapter of Part 1, devoted to the general properties of integral equations, we shall undertake a detailed investigation of some properties of the resolvent kernel, namely the expansion of the resolvent kernel $\mathfrak{N}(x, y, \lambda)$ in the neighbourhood of an eigenvalue λ_0 as pole of this meromorphic function.

We have already shown that the resolvent kernel of the kernel $N(x, y)$ satisfies the integral equations

$$\begin{aligned} \mathfrak{N}(x, y, \lambda) &= N(x, y) + \lambda \int_{\Omega} N(x, s)\, \mathfrak{N}(s, y, \lambda)\, ds, \\ \mathfrak{N}(x, y, \mu) &= N(x, y) + \mu \int_{\Omega} \mathfrak{N}(x, s, \mu)\, N(s, y)\, ds. \end{aligned} \tag{1}$$

From these equations it is possible to derive an integral equation not containing the kernel N, which is satisfied by all the resolvent kernels. For, on the basis of equations (1) we have

$$\begin{aligned} &\mathfrak{N}(x, y, \lambda) - \mathfrak{N}(x, y, \mu) \\ &\quad = \lambda \int_{\Omega} N(x, s)\, \mathfrak{N}(s, y, \lambda)\, ds - \mu \int_{\Omega} \mathfrak{N}(x, s, \mu)\, N(s, y)\, ds. \end{aligned} \tag{2}$$

Now, if in the first equation (1) we replace x by t, multiply both sides by $\mu \mathfrak{N}(x, t, \mu)$ and integrate, and in the second we replace y by t, multiply both sides by $\lambda \mathfrak{N}(t, y, \lambda)$ and integrate, then after subtracting the resulting equations we obtain

$$\begin{aligned} &(\mu - \lambda) \int_{\Omega} \mathfrak{N}(x, t, \mu)\, \mathfrak{N}(t, y, \lambda)\, dt \\ &\quad = \mu \int_{\Omega} N(t, y)\, \mathfrak{N}(x, t, \mu)\, dt - \lambda \int_{\Omega} N(x, t)\, \mathfrak{N}(t, y, \lambda)\, dt. \end{aligned}$$

Hence, by comparing with equality (2), it follows that

$$\mathfrak{R}(x, y, \lambda) - \mathfrak{R}(x, y, \mu) = (\lambda - \mu) \int_\Omega \mathfrak{R}(x, t, \mu) \mathfrak{R}(t, y, \lambda) \, dt . \quad (3)$$

This is just the *integral equation of all the resolvent kernels.*

§ 2. Orthogonal kernels

The notion of orthogonal kernels was introduced by E. GOURSAT* who pointed out their importance in the theory of Fredholm equations. Two kernels $P(x, y)$ and $Q(x, y)$ are called *orthogonal* if

$$\int_\Omega P(x, s) Q(s, y) \, ds = 0 , \qquad \int_\Omega Q(x, s) P(s, y) \, ds = 0 \quad (4)$$

for every pair of points x and y of the domain Ω.

If only one of the relations (4) holds, then the kernels P and Q are called *semi-orthogonal.*

Letting P_* and Q_* denote the resolvent kernels of the kernels P and Q, respectively, we have

$$P_*(x, y, \lambda) = \sum_{n=0}^{\infty} \lambda^n P_n(x, y) , \qquad Q_*(x, y, \lambda) = \sum_{n=0}^{\infty} \lambda^n Q_n(x, y) \quad (5)$$

for sufficiently small values of $|\lambda|$, where P_n and Q_n denote the iterated kernels. Equality (5) implies directly that if the kernels P and Q are orthogonal, then

$$\int_\Omega P(x, s) Q_*(s, y, \lambda) \, ds = 0 \quad \text{and} \quad \int_\Omega Q(x, s) P_*(s, y, \lambda) \, ds = 0 . \quad (6)$$

We may extend these equalities by analytic continuation to every value of λ not equal to an eigenvalue.

* Sur les équations intégrales, *Comptes Rendus*, Paris 1907.

THEOREM 1. *If the kernels $P(x, y)$ and $Q(x, y)$ are orthogonal then their sum*

$$N(x, y) = P(x, y) + Q(x, y)$$

has a resolvent kernel which is the sum of the resolvent kernels of the given kernels P and Q:

$$\mathfrak{N}(x, y, \lambda) = P_*(x, y, \lambda) + Q_*(x, y, \lambda).$$

In order to prove this property, consider the equations satisfied by the resolvent kernels

$$\begin{aligned} P_*(x, y, \lambda) &= P(x, y) + \lambda \int_\Omega P(x, s) P_*(s, y, \lambda)\, ds, \\ Q_*(x, y, \lambda) &= Q(x, y) + \lambda \int_\Omega Q(x, s) Q_*(s, y, \lambda)\, ds. \end{aligned} \tag{7}$$

From them, on the basis of equality (6) it follows that

$$\begin{aligned} &P_*(x, y, \lambda) + Q_*(x, y, \lambda) \\ &\quad = P(x, y) + Q(x, y) + \\ &\qquad + \lambda \int_\Omega [P(x, s) P_*(s, y, \lambda) + Q(x, s) Q_*(s, y, \lambda)]\, ds \\ &\quad = P(x, y) + Q(x, y) + \\ &\quad + \lambda \int_\Omega [P(x, s) + Q(x, s)][P_*(s, y, \lambda) + Q_*(s, y, \lambda)]\, ds. \end{aligned}$$

This equality says that $P_* + Q_*$ is a resolvent kernel of the kerne $P+Q$, which completes the proof.

THEOREM 2. *If the kernels P and Q are orthogonal or semi-orthogonal, then the Fredholm first function $D_N(\lambda)$ of the sum $N(x, y) = P(x, y) + Q(x, y)$ of the kernels P and Q is equal to the product of the Fredholm functions $D_P(\lambda)$ and $D_Q(\lambda)$ of these kernels:*

$$D_N(\lambda) = D_P(\lambda) D_Q(\lambda). \tag{8}$$

We shall derive this property from the expansion

$$\log D(\lambda) = -\sum_{n=1}^{\infty} \frac{\lambda^n}{n} \int_\Omega N_n(s, s)\, ds \qquad (N_1 = N).$$

For if the traces of the kernels P and Q are denoted by p_n and q_n,

$$p_n = \int_\Omega P_n(s, s)\, ds, \qquad q_n = \int_\Omega Q_n(s, s)\, ds, \tag{9}$$

then

$$\log D_P(\lambda) = -\sum_{n=1}^{\infty} \frac{\lambda^n}{n} p_n,$$
$$\log D_Q(\lambda) = -\sum_{n=1}^{\infty} \frac{\lambda^n}{n} q_n, \tag{10}$$

whence

$$\log D_P(\lambda) D_Q(\lambda) = -\sum_{n=1}^{\infty} \frac{\lambda^n}{n} (p_n+q_n). \tag{11}$$

We shall show that if the kernels P and Q are semi-orthogonal, then the numbers p_n+q_n are traces of the kernel $N = P+Q$. First of all we see that p_1+q_1 is the first trace of the kernel N, since

$$\int_\Omega N(s, s)\, ds = p_1+q_1.$$

In order to prove this property for every index n note that

$$N_n(x, y) = \int_\Omega \dots \int_\Omega N(x, s_1) N(s_1, s_2) \dots N(s_{n-1}, y)\, ds_1\, ds_2 \dots ds_{n-1}.$$

Consequently, the n-th trace of the kernel N is

$$\int_\Omega N_n(x, x)\, dx$$
$$= \int_\Omega \dots \int_\Omega [P(x, s_1)+Q(x, s_1)] [P(s_1, s_2)+Q(s_1, s_2)] \dots$$
$$\dots [P(s_{n-1}, x)+Q(s_{n-1}, x)]\, ds_1\, ds_2 \dots ds_{n-1}\, dx.$$

If the kernels P and Q are orthogonal or semi-orthogonal, then in the above expression the integrals of all the products containing at least one pair of different kernels P and Q vanish, and all that remains is

$$\int_\Omega N_n(x, x)\, dx$$
$$= \int_\Omega \dots \int_\Omega P(x, s_1) P(s_1, s_2) \dots P(s_{n-1}, x)\, ds_1 \dots ds_{n-1}\, dx +$$
$$+ \int_\Omega \dots \int_\Omega Q(x, s_1) Q(s_1, s_2) \dots Q(s_{n-1}, x)\, ds_1 \dots ds_{n-1}\, dx$$
$$= \int_\Omega P_n(x, x)\, dx + \int_\Omega Q_n(x, x)\, dx = p_n+q_n.$$

This result combined with equality (11) allows one to conclude that

$$D_N(\lambda) = D_P(\lambda) D_Q(\lambda).$$

This completes the proof.

§ 3. Investigation of the resolvent kernel in the neighbourhood of an eigenvalue

If an eigenvalue $\lambda = c$ is a p-th order pole of the resolven kernel $\mathfrak{R}(x, y, \lambda)$ of a given kernel $N(x, y)$, then according to Laurent's Theorem, the expansion of the resolvent kernel in the neighbourhood of that eigenvalue has the form

$$\mathfrak{R}(x, y, \lambda) = \frac{B_p(x, y)}{(\lambda-c)^p} + \frac{B_{p-1}(x, y)}{(\lambda-c)^{p-1}} + \ldots + \frac{B_1(x, y)}{(\lambda-c)} + \\ + \sum_{\nu=0}^{\infty} A_\nu(x, y)(\lambda-c)^\nu, \quad (12)$$

where the function $B_p(x, y)$ is not identically zero. Substituting expression (12) in the integral equation

$$\mathfrak{R}(x, y, \lambda) = N(x, y) + \lambda \int_\Omega N(x, s) \mathfrak{R}(s, y, \lambda)\, ds, \quad (13)$$

satisfied by the resolvent kernel, we have

$$\frac{B_p(x, y)}{(\lambda-c)^p} + \ldots + \frac{B_1(x, y)}{\lambda-c} + \sum_{\nu=0}^{\infty} A_\nu(x, y)(\lambda-c)^\nu$$

$$= N(x, y) + \lambda \int_\Omega N(x, s) \times$$

$$\times \left[\frac{B_p(s, y)}{(\lambda-c)^p} + \ldots + \frac{B_1(s, y)}{\lambda-c} + \sum_{\nu=0}^{\infty} A_\nu(s, y)(\lambda-c)^\nu \right] ds. \quad (14)$$

Equating the coefficients of $(\lambda-c)^{-p}$ we obtain

$$B_p(x, y) = c \int_\Omega N(x, s) B_p(s, y)\, ds, \quad (15)$$

which indicates that the function $B_p(x, y)$, for fixed y is an eigenfunction of the integral equation corresponding to the eigenvalue c.

In a similar way, using the second integral equation of the resolvent kernel, it is possible to show that the function $B_p(y, x)$ for fixed y is a solution of the associated equation.

Now let us substitute expression (12) for resolvent kernel in the neighbourhood of a pole $\lambda = c$, into the general integral equation (3) of resolvent kernels, replacing the variable of integration t by s. We obtain

$$\sum_{\nu=1}^{p} B_\nu(x, y)\left[\frac{1}{(\lambda-c)^\nu}-\frac{1}{(\mu-c)^\nu}\right]+ \\ +\sum_{i=0}^{\infty} A_i(x, y)[(\lambda-c)^i-(\mu-c)^i]$$

$$= (\lambda-\mu)\int\limits_{\Omega}\left[\sum_{\nu=1}^{p} B_\nu(x, s)\frac{1}{(\lambda-c)^\nu}+\sum_{i=0}^{\infty} A_i(x, s)(\lambda-c)^i\right]\times \\ \times\left[\sum_{\nu=1}^{p} B_\nu(s, y)\frac{1}{(\mu-c)^\nu}+\sum_{\nu=0}^{\infty} A_\nu(s, y)(\mu-c)^\nu\right] ds. \tag{16}$$

Now, using the notation $h = \lambda-c$, $k = \mu-c$, and dividing both sides by $h-c$, we have

$$-\sum_{\nu=1}^{p}\frac{B_\nu(x, y)}{hk}\left[\frac{1}{h^{\nu-1}}+\frac{1}{h^{\nu-2}k}+\ldots+\frac{1}{k^{\nu-1}}\right]+ \\ +\sum_{i=1}^{\infty} A_i(x, y)(h^{i-1}+h^{i-2}k+\ldots+k^{i-1})$$

$$=\int\limits_{\Omega}\left[\sum_{\nu=1}^{p}\frac{1}{h^\nu}B_\nu(x, s)+\sum_{i=0}^{\infty} A_i(x, s)h^i\right]\times \\ \times\left[\sum_{\nu=1}^{p}\frac{1}{k^\nu}B_\nu(s, y)+\sum_{i=0}^{\infty} A_i(s, y)k^i\right] ds \tag{17}$$

for all values of $h \neq 0$, $k \neq 0$ in a certain interval.

We see that the left-hand side of equality (17) contains only terms of the form $1/h^\alpha k^\beta$ or $h^\alpha k^\beta$ where α and β are non-negative integers. Consequently, the terms on the right-hand side containing factors of the form k^i/h^ν or h^ν/k^i, where i, ν are non-negative integers, should be equal to zero. We obtain the following system of equations:

$$\begin{aligned}&\int_{\Omega} B_\nu(x,s)A_i(s,y)\,ds=0,\\&\int_{\Omega} B_\nu(s,y)A_i(x,s)\,ds=0\end{aligned}\qquad\begin{pmatrix}\nu=1,2,\dots,p\\ i=1,2,\dots,\infty\end{pmatrix}. \tag{18}$$

Now if we denote the *principal part* of the resolvent kernel $\mathfrak{R}$ in the neighbourhood of a pole c by G:

$$G(x,y,\lambda)=\frac{B_p(x,y)}{(\lambda-c)^p}+\frac{B_{p-1}(x,y)}{(\lambda-c)^{p-1}}+\dots+\frac{B_1(x,y)}{\lambda-c}, \tag{19}$$

and the *regular part* by H,

$$H(x,y,\lambda)=\sum_{\nu=0}^{\infty}A_\nu(x,y)(\lambda-c)^\nu, \tag{20}$$

then from equation (18) we obtain the following important conclusion:

The principal part of a resolvent kernel is orthogonal to its regular part in the neighbourhood of a pole, i.e.

$$\begin{aligned}&\int_{\Omega} G(x,s,\lambda)H(s,y,\mu)\,ds=0,\\&\int_{\Omega} H(x,s,\mu)G(s,y,\lambda)\,ds=0.\end{aligned} \tag{21}$$

Even though they have been derived from equality (17), requiring the convergence of the respective series, equations (21) hold for all values of the parameters λ and μ not equal to eigenvalues. Indeed, the principal part G is simply the rational function of the parameter λ, while the regular part H is the branch of the meromorphic function of the parameter μ not having a pole $\mu=c$ and consequently may be a single-valued analytic extension.

Now if in identity (17) we compare on both sides those coefficients of the powers of $1/h$ and $1/k$ which belong only to the principal part, we obtain the equation

$$G(x,y,\lambda)-G(x,y,\mu)=(\lambda-\mu)\int_{\Omega} G(x,s,\lambda)G(s,y,\mu)\,ds. \tag{22}$$

Similarly, if we compare the coefficients of the powers belonging only to the regular part, we obtain

$$H(x,y,\lambda)-H(x,y,\mu)=(\lambda-\mu)\int_{\Omega} H(x,s,\lambda)H(s,y,\mu)\,ds, \quad (23)$$

i.e. *the principal part and the regular part satisfy the general equation of resolvent kernels.*

Let us also express

$$G(x,y,0)=P(x,y), \qquad H(x,y,0)=Q(x,y). \quad (24)$$

Since

$$\mathfrak{N}(x,y,0)=N(x,y),$$

we have

$$P(x,y)+Q(x,y)=N(x,y). \quad (25)$$

Substituting $\mu = 0$ in equations (22) and (23), we obtain

$$\begin{aligned} G(x,y,\lambda) &= P(x,y)+\lambda\int_{\Omega} G(x,s,\lambda)P(s,y)\,ds, \\ H(x,y,\lambda) &= Q(x,y)+\lambda\int_{\Omega} H(x,s,\lambda)Q(s,y)\,ds. \end{aligned} \quad (26)$$

These equations express that the principal part $G(x, y, \lambda)$ is the resolvent kernel for the kernel

$$P(x,y)=G(x,y,0),$$

and the regular part $H(x, y, \lambda)$ is the resolvent kernel for the kernel

$$Q(x,y)=H(x,y,0).$$

We call the function $P(x, y, 0)$ the *principal kernel* for the eigenvalue $\lambda = c$. In view of (12), this function is expressed by the formula

$$P(x,y)=\frac{B_p(x,y)}{(-c)^p}+\frac{B_{p-1}(x,y)}{(-c)^{p-1}}+\ldots+\frac{B_1(x,y)}{(-c)}. \quad (27)$$

§ 4. Principal functions

We shall now acquaint ourselves in greater detail with the structure of functions $B_\nu(x, y)$ which occur in the expression for the principal part of the resolvent kernel. With this aim, we shall first give a definition and a lemma.

DEFINITION. *Two sequences in* $L^2(\Omega)$:

$$\varphi_1(x), \varphi_2(x), \ldots, \varphi_n(x), \ldots,$$
$$\psi_1(x), \psi_2(x), \ldots, \psi_n(x), \ldots,$$

constitute a biorthogonal system if

$$\int_\Omega \varphi_i(x)\psi_k(x)\,dx = \delta_{ik},$$

where δ_{ik} *is the Kronecker delta.*

Here we have adopted a definition of orthogonality differing from that in Chapter IV as, although the present argument may also be extended to complex functions, the above definition is more convenient.

LEMMA. *If a function* $\Phi(x, y)$, *integrable together with the square of its modulus, with a positive norm has a finite trace and satisfies the equation*

$$\Phi(x, y) = \int_\Omega \Phi(x, s)\Phi(s, y)\,ds, \tag{28}$$

then it has the form

$$\Phi(x, y) = \sum_{\nu=1}^{n} \varphi_\nu(x)\psi_\nu(y), \tag{29}$$

where the two sequences of functions $\varphi_\nu(x)$ *and* $\psi_\nu(y)$ *form a biorthogonal system.*

Assumption (28) implies directly that all the iterated kernels of the kernel Φ are identical, since

$$\Phi_{n+1}(x, y) = \int_\Omega \Phi(x, s)\Phi_n(s, y)\,ds = \Phi(x, y), \tag{30}$$

if $\Phi_n(x, y) = \Phi(x, y)$. Hence it follows that all the traces of the kernel Φ must be equal to the integer

$$m = \int_\Omega \Phi(s, s)\,ds.$$

Indeed, in view of property (30), we have *

$$\log D(\lambda) = m\left[-\frac{\lambda}{1} - \frac{\lambda^2}{2} - \ldots - \frac{\lambda^n}{n} - \ldots\right] = m\log(1-\lambda),$$

* Cf. formula (70) on p. 49.

and hence

$$D(\lambda) = (1-\lambda)^m. \tag{31}$$

Thus, m is an integer.

Now, let us form the function

$$\Phi(x, y) - \frac{\Phi(x_1, y)\,\Phi(x, y_1)}{\Phi(x_1, y_1)} = \Phi_1(x, y), \tag{32}$$

where, in accordance with the hypothesis, the values x_1, y_1 are chosen so that $\Phi(x_1, y_1) \neq 0$. *This function also satisfies equation* (28) *and its trace is equal to* $m-1$.

In fact, we have

$$\int_\Omega \Phi_1(x, s)\,\Phi_1(s, y)\,ds$$

$$= \int_\Omega \left[\Phi(x, s) - \frac{\Phi(x, y_1)\,\Phi(x_1, s)}{\Phi(x_1, y_1)}\right] \times$$

$$\times \left[\Phi(s, y) - \frac{\Phi(s, y_1)\,\Phi(x_1, y)}{\Phi(x_1, y_1)}\right] ds$$

$$= \Phi(x, y) - \frac{\Phi(x, y_1)\,\Phi(x_1, y)}{\Phi(x_1, y_1)} = \Phi_1(x, y),$$

and the trace is equal to

$$\int_\Omega \Phi_1(s, s)\,ds = \int_\Omega \Phi(s, s)\,ds - \int_\Omega \frac{\Phi(x_1, s)\,\Phi(s, y_1)}{\Phi(x_1, y_1)}\,ds = m-1.$$

In the case $\Phi_1 = 0$, the theorem is proved. Otherwise, applying the same process to the function Φ_1, i.e. investigating the function

$$\Phi_1(x, y) - \frac{\Phi_1(x_2, y)\,\Phi(x, y_2)}{\Phi_1(x_2, y_2)} = \Phi_2(x, y),$$

where $\Phi_1(x_2, y_2) \neq 0$, we again find that the function satisfies equation (28) and that its trace is equal to $m-2$.

Repeating the above process, we conclude that the function $\Phi(x, y)$ has the form

$$\Phi(x, y)=\varphi_1(x)\psi_1(y)+\varphi_2(x)\psi_2(y)+ \\ +\ldots+\varphi_n(x)\psi_n(y)+\kappa(x, y), \quad (33)$$

where the function $\kappa(x, y)$ has zero trace

$$\int_\Omega \kappa(s, s)\, ds=0 .$$

We shall now show that *the function* $\kappa(x, y)$ *is identically zero.*

For, suppose this were not the case. Then, since the function $\kappa(x, y)$ satisfies equation (28), all the iterated kernels of the function κ are equal to that function and its resolvent kernel has the form

$$\kappa(x, y)(1+\lambda+\lambda^2+\lambda^3+\ldots)=\frac{\kappa(x, y)}{1-\lambda},$$

which is impossible, since, in view of (31), we have $D(\lambda) = 1$. Consequently, $\kappa(x, y) = 0$ must hold and finally the function $\Phi(x, y)$ has form (29).

We shall also show that the functions $\varphi_\nu(x)$ and $\psi_\nu(x)$ form a *biorthogonal system.* Indeed, substituting expression (29) in equation (28) we have

$$\sum_{\nu=1}^{n}\varphi_\nu(x)\psi_\nu(y)=\sum_{\nu, i=1}^{n}\varphi_\nu(x)\psi_i(y)\int_\Omega \varphi_i(s)\psi_\nu(s)\, ds,$$

but it may always be assumed that the functions φ_ν and ψ_ν form two linearly independent systems, and consequently

$$\int_\Omega \varphi_i(s)\psi_\nu(s)\, ds=\delta_{i\nu}$$

must hold, which was to be proved.

Conversely: *a function of form* (29) *satisfies equation* (28) *and its trace is an integer.*

The lemma just proved makes it possible to investigate the structure of the coefficients $B_\nu(x, y)$ occurring in the Laurent expansion of the resolvent kernel in the neighbourhood of an eigenvalue $\lambda = c$:

$$\mathfrak{R}(x, y, \lambda) = \frac{B_p(x, y)}{(\lambda-c)^p} + \ldots + \frac{B_1(x, y)}{\lambda-c} + \sum_{\nu=0}^{\infty} A_\nu(x, y)(\lambda-c)^\nu .$$

For, if in identity (17) on p. 169 we compare the expressions containing the powers of h and k in the denominator only, we obtain the equalities

$$B_{\mu+\nu-1}(x, y) = \int_\Omega B_\mu(x, s) B_\nu(s, y)\, ds \qquad (\mu+\nu \leqq p+1). \tag{34}$$

Let us begin with the case $\mu = 1$, $\nu = 1$. We then have

$$B_1(x, y) = \int_\Omega B_1(x, s) B_1(s, y)\, ds, \tag{35}$$

whence, on the basis of the lemma, it follows that the coefficient $B_1(x, y)$ has the form

$$B_1(x, y) = \sum_{\nu=1}^{n} \varphi_\nu(x) \psi_\nu(y), \tag{36}$$

where the sequences of functions $\varphi_\nu(x)$ and $\psi_\nu(y)$ form a bi-orthogonal system.

From relations (34) we have

$$B_2(x, y) = \int_\Omega B_1(x, s) B_2(s, y)\, ds = \int_\Omega B_2(x, s) B_1(s, y)\, ds, \tag{37}$$

from which, in view of (36), it follows that the coefficient B_2 can be expressed in the form

$$B_2(x, y) = \sum_{i,k=1}^{n} a_{ik} \varphi_i(x) \psi_k(y). \tag{38}$$

Again using the relations (34), we have

$$B_3(x, y) = \int_\Omega B_2(x, s) B_2(s, y)\, ds,$$

$$B_4(x, y) = \int_\Omega B_3(x, s) B_2(s, y)\, ds,$$

$$\ldots\ldots\ldots\ldots\ldots\ldots\ldots\ldots$$

$$B_p(x, y) = \int_\Omega B_{p-1}(x, s) B_2(s, y)\, ds,$$

whence we see that *each of the coefficients B may be expressed as a certain sum of the functions* $\varphi_i(x)$ *and* $\psi_k(y)$. We call these functions the *principal functions* corresponding to an eigenvalue $\lambda = c$.

From formula (27) on p. 171 we see that *the principal kernel* $P(x, y) = G(x, y, 0)$ *is also a bilinear form of the principal functions* $\varphi_i(x)$ *and* $\psi_k(y)$.

In the case of a single pole ($p = 1$) the coefficient B_1, according to equation (15) on p. 168, is an eigenfunction and we have

$$\sum_{\nu=1}^{n} \varphi_\nu(x)\psi_\nu(y) = c\int_{\Omega} N(x, s) \sum_{\nu=1}^{n} \varphi_\nu(s)\psi_\nu(y)\, ds .$$

Also, since the functions ψ_ν are linearly independent, belonging to a biorthogonal system, we have

$$\varphi_\nu(x) = c\int_{\Omega} N(x, s)\varphi_\nu(s)\, ds \qquad (\nu = 1, 2, \dots, n).$$

In the same fashion we show that

$$\psi_\nu(x) = c\int_{\Omega} N(s, x)\psi_\nu(s)\, ds .$$

In the case of a single pole *the principal functions* $\varphi_\nu(x)$ *are at the same time eigenfunctions of the given integral equation and the functions* $\psi_\nu(x)$ *are eigenfunctions of the associated equations.*

When a kernel is real *symmetric*, we have $N(x, y) = N(y, x)$. Then the pole is simple and the functions φ_ν and ψ_ν are equal, and the principal part of the resolvent kernel in the neighbourhood of a pole $\lambda = c$ has the form

$$\sum_{\nu=1}^{n} \frac{\varphi_\nu(x)\varphi_\nu(y)}{\lambda - c},$$

in accordance with the result obtained in the investigations of the symmetric kernel.

§ 5. Genus of the function $D(\lambda)$

In conclusion, we give a certain property of the entire Fredholm function $D(\lambda)$.

From the *Weierstrass* theorem on the expansion of an entire function in factors *, we know that:

If $\{\lambda_n\}$ *is a sequence of zeros of an entire function* $F(z)$ *repeated the same number of times as the rank, and if* $k+1$ *is the smallest integer such that the series*

$$\sum_{n=1}^{\infty}\left(\frac{1}{\lambda_n}\right)^{k+1} \tag{39}$$

converges, then the function $F(z)$ *may be represented in the form of the infinite product*

$$F(z) = e^{g(z)}\prod_{\nu=1}^{\infty}\left(1-\frac{\lambda}{\lambda_\nu}\right)\exp\left(\frac{\lambda}{\lambda_\nu}+\frac{\lambda^2}{2\lambda_\nu^2}+\dots+\frac{\lambda^k}{k\lambda_\nu^k}\right) \tag{40}$$

where $g(z)$ *is an entire function.*

Now in the case when $g(z)$ is a polynomial of degree m, then the *genus* of the entire function $F(z)$ is the greater of the two numbers m and k.

The genus of an entire function is connected with the growth of the modulus of the coefficients a_n of the expansion in an always convergent series of the given entire function $F(z)$:

$$F(z) = \sum_{n=0}^{\infty} a_n z^n. \tag{41}$$

In this connection, J. Hadamard has proved the following theorem:

If

$$\lim_{n\to\infty} n^{\alpha}\sqrt[n]{|a_n|} = 0, \tag{42}$$

then the genus of the function $F(z)$ *is at most equal to the number* $1/\alpha$.

---

* See the Author's *Analiza matematyczna* (*Mathematical Analysis*), vol. IV, p. 77.

Now, we have seen that, if a kernel N is bounded, then the moduli of the coefficients in the series expansion of the entire function $D(\lambda)$ are smaller than

$$\frac{M^n n^{n/2}}{n!} V^n,$$

where M is the upper bound of the modulus of the kernel N, and V is the volume of the domain of integration. Hence it follows that for the function $D(\lambda) = \sum_{n=0}^{\infty} a_n \lambda^n$, the product $n^\alpha \sqrt[n]{|a_n|}$ tends to zero when $\alpha < 1/2$, and hence the genus of Fredholm function is at most equal to 2.

Since we also know that the series of reciprocals of the powers of the eigenvalues

$$\sum_{n=1}^{\infty} \frac{1}{\lambda_n^p}$$

converges when $p \geqq 2$, we conclude that the entire Fredholm function $D(\lambda)$ may be expanded as the infinite product

$$D(\lambda) = e^{a\lambda + b\lambda^2} \prod_{\nu=1}^{\infty} \left(1 - \frac{\lambda}{\lambda_\nu}\right) e^{\lambda/\lambda_\nu}, \tag{43}$$

where a and b are certain constants which are either both zero, or both non-zero.

If the kernel N has no eigenvalues, then the corresponding Fredholm function has the form

$$D(\lambda) = e^{a\lambda + b\lambda^2}. \tag{44}$$

And since

$$\log D(\lambda) = -\sum_{n=1}^{\infty} \int_{\Omega} N_n(s, s)\, ds,$$

we draw the following conclusion:

For a kernel N to have no eigenvalues, it is necessary and sufficient that its traces, beginning with $n = 3$, *be equal to zero.*

PART 2

Systems of Linear Integral Equations. Non-linear Integral Equations. Applications of Integral Equations in the Theory of Differential Equations

With an Appendix by R. Sikorski
on Schauder's Theorem

Translated by

A. KACNER

CHAPTER VIII

SYSTEMS OF LINEAR INTEGRAL EQUATIONS. LINEAR INTEGRO-DIFFERENTIAL EQUATIONS

§ 1. System of Fredholm integral equations

A system of n Fredholm integral equations of the second kind can be written in the form

$$\varphi_\alpha(x) = f_\alpha(x) + \lambda \int_\Omega \sum_{\beta=1}^{n} N_{\alpha\beta}(x, y)\, \varphi_\beta(y)\, dy \qquad (\alpha = 1, 2, \ldots, n), \quad (1)$$

where $\varphi_1(x), \varphi_2(x), \ldots, \varphi_n(x)$ are the unknown functions in the region Ω, $f_\alpha(x)$ is defined in the same region, and $N_{\alpha\beta}(x, y)$ are known functions of the pair of points x and y in Ω. We assume that functions f_α and $N_{\alpha\beta}$ are integrable, as in the theory of the Fredholm equation.

The system of integral equations (1) can easily be reduced to one Fredholm equation. To do this let us consider regions Ω_2, $\Omega_3, \ldots, \Omega_n$ obtained by a parallel displacement of the region $\Omega_1 = \Omega$, no pair of which has common points. Let $F(x)$ denote a function in the domain $\Omega_1 + \Omega_2 + \ldots + \Omega_n$ defined by the relations

$$F(x_\alpha) = f_\alpha(x_1) \qquad (\alpha = 1, 2, \ldots, n), \quad (2)$$

where x_α is a point of Ω_α corresponding to a point x_1 of $\Omega_1 = \Omega$.

Further, let $M(x, y)$ denote a function of two variables in $\Omega_1 + \Omega_2 + \ldots + \Omega_n$ defined by the relations

$$M(x_\alpha, y_\beta) = N_{\alpha\beta}(x_1, y_1) \qquad (\alpha, \beta = 1, 2, \ldots, n), \quad (3)$$

where $x_\alpha \in \Omega_\alpha$, $y_\beta \in \Omega_\beta$.

It follows from the foregoing that if the functions $\varphi_1(x)$, $\varphi_2(x), \ldots, \varphi_n(x)$ satisfy equations (1) in the region Ω, then the function $\Phi(x)$, defined in $\Omega_1+\Omega_2+\ldots+\Omega_n$ by the relations

$$\Phi(x_\alpha) = \varphi_\alpha(x_1), \quad x_\alpha \in \Omega_\alpha \quad (\alpha = 1, 2, \ldots, n), \tag{4}$$

satisfies the equation

$$\Phi(x) = F(x) + \lambda \int_{\Pi} M(x, y)\Phi(y)\, dy \tag{5}$$

where $\Pi = \Omega_1+\Omega_2+\ldots+\Omega_n$, and conversely, if $\Phi(x)$ is a solution of (5), then the values of this function in $\Omega_1, \Omega_2, \ldots, \Omega_n$ define a system of n functions in Ω, $\varphi_\alpha(x_1) = \Phi(x_\alpha)$ ($\alpha = 1, 2, \ldots, n$) which constitutes a solution of the system of equations (1). Thus *one Fredholm equation* (5) *with one unknown function* $\Phi(x)$ *is equivalent to the considered system of equations* (1).

Consequently, the theory of a system of Fredholm integral equations can be reduced to the familiar theory of one Fredholm equation and, moreover, no new difficulties arise. This remark will frequently be used in applications.

§ 2. System of Volterra integral equations

A system of Volterra integral equations can be written in the form

$$\varphi_\alpha(x) = f_\alpha(x) + \lambda \int_a^x \sum_{\beta=1}^n N_{\alpha\beta}(x, y)\varphi_\beta(y)\, dy, \tag{6}$$

where $\varphi_1, \varphi_2, \ldots, \varphi_n$ denote the unknown functions in the interval (a, b); the known functions $f_\alpha(x)$ are defined in the same interval, and the functions $N_{\alpha\beta}(x, y)$ are defined in the triangle

$$a \leqq x \leqq b, \quad a \leqq y \leqq x. \tag{7}$$

Concerning $f_\alpha(x)$ and $N_{\alpha\beta}(x, y)$ we make the same assumptions as for the functions $f(x)$ and $N(x, y)$ in the theory of one Volterra equation. Equations (6) will be solved directly by the iteration method in a manner similar to the case of one equation. Thus we observe that if the functions $\varphi_1, \varphi_2, \ldots, \varphi_n$ satisfy system (6), then they also satisfy the iterated system

$$\varphi_\alpha(x) = f_\alpha(x) + \lambda \int_a^x \sum_{\beta=1}^n N_{\alpha\beta}(x, y) f_\beta(y)\, dy +$$

$$+ \lambda^2 \int_a^x \sum_{\beta=1}^n N_{\alpha\beta}(x, t) \Big[\int_a^t \sum_{\gamma=1}^n N_{\beta\gamma}(t, y) \varphi_\gamma(y)\, dy \Big] dt$$

or

$$\varphi_\alpha(x) = f_\alpha(x) + \lambda \int_a^x \sum_{\beta=1}^n N_{\alpha\beta}(x, y) f_\beta(y)\, dy +$$

$$+ \lambda^2 \int_a^x \sum_{\beta=1}^n N_{\alpha\beta}^{(1)}(x, y) \varphi_\beta(y)\, dy, \qquad (8)$$

where

$$N_{\alpha\beta}^{(1)}(x, y) = \sum_{\gamma=1}^n \int_y^x N_{\alpha\gamma}(x, t) N_{\gamma\beta}(t, y)\, dt.$$

Repeating this iteration a number of times, we find, as before, that if there exists a system of functions $\varphi_1, \varphi_2, \ldots, \varphi_n$ which satisfies (6), then it is unique and given by the formulae

$$\varphi_\alpha(x) = f_\alpha(x) + \lambda \int_a^x \sum_{\beta=1}^n \mathfrak{N}_{\alpha\beta}(x, y, \lambda) f_\beta(y)\, dy$$

$$(\alpha = 1, 2, \ldots, n). \qquad (9)$$

The functions $\mathfrak{N}_{\alpha\beta}$ are the sums of the series

$$\mathfrak{N}_{\alpha\beta}(x, y, \lambda) = N_{\alpha\beta}(x, y) + \lambda N_{\alpha\beta}^{(1)}(x, y) + \ldots +$$

$$+ \lambda^\nu N_{\alpha\beta}^{(\nu)}(x, y) + \ldots, \qquad (10)$$

the $N_{\alpha\beta}^{(\nu)}$ being defined by the recursive formulae

$$N_{\alpha\beta}^{(\nu+1)}(x, y) = \sum_{\gamma=1}^n \int_y^x N_{\alpha\gamma}(x, t) N_{\gamma\beta}^{(\nu)}(t, y)\, dt. \qquad (11)$$

It can easily be proved, as for the case of one Volterra equation, that *the series* (10) *are absolutely and uniformly convergent for every value of the parameter* λ, *and that the functions* (9) *constitute the required solution of* (6).

§ 3. Linear integro-differential equation

Consider the linear integro-differential equation in the form

$$\varphi(x) = f(x) + \lambda \int_a^b \sum_{\nu=0}^{n} N_\nu(x, y)\, \varphi^{(\nu)}(y)\, dy, \tag{12}$$

where $\varphi^{(\nu)}(x)$ denotes νth derivative of the unknown function φ, and $\varphi^{(0)} = \varphi$.

We assume that the given function $f(x)$ has an n-th derivative ($n \geqq 1$) continuous in the interval (a, b). Moreover, we make the further assumption that the functions $N_\nu(x, y)$ and their derivatives with respect to x of order n inclusive, are defined in the square

$$a \leqq x \leqq b, \quad a \leqq y \leqq b$$

and that they are continuous with respect to both variables in this square.

To solve equation (12) observe that if there exists a solution $\varphi(x)$, then it satisfies the following equations derived by differentiating both sides of (12) α times:

$$\varphi^{(\alpha)}(x) = f^{(\alpha)}(x) + \lambda \int_a^b \sum_{\nu=0}^{n} N_\nu^{(\alpha)}(x, y)\, \varphi^{(\nu)}(y)\, dy \qquad (\alpha = 1, 2, \ldots, n), \tag{13}$$

where $N_\nu^{(\alpha)}(x, y)$ denotes the αth derivative with respect to x of $N_\nu(x, y)$.

Consider now the system of $n+1$ integral equations

$$\psi_\alpha(x) = f^{(\alpha)}(x) + \lambda \int_a^b \sum_{\nu=0}^{n} N_\nu^{(\alpha)}(x, y)\, \psi_\alpha(y)\, dy \qquad (\alpha = 0, 1, 2, \ldots, n), \tag{14}$$

the unknown functions being $\psi_0, \psi_1, \ldots, \psi_n$, and $f^{(0)}(x) = f(x)$, $N_\nu^{(0)}(x, y) = N_\nu(x, y)$.

We know (§ 1) that the solution of the system of equations (14) is reducible to the solution of one Fredholm equation with one unknown function. Having obtained the solution $\psi_0, \psi_1, \ldots$ $\ldots, \psi_n$ of (14) we find that function $\varphi(x) = \psi_0(x)$ constitutes the solution of the considered integro-differential equation (12).

In fact, equations (14) imply the relations

$$\frac{d^\alpha}{dx^\alpha}[\psi_0(x)] = \psi_\alpha(x) \qquad (\alpha = 1, 2, \ldots, n),$$

and hence

$$\psi_0(x) = f(x) + \lambda \int_a^b \sum_{\nu=0}^n N_\nu(x, y)\psi_0^{(\nu)}(y)\,dy. \tag{15}$$

Conversely, if $\varphi(x)$ is the solution of equation (12) then system of functions $\varphi_0 = \varphi(x)$, $\psi_1 = \varphi'(x), \ldots, \psi_n = \varphi^{(n)}(x)$ is the solution of the system of equations (14). Equations (12) and system (14) are in a sense equivalent. In particular, if the Fredholm equation to which the system (14) is reduced has a unique solution, then the considered equation (12) also has a unique solution.

CHAPTER IX

NON-LINEAR INTEGRAL EQUATIONS

§ 1. Non-linear integral Fredholm equation of the second kind

By a *non-linear integral equation* we mean any integral equation which does not belong to the types of linear integral equations investigated in Part I. There exist numerous types of non-linear integral equations. We shall examine here only the most important ones.

Unlike linear equations we cannot, in general, solve non-linear equations; we can do so only for sufficiently small values of the diameter of the region of integration, by employing the method of successive approximations or the topological Schauder method.

The non-linear Fredholm equation of the second kind can be written in the form

$$\varphi(x) = f(x) + \lambda \int_{\Omega} F[x, y, \varphi(y)]\, dy, \tag{1}$$

where $\varphi(x)$ is the unknown function x in the region Ω.* We assume the following:

1) $f(x)$ is a known real function, which is defined bounded and continuous in Ω.

2) $F(x, y, u)$ is a known real function of a pair of points x and y of Ω and the real variable u in the interval $a \leqq u \leqq b$. This function is bounded, continuous and, moreover, it satisfies the Lipschitz condition with respect to the variable u.

Let m_1 and m_2 denote the lower and upper bounds of $f(x)$, respectively, i.e. $m_1 \leqq f(x) \leqq m_2$, and M the upper bound of the absolute values of F, $|F(x, y, u)| \leqq M$.

---

* Ω is assumed to be an open set.

We assume that

$$a < m_1 \leqq m_2 < b. \tag{2}$$

Equation (1) will be solved by the method of successive approximations. We therefore construct the sequence of functions

$$\varphi_0(x), \varphi_1(x), \varphi_2(x), \ldots, \varphi_n(x), \ldots \tag{3}$$

by means of the recursive relation

$$\varphi_{n+1}(x) = f(x) + \lambda \int_{\Omega} F[x, y, \varphi_n(y)]\, dy, \tag{4}$$

where the initial function $\varphi_0(x)$ is an arbitrary continuous function which satisfies the condition

$$a \leqq \varphi_0(x) \leqq b \tag{5}$$

in Ω.

We first consider the existence of the terms of the sequence (3) for any n. Let us assume that the function $\varphi_n(x)$ satisfies the condition

$$a \leqq \varphi_n(x) \leqq b. \tag{6}$$

Then we have

$$|\varphi_{n+1}(x) - f(x)| \leqq |\lambda|\, MV,$$

where V denotes the volume of Ω; therefore the function $\varphi_{n+1}(x)$ also satisfies condition $a \leqq \varphi_{n+1}(x) \leqq b$ when λ satisfies the inequality

$$|\lambda| \leqq \min\left(\frac{m_1 - a}{MV}, \frac{b - m_2}{MV}\right). \tag{7}$$

Hence, by induction we infer that *the functions* (3) *exist for all n, and that they satisfy condition* (6) *when the parameter* λ *satisfies* (7).

To prove the convergence of the series (3), we estimate the decrease in the difference between successive approximations.

Thus, from the recursive relation (4) it follows that

$$\varphi_{n+1}(x)-\varphi_n(x) = \lambda \int_\Omega \{F[x, y, \varphi_n(y)]-F[x, y, \varphi_{n-1}(y)]\} dy, \quad (8)$$

and since we assumed the validity of the Lipschitz condition

$$|F[x, y, \varphi_n]-F[x, y, \varphi_{n-1}]| \leqq k|\varphi_n-\varphi_{n-1}|$$

(k a positive constant) for arbitrary values of φ_n and φ_{n-1} from the interval (a, b), we obtain

$$|\varphi_{n+1}(x)-\varphi_n(x)| \leqq k|\lambda| \int_\Omega |\varphi_n-\varphi_{n-1}| dy.$$

Since

$$|\varphi_2(x)-\varphi_1(x)| \leqq k|\lambda| \int_\Omega |\varphi_1-\varphi_0| dy \leqq k|\lambda| V(b-a),$$

we infer by induction that the following inequality holds for all n:

$$|\varphi_{n+1}(x)-\varphi_n(x)| \leqq (b-a)|k\lambda V|^n. \quad (9)$$

If we now observe that

$$\varphi_n(x) = \varphi_0(x)+ \sum_{\nu=1}^{n} [\varphi_\nu(x)-\varphi_{\nu-1}(x)],$$

we find, in view of inequality (9), that the sequence of approximations (3) tends uniformly to the limit function $\varphi(x) = \lim \varphi_n(x)$ when the condition

$$|k\lambda V| < 1 \quad (10)$$

is satisfied.

$\lim \varphi_n(x)$ is evidently the solution of the integral equation (1).

We now prove that the solution obtained is unique.

In fact if there exists another solution $\psi(x)$ of equation (1), we have

$$\psi(x) = f(x)+\lambda \int_\Omega F[x, y, \psi(y)] dy.$$

Hence, bearing in mind relation (1), for all n we have

$$\varphi(x)-\psi(x)=\lambda\int_{\Omega}\{F[x,y,\varphi(y)]-F[x,y,\psi(y)]\}\,dy,$$

consequently

$$|\varphi(x)-\psi(x)|\leqq|\lambda|\,k\int_{\Omega}|\varphi-\psi|\,dy$$

and the upper bound of the difference satisfies the inequality

$$\sup|\varphi-\psi|\leqq|\lambda|\,kV\sup|\varphi-\psi|,$$

which contradicts assumption (10). Thus we have $\varphi=\psi$ and the solution is unique.

Finally, we may state that the considered integral equation (1) has the unique solution $\lim\varphi_n(x)$ when the parameter λ satisfies the condition

$$|\lambda|<\min\left(\frac{m_1-a}{MV},\frac{b-m_2}{MV},\frac{1}{kV}\right). \qquad (11)$$

The argument can easily be extended to the case of a system of p integral equations of the form

$$\varphi_\alpha(x)=f_\alpha(x)+\lambda\int_{\Omega}F_\alpha[x,y,\varphi_1(y),\varphi_2(y),\dots,\varphi_p(y)]\,dy$$
$$(\alpha=1,2,\dots,p). \qquad (12)$$

We assume the following:

1) $f_\alpha(x)$ are known real functions which are defined, bounded and continuous in Ω.

2) $F_\alpha(x,y,u_1,u_2,\dots,u_p)$ are known real functions of pair of points x and y of Ω and the real variables $u_1,u_2,\dots,u_p$ where $a_\alpha\leqq u_\alpha\leqq b_\alpha$ $(\alpha=1,2,\dots,p)$, respectively; these functions are bounded, continuous and they satisfy the Lipschitz condition with respect to variables $u_1,u_2,\dots,u_p$.

Let $m_1^{(\alpha)}$ and $m_2^{(\alpha)}$ denote the lower and upper bounds of functions $f_\alpha(x)$, respectively, i.e. $m_1^{(\alpha)}\leqq f_\alpha(x)\leqq m_2^{(\alpha)}$, and M_α the upper bounds of the absolute values of the functions F_α, $|F_\alpha(x,y,u_1,u_2,\dots,u_p)|\leqq M_\alpha$.

We assume that

$$a_\alpha<m_1^{(\alpha)}\leqq m_2^{(\alpha)}<b_\alpha. \qquad (13)$$

To solve system (13) by the method of successive approximations we construct p functional sequences

$$\varphi_\alpha^{(0)}(x), \varphi_\alpha^{(1)}(x), \dots, \varphi_\alpha^{(n)}(x), \dots \quad (\alpha = 1, 2, \dots, p) \tag{14}$$

by means of the recursive relation

$$\varphi_\alpha^{(n+1)}(x) = f_\alpha(x) + \lambda \int_\Omega F_\alpha[x, y, \varphi_1^{(n)}(y), \varphi_2^{(n)}(y), \dots, \varphi_p^{(n)}(y)]\, dy$$
$$(\alpha = 1, 2, \dots, p), \tag{15}$$

the initial functions $\varphi_\alpha^{(0)}(x)$ being arbitrary continuous functions which satisfy the condition

$$a_\alpha \leqq \varphi_\alpha^{(0)}(x) \leqq b_\alpha$$

in the region Ω. As before we shall prove that the functions (14) satisfy the condition

$$a_\alpha \leqq \varphi_\alpha^{(n)}(x) \leqq b_\alpha \tag{16}$$

for all n, provided that the parameter λ satisfies the inequality

$$|\lambda| \leqq \min\left(\frac{m_1^{(\alpha)} - a_\alpha}{M_\alpha V}, \frac{b_\alpha - m_2^{(\alpha)}}{M_\alpha V}\right). \tag{17}$$

To prove the convergence of series (14), consider the differences

$$\varphi_\alpha^{(n+1)}(x) - \varphi_\alpha^{(n)}(x) = \lambda \int_\Omega \{F[x, y, \varphi_1^{(n)}(y), \dots, \varphi_p^{(n)}(y)] -$$
$$- F[x, y, \varphi_1^{n-1}(y), \dots, \varphi_p^{(n-1)}(y)]\}\, dy. \tag{18}$$

Hence, in view of the assumed Lipschitz condition for the functions $F_\alpha(x, y, u_1, u_2, \dots, u_p)$ with respect to the variables $u_1, u_2, \dots, u_p$, we arrive at the inequalities

$$|\varphi_\alpha^{(n+1)}(x) - \varphi_\alpha^{(n)}(x)| < k|\lambda| \int_\Omega \sum_{\alpha=1}^{p} |\varphi_\alpha^{(n)}(y) - \varphi_\alpha^{(n-1)}(y)|\, dy, \tag{19}$$

where k denotes the known positive Lipschitz coefficient. Inequality (19) implies the inequalities

$$|\varphi_\alpha^{(2)}(x) - \varphi_\alpha^{(1)}(x)| < k|\lambda| VpA,$$

where A denotes the largest of the p differences $b_\alpha - a_\alpha$; hence, by induction, we infer that the following inequalities hold for all n:

$$|\varphi_\alpha^{(n+1)}(x) - \varphi_\alpha^{(n)}(x)| < A(k|\lambda| Vp)^n. \tag{20}$$

This implies the absolute and uniform convergence of series (14), provided $k|\lambda| Vp < 1$. Finally, we may state that *the system of integral equations* (15) *has a solution constructed from the system of limit functions* $\varphi_\alpha^{(n)}(x)$ *of series* (14), *when the parameter* λ *satisfies the condition*

$$|\lambda| < \min\left(\frac{m_1^{(\alpha)} - a_\alpha}{M_\alpha V}, \frac{b_\alpha - m_2^{(\alpha)}}{M_\alpha V}, \frac{1}{kVp}\right).$$

As for the case of one equation, we can prove that the derived solution is unique.

§ 2. Non-linear Volterra equations

A non-linear Volterra equation of the second kind has the form

$$\varphi(x) = f(x) + \lambda \int_a^x F[x, y, \varphi(y)]\, dy. \tag{21}$$

We assume that the known function $f(x)$ is defined and continuous in the interval (a, b), that the function $F(x, y, u)$ is defined and continuous with respect to all variables in the domain

$$a \leqq x \leqq b, \quad a \leqq y \leqq x, \quad p \leqq u \leqq q \tag{22}$$

and, moreover, that $p < m_1 \leqq m_2 < q$ where m_1 and m_2 denote the lower and upper bounds of function $f(x)$, respectively. We make also the assumption that the function $F(x, y, u)$ satisfies the Lipschitz condition with respect to u in the region (22), i.e.

$$|F(x, y, u') - F(x, y, u'')| < k|u' - u''|, \tag{23}$$

k being a positive constant.

Applying the method of successive approximations we again construct the sequence of functions

$$\varphi_0(x), \varphi_1(x), \dots, \varphi_n(x), \dots \tag{24}$$

by means of the recursive relation

$$\varphi_{n+1}(x) = f(x) + \lambda \int_a^x F[x, y, \varphi_n(y)]\, dy. \tag{25}$$

In a known way we find that the sequence (24) is defined for all n when the parameter λ satisfies the condition

$$|\lambda| < \min\left(\frac{m_1 - a}{M(b-a)}, \frac{b - m_2}{M(b-a)}\right), \tag{26}$$

M being the upper bound of the function $|F|$.

We now prove the convergence of sequence (24), the only assumption being (26). Thus, according to relation (25) and the assumed inequality (23), we have

$$|\varphi_{n+1}(x) - \varphi_n(x)| < k|\lambda| \int_a^x |\varphi_n(y) - \varphi_{n-1}(y)|\, dy. \tag{27}$$

This implies successively

$$|\varphi_2(x) - \varphi_1(x)| < k|\lambda| \int_a^x |\varphi_1(y) - \varphi_0(y)|\, dy < k|\lambda| . |p-q| . |x-a|,$$

$$|\varphi_3(x) - \varphi_2(x)| < k^2 |\lambda|^2 |p-q| \frac{|x-a|^2}{2},$$

$$|\varphi_4(x) - \varphi_3(x)| < k^3 |\lambda|^3 . |p-q| \frac{|x-a|^3}{1.2.3},$$

. . . .

Generally, by induction we conclude that the following inequality holds for all n:

$$|\varphi_{n+1}(x) - \varphi_n(x)| < |p-q|\, |k\lambda|^n \frac{|x-a|^n}{n!}. \tag{28}$$

Thus, without decreasing the modulus of λ we may state that *the series*

$$\varphi_0(x)+\sum_{\nu=0}^{\infty}[\varphi_{\nu+1}(x)-\varphi_\nu(x)]$$

is absolutely and uniformly convergent and its sum $\varphi(x) = \lim\varphi_n(x)$ *is the solution of the integral equation* (21), *under the assumption* (26).

As in the preceding section we can prove that this solution is unique.

We now proceed to investigate a *non-linear Volterra equation of the first kind*; we write it in the form

$$\int_a^x F[x, y, \varphi(y)]\,dy = f(x), \tag{29}$$

where $F(x,y,u)$ and $f(x)$ are defined and continuous in the domain

$$a \leqq x \leqq b, \quad a \leqq y \leqq b, \quad p \leqq u \leqq q \tag{30}$$

and, moreover, $f(0) = 0$. Assuming also that $F(x,y,u)$ and $f(x)$ have continuous derivatives with respect to the variables x, y, u, we may then say that a function which satisfies equation (29) also satisfies the equation derived by differentiating equation (29)

$$F[x, x, \varphi(x)]+\int_a^x F'_x[x, y, \varphi(y)]\,dy = f'(x). \tag{31}$$

Conversely, a function which satisfies equation (31) also satisfies equation (29), for $f(0) = 0$.

To solve equation (31) we also assume that F and f have continuous second derivatives with respect to the variable x. Then we are in a position to state that function φ which satisfies equation (31) and is differentiable, also satisfies the equation

$$2F'_x[x, x, \varphi(x)]+F'_y[x, x, \varphi(x)]+F'_u[x, x, \varphi(x)]\,\varphi'(x)+$$

$$+\int_a^x F''_{xx}[x, y, \varphi(y)]\,dy = f''(x) \tag{32}$$

derived by differentiating both sides of equation (31) with respect to x.

Assume that there exists at least one root u_0 of the equation

$$F(a, a, u_0) = f'(a) \tag{33}$$

in the interval (p,q). Then, on the basis of (32), we may state that a function which satisfies equation (31) also satisfies the integral equation

$$\varphi(x) = u_0 + \int_a^x \frac{f''(t) - 2F'_x[t, t, \varphi(t)] - F'_u[t, t, \varphi(t)]}{F'_u[t, t, \varphi(t)]} dt -$$

$$- \int_a^x \int_a^t \frac{F''_{xx}[t, y, \varphi(y)]}{F'_u[t, t, \varphi(t)]} dy\, dt \tag{34}$$

assuming that $F'_u(x, x, u) \neq 0$ in the domain (30), and that $\varphi(a) = u_0$. Conversely, a function which satisfies equation (34) also satisfies *equation* (32) and hence, according to relation (33), it satisfies equation (31), and finally, the considered equation (29) as well.

Thus the solution of equation (29) has been reduced to the solution of equation (34) to which we can apply the method of successive approximations, assuming that the derivatives of F and $F''_{xx}(x, y, u)$ satisfy the Lipschitz condition with respect to u.

We omit the argument, similar to the one used before, which proves that *equation* (34) *has a unique solution corresponding to the root* u_0, *provided the difference* $x-a$ *is sufficiently small.*

This solution is also a solution of the considered equation (29). There may be other solutions of equation (29) when equation (33) has several roots.

As in equation (29), we may investigate (see [48]) an integro-differential equation of the form

$$\int_a^x F[x, y, \varphi(y), \varphi'(y)]\, dy = f(x).$$

CHAPTER X

FIXED POINT THEOREMS AND NON-LINEAR INTEGRAL EQUATIONS

§ 1. Banach's Fixed Point Theorem

We proceed to clarify the geometrical nature of the problem of solving the integral equation

$$\varphi(x) = \int_{\Omega} F[x, y, \varphi(y)]\, dy \tag{1}$$

in the function space, i.e. in a space the points of which are certain functions (see Part 1, p. 115). The right-hand side of the integral equation (1) defines a functional operation which associates with a set of functions $\varphi(x)$, i.e. a set of points of the function space, points $\psi(x)$ of this space according to the formula

$$\psi(x) = \int_{\Omega} F[x, y, \varphi(y)]\, dy. \tag{2}$$

The problem of solution of the integral equation (1) can be thought geometrically as finding a point φ^* of the function space which corresponds to itself under the transformation (2); this point is called the *fixed point* of the function space with respect to the operation (2).

This is the geometrical meaning of not only equations of the form (1), but also of all integral equations to which we apply the method of successive approximation.

The above procedure may be expressed by means of a general theorem on fixed points, which constitutes an extension to equations more general than integral equations, i.e. to equations of the form

$$\varphi = \hat{A}(\varphi),$$

where $\hat{A}$ is an operator, i.e. a symbol of an operation in the function space.

Prior to the proof of the theorem we present some definitions concerning metric space which has already been dealt with in Part 1 (p. 115).

DEFINITION 1. *The sequence of points* $\{\varphi_n\}$ *of a metric space is called convergent to a point* φ *of this space, if the sequence of distances* $\delta(\varphi_n, \varphi)$ *tends to zero as* $n \to \infty$.

If the sequence of points $\{\varphi_n\}$ is convergent to a point φ, then the Cauchy convergence condition is satisfied. This is so, since from the triangle inequality, for any positive integers n and p, it follows that

$$\delta(\varphi_n, \varphi_{n+p}) \leqq \delta(\varphi_n, \varphi) + \delta(\varphi_{n+p}, \varphi),$$

and since the sequence converges to the point φ, for any positive ε, there exists an index N_ε such that $\delta(\varphi_n, \varphi) < \varepsilon/2$ and $\delta(\varphi_{n+p}, \varphi) < \varepsilon/2$ when $n > N_\varepsilon$; thus

$$\delta(\varphi_n, \varphi_{n+p}) < \varepsilon, \tag{3}$$

when $n > N_\varepsilon$, p being arbitrary.

The Cauchy condition is therefore a necessary condition for the convergence of a sequence of points in a metric space. However, this condition is not always sufficient; in fact, it is easy to give an example of a metric space in which there exist sequences of points which satisfy the Cauchy condition but do not converge to any point of the considered space.

DEFINITION 2. *A metric space is called complete if the Cauchy condition is sufficient for the convergence of a sequence of points of the space, i.e. if the sequence of points* $\{\varphi_n\}$ *of this space satisfies condition* (3) *then there exists a point of the space* φ, *such that* $\delta(\varphi_n, \varphi) \to 0$ *as* $n \to \infty$.

An example of a complete metric space is evidently ordinary Euclidean space, and an example of a complete square function space is provided by the space L^2 of functions quadratically integrable (cf. pp. 117 *et seq.*).

THE BANACH–CACCIOPOLI THEOREM. *If in a complete metric space an operation A associates with every two points f and g, points $\hat{A}(f)$ and $\hat{A}(g)$ of this space, the distances of which satisfy the inequality*

$$\delta[\hat{A}(f), \hat{A}(g)] \leqq \alpha\delta(f, g), \tag{4}$$

the positive constant α being smaller than unity, and independent of the pair f and g, then there exists a unique point φ of the space, which satisfies the equation

$$\varphi = \hat{A}(\varphi),$$

i.e. point fixed with respect to the operation $\hat{A}$.

This theorem is proved, [1] and [4], by the method of successive approximations. Starting from an arbitrary point φ_0 of the considered space, we construct the infinite sequence of points

$$\varphi_0, \varphi_1, \varphi_2, \ldots, \varphi_n, \varphi_{n+1}, \ldots \tag{5}$$

by means of the operation

$$\varphi_{n+1} = \hat{A}(\varphi_n). \tag{6}$$

In accordance with assumption (4) we obtain, successively,

$$\begin{aligned} &\delta(\varphi_1, \varphi_2) \leqq \alpha\delta(\varphi_0, \varphi_1), \\ &\delta(\varphi_2, \varphi_3) \leqq \alpha^2\delta(\varphi_0, \varphi_1), \\ &\cdots\cdots\cdots\cdots \\ &\delta(\varphi_n, \varphi_{n+1}) \leqq \alpha^n\delta(\varphi_0, \varphi_1). \end{aligned} \tag{7}$$

Further, in view of the triangle inequality we have

$$\begin{aligned} \delta(\varphi_n, \varphi_{n+2}) &\leqq \delta(\varphi_n, \varphi_{n+1}) + \delta(\varphi_{n+1}, \varphi_{n+2}), \\ \delta(\varphi_n, \varphi_{n+3}) &\leqq \delta(\varphi_n, \varphi_{n+2}) + \delta(\varphi_{n+2}, \varphi_{n+3}) \\ &\leqq \delta(\varphi_n, \varphi_{n+1}) + \delta(\varphi_{n+1}, \varphi_{n+2}) + \delta(\varphi_{n+2}, \varphi_{n+3}). \end{aligned}$$

Generally, for any positive integers n and p we conclude by induction that the inequality

$$\delta(\varphi_n, \varphi_{n+p}) \leqq \sum_{\nu=n}^{n+p-1} \delta(\varphi_\nu, \varphi_{\nu+1})$$

holds. Consequently, taking into account inequality (7)

$$\delta(\varphi_n, \varphi_{n+p}) \leqq \sum_{\nu=n}^{n+p-1} \alpha^\nu \delta(\varphi_0, \varphi_1) < \frac{\alpha^n}{1-\alpha} \delta(\varphi_0, \varphi_1).$$

Thus for an arbitrary $\varepsilon > 0$, we can find N_ε such that $\delta(\varphi_n, \varphi_{n+1}) < \varepsilon$ for $n > N_\varepsilon$, and the Cauchy condition is satisfied. According to the definition of a complete space, there exists a point φ of the space to which the sequence $\{\varphi_n\}$ converges. We now prove that this limit point is exactly the fixed point, i.e. it satisfies the equation $\varphi = \hat{A}(\varphi)$. In fact, we have

$$\delta[\varphi, \hat{A}(\varphi)] < \delta(\varphi, \varphi_{n+1}) + \delta[\varphi_{n+1}, \hat{A}(\varphi)]$$

$$= \delta(\varphi, \varphi_{n+1}) + \delta[\hat{A}(\varphi_n), \hat{A}(\varphi)] \leqq \delta(\varphi, \varphi_{n+1}) + \alpha\delta(\varphi, \varphi_n).$$

But $\delta(\varphi, \varphi_n) \to 0$ as $n \to \infty$, and hence $\delta[\varphi, \hat{A}(\varphi)] = 0$, i.e. $\varphi = \hat{A}(\varphi)$.

We prove also that this fixed point φ is unique. Thus, if there exists another fixed point $\overline{\varphi}$, say, then $\delta(\varphi, \overline{\varphi}) = \delta[\hat{A}(\varphi), \hat{A}(\overline{\varphi})] \leqq \alpha\delta(\varphi, \overline{\varphi})$ which is impossible if $\delta(\varphi, \overline{\varphi}) \neq 0$. Thus $\delta(\varphi, \varphi) = 0$, i.e. $\varphi = \overline{\varphi}$.

Observe that to prove the uniqueness of the fixed point an assumption weaker than that in the above theorem of Banach is sufficient. Namely we have the following *theorem on uniqueness*, given by Cacciopoli:

If the transformation of a set in a metric space onto a subset decreases the distance between every pair of points of the considered set, then there exists at most one fixed point.

Let $\hat{A}$ denote the operation. Then, in accordance with the assumption, for every pair of points f and g under consideration we have

$$\delta[\hat{A}(f), \hat{A}(g)] < \delta(f, g). \tag{8}$$

If we assume that there exist two distinct fixed points φ and ψ, i.e. points for which

$$\varphi = \hat{A}(\varphi) \quad \text{and} \quad \psi = \hat{A}(\psi),$$

then

$$\delta[\hat{A}(\varphi), \hat{A}(\psi)] = \delta(\varphi, \psi),$$

on the other hand, by virtue of the assumption,

$$\delta[\hat{A}(\varphi), \hat{A}(\psi)] < \delta(\varphi, \psi),$$

we arrive at a contradiction, and therefore the points φ and ψ cannot be distinct.

The above theorem can be applied to solving integral and differential equations, but actually it yields no new results compared with the method of successive approximations, and does not provide us with a proof under assumptions weaker than those in the classical method. In this respect, the Schauder Theorem is considerably more impoıtant, since it yields a new method of proof of the existence of solutions of integral equations and, moreover, under much more general assumptions than those of the classical method.

§ 2. Schauder's Fixed Point Theorem

The classical method of successive approximations which is such a powerful method of investigating differential equations and some integral equations, (e.g. non-linear Fredholm equations (1)), fails if the assumptions are any weaker; for example, it fails when we assume that function $F(x, y, u)$ in the integrand of equation (1) satisfies the Hölder condition with exponent smaller than unity, i.e. it certainly fails when we simply assume the continuity of the function F with respect to the variable u.

It is to the credit of modern mathematics that it provides us with an entirely new method based on topological considerations, which makes it possible to obtain proofs of existence of solutions of numerous integral equations where classical methods are useless. These proofs are based exactly on the fixed point theorem proved by the Polish mathematician J. Schauder who perished tragically in 1942. These proofs constitute a beautiful and bold application of topological considerations to function space. Before formulating the Schauder Theorem we present a few definitions on which the theorem is based.

Definition 3. *By a closed set, we mean a set which contains all its condensation points.*

DEFINITION 4. *By a line segment connecting points f and g of a linear function space* (cf. Part 1, p. 115) *we mean the set of all functions of the form* $(1-\lambda)f+\lambda g$ *obtained by varying the parameter* λ *in a continuous way in the interval* (0,1).

DEFINITION 5. *A set of points of a linear space is called convex, if the line segment joining any two points of the set consists of points of the considered set only.*

DEFINITION 6. *A set of points of a normed function space is called bounded if the set of norms of all points of the considered set is bounded.*

DEFINITION 7. *A set of points of a metric space is called relatively compact if every infinite subset of the considered set contains a convergent sequence.*

A set of points is called compact if, moreover, the limit points of the extracted convergent sets belong to the set.

DEFINITION 8. *An operation* $\hat{A}$ *in a function space is called continuous if it transforms every sequence of points* $\{\varphi_n\}$ *of this space convergent to a point* φ, *into a sequence of points* $\{\hat{A}(\varphi_n)\}$ *convergent to the transformed point* $\hat{A}(\varphi)$, *i.e. if* $\delta(\varphi_n, \varphi) \to 0$ *implies* $\delta[\hat{A}(\varphi_n), \hat{A}(\varphi)] \to 0$.

DEFINITION 9. *A linear space in which every point* x *is associated with a non-negative number* $||x||$, *called its norm, and satisfying the conditions*

$$\|x+y\| \leqq \|x\|+\|y\|, \qquad \|\lambda x\| = |\lambda| . \|x\|, \tag{9}$$

where λ *is an arbitrary real or complex number, is called a normed linear space.*

DEFINITION 10. *If a space is linear, normed, metric and complete then it is called a Banach space.*

According to Weierstrass' Theorem, every infinite bounded set of points in a Euclidean space has at least one condensation point, and therefore from this set we can always extract a convergent sequence, and the considered set is always compact. On the other hand, a bounded set of points of a function space may not be compact. Consider in the space $L^2(\Omega)$ of functions which are integrable together with the square of their moduli, an orthonormal system of functions $\{\varphi_n(x)\}$. Then we have for $m \neq n$

$$\delta(\varphi_m, \varphi_n) = \|\varphi_m - \varphi_n\|$$
$$= \sqrt{\int\limits_{\Omega} |\varphi_m - \varphi_n|^2 \, dx} = \sqrt{\|\varphi_m\|^2 + \|\varphi_n\|^2} = \sqrt{2},$$

consequently from this set we cannot extract a convergent sequence, and therefore it is not compact. For this reason the concept of compactness of a set of points in a function space is essential. This concept played an important rôle in modern investigations into the theory of analytic functions (the normal family of Montel functions) and in the proofs of existence of solutions of differential and integral equations.

We are now in a position to state the following basic theorem (see [55]):

THE SCHAUDER THEOREM. *If in a Banach space a continuous operation transforms a closed convex set of points into a compact subset, then there exists at least one fixed point of the operation.*

The proof of the theorem, worked out by R. SIKORSKI, is given in the Appendix to this volume.

§ 3. Applications of the Schauder Theorem to integral equations

We have already stated that the Schauder Fixed Point Theorem makes it possible to prove the existence of solutions of non-linear integral equations under very general conditions, where the classical theory is inapplicable. We present, for the time being, only a few examples taken from the numerous ones available. We emphasize, however, that the Schauder Theorem also yields important results in the field of boundary-value problems in the theory of partial differential equations.

Before presenting the examples, we give some definitions and an important theorem on continuous functions, which we shall use later.

DEFINITION 11. *We say that a family of functions is uniformly bounded if there exists a positive number which exceeds all absolute values of the considered functions.*

DEFINITION 12. *A family of functions, defined in the same domain Ω, is said to be equicontinuous if, for any ε, there exists a number $\eta(\varepsilon)$, depending on ε only, such that all functions $f(x)$ of the family satisfy the inequality $|f(x')-f(x'')| < \varepsilon$ when the distance between the two arbitrary points x' and x'' of domain Ω is smaller than $\eta(\varepsilon)$.*

ARZÉLA'S THEOREM. *Every infinite family of functions which are uniformly bounded, equi-continuous and defined in the same bounded domain, contains a uniformly convergent sequence of functions, i.e. is relatively compact.*

The proof of the theorem the reader may find in the monograph of R. SIKORSKI [78].

Consider the non-linear Fredholm integral equation

$$\varphi(x) = \lambda \int_{\Omega} F[x, y, \varphi(y)]\, dy, \tag{10}$$

dealt with in the preceding chapter. We make the following weaker assumptions: the known real function $F(x, y, u)$ is defined and continuous with respect to the set of variables, in a closed and bounded domain

$$[x \in \Omega,\ y \in \Omega,\ |u| \leqq R]. \tag{11}$$

It turns out that under this assumption equation (10) cannot be solved by means of the classical method of successive approximation; it can, however, be solved by employing the Schauder Theorem.

To this end, let us find whether the functional operation

$$\psi(x) = \hat{A}[\varphi(x)] = \lambda \int_{\Omega} F[x, y, \varphi(y)]\, dy \tag{12}$$

satisfies the assumptions of the Schauder Theorem. Consider therefore a function space E the points of which are all real continuous functions $\varphi(x)$ defined in the closed set Ω. The space E is linear since both addition of its elements and multiplication by real numbers are defined. For the distance between two arbitrary points $\varphi(x)$ and $g(x)$ of the space we take

$$\delta(\varphi, g) = \sup |\varphi(x) - g(x)|, \tag{13}$$

for the norm of point φ we take its distance from zero,

$$\|\varphi\| = \delta(\varphi, 0) = \sup|\varphi(x)|. \tag{14}$$

This definition of distance (13) satisfies all general conditions (see Part 1, formula (47), p. 115), and the norm (14) satisfies conditions (9). The space E is therefore a normed metric space.

According to Definition 1 and the definition of distance (13) every sequence $\{\varphi_n\}$ of points of E is convergent to a point of this space if, and only if, $\sup|\varphi_n - \varphi| \to 0$, i.e. if, and only if, the sequence of functions $\{\varphi_n(x)\}$ is uniformly convergent in the set Ω. If an arbitrary sequence of points $\{\varphi_n\}$ of E satisfies the Cauchy condition, then in accordance with the definition of distance (13) we have

$$\delta(\varphi_n, \varphi_{n+p}) = \sup|\varphi_n(x) - \varphi_{n+p}(x)| < \varepsilon,$$

when $n > N_\varepsilon$; therefore the function sequence $\{\varphi_n(x)\}$ is uniformly convergent. But its limit $\varphi(x)$ is then a continuous function in the set Ω and is a point of the space E, which implies that the sequence of points $\{\varphi_n\}$ converges to the point φ, since $\delta(\varphi_n, \varphi) \to 0$ as $n \to \infty$. The Cauchy condition is therefore a sufficient condition for convergence of sequences of points of the space E, and this space, in accordance with Definition 3, is complete.

The space E is therefore a Banach space.

Consider now, in the space of continuous functions E, a set S of points which satisfy the condition

$$\|\varphi\| = \delta(\varphi, 0) \leqq R.$$

The closed set S is called a *sphere* with centre 0 and radius R.

According to Definitions 4 and 5, the set S is convex. In fact, if φ_1 and φ_2 are arbitary points of S, i.e. points such that

$$|\varphi_1(x)| \leqq R \quad \text{and} \quad |\varphi_2(x)| \leqq R,$$

then every point of the line segment joining these points is defined by the formula $(1-\alpha)\varphi_1 + \alpha\varphi_2$ where $0 \leqq \alpha \leqq 1$, and we obtain

$$|(1-\alpha)\varphi_1(x) + \alpha\varphi_2(x)| \leqq (1-\alpha)|\varphi_1(x)| + \alpha|\varphi_2(x)| \leqq R,$$

consequently all points of this segment belong to S and this set is convex.

According to assumption (11), operation (12) is defined in S and associates with every point $\varphi \in S$ a point $\psi \in E$. The fixed point of operation (12) is exactly the solution of the integral equation (10).

Since E is a Banach space, to prove the existence of a fixed point on the basis of Schauder's Theorem, it is sufficient to establish the following three properties of transformation (12):

1) Every transformed point ψ belongs to the set S.
2) Operation (12) is continuous.
3) The set S' of all transformed points of the set S is compact.

The first property holds for (12), if the absolute value of the parameter λ is sufficiently small. For, if M is the upper bound of the modulus of $F(x, y, u)$ in the domain (11), and V is the measure of the set Ω, we have

$$|\psi| \leqq R, \quad \text{when} \quad |\lambda| \leqq \frac{R}{MV} \tag{15}$$

and the point ψ belongs to the sphere S.

To prove that the operation is continuous in the sense of Definition 8, consider an arbitrary sequence $\{\varphi_n\}$ of points of S convergent to a point $\varphi \in S$; we shall prove that the sequence of the transformed points $\psi_n = \hat{A}(\varphi_n)$ converges to the point $\psi = \hat{A}(\varphi)$.

According to formula (12), we have

$$\psi_n - \psi = \hat{A}(\varphi_n) - \hat{A}(\varphi) = \lambda \int_{\Omega} \{F[x, y, \varphi_n(y)] - F[x, y, \varphi(y)]\} \, dy.$$

Now it follows from the assumption of the continuity of F, that for any $\varepsilon > 0$

$$|F(x, y, \varphi_n) - F(x, y, \varphi)| < \varepsilon, \quad \text{when} \quad |\varphi_n - \varphi| < \eta_\varepsilon,$$

and hence

$$|\psi_n - \psi| < |\lambda| \, V\varepsilon, \quad \text{when} \quad |\varphi_n - \varphi| < \eta_\varepsilon. \tag{16}$$

This implies that

$$\delta(\psi_n, \psi) \to 0, \quad \text{when} \quad \delta(\varphi_n, \varphi) \to 0 \tag{17}$$

and operation (12) is continuous.

To prove that S' is relatively compact observe that S' is a set of continuous functions which are uniformly bounded, since $|\psi(x)| \leqq R$; furthermore, these functions are equi-continuous since

$$|\psi(x') - \psi(x'')| < \lambda \int_{\Omega} |F[x', y, \varphi(y)] - F[x'', y, \varphi(y)]| \, dy.$$

Since in view of the continuity of F, for every positive ε and every function $\varphi \in S$ the inequality

$$|F(x', y, \varphi) - F(x'', y, \varphi)| < \frac{\varepsilon}{|\lambda| V}$$

holds when the distance $|x'x''|$ is smaller than η'_ε, depending only on ε, it follows that all functions of S' simultaneously satisfy the condition

$$|\psi(x') - \psi(x'')| < \varepsilon, \quad \text{when} \quad |x'x''| < \eta'_\varepsilon.$$

Hence, taking into account Arzela's Theorem we conclude that every infinite subset of S' contains a limit point, and hence S' is relatively compact. Thus, all the conditions of Schauder's Theorem are satisfied and we infer that *there exists at least one solution φ of the integral equation* (10) *when $|\lambda|$ is sufficiently small.*

Remark. The merit of the method based on the Schauder Theorem is not only the proof of existence of solutions of integral equations under weaker assumptions, for which the method of successive approximations fails, but also the proof of the existence of solutions of certain non-linear integral equations without limitation of the parameter; this could not be done by classical methods.

Assume that function $F(x, y, u)$ in the integral equation (10) is defined and continuous in the domain

$$[x \in \Omega, y \in \Omega, -\infty < u < +\infty] \tag{18}$$

and that it satisfies the condition

$$|F(x, y, u)| < ku^\beta, \tag{19}$$

where $0 \leqq \beta < 1$ and k is a positive constant. In the Banach space E, consider a set S of continuous functions which satisfy the inequality

$$|\varphi(x)| \leqq \rho,$$

ρ being an arbitrary positive number. The set S' of the points $\psi(x)$, transformed by means of operation (12), is a subset of S if the inequality

$$|\lambda| V k \rho^{\beta} \leqq \rho$$

holds. Since $\beta < 1$, however, we can always choose ρ sufficiently large in order that the latter inequality be satisfied.

The remaining argument is analogous to the preceding one and leads to the interesting conclusion that under assumption (19), in the region (18) there exists at least one solution of the integral equation (10) for any value of the parameter λ. The following are examples of integral equations to which this result may be applied:

$$\varphi(x) = \lambda \int_{\Omega} [A_0(x, y)|\varphi(y)|^{\beta} + B_0(x, y)] \cos^{\alpha}[\varphi(y)]\, dy,$$

$$\varphi(x) = \lambda \int_{\Omega} \frac{\sum_{\nu=0}^{p} A_{\nu}(x, y)[\varphi(y)]^{\nu}}{\sum_{\nu=0}^{q} B_{\nu}(x, y)[\varphi(y)]^{\nu}} |\varphi(y)|^{\beta}\, dy;$$

β denotes a non-negative constant smaller than unity; α, p and q are positive integers and $p \leqq q$; $A(x, y)$ and $B(x, y)$ are real continuous functions of the pair of points x and y of the closed domain Ω, and $\sum_{\nu} B_{\nu}(x, y) u^{\nu} \neq 0$ in the region (18). Other applications were presented by the author in his paper [53].

We now apply our argument to a system of integral equations with weak singularities which, for the sake of generality, we write in the form

$$\varphi_p(x) = \lambda \int_{\Omega} \frac{F_{\nu}[x, y, \varphi_1(y), \varphi_2(y), \ldots, \varphi_p(y)]}{|xy|^{\alpha_{\nu}}}\, dy \qquad (\nu = 1, 2, \ldots, p), \qquad (20)$$

$|xy|$ denotes the distance between two points x and y of a closed bounded region Ω, and the constant non-negative exponents α_ν are smaller than the number of dimensions of Ω in the Euclidean space. We assume that the functions $F_\nu(x, y, u_1, u_2, \ldots, u_p)$ of $p+2$ variables are defined and continuous in the domain

$$[x \in \Omega, y \in \Omega, |u_1| \leqq R, \quad |u_2| \leqq R, \quad \ldots, \quad |u_p| \leqq R]. \tag{21}$$

To solve the system of equations (20) consider the space E the points of which are all p-tuples $U = [\varphi_1, \varphi_2, \ldots, \varphi_p]$ of functions $\varphi_\nu(x)$ which are defined and continuous in the closed region Ω. E is linear if we define the sum of two points $U = [\varphi_1, \varphi_2, \ldots, \varphi_p]$ and $V = [g_1, g_2, \ldots, g_p]$ and the product of U by a real number γ, by the formulae

$$U + V = [\varphi_1 + g_1, \varphi_2 + g_2, \ldots, \varphi_p + g_p],$$
$$\gamma U = [\gamma\varphi_1, \gamma\varphi_2, \ldots, \gamma\varphi_p].$$

These operations obey the usual rules of algebra.

The distance between two points $U = [\varphi_1, \varphi_2, \ldots, \varphi_p]$ and $V = [g_1, g_2, \ldots, g_p]$ of the space is defined as

$$\delta(U, V) = \sum_{\nu=1}^{p} \sup |\varphi_\nu(x) - g_\nu(x)|, \tag{22}$$

and the norm of the point U as the distance $\delta(U, \Theta)$ of this point from zero $\Theta = [0, 0, \ldots, 0]$

$$\|U\| = \delta(U, \Theta) = \sum_{\nu=1}^{p} \sup |\varphi_\nu(x)|. \tag{23}$$

It follows that E is metric and normed since (23) satisfies the conditions for the norm (9). Every sequence of points $U_n = [\varphi_1^{(n)}, \varphi_2^{(n)}, \ldots, \varphi_p^{(n)}]$ of the space E is convergent to a point $U = [\varphi_1, \varphi_2, \ldots, \varphi_p]$ of this space if, and only if, $\sup |\varphi_\nu^{(n)} - \varphi_\nu| \to 0$ for any $\nu = 1, 2, \ldots, p$, i.e. when the functions $\varphi_\nu^{(n)}$ tend uniformly to the functions φ_ν; in other words, when the Cauchy condition is satisfied, $\delta(U_n, U_{n+1}) < \varepsilon$, and the space is complete.

Thus, E is a Banach space.

Consider now in E a closed set S of all points $U = [\varphi_1, \varphi_2, \dots, \varphi_p]$ which satisfy the inequality

$$|\varphi_\nu(x)| \leqq R, \tag{24}$$

the constant R being the same as in inequalities (21). The set S is convex. In fact, if $U = [\varphi_1, \varphi_2, \dots, \varphi_p]$ and $V = [g_1, g_2, \dots, g_p]$ are two points of S, i.e. points such that

$$|\varphi_\nu(x)| \leqq R \quad \text{and} \quad |g_\nu(x)| \leqq R,$$

then all points $(1-\gamma)U+\gamma V$ of the line segment joining U and V also satisfy inequality (24), for

$$|(1-\gamma)\varphi_\nu(x)+\gamma g_\nu(x)| \leqq (1-\gamma)|\varphi_\nu(x)|+\gamma|g_\nu(x)| \leqq R,$$

when $0 \leqq \gamma \leqq 1$.

Apply now to all points $U = [\varphi_1, \varphi_2, \dots, \varphi_p]$ of S the functional operation defined by the formulae

$$\psi_\nu(x) = \lambda \int\limits_\Omega \frac{F_\nu[x, y, \varphi_1(y), \varphi_2(y), \dots, \varphi_p(y)]}{|xy|^{\alpha_\nu}}\, dy \qquad (\nu = 1, 2, \dots, p). \tag{25}$$

This operation associates with the point $U = [\varphi_1, \varphi_2, \dots, \varphi_p]$ of S a point $U' = [\psi_1, \psi_2, \dots, \psi_p]$ of the same set, provided the absolute value of the parameter λ is sufficiently small, i.e. provided that for any $\nu = 1, 2, \dots, p$ we have

$$|\lambda|\, M_\nu \int\limits_\Omega \frac{dy}{|xy|^{\alpha_\nu}} \leqq R, \tag{26}$$

where M_ν is the upper bound of $|F_\nu|$ in the domain (21). If $\varepsilon > \alpha_\nu$ is the number of dimensions of Ω, then

$$\omega_s = \frac{2(\sqrt{\pi})^s}{\Gamma(s/2)}$$

is the surface area of the p-dimensional sphere of unit radius, and we obtain

$$\int\limits_\Omega \frac{dy}{|xy|^{\alpha_\nu}} \leqq \int\limits_0^L \frac{\omega\rho^{s-1}}{\rho\alpha_\nu}\, d\rho = \frac{\omega_s}{s-\alpha_\nu} L^{s-\alpha_\nu} = l_\nu, \tag{27}$$

where L denotes the diameter of Ω. Condition (26) is therefore satisfied if λ is such that

$$|\lambda| \leqq \min\left(\frac{(s-\alpha_1)R}{M_1\,\omega_s L^{s-\alpha_1}}, \frac{(s-\alpha_2)R}{M_2\,\omega_s L^{s-\alpha_2}}, \ldots, \frac{(s-\alpha_p)R}{M_p\,\omega_s L^{s-\alpha_p}}\right). \tag{28}$$

To establish, using Schauder's Theorem, the existence of a fixed point of operation (25) it is now sufficient to prove that this operation is continuous and that the set S' of the transformed points of S is relatively compact.

Consider therefore in S a sequence $\{U_n\}$ of points $U_n = [\varphi_1^{(n)}, \varphi_2^{(n)}, \ldots, \varphi_p^{(n)}]$ convergent to the point $U = [\varphi_1, \varphi_2, \ldots, \varphi_p]$. Thus we have

$$\delta(U_n, U) = \sum_{\nu=1}^{p} \sup|\varphi_\nu^n(x) - \varphi_\nu(x)| \to 0, \quad \text{when} \quad n \to \infty. \tag{29}$$

If $\{U_n' = [\psi_1^{(n)}, \psi_2^{(n)}, \ldots, \psi_p^{(n)}]\}$ is the sequence of points corresponding to points U_n in accordance with operation (25) and $U' = [\psi_1, \psi_2, \ldots, \psi_n]$ corresponds to the limit point U in accordance with this operation, then we obtain

$$\begin{aligned}\psi_\nu^{(n)}(x) - \psi_\nu(x) &= \lambda \int_\Omega \frac{F_\nu[x, y, \varphi_1^{(n)}(y), \varphi_2^{(n)}(y), \ldots, \varphi_p^{(n)}(y)]}{|xy|^{\alpha_\nu}} - \\ &\quad - \frac{F_\nu[x, y, \varphi_1(y), \varphi_2(y), \ldots, \varphi_p(y)]}{|xy|^{\alpha_\nu}}\, dy.\end{aligned} \tag{30}$$

Since, by assumption (29) all differences $\varphi_\nu^{(n)} - \varphi_\nu$ tend uniformly to zero in Ω when $n \to \infty$, and the functions F_ν are continuous, for an arbitrary $\varepsilon > 0$, we can find a number N_ε such that, for all ν,

$$\begin{aligned}|F_\nu[x, y, \varphi_1^{(n)}(y), \varphi_2^{(n)}(y), \ldots, \varphi_p^{(n)}(y)] - \\ - F_\nu[x, y, \varphi_1(y), \varphi_2(y), \ldots, \varphi_p(y)]| < \varepsilon,\end{aligned}$$

when $n > N_\varepsilon$, and then all differences (30) satisfy the inequalities

$$|\psi_\nu^{(n)}(x) - \psi_\nu(x)| \leqq |\lambda|\,\varepsilon \int_\Omega \frac{dy}{|xy|^{\alpha_\nu}} \leqq |\lambda| \frac{\omega_s L^{s-\alpha_\nu}}{s-\alpha_\nu}\,\varepsilon,$$

when $n > N_\varepsilon$, i.e. they tend uniformly to zero in Ω as $n \to \infty$. It follows therefore that $\delta(U'_n, U') \to 0$ as $n \to \infty$ and thus the point U' is the limit of the sequence $\{U'_n\}$ and the functional operation defined by formulae (25) is continuous. To prove finally that S' is relatively compact we apply Arzela's Theorem. Thus, first of all, the set of functions (25) is uniformly bounded since all functions satisfy the inequality $|\psi_\nu(x)| < R$. We have also to prove that the functions (25) are equi-continuous, i.e. given $\varepsilon > 0$, there exists a number η, such that all the functions (25) satisfy the condition

$$|\psi_\nu(x') - \psi_\nu(x'')| < \varepsilon, \quad \text{when} \quad |x'x''| < \eta. \tag{31}$$

To this end, decompose the difference (31) into the following two terms:

$$\psi_\nu(x') - \psi_\nu(x'') = \lambda \int_\Omega \left\{ \frac{F_\nu[x', y, \varphi_1(y), \varphi_2(y), \ldots, \varphi_p(y)]}{|x'y|^{\alpha_\nu}} - \frac{F_\nu[x'', y, \varphi_1(y), \varphi_2(y), \ldots, \varphi_p(y)]}{|x'y|^{\alpha_\nu}} \right\} dy +$$

$$+ \lambda \int_\Omega F_\nu[x'', y, \varphi_1(y), \varphi_2(y), \ldots, \varphi_p(y)] \times \left(\frac{1}{|x'y|^{\alpha_\nu}} - \frac{1}{|x''y|^{\alpha_\nu}} \right) dy. \tag{32}$$

In view of the continuity of the functions F_ν, for an arbitrary positive ε, we can find a number η_1 such that

$$|\lambda| . |F_\nu[x', y, \varphi_1, \varphi_2, \ldots, \varphi_p] - F_\nu[x'', y, \varphi_1, \varphi_2, \ldots, \varphi_p]| < \frac{\varepsilon}{2l}$$

for all functions φ_ν of the set S when $|x'x''| < \eta_1$, where l denotes the greatest of the numbers l_ν in formula (27). The absolute value of the first term of sum (32) is then, in accordance with inequality (27), smaller than $\varepsilon/2$. To make the absolute value of the second term of the sum (32) smaller than $\varepsilon/2$ by bringing closer the points x' and x'', observe that

$$\left|\lambda \int_{\Omega} F_\nu[x'', y, \varphi_1(y), \varphi_2(y), \dots, \varphi_p(y)] \left(\frac{1}{|x'y|^{\alpha_\nu}} - \frac{1}{|x''y|^{\alpha_\nu}}\right) dy\right|$$

$$\leq M|\lambda| \int_{\Omega} \left|\frac{1}{|x'y|^{\alpha_\nu}} - \frac{1}{|x''y|^{\alpha_\nu}}\right| dy, \quad (33)$$

where M denotes the least upper bound of the functions $|F_\nu|$. Now surround the point x' by a sphere K with centre x', and decompose the integral on the right side of inequality (33) into two parts

$$\int_{\Omega} \left|\frac{1}{|x'y|^{\alpha_\nu}} - \frac{1}{|x''y|^{\alpha_\nu}}\right| dy$$

$$= \int_{K^*} \left|\frac{1}{|x'y|^{\alpha_\nu}} - \frac{1}{|x''y|^{\alpha_\nu}}\right| dy + \int_{\Omega - K^*} \left|\frac{1}{|x'y|^{\alpha_\nu}} - \frac{1}{|x''y|^{\alpha_\nu}}\right| dy, \quad (34)$$

integration being carried out over the region $K^* = \Omega K$ and the remaining region $\Omega - K^*$, respectively. The radius r_ε of the sphere K can be selected sufficiently small, so that

$$\int_{K^*} \frac{dy}{|x''y|^{\alpha_\nu}} < \frac{\varepsilon}{6M|\lambda|} \quad (35)$$

for every point x'' and for all $\nu = 1, 2, \dots, p$. Since x' is inside $\Omega - K^*$, for a fixed radius r_ε of the sphere K we can now choose a number η_2, independent of x' and ν, such that

$$\left|\frac{1}{|x'y|^{\alpha_\nu}} - \frac{1}{|x''y|^{\alpha_\nu}}\right| < \frac{\varepsilon}{6MV|\lambda|}, \quad \text{when} \quad |x'x''| < \eta_2 \quad (36)$$

for every point y inside K; V denotes the volume of Ω.

Finally on the basis of formulae (33), (34), (35) and (36) we infer that the absolute value of integral (33) is smaller than $\varepsilon/2$ when $|x'x''| < \eta_2$, i.e. we have

$$|\psi_\nu(x') - \psi_\nu(x'')| < \varepsilon \quad (37)$$

for every function ψ_ν and for every pair of points x' and x'' of Ω, the distance between which is less than the smaller of the two numbers η_1 and η_2. Thus, the functions (25) are equi-continuous. Thus, from Arzela's Theorem, we infer that S is relatively compact.

The above properties of transformation (25) and properties of the sets S and S' make it possible to apply Schauder's Theorem which implies that *there exists a fixed point of transformation* (25) *in* S, *i.e. there exists a system of continuous functions* $\varphi_1(x), \varphi_2(x), \ldots, \varphi_p(x)$ *which satisfy the system of integral equations* (19).

To conclude this section, we present a remark concerning a particular form of the integral equation

$$\varphi(x) = \lambda \int_\Omega K(x, y) f[y, \varphi(y)]\, dy \tag{38}$$

called the *Hammerstein equation*; $K(x, y)$ and $f(y, u)$ are known functions. This equation was investigated by Hammerstein using the method of classical analysis. Equation (38) was subsequently the subject of investigations of the Soviet mathematician NEMYTZKI [39] who, under weaker assumptions (functions K and f are square-integrable) examined equation (38) employing Schauder's Fixed Point Theorem.

§ 4. Integral equations with an infinite number of unknown functions

We proceed to investigate a system of integral equations with an infinite number of unknown functions

$$\varphi_1(x), \varphi_2(x), \ldots, \varphi_n(x), \ldots \tag{39}$$

We write it in the form

$$\varphi_n(x) = \lambda \int_\Omega F_n[x, y, \varphi_1(y), \varphi_2(y), \ldots]\, dy \quad (n = 1, 2, \ldots), \tag{40}$$

where $F_n(x, y, u_1, u_2, \ldots)$ are known functions of an infinite number of variables, defined in the closed domain

$$[x \in \Omega, y \in \Omega, |u_1| \leqq R, |u_2| \leqq R, \ldots, |u_n| \leqq R, \ldots]; \tag{41}$$

as before, Ω denotes a bounded closed region in Euclidean space. Assume that the known functions F_n are continuous in the sense that for any $\varepsilon > 0$ and for a given function F_n, at an arbitrary point $(x^0, y^0, u_1^0, u_2^0, \ldots)$ of set (41) there exist η and N such that

$$|F_n(x, y, u_1, u_2, \ldots) - F_n(x^0, y^0, u_1^0, u_2^0, \ldots)| < \varepsilon, \qquad (42)$$

when

$$|xx^0| < \eta, \quad |yy^0| < \eta, \quad |u_\nu - u_\nu^0| < \eta \quad (\nu = 1, 2, \ldots, N).$$

Assume, moreover, that the functions F_n are uniformly bounded, i.e. $|F_n| \leqq M$.

The proof of the existence of a solution of system (40) is based on Fréchet's Theorem [7] on the relative compactness of a set, which is stated without proof.

FRÉCHET'S THEOREM. *In order that a set X of points in a complete metric space E be relatively compact it is necessary and sufficient that, given $\varepsilon > 0$, there exists in E a relatively compact set Y_ε, such that to every point $x \in X$ there corresponds a point $y \in Y_\varepsilon$, the distance between x and y being smaller than ε.*

We first prove that every function F_n is uniformly continuous in the domain (41). To this end, consider the space T the points of which are all sequences $A(x, y, u_1, u_2, \ldots)$ constructed of the pairs (x, y) of points of the Euclidean space in which the region Ω is located, and of arbitrary real and bounded sequences $u_1, u_2, \ldots$ We define the distance $\delta(A, B)$ between two points $A(x, y, u_1, u_2, \ldots)$ and $B(x', y', u_1', u_2', \ldots)$ of T by the formula

$$\delta(A, B) = |xx'| + |yy'| + \sum_{\nu=1}^{\infty} \frac{1}{2^\nu} |u_\nu - u_\nu'|, \qquad (43)$$

the series being always convergent in view of the boundedness of the sequences $\{u_\nu\}$ and $\{u_\nu'\}$.

Thus the space T is a metric space. It is also complete, since it is evident that the Cauchy condition is sufficient for the convergence of the set of points $A_1, A_2, \ldots$ of the considered space.

The functions F_n are defined and uniformly bounded in the set of points T^* of T, defined by inequalities (41). We prove that T^* is relatively compact in T.

In fact, given $\varepsilon > 0$, we can associate with every point $A(x, y, u_1, u_2, \ldots)$ of T^* a point $A'(x, y, u_1, u_2, \ldots, u_{N_\varepsilon}, 0, 0, \ldots)$

of this set (the terms with indices greater than N_ε are zeros) such that

$$\delta(A, A') = \sum_{\nu=N_\varepsilon+1}^{\infty} \frac{1}{2^\nu} |u_\nu| < \varepsilon.$$

But the set of points A' with a finite number of components which satisfy condition (31) is compact and hence, in accordance with Fréchet's Theorem, T^* is relatively compact in T.

Observe now that the function F_n, continuous in the sense of (42), is also continuous in the sense of the metric (43). In fact, given $\varepsilon > 0$, there exists η such that

$$|F_n(A) - F_n(A_0)| < \varepsilon,$$

when $A(x, y, u_1, u_2, \dots)$ and $A(x^0, y^0, u_1^0, u_2^0, \dots)$ satisfy the inequality

$$\delta(A, A_0) = |xx^0| + |yy^0| + \sum_{\nu=1}^{\infty} \frac{1}{2^\nu} |u_\nu - u_\nu^0| < \frac{\eta}{2^N},$$

since then we have

$$|xx^0| < \eta, \quad |yy^0| < \eta, \quad |u_\nu - u_\nu^0| < \eta \quad (\nu = 1, 2, \dots, N),$$

N being selected for ε in accordance with assumption (42).

Conversely, when $F_n(A)$ is continuous in the sense of metric (43), for any $\varepsilon > 0$ there exists $\eta_1 > 0$ such that

$$|F_n(A) - F_n(A_0)| < \varepsilon, \quad \text{when} \quad \delta(A, A_0) < \eta_1.$$

With this ε, we now select an integer $N_1(\varepsilon)$ such that

$$2R \sum_{N_1+1}^{\infty} \frac{1}{2^\nu} \leqq \frac{\eta_1}{4};$$

then $\delta(A, A_0) < \eta_1$ when

$$|xx^0| < \frac{\eta_1}{4}, \quad |yy^0| < \frac{\eta_1}{4}, \quad |u_\nu - u_\nu^0| < \frac{\eta_1}{4}$$

$$(\nu = 1, 2, \dots, N_1),$$

and this means that F_n is continuous in the sense of (42).

We finally deduce that every function F_n, continuous at all points of the set T^*, is uniformly continuous in this set with respect to the metric (43).

To investigate the system of equations (40), consider a function space E^∞, the points of which are all infinite bounded sequences $U = [\varphi_1(x), \varphi_2(x), \ldots, \varphi_n(x), \ldots]$ or briefly $U = \{\varphi_n(x)\}$, constructed from real functions, defined and continuous in a closed region Ω. E^∞ is linear if we take the following definition of the product of the point $U = \{\varphi_n\}$ by a real number γ,

$$\gamma U = \{\gamma \varphi_n\}$$

and the definition of a sum of two points $U = \{\varphi_n\}$ and $V = \{g_n\}$,

$$U+V = \{\varphi_n + g_n\}.$$

We define the distance $\delta(U, V)$ between two points $U = \{\varphi_n\}$ and $V = \{g_n\}$ of E^∞ as the sum of the convergent series

$$\delta(U, V) = \sum_{n=1}^{\infty} \frac{1}{2^n} \sup |\varphi_n(x) - g_n(x)|, \tag{44}$$

the norm of $U = \{\varphi_n\}$ being defined as its distance from $\Theta = [0, 0, \ldots]$:

$$\|U\| = \delta(U, \Theta) = \sum_{n=1}^{\infty} \frac{1}{2^n} \sup |\varphi_n(x)|. \tag{45}$$

E^∞ with distance and norm thus defined, evidently satisfies all the postulates of a normed metric space. As before, the Cauchy condition is sufficient for the convergence of a sequence of points $U_1, U_2, \ldots$ of E^∞, and this space is complete.

Thus, E^∞ is a Banach space.

Consider now in E^∞ the closed set S of all points $U = \{\varphi_n\}$ which satisfy the inequality

$$|\varphi_n(x)| \leqq R. \tag{46}$$

This set is convex, since all points of the line segment $(1-\gamma)U + \gamma V$ joining the two points $U = \{\varphi_n\}$ and $V = \{g_n\}$ of S satisfy the inequality

$$|(1-\gamma)\varphi_n(x) + \gamma g_n(x)| \leqq (1-\gamma)|\varphi_n(x)| + \gamma |g_n(x)| \leqq R,$$

when γ lies within the interval (0,1). In other words, these points belong to S.

Bearing in mind the system of integral equations (40), let us now transform S, associating with every point $U = \{\varphi_n\}$ of S a point $U' = \{\psi_n\}$ of E^∞ in accordance with the formula

$$\psi_n(x) = \lambda \int_\Omega F_n[x, y, \varphi_1(y), \varphi_2(y), \ldots]\, dy \quad (n = 1, 2, \ldots). \quad (47)$$

Since $|\psi_n| < |\lambda| MV$, where V denotes the measure of Ω, the point $U = \{\psi_n\}$ belongs to S if the condition $|\lambda| MV < R$ is satisfied, i.e. when $|\lambda|$ is sufficiently small,

$$|\lambda| \leqq \frac{R}{MV}.$$

We now prove that operation (47) is continuous in E^∞. Consider, therefore, in S an arbitrary sequence $\{U_\nu\}$ of points $U_\nu = [\varphi_1^\nu, \varphi_2^\nu, \ldots]$ converging to the point $U = [\varphi_1, \varphi_2, \ldots]$. Then, in view of definition (44),

$$\delta(U_\nu, U) = \sum_{n=1}^{\infty} \frac{1}{2^n} \sup |\varphi_n^\nu(x) - \varphi_n(x)| \to 0, \quad \text{when} \quad \nu \to \infty. \quad (48)$$

If $\{U'_\nu\}$ is a sequence of points $U'_\nu = [\psi_1^\nu, \psi_2^\nu, \ldots]$ of E^∞ which correspond to the points U_ν under the transformation (47), then, for arbitrary integers n and ν, we have

$$\psi_n^\nu(x) - \psi_n(x) = \lambda \int_\Omega \{F_n[x, y, \varphi_1^\nu(y), \varphi_2^\nu(y), \ldots] -$$
$$- F_n[x, y, \varphi_1(y), \varphi_2(y), \ldots]\}\, dy.$$

By virtue of assumption (48) and the uniform continuity of the functions F_n, for every $\varepsilon > 0$ we can find an index $N_n(\varepsilon)$ which may depend on n, such that

$$|F_n[x, y, \varphi_1^\nu(y), \varphi_2^\nu(y), \ldots] - F_n[x, y, \varphi_1(y), \varphi_2(y), \ldots]| < \varepsilon,$$

when $\nu > N_n(\varepsilon)$, for an arbitrary pair of points x, y in Ω. Thus we have

$$|\psi_n^\nu(x) - \psi_n(x)| \leqq |\lambda| \varepsilon V, \quad \text{when} \quad \nu > N_n(\varepsilon). \quad (49)$$

Observe now that for any n and ν, the functions ψ_n^ν satisfy the inequality

$$|\psi_n^\nu(x)| \leqq R.$$

Thus, we can select a sufficiently large index $n_0(\varepsilon)$, depending only on ε, such that

$$\sum_{n=n_0(\varepsilon)+1}^{\infty} \frac{1}{2^n} \sup |\psi_n^\nu - \psi_n(x)| \leqq \varepsilon \tag{50}$$

for arbitrary ν. After having fixed $n_0(\varepsilon)$ we get, taking into account (49), the following inequality:

$$\sum_{n=1}^{n_0(\varepsilon)} \frac{1}{2^n} \sup |\psi_n^\nu(x) - \psi_n(x)| \leqq |\lambda| \varepsilon V, \quad \text{when} \quad \nu > \overline{N}(\varepsilon), \tag{51}$$

where $\overline{N}(\varepsilon) = \sup N_n(\varepsilon)$ $(n = 1, 2, \ldots, n_0(\varepsilon))$. In view of inequalities (50) and (51), this implies that

$$\delta(U'_\nu, U') = \sum_{n=1}^{\infty} \frac{1}{2^n} \sup |\psi_n^\nu(x) - \psi_n(x)| \leqq (1 + |\lambda| V) \varepsilon,$$

when $\nu > \overline{N}(\varepsilon)$; thus $\delta(U'_\nu, U') \to 0$ as $\nu \to \infty$ and the transformation defined by formula (47) is continuous in E^∞.

We shall now prove that S' (the transformed set S) is compact. For this purpose, given $\varepsilon > 0$, construct a set S''_ε of points, associating with every point $U' = [\psi_1, \psi_2, \ldots]$ a point $U''_\varepsilon = [\psi_1, \psi_2, \ldots, \psi_{N_\varepsilon}, 0, 0, \ldots]$ of S' such that

$$\delta(U', U''_\varepsilon) = \sum_{n=N_\varepsilon+1}^{\infty} \frac{1}{2^n} \sup |\psi_n(x)| \leqq \frac{R}{2^{N_\varepsilon}} < \varepsilon. \tag{52}$$

But the set of points U''_ε (sequences with a finite number of non-zero terms) is relatively compact, on the basis of properties analogous to those of differences (42) examined before, and in view of Arzela's Theorem. Hence, taking into account Fréchet's Theorem, we infer that S' is relatively compact. All the conditions of Schauder's Theorem are therefore satisfied, and hence there exists in S a fixed point with respect to transformation (27), i.e. there exists a solution $\{\varphi_n\}$ of the system of integral equations with an inifinite number of unknown functions.

Other types of integral equations with an infinite number of unknown functions were recently investigated by the author in his paper [35].

CHAPTER XI

APPLICATION OF INTEGRAL EQUATIONS TO ORDINARY DIFFERENTIAL EQUATIONS

§ 1. Initial value problems

The theory of the Volterra equation makes it possible to solve in a simple way initial value problems for a linear ordinary differential equation of an arbitrary order. Consider therefore a linear differential equation of order n:

$$\frac{d^n y}{dx^n} + p_1(x)\frac{d^{n-1}y}{dx^{n-1}} + \ldots + p_{n-1}(x)\frac{dy}{dx} + p_n(x)\,y = f(x), \qquad (1)$$

where $p_1(x), p_2(x), \ldots, p_n(x)$ and $f(x)$ are functions defined and continuous in the closed interval $[a, b]$. We require a solution $y(x)$ of equation (1) which, at a selected point x_0 of the interval $[a, b]$, satisfies certain prescribed conditions

$$y(x_0) = q_0, \quad y'(x_0) = q_1, \quad \ldots, \quad y^{(n-1)}(x_0) = q_{n-1}. \qquad (2)$$

We introduce the unknown function

$$\varphi(x) = \frac{d^n y}{dx^n}. \qquad (3)$$

In view of the initial condition (2), we have

$$\frac{d^{n-1}y}{dx^{n-1}} = \int_{x_0}^{x} \varphi(t)\,dt + q_{n-1},$$

$$\frac{d^{n-2}y}{dx^{n-2}} = \int_{x_0}^{x} (x-t)\,\varphi(t)\,dt + q_{n-1}(x-x_0) + q_{n-2},$$

. . . .

$$\frac{dy}{dx}=\int_{x_0}^{x}\frac{(x-t)^{n-2}}{(n-2)!}\varphi(t)\,dt+\frac{q_{n-1}}{(n-2)!}(x-x_0)^{n-2}+$$

$$+\frac{q_{n-2}}{(n-3)!}(x-x_0)^{n-3}+\ldots+q_2(x-x_0)+q_1,$$

$$y=\int_{x_0}^{x}\frac{(x-t)^{n-1}}{(n-1)!}\varphi(t)\,dt+\frac{q_{n-1}}{(n-1)!}(x-x_0)^{n-1}+$$

$$+\frac{q_{n-2}}{(n-2)!}(x-x_0)^{n-2}+\ldots+q_1(x-x_0)+q_0.$$

Thus we may state that if $y(x)$ satisfies equation (1) and the initial conditions (2), then the function (3) satisfies the integral equation

$$\varphi(x)+\int_{x_0}^{x}\left[p_1(x)+p_2(x)(x-t)+\ldots+p_{n-1}(x)\frac{(x-t)^{n-2}}{(n-2)!}+\right.$$

$$\left.+p_n(x)\frac{(x-t)^{n-1}}{(n-1)!}\right]\varphi(t)\,dt+$$

$$+p_1(x)q_{n-1}+p_2(x)[q_{n-1}(x-x_0)+q_{n-2}]+\ldots+$$

$$+p_n(x)\left[\frac{q_{n-1}}{(n-1)!}(x-x_0)^{n-1}+\ldots+q_1(x-x_0)+q_0\right]=f(x) \quad (4)$$

and, conversely, if $\varphi(x)$ satisfies the integral equation (4) in the interval $[a, b]$, then the function

$$y(x)=\int_{x_0}^{x}\frac{(x-t)^{n-1}}{(n-1)!}\varphi(t)\,dt+$$

$$+\frac{q_{n-1}}{(n-1)!}(x-x_0)^{n-1}+\ldots+q_1(x-x_0)+q_0 \quad (5)$$

satisfies the differential equation (1) and conditions (2). Equation (4) is the well-known Volterra equation, the kernel of which is

$$N(x, t) = p_1(x) + p_2(x)(x-t) + \ldots + p_n(x)\,\frac{(x-t)^{n-1}}{(n-1)!} \tag{6}$$

defined and continuous in the strip $a \leqq x \leqq b$, $-\infty < t < \infty$, and the equation has a unique continuous solution in the interval $[a, b]$ (see Part 1, formula (12), p. 11). Thus *in the interval* $[a, b]$ *there exists a unique solution* y (*of class* C_n) *of the differential equation* (1), *given by formula* (5), *which satisfies the initial conditions* (2), *where* φ *is the solution of the Volterra equation* (4).

§ 2. Boundary value problems

By a *boundary value problem* for an ordinary differential equation of nth order we mean the problem of determining the solution of the equation in a certain interval, on the boundaries of which the solution and its derivatives of order not higher than $n-1$ take on prescribed values, or satisfy given relations. These problems lead to Fredholm integral equations.

The simplest boundary value problem has already been presented in the Introduction to Part 1. It consists in determining the solution of the differential equation of the second order

$$\frac{d^2 y}{dx^2} + \lambda p(x) y = q(x), \tag{7}$$

which takes given values on the boundaries of an interval $[a, b]$. By a simple substitution we can always reduce the problem to the case when both boundary values are zero; we have therefore the conditions

$$y(a) = 0 \quad \text{and} \quad y(b) = 0. \tag{8}$$

The functions $p(x)$ and $q(x)$ are known and continuous in the interval $[a, b]$, while λ is a parameter. We proved (see Part 1, p. 4) that the solution y of the problem satisfies the Fredholm equation

$$y(x) = -\lambda \int_a^b G(x, t)\,p(t)\,y(t)\,dt + \int_a^b G(x, t)\,q(t)\,dt, \tag{9}$$

where $G(x, t)$ is the so-called *Green's Function* defined by the formulae

$$G(x,t)=\begin{cases}\dfrac{(x-a)(t-b)}{b-a}, & \text{when} \quad x \leqq t;\\[2ex] \dfrac{(x-b)(t-a)}{b-a}, & \text{when} \quad x \geqq t.\end{cases} \tag{10}$$

Conversely, the solution of the Fredholm equation (9) satisfies the differential equation (7) in the interval $[a, b]$, and the boundary conditions (8).

The function $G(x, t)$ in equation (9) is symmetric,

$$G(x,t) = G(t,x),$$

consequently the kernel of equation (9) is of the Schmidt type (see Part 1, p. 152) and the equation can be reduced by the substitution $\varphi(x) = y(x)\sqrt{p(x)}$ to an equation with a symmetric kernel,

$$\varphi(x) = -\lambda \int_a^b G(x,t)\sqrt{p(x)p(t)}\,\varphi(t)\,dt +$$

$$+\sqrt{p(x)}\int_a^b G(x,t)\,q(t)\,dt, \tag{11}$$

assuming that function $p(x)$ is non-negative.

The properties of an equation with a symmetric kernel (see Part 1, p. 121) make it possible to draw interesting conclusions concerning the considered boundary problem; a straightforward proof of these properties in the general case would not be easy.

First, since the kernel of equation (11) is not degenerate, i.e. it is not a sum of the products $\sum_\nu K_\nu(x)\,L_\nu(y)$ of functions of one variable defined independently in the interval (a, b), it has an infinite number of real eigenvalues (see Part 1, p. 132) $\lambda_1, \lambda_2, \ldots$

In fact, observe that in the case $p = 1$, the eigensolutions of the homogeneous integral equation

$$\varphi(x) = -\lambda \int_a^b G(x,t)\,\varphi(t)\,dt$$

are the non-zero solutions of the differential equation

$$\frac{d^2y}{dx^2}+\lambda y=0$$

which vanish at the end-points of the interval (a, b). These solutions exist for an infinite number of eigenvalues

$$\lambda_\nu=\left(\frac{\nu\pi}{b-a}\right)^2 \qquad (\nu=1,2,\ldots)$$

and are given by the formula

$$\varphi_\nu(x)=\sin\frac{\nu\pi}{b-a}x.$$

Thus, the kernel $G(x, t)$ and therefore the kernel of equation (11) as well, are not degenerate.

Since the kernel $-G(x,t)\sqrt{p(x)\,p(t)}$ of equation (11) *is positive* (in the sense of the Definition 3, Part 1, p. 150) *all its eigenvalues are positive and their sequence tends to infinity.*

Now the second Fredholm Theorem implies that *the homogeneous differential equation*

$$\frac{d^2y}{dx^2}+\lambda p(x)\,y=0$$

has a non-zero solution (vanishing at the end-points of the interval) only if the parameter $+\lambda$ *has the same eigenvalues as the kernel of equation* (11). The appropriate solutions are expressed in terms of the eigensolutions of this equation. Since the kernel of equation (11) is positive, continuous, and bounded, it follows from Mercer's Theorem (see Part 1, p. 150) that this kernel is the sum of its Fourier series

$$-G(x,t)\sqrt{p(x)\,p(t)}=\sum_{n=1}^{\infty}\frac{\varphi_n(x)\,\varphi_n(y)}{\lambda_n}$$

which is absolutely and uniformly convergent with respect to the pair of variables x and y. The sequence $\{\varphi_n(x)\}$ is an orthonormal system of eigensolutions of the homogeneous equation corresponding to (11).

If the differential equation is not homogeneous, i.e. if it has the form

$$\frac{d^2y}{dx^2}+\lambda p(x)\,y = q(x)$$

and λ is equal to one of the eigenvalues of the kernel of equation (11), then according to the Fredholm's Third Theorem, *the solution of this equation which satisfies the boundary conditions* (8) *exists only if function* $q(x)$ *satisfies the orthogonality conditions*

$$\int_a^b\int_a^b \Phi_\nu(x)\sqrt{p(x)}\,G(x,t)\,q(t)\,dt\,dx = 0 \tag{12}$$

for all fundamental solutions $\Phi_\nu(x)$ *of the integral equation* (11), *corresponding to the eigenvalue* λ.

This result has a beautiful direct interpretation in the theory of vibrations of strings or longitudinal vibrations of rods.

Let us now examine another boundary value problem for equation (7):

$$y(a) = 0 \quad \text{and} \quad \left(\frac{dy}{dx}\right)_{x=b} = 0. \tag{13}$$

These boundary conditions occur in the problem of longitudinal vibrations of a rod fixed at one end and free at the other. As before, we first seek the solution of the equation

$$\frac{d^2y}{dx^2} = f(x),$$

where $f(x)$ is a known continuous function satisfying conditions (13). Requiring that the general solution of this equation

$$y = \int_a^x (x-t)\,f(t)\,dt + C_1 x + C_2$$

satisfy conditions (13), we obtain

$$C_1 a + C_2 = 0 \quad \text{and} \quad \int_a^b f(t)\,dt + C_1 = 0.$$

Hence

$$y = \int_a^x (x-t) f(t)\,dt - \int_a^b x f(t)\,dt + \int_a^b a f(t)\,dt$$

or

$$y = \int_a^b G^*(x, t) f(t)\,dt, \tag{14}$$

the new Green's Function having the form

$$G^*(x, t) = \begin{cases} a-x, & \text{when} \quad x \leqq t, \\ a-t, & \text{when} \quad x \geqq t. \end{cases} \tag{15}$$

This function is also symmetric.

Thus the solution $y(x)$ which satisfies the boundary conditions (13) *is a solution of the integral equation*

$$y(x) = \lambda \int_a^b G^*(x, t)\, p(t)\, y(t)\,dt + \int_a^b G^*(x, t)\, q(t)\,dt \tag{16}$$

and conversely. This is a Fredholm equation with Schmidt kernel.

We now proceed to find the solution of the differential equation of the fourth order

$$\frac{d^4 y}{dx^4} = \lambda p(x)\, y + q(x) \tag{17}$$

which satisfies the boundary conditions

$$y = 0 \quad \text{and} \quad \frac{dy}{dx} = 0 \quad \text{for} \quad x = a \quad \text{and} \quad x = b; \tag{18}$$

$p(x)$ and $q(x)$, as before are known continuous functions in the interval (a, b). This problem occurs in the theory of deformation of a rod fixed at both ends.

The general solution of the equation

$$\frac{d^4 y}{dx^4} = f(x)$$

has the form

$$y(x) = \int_a^x \frac{(x-t)^3}{6} f(t)\,dt + \\ + C_1 (x-a)^3 + C_2 (x-a)^2 + C_3 (x-a) + C_4 .$$

Requiring that the boundary conditions (18) be satisfied, we obtain $C_3 = 0$, $C_4 = 0$ and the system of equations

$$C_1(b-a)^3 + C_2(b-a)^2 + \int_a^b \frac{(b-t)^3}{6} f(t)\,dt = 0,$$

$$3C_1(b-a)^2 + 2C_2(b-a) + \int_a^b \frac{(b-t)^2}{2} f(t)\,dt = 0.$$

Hence

$$y(x) = \int_a^b G_*(x, t) f(t)\,dt, \tag{19}$$

where

$$G_*(x, t) = \begin{cases} \frac{1}{6}(x-t)^3 + \frac{1}{6}(x-a)^2\left(\frac{b-t}{b-a}\right)^2\left[(x-a)\frac{-b+3a-2t}{b-a} + \right. \\ \qquad \left. + 3(t-a)\right], \quad \text{when} \quad t \leqq x; \\ \frac{1}{6}(x-a)^2\left(\frac{b-t}{b-a}\right)^2\left[(x-a)\frac{-b+3a-2t}{b-a} + 3(t-a)\right], \\ \qquad \text{when} \quad t \geqq x. \end{cases} \tag{20}$$

It follows from these results that *the function* $y(x)$ *satisfying the differential equation* (17) *and the boundary conditions* (18) *is a solution of the integral equation*

$$y(x) = \lambda \int_a^b G_*(x, t) p(t) y(t)\,dt + \int_a^b G_*(x, t) q(t)\,dt \tag{21}$$

and conversely. Thus the problem has been reduced to a Fredholm integral equation.

§ 3. Determination of periodic solutions

Consider the ordinary differential equation

$$\frac{d^2y}{dx^2} = \lambda p(x) y + q(x), \tag{22}$$

$p(x)$ and $q(x)$ being known continuous periodic functions with period ω. If these functions are defined and continuous in the interval $(0, \omega)$ only, but their right limits at the point $x = 0$ are equal to the corresponding left limits at the point $x = \omega$,

$$p(+0) = p(\omega - 0) \quad \text{and} \quad q(+0) = q(\omega - 0), \tag{23}$$

then we can define functions continued to the interval $(-\infty, +\infty)$, which are continuous and periodic with period ω, and are equal to the considered functions in interval $(0, \omega)$.

We now seek a periodic solution of equation (22) with period ω, which has continuous derivatives of second order. A necessary and sufficient condition for the existence of this solution $y(x)$ is that the following relations be satisfied:

$$y(+0) = y(\omega - 0) \quad \text{and} \quad y'(+0) = y'(\omega - 0) \tag{24}$$

for the boundary values of the function $y(x)$ and its derivative $y'(x)$, since the periodicity of the second derivative follows from relation (22).

As before, we first take the differential equation

$$\frac{d^2y}{dx^2} = f(x), \tag{25}$$

where $f(x)$ is a known continuous function in the interval $(0, \omega)$, satisfying the condition $f(+0) = f(\omega - 0)$. Every solution of this equation can be represented in the form

$$y(x) = \int_0^x (x - t) f(t)\, dt + C_1 x + C_2, \tag{26}$$

where C_1 and C_2 are constants. Requiring that conditions (24) be satisfied, we are led to the following two equations:

$$\int_0^\omega (\omega - t) f(t)\, dt + C_1 \omega = 0 \quad \text{and} \quad \int_0^\omega f(t)\, dt = 0. \tag{27}$$

If the known function $f(x)$ satisfies the second equation (27) then every periodic solution of equation (25) with continuous second derivatives is given by the formula

$$y(x) = \int_0^x (x-t)f(t)\,dt - \frac{x}{\omega}\int_0^\omega (\omega-t)f(t)\,dt + C_2, \tag{28}$$

where C_2 is an arbitrary constant. Solution (28) can also be written in the form

$$y(x) = \int_0^\omega K(x,t)f(t)\,dt + C_2, \tag{28'}$$

where $K(x, t)$ denotes the function

$$K(x,t) = \begin{cases} \dfrac{t}{\omega}(x-\omega), & \text{when} \quad t \leqq x; \\ \dfrac{x}{\omega}(t-\omega), & \text{when} \quad t \geqq x. \end{cases} \tag{29}$$

Relation (28) implies that *if there exists a periodic solution* $y(x)$ *of equation* (22) *with continuous second derivatives, then this solution satisfies the integral equation*

$$y(x) = \int_0^\omega K(x,t)[\lambda p(t)y(t)+q(t)]\,dt + C_2 \tag{30}$$

and an equation obtained by substituting the right-hand side of equation (22) *into the second equation* (27)

$$\int_0^\omega [\lambda p(t)y(t)+q(t)]\,dt = 0. \tag{31}$$

Conversely, the function $y(x)$ which satisfies the system of equations (30) and (31) is the required periodic solution of the differential equation (22). The value of the constant C_2 in equation (30) is not arbitrary any more; we determine it in such a way that the second equation (31) is satisfied. This we do by substituting expression (30) for $y(x)$ into equation (31), and we arrive at the equation

$$\lambda^2 \int_0^\omega \Big[\int_0^\omega p(t) K(t,\tau)\, dt\Big] p(\tau) y(\tau)\, d\tau +$$

$$+\lambda \int_0^\omega \int_0^\omega p(t) q(\tau) K(t,\tau)\, dt\, d\tau + \int_0^\omega q(t)\, dt + \lambda C_2 \int_0^\omega p(t)\, dt = 0. \quad (32)$$

Eliminating the unknown constant C_2 from equations (30) and (32), assuming that

$$\lambda \int_0^\omega p(t)\, dt \neq 0, \quad (33)$$

we obtain for the unknown function $y(t)$ the Fredholm equation

$$y(x) = \lambda \int_0^\omega \left[K(x,t) - \frac{\int_0^\omega K(\tau,t) p(\tau)\, d\tau}{\int_0^\omega p(\tau)\, d\tau} \right] p(t) y(t)\, dt +$$

$$+ \int_0^\omega K(x,t) q(t)\, dt - \frac{\int_0^\omega \int_0^\omega p(t) q(\tau) K(t,\tau)\, dt\, d\tau}{\int_0^\omega p(t)\, dt} - \frac{\int_0^\omega q(t)\, dt}{\int_0^\omega p(t)\, dt}. \quad (34)$$

If λ is not an eigenvalue of the kernel of this equation, then equation (34) has a unique solution $y(x)$ given by the familiar Fredholm formula. *This solution continued into the interval* $(-\infty, +\infty)$ *is the required unique periodic solution of the differential equation* (22), *provided* (33) *is satisfied.* In fact, the solution $y(x)$ of equation (34), assuming the validity of (33), satisfies the system of equations (30) and (31), provided that the constant C_2 is given by equation (32). Consequently, the obtained function $y(x)$ satisfies conditions (24) and the differential equation (22).

CHAPTER XII

APPLICATIONS OF INTEGRAL EQUATIONS TO POTENTIAL THEORY AND DIFFERENTIAL EQUATIONS OF ELLIPTIC TYPE

§ 1. Dirichlet and von Neumann problems

The most important achievement of the theory of integral equations consists in the solution of numerous boundary value problems in the theory of partial differential equations of the second order. The boundary value problems for equations of elliptic type lead to Fredholm equations, while the boundary value problems for parabolic and hyperbolic equations yield Volterra integral equations.

We first examine the application of the theory of Fredholm equation to the solution of the Dirichlet and von Neumann problems. This application constitutes a particularly important and interesting illustration of the Fredholm theorems.

It is known ([24], vol. I, and [42], vol. IV) that the *Dirichlet problem* consists in the determination of a function harmonic in a region and continuous in the closure of this region, which takes *a priori* prescribed boundary values while the *von Neumann problem* consists in the determination of a function harmonic in a region and continuous in its closure, the normal derivative of which takes *a priori* prescribed boundary values.

These problems solved by means of the theory of Fredholm equation are closely connected and we shall treat them jointly. The two problems considered will at once be solved for the case of a three-dimensional region.

An investigation of these problems for the case of a plane region is based on the properties of the logarithmic potential;

we shall later return to the plane problems and carry out more detailed investigations, in connection with singular integral equations.

Consider therefore a three-dimensional bounded region Ω the boundary of which is a closed surface S, and two arbitrary continuous functions $f(P)$ and $g(P)$ defined on S (Fig. 1). We

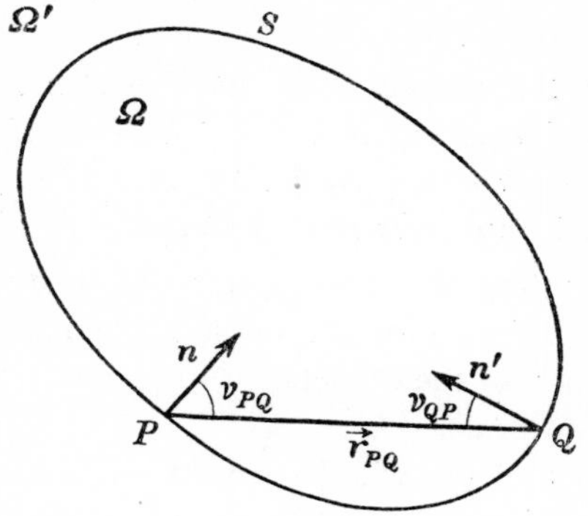

Fig. 1

seek two functions $u(A)$ and $v(A)$ which are harmonic in the region Ω, i.e. which satisfy the Laplace equation

$$\Delta u = 0 \quad \text{and} \quad \Delta v = 0$$

at all interior points $A(x, y, z)$ of Ω and are continuous in the closure $\Omega + S$; they have to satisfy the boundary conditions

$$u(A) \underset{A \to P}{\to} f(P) \quad \text{(Dirichlet problem)}, \tag{1}$$

$$\frac{du(A)}{dn_P} \underset{A \to P}{\to} g(P) \quad \text{(von Neumann problem)}. \tag{2}$$

The Dirichlet and von Neumann problems for a bounded region Ω are called *interior*. Similarly, for an unbounded region Ω located outside the surface S, they are said to be *exterior*.

We assume that the closed surface S satisfies the following conditions called the *Liapunov conditions*:

1. *The surface S has a tangent plane at every point P and the angle ν_{PQ} between the normals to the surface at two arbitrary points P and Q, satisfies the inequality*

$$|\nu_{PQ}| \leqq C r_{PQ}^{\kappa} \quad (0 < \kappa \leqq 1), \tag{3}$$

where r_{PQ} denotes the distance between the points P and Q, the exponent κ is a positive number not exceeding unity, and C is a known positive coefficient.

2. *There exists a number δ so small that a sphere of radius δ and centre $P \in S$ cuts out in the neighbourhood of every point $P \in S$, a part of the surface, such that an arbitrary line parallel to the normal at P intersects this part at at most one point.*

It is worth noting that assumption (3) is stronger than the assumption of continuity of the tangent plane, but it is weaker that the assumption of the existence of principal radii of curvature of surface S.

Problems (1) and (2) will be solved using the properties of Newtonian potential of a surface and double distributions. First, we seek the solution of the Dirichlet problem in the form of a potential u of double distribution of density $\varphi(P)$ over the surface S

$$u(A) = \iint_S \frac{\cos \nu_{QA}}{r_{AQ}^2} \varphi(Q)\, d\sigma_Q, \tag{4}$$

while the solution of the von Neumann problem is represented in the form of a potential of surface distribution of density $\psi(P)$ over the surface S

$$v(A) = \iint_S \frac{\psi(Q)}{r_{AQ}}\, d\sigma_Q, \tag{5}$$

where r_{AQ} denotes the distance of a point A of Ω from a point Q of S, and ν_{QA} is the angle between the vector $\overrightarrow{QA}$ and normal Qn at the point Q of S, directed towards the interior of Ω.

If the functions $\varphi(P)$ and $\psi(P)$ are continuous then functions (4) and (5) are harmonic in the regions Ω and Ω', and the interior boundary values of functions u and dv/dn (i.e. with respect to the region Ω) are the following:

$$\lim_{A\to P} u(A) = 2\pi\varphi(P) + \iint_S \frac{\cos\nu_{QP}}{r_{PQ}^2}\varphi(Q)\,d\sigma_Q,$$
$$\lim_{A\to P}\frac{dv(A)}{dn_P} = -2\pi\psi(P) + \iint_S \frac{\cos\nu_{PQ}}{r_{PQ}^2}\psi(Q)\,d\sigma_Q \tag{6}$$

(see Theorem 9 on p. 322). On the other hand, the exterior boundary values (i.e. with respect to the exterior region Ω') are the following:

$$\lim_{A\to P} u(A) = -2\pi\varphi(P) + \iint_S \frac{\cos\nu_{QP}}{r_{PQ}^2}\varphi(Q)\,d\sigma_Q,$$
$$\lim_{A\to P}\frac{dv(A)}{dn_P} = 2\pi\psi(P) + \iint_S \frac{\cos\nu_{PQ}}{r_{PQ}^2}\psi(Q)\,d\sigma_Q, \tag{6'}$$

where ν_{PQ} denotes the angle between vector $\vec{r}_{PQ}$ and the inward drawn normal to the surface S at the point P, and ν_{QP} is the angle between the vector $\vec{r}_{QP}$ and the interior normal at Q (Fig. 1).

In accordance with the formulation of the Dirichlet and von Neumann problems, we require that the boundary values (6) or (6′) be equal to the *a priori* known values of functions $f(P)$ and $g(P)$; hence we obtain two Fredholm integral equations for the determination of the unknown densities $\varphi(P)$ and $\psi(P)$:

$$\varphi(P) = \frac{\lambda}{2\pi}\iint_S \frac{\cos\nu_{QP}}{r_{PQ}^2}\varphi(Q)\,d\sigma_Q - \frac{\lambda}{2\pi}f(P),$$
$$\psi(P) = \frac{\lambda}{2\pi}\iint_S \frac{\cos\nu_{PQ}}{r_{PQ}^2}\psi(Q)\,d\sigma_Q - \frac{\lambda}{2\pi}g(P). \tag{7}$$

For $\lambda = -1$ the first equation corresponds to the interior Dirichlet problem, and the second to the exterior von Neumann problem, while for $\lambda = +1$ the converse is true, i.e. the first equation corresponds to the exterior Dirichlet problem and the second to the interior uon Neumann problem.

It is readily seen that equations (7) are adjoint and it is for this reason that we treat the two problems together.

We now prove that the kernels of equations (7) possess weak singularities if the Liapunov conditions are satisfied. To this end, we first prove that $\cos \nu_{PQ}$ and $\cos \nu_{QP}$ tend to zero as $r^{\varkappa}_{PQ}$, when the distance between P and Q tends to zero. Consider, therefore, a rectangular system of axes $P\xi\eta\zeta$ the origin being an arbitrary point P of S; the axis $P\zeta$ is directed towards the interior of Ω. Thus the axes $P\xi$ and $P\eta$ are located in the tangent plane to the surface S at P. According to our assumption, there exists a small part S_P of the surface S at the point P, such that every point $Q'(\xi, \eta, 0)$ of the projection S'_P of this part onto the tangent plane $P\xi\eta$ is the projection of only one point $Q(\xi, \eta, \zeta)$ of S_P. Our assumption of the existence of the tangent plane implies that the coordinate ζ is a function $\zeta = f(\xi, \eta)$ of the coordinates ξ and η, defined in S'_P and possessing continuous derivatives ζ'_ξ and ζ'_η; moreover, the choice of the axis $P\zeta$ implies that these derivatives vanish at P

$$f'_\xi(0, 0) = 0 \quad \text{and} \quad f'_\eta(0, 0) = 0. \tag{8}$$

Let α, β and γ denote the angles between the normal to S_P at the point $Q(\xi, \eta, \zeta)$ and the coordinate axes $P\xi\eta\zeta$. Then we have

$$\begin{aligned} |\cos\alpha| &= \frac{|\zeta'_\xi|}{\sqrt{1+\zeta'^2_\xi+\zeta'^2_\eta}}, \\ |\cos\beta| &= \frac{|\zeta'_\eta|}{\sqrt{1+\zeta'^2_\xi+\zeta'^2_\eta}}, \\ |\cos\gamma| &= \frac{1}{\sqrt{1+\zeta'^2_\xi+\zeta'^2_\eta}}. \end{aligned} \tag{9}$$

We may always assume that S_P is so small that at all points Q belonging to it

$$\frac{1}{2} \leqq \cos\gamma \leqq 1. \tag{10}$$

Observe now that

$$\cos\alpha = \sin\gamma\cos\alpha' \quad \text{and} \quad \cos\beta = \sin\gamma\cos\beta', \tag{11}$$

where α' and β' are the angles between the projection of the normal Qn onto the tangent plane $P\xi\eta$ and the axes $P\xi$ and $P\eta$. Hence, in view of the Liapunov condition (3) and the result $0 < \sin\gamma < \gamma$ when $0 < \gamma < \pi/2$, we have

$$|\cos\alpha| \leqq \gamma \leqq Cr_{PQ}^{\kappa} \quad \text{and} \quad |\cos\beta| \leqq \gamma \leqq Cr_{PQ}^{\kappa}, \tag{12}$$

which implies the inequalities

$$|\zeta'_{\xi}| = \frac{|\cos\alpha|}{|\cos\gamma|} \leqq 2Cr_{PQ}^{\kappa} \quad \text{and} \quad |\zeta'_{\eta}| = \frac{|\cos\beta|}{|\cos\gamma|} \leqq 2Cr_{PQ}^{\kappa} \tag{13}$$

satisfied at all points $Q \in S_P$.

In accordance with the theorem on increments, we have

$$\zeta(\xi,\eta) = \zeta'_{\xi}(\theta\xi,\theta\eta)\,\xi + \zeta'_{\eta}(\theta\xi,\theta\eta)\,\eta \quad (0 < \theta < 1), \tag{14}$$

and, moreover, there exists a positive constant k such that

$$1 \leqq \frac{r_{PQ}}{\sqrt{\xi^2+\eta^2}} \leqq k. \tag{15}$$

Consequently, in view of inequality (13) we find that the function ζ satisfies the inequality

$$|\zeta(\xi,\eta)| \leqq 4Ck^{\kappa}\, r_{PQ}^{\kappa+1}, \tag{16}$$

and therefore

$$|\cos\nu_{PQ}| = \left|\frac{\zeta}{r_{PQ}}\right| \leqq 4Ck^{\kappa}\, r_{PQ}^{\kappa} \tag{17}$$

according to the former statement.

To derive a similar inequality for $\cos\nu_{QP}$, observe that

$$|\cos\nu_{QP}| = \left|\frac{\xi}{r_{PQ}}\cos\alpha + \frac{\eta}{r_{PQ}}\cos\beta + \frac{\zeta}{r_{PQ}}\cos\gamma\right|$$

$$\leqq |\cos\alpha| + |\cos\beta| + \left|\frac{\zeta}{r_{PQ}}\right|,$$

and taking into account inequalities (12) and (17),

$$|\cos \nu_{QP}| \leqq 2C(2k^{\kappa}+1)\, r_{PQ}^{\kappa}\,. \tag{18}$$

This implies that the kernels of the integral equations (7) satisfy the inequalities

$$\left|\frac{\cos \nu_{QP}}{r_{PQ}^2}\right| \leqq \frac{k_1}{r_{PQ}^{2-\kappa}} \quad \text{and} \quad \left|\frac{\cos \nu_{PQ}}{r_{PQ}^2}\right| \leqq \frac{k_1}{r_{PQ}^{2-\kappa}} \quad (0<\kappa\leqq 1), \tag{19}$$

where k_1 is a positive constant which can always be selected so that inequalities (19) are satisfied, not only for the points of S'_P, but also for an arbitrary pair of points P and Q of S. Thus, the integral equations (7) possess weak singularities.

In the particular case, when in the Liapunov inequality $\kappa = 1$, the kernels of the integral equations satisfy the inequality

$$\left|\frac{\cos \nu_{QP}}{r_{PQ}^2}\right| \leqq \frac{k_1}{r_{PQ}} \quad \text{and} \quad \left|\frac{\cos \nu_{PQ}}{r_{PQ}^2}\right| \leqq \frac{k_1}{r_{PQ}}, \tag{19'}$$

and therefore the singularity is the weakest. This case occurs for instance when S has principal radii of curvature, i.e. for surface most frequently encountered in applications.

According to the theory of iteration of the integral equation (Part 1, pp. 80–96) we infer, in view of inequality (19), that the integral equations (7), by means of a finite number of iterations, can be reduced to equivalent equations, the kernels of which are bounded and to which the Fredholm Theorems may be applied.

To deduce conclusions concerning the existence of solutions of the Dirichlet and von Neumann problems, we derive a few properties of equations (7).

THEOREM 1. *The value* $\lambda = -1$ *is not an eigenvalue of the adjoint equations* (7).

In proving this theorem the convenience of the joint treatment of equations (7) becomes clear, since the proof of this property for one equation implies the same for the other.

The validity of the theorem is evident from the second equation (7). In fact, the density of the surface distribution, the potential of which

$$V(A) = \iint_S \frac{\psi(Q)\, d\sigma_Q}{r_{AQ}} \tag{20}$$

satisfies, on S, the exterior boundary condition

$$\lim_{A \to P} \frac{dV(A)}{dn_P} = 0, \tag{21}$$

satisfies the homogeneous equation

$$\psi(P) = -\frac{1}{2\pi} \iint_S \frac{\cos \nu_{PQ}}{r_{PQ}^2} \psi(Q)\, d\sigma_Q. \tag{22}$$

We now prove that this potential (20) must be constant, and equal to zero in the whole space. To this end, consider, in the exterior region Ω', a spherical surface Γ, with centre in Ω, and radius R sufficiently large for the sphere to surround S. Let us now apply to region Ω'_1, located between the surfaces S and Γ, the known relation

$$\iint_S V \frac{dV}{dn}\, d\sigma + \iint_\Gamma V \frac{dV}{dn}\, d\sigma = \iiint_{\Omega'_1} \left[\left(\frac{\partial V}{\partial x}\right)^2 + \left(\frac{\partial V}{\partial y}\right)^2 + \left(\frac{\partial V}{\partial z}\right)^2\right] d\tau \tag{23}$$

which is a corollary of Green's Theorem.* In view of the uniform convergence to zero (21) of the derivative of the potential V along the normal, the first integral in relation (23) vanishes. Moreover, the second integral tends to zero when the radius

---

* The spatial integral in relation (23) is meaningful, since the first derivatives of potential (20) of surface distribution with continuous density behave (tend to infinity) as the logarithm of the distance from A to the surface S.

R of Γ tends to infinity, for V and dV/dn tend to zero as R^{-1} and R^{-2}; thus we have

$$\left| \iint_{\Gamma} V \frac{dV}{dn} d\sigma \right| < \frac{k}{R^3} 4\pi R^2 ,$$

where k is a constant. Since the integrand in the right-hand side of relation (23) is non-negative, we obtain

$$\frac{\partial V}{\partial x} = 0, \quad \frac{\partial V}{\partial y} = 0, \quad \frac{\partial V}{\partial z} = 0,$$

i.e. $V = \text{const}$ in the exterior region Ω'. The continuity of potential (20) implies now that the interior boundary value of potential (20) is constant, i.e. the potential is constant in the interior of Ω. Therefore, for Ω we have

$$\lim_{A \to P} \frac{dV(A)}{dn_P} = 0 .$$

It is known from potential theory that the difference between the boundary values of the normal derivative of the potential of the surface distribution (20) is equal to $4\pi \psi(P)$; therefore, we finally conclude that the homogeneous integral equation (22) has only the zero solution, $\psi = 0$. Consequently, the adjoint equation

$$\varphi(P) = -\frac{\lambda}{2\pi} \iint_{S} \frac{\cos \nu_{QP}}{r_{PQ}^2} \varphi(Q) \, d\sigma_Q$$

also has the zero solution only, and the value $\lambda = -1$ is not an eigenvalue of the kernels of equations (7).

These results imply that for the value $\lambda = -1$ the adjoint integral equations (7) have unique solutions which can be derived by applying the first Fredholm Theorem to the equations, iterated with respect to (7) a sufficient number of times, ensuring that the iterated equations have bounded kernels and are equivalent to equations (7).

Thus the interior Dirichlet problem and the exterior Neumann problem with respect to the given surface S have a solution for arbitrary boundary functions $f(P)$ and $g(P)$, expressed by the potentials (4) and (5).

It is known that the solution of the interior Dirichlet problem and the exterior von Neumann problem (the latter vanishing at infinity) are unique.

THEOREM 2. *The value* $\lambda = +1$ *is the eigenvalue of the kernels of the adjoint equations* (7), *of order unity.*

This property follows at once from the first equation (7), since the homogeneous equation

$$\varphi(P) = \frac{1}{2\pi} \iint_S \frac{\cos \nu_{QP}}{r_{PQ}^2} \varphi(Q)\, d\sigma_Q \tag{24}$$

has the obvious solution, equal to an arbitrary constant, $\varphi(P) = \text{const}$, which does not necessarily vanish.

It follows that the adjoint homogeneous equation

$$\psi(P) = \frac{1}{2\pi} \iint_S \frac{\cos \nu_{PQ}}{r_{PQ}^2} \psi(Q)\, d\sigma_Q \tag{24'}$$

has also a non-zero solution ψ. This solution is the density of the surface distribution of potential (20) which satisfies the boundary condition

$$\left(\frac{dV}{dn}\right)_P = 0. \tag{25}$$

The non-zero solution of equation (24′) is therefore a density of electricity in the state of equilibrium, which is distributed over the conducting surface S; in other words, the potential of surface distribution ψ^* yields a constant value of V^*:

$$V^* = \iint_S \frac{\psi^*(Q)\, d\sigma_Q}{r_{PQ}} \tag{26}$$

on S and in the interior of Ω.

According to a familiar theorem of potential theory, on the difference of the boundary values of derivatives of a potential of surface distribution, we find, taking into account (25), that the value of $\psi^*(Q)$ is proportional to the exterior boundary value of the derivative of the potential based on this function,

$$\psi^*(Q) = -\frac{1}{4\pi}\left(\frac{dV}{dn}\right)_{Q(\text{ext})}. \tag{27}$$

Thus the boundary value V^* of the potential cannot vanish. In fact, if $V^* = 0$, $V(x, y, z)$ being a harmonic function equal to zero on S and at infinity, vanishes in the whole region Ω' and consequently $dV/dn = 0$ at all points of S, and hence also $\psi^* = 0$, contrary to the assumption that ψ^* is an eigensolution.

We now proceed to prove that if $V^* > 0$, then $\psi^*(Q) \geqq 0$; if $V^* < 0$, $\psi^* \leqq 0$, and of course the converse, too.

In fact, if $V^* > 0$ the value V^* is the upper bound in Ω' of the potential constructed on the basis of $\psi^*(P)$, since this potential vanishes at infinity and cannot attain its upper bound in the interior of Ω' (as a harmonic function). Thus

$$\psi^*(Q) = -\frac{1}{4\pi}\left(\frac{dV}{dn}\right)_{Q(\text{ext})} \geqq 0.$$

A similar result occurs for $V^* < 0$.

We now prove that the non-zero solution of equation (24′) is unique, to within an arbitrary factor, i.e. that every such solution of equation (24′) is proportional to one of them.

Consider, therefore, two non-zero solutions $\psi_1(P)$ and $\psi_2(P)$ of equation (24′), and the corresponding constant potentials on the surface S

$$V_1 = \iint\limits_S \frac{\psi_1(Q)\, d\sigma_Q}{r_{PQ}} \quad \text{and} \quad V_2 = \iint\limits_S \frac{\psi_2(Q)\, d\sigma_Q}{r_{PQ}}.$$

We know that they do not vanish, and consequently the function

$$\psi_3(Q) = \psi_1(Q) + C\psi_2(Q)$$

which is a linear combination of ψ_1 and ψ_2, induces on S a constant potential

$$V_3 = V_1 + CV_2.$$

Thus if we select $C = -V_1/V_2$, then $V_3 = 0$ and therefore, as we have already proved, the corresponding density vanishes everywhere

$$\psi_3(Q) = \psi_1(Q) + C\psi_2(Q) = 0.$$

Thus two distinct densities are proportional, for their quotient is constant at all points and equal to the quotient of the corresponding potentials. Consequently, the quotient of the total quantity of electricity on S, $\iint\limits_S \psi^*(Q)\,dS$, to the corresponding potential has a constant value depending only on the shape of S; this quotient is called the electrostatic capacity of the conductor.

Thus the order of the eigenvalue $\lambda = +1$ is equal to unity.

It follows from Theorem 2 that the non-homogeneous integral equations (7), for $\lambda = +1$, do not always have solutions, for, in accordance with the Third Fredholm Theorem, a necessary and sufficient condition of the existence of a solution of the first equation (7) is the orthogonality of the function $f(P)$ to the eigensolution ψ^* of the adjoint equation

$$\iint\limits_S f(P)\,\psi^*(P)\,d\sigma_P = 0, \tag{28}$$

and a necessary and sufficient condition for the existence of a solution of the second equation (7) is the orthogonality of the function $g(P)$ to the eigensolution $\varphi(P) = \text{const} \neq 0$ of the first equation

$$\iint\limits_S g(P)\,d\sigma_P = 0. \tag{29}$$

If either of conditions (28) or (29) is satisfied, there exists a solution of the exterior Dirichlet problem expressed by the potential of double surface distribution (4) and a solution of the interior Neumann problem expressed by the potential of the surface distribution (5).

If the prescribed function $f(P)$ does not satisfy condition (28), then the first integral equation (7) has no solution for $\lambda = 1$. However, the conclusion then that the exterior Dirichlet problem has no solution would not be true. In fact, applying the Kelvin transformation we reduce the exterior Dirichlet problem to an interior one, and then we infer that for any boundary function $f(P)$ there exists a harmonic function in the exterior region Ω' which is regular and vanishes at infinity. Thus if $f(P)$ does not satisfy condition (28) the solution of the exterior Dirichlet problem exists, but cannot be represented by means of the potential of double distribution. When condition (28) is not satisfied the solution of the exterior Dirichlet problem can also be obtained without employing the Kelvin transformation. For, we seek the solution in region Ω' in form of the sum

$$V(M) = \iint_S \frac{\cos \nu_{QM}}{r_{MQ}^2} \varphi(Q)\, d\sigma_Q + \frac{\alpha}{r_{OM}} \tag{30}$$

of a potential of double distribution of density φ and a potential of a constant point 0 inside Ω, the charge α of which is for the time being arbitrary. The requirement that the function (30) takes the prescribed boundary value $f(P)$ leads to the integral equation

$$2\pi \varphi(P) + \iint_S \frac{\cos \nu_{QP}}{r_{PQ}^2} \varphi(Q)\, d\sigma_Q = f(P) - \frac{\alpha}{r_{OP}},$$

which, in accordance with the Third Fredholm Theorem, has the solution $\varphi(P)$ if, and only if, the condition of orthogonality

$$\iint_S \left[f(P) - \frac{\alpha}{r_{OP}} \psi^*(P) \right] d\sigma_P = 0$$

is satisfied. This determines the constant α, since we evidently have

$$\iint_S \frac{\psi^*(P)}{r_{OP}}\, d\sigma_P \neq 0$$

in view of the constant sign of $\psi^*(P)$ on S.

If the known function $g(P)$ in the interior von Neumann problem ($\lambda = 1$) does not satisfy condition (29) then not only does the second integral equation (7) have no solution, but also the von Neumann problem itself cannot be solved. In fact, the Green–Ostrogradski Theorem

$$\iint\limits_{S} \left(\frac{dV}{dn}\right)_{\text{int.}} d\sigma = \iiint\limits_{\Omega} \Delta V \, d\tau = 0$$

implies that inequality (29) is a necessary condition for the existence of a solution of the interior von Neumann problem.

§ 2. Mixed boundary problems

A mixed boundary problem consists in the determination of a harmonic function $u(x, y, z)$ in the interior of a region Ω, continuous in the closure of Ω, and possessing a derivative in the direction of the interior normal du/dn at all points P of S. This derivative has, at all points of S, to satisfy a prescribed linear relation between the boundary value of the normal derivative $(du/dn)_P$ and the boundary value of the function itself, $u(P)$:

$$\left(\frac{du}{dn}\right)_P + a(P)\, u(P) = f(P). \tag{31}$$

We assume that the known functions $a(P)$ and $f(P)$ are defined and continuous on S. Our considerations will concern the interior region Ω; a similar argument may be carried out for the exterior region Ω'.

We seek the solution of the problem in the form of a potential of surface distribution

$$u(A) = \iint\limits_{S} \frac{\psi(Q)}{r_{AQ}} \, d\sigma_Q \tag{32}$$

with density $\psi(Q)$. Using formula (6) for the interior boundary value of the derivative of the potential of surface distribution, we can state that the function (32) satisfies the boundary condition

(31) if, and only if, the unknown density $\psi(P)$ is a solution of the Fredholm integral equation

$$-2\pi\psi(P)+\iint_S\left[\frac{\cos\nu_{PQ}}{r_{PQ}^2}+a(P)\frac{1}{r_{PQ}}\right]\psi(Q)\,d\sigma_Q=f(P). \tag{33}$$

If we assume, as before, that surface S satisfies the Liapunov conditions, then in accordance with inequality (19) the kernel of equation (33) has a weak singularity, and the equation is equivalent to the equation iterated a sufficient number of times with a bounded kernel, to which the Fredholm theorems may be applied.

We now prove that *when the known function $a(P)$ takes negative values only, $a(P)\leqq 0$ (but does not identically vanish), the homogeneous equation corresponding to (33) has only the zero solution $\psi = 0$.*

In fact, if ψ is a solution of the homogeneous equation ($f=0$), then the potential (32) satisfies the boundary condition

$$\left(\frac{du}{dn}\right)_P+a(P)\,u(P)=0. \tag{34}$$

Applying now a known corollary of the Green–Ostrogradski Theorem (see footnote on p. 237), we have

$$\iiint_\Omega\left[\left(\frac{\partial u}{\partial x}\right)^2+\left(\frac{\partial u}{\partial y}\right)^2+\left(\frac{\partial u}{\partial z}\right)^2\right]dA$$

$$=-\iint_S u\,\frac{du}{dn}\,d\sigma_P=+\iint_S a(P)\,u^2\,d\sigma_P.$$

Thus, if $a(P)\leqq 0$ we have $u=0$ on the boundary and in the interior of Ω. Consequently, as before, we infer that $\psi(P)=0$ at all points of surface S.

The homogeneous integral equation has therefore, in the case $a\leqq 0$, only the zero solution. Thus, according to the first Fredholm theorem, equation (33) has the unique solution $\psi(P)$ for an arbitrary continuous function $f(P)$. Potential (32), constructed on the basis of the function ψ, is a solution of the mixed boundary problem. In the considered case, $a(P) \leqq 0$, the solution u of the mixed boundary problem is unique; in fact, if there exist two solutions u_1 and u_2, then their difference, $w = u_1 - u_2$, is a harmonic function in Ω, which satisfies on its boundary the homogeneous relation

$$\left(\frac{dw}{dn}\right)_P + a(P)\,w(P) = 0$$

identical with relation (34); therefore, repeating the argument, we obtain $w = u_1 - u_2 = 0$ in Ω.

If the given function $a(P)$ does not satisfy the inequality $a \leqq 0$, then, for the integral equation (33), the conditions of the First or Third Fredholm equation could be satisfied, and for any continuous function $f(P)$, either a unique solution ψ exists, or the solution exists only when function $f(P)$ satisfies the familiar conditions of orthogonality.

§ 3. Green's Function and its properties

Green's Function is an auxiliary function which plays a principal rôle in the reduction to an integral equation of boundary value problems for differential equations, more general than the Laplace equation.

The term *Green's Function* is commonly used not only for the Laplace equation; it depends on the form of the differential equation, the boundary conditions and on the region.

Let us recall the original definition of Green's Function for the Dirichlet problem applied to the Laplace equation. By *Green's Function of first kind* we mean a function $G(A, B)$ of a pair of distinct points A and B, defined in the interior of the region Ω bounded by a surface S, which satisfies the following conditions.

1. *$G(A, B)$ is the difference of two functions,*

$$G(A, B) = \frac{1}{r_{AB}} - g(A, B), \tag{35}$$

the first of which has a singularity when A tends to B, while the second satisfies the Laplace equation

$$\Delta_A g(A, B) = 0 \tag{36}$$

with respect to an arbitrary interior point A, even when A coincides with B.

2. *G(A, B) tends to zero when A tends to an arbitrary point P, located on the bounded surface S*

$$G(A, B) \to 0, \quad \text{when} \quad A \to P \in S, \tag{37}$$

B being fixed.

Formula (35) and equation (36) imply that function $G(A, B)$ also satisfies Laplace's equation

$$\Delta_A G(A, B) = 0$$

at all interior points $A \neq B$. B is called a *pole of the Green's Function.* It follows from assumptions (35), (36) and (37) that function $g(A, B)$ is a harmonic function with respect to the coordinates of A in the whole region Ω, which has the following boundary values at points of the surface S:

$$\lim_{A \to P} g(A, B) = \frac{1}{r_{PB}}. \tag{38}$$

Consequently, the determination of $g(A, B)$, and therefore also of $G(A, B)$, consists in solving the Dirichlet problem with the boundary condition (38). Thus, in accordance with the previous results, $g(A, B)$ exists and can be expressed in the form of a potential of double surface distribution

$$g(A, B) = \iint_S \frac{\cos \nu_{QP}}{r_{PQ}^2} \varphi(Q, B)\, d\sigma_Q, \tag{39}$$

where $\varphi(Q, B)$ is the unique solution of the Fredholm equation

$$2\pi \varphi(P, B) + \iint_S \frac{\cos \nu_{QP}}{r_{PQ}^2} \varphi(Q, B)\, d\sigma_Q = \frac{1}{r_{PB}}, \tag{40}$$

B being an interior point, which plays the rôle of a parameter. We assume of course that S satisfies the Liapunov conditions (p. 231).

We now prove that the regular component of the Green's Function can also be determined by expressing it simply in the form of a potential of surface distribution

$$g(A, B) = \iint_S \frac{\psi(Q, B)}{r_{AQ}} d\sigma_Q. \tag{41}$$

The physical interpretation is the following: it is the potential of electric charge with density $\psi(Q, B)$ induced on the surface S by a unit point charge at an interior point B.

In fact, if B is an interior point of Ω, then the function

$$g_{\text{ext}}(A, B) = \frac{1}{r_{AB}} \tag{42}$$

is harmonic in the unbounded region Ω' located outside the surface S, it takes the boundary values

$$\lim_{A \to P} g_{\text{ext}}(A, B) = \frac{1}{r_{PB}} \tag{43}$$

at points of S and vanishes at infinity. Consequently, this function is also the solution of the exterior von Neumann problem, for it satisfies the boundary condition

$$\lim_{A \to P} \frac{d}{dn_P} [g_{\text{ext}}(A, B)] = \frac{d}{dn_P} \left(\frac{1}{r_{PB}} \right), \tag{44}$$

Thus, seeking an expression for function (42) in the form of a potential of surface distribution (41), we obtain, as we already know (see p. 233), for the determination of the density ψ, the Fredholm integral equation

$$2\pi \psi(P, B) + \iint_S \frac{\cos \nu_{PQ}}{r_{PQ}^2} \psi(Q, B) d\sigma_Q = \frac{d}{dn_P} \left(\frac{1}{r_{PB}} \right). \tag{45}$$

We know that this equation has the unique solution ψ and that there exists one solution of the exterior Neumann problem which uniformly tends to zero at infinity. Consequently, at points A located outside S the potential of surface distribution (41) with density ψ satisfying equation (45) is identical with the function (42). Since the potential of surface distribution is continuous in passing through S, the function (41) is harmonic in the interior of Ω, and on S it takes the same boundary values (43) as the exterior function (41). The function defined by formula (41), in which ψ has been replaced by a solution of equation (45), is therefore the regular component $g(A, B)$ of the Green's Function.

It can easily be proved, using the properties of harmonic functions, that the density $\psi(P, B)$ is positive at all points of S and that the total charge is equal to unity

$$\iint_S \psi(P, B)\, d\sigma_P = 1$$

independent of the position of B in Ω. This property of Green's Function simplifies the investigation of the properties of its derivatives, since the investigation of a potential of surface distribution is easier than that of a potential of double layer.

It can be proved that $G(A, B)$ and consequently, also $g(A, B)$, are symmetric, i.e. $G(A, B) = G(B, A)$. This property is of primary importance in the boundary problems treated from the point of view of integral equations.

It follows directly from the elementary properties of harmonic functions that G and g satisfy the following important inequalities:

$$0 < G(A, B) < \frac{1}{r_{AB}} \quad \text{and} \quad 0 < g(A, B) < \frac{1}{r_{AB}} \tag{46}$$

for every pair of distinct points A and B in the interior of Ω. The second inequality (46) seems to contradict the assumption that $g(A, B)$ is harmonic even when A coincides with B. However, there is in fact no contradiction since, although $g(A, B)$ remains bounded and regular when A tends to an interior point B it is unbounded when points A and B tend to the same point P on the boundary S of Ω.

It is important for applications to boundary-value problems, to estimate the unboundedness of the derivatives of the functions $G(A, B)$ and $g(A, B)$. These investigations for the case of two variables, were carried out by E. PICARD by means of a conformal mapping onto a circle. The derivatives of the Green's Function in space were investigated by the Polish mathematician ZAREMBA [92] using properties of the Newtonian potential; he proved that the first and second derivatives of $g(A, B)$ with respect to the coordinates of the point A satisfy the inequalities

$$|D_1 g(A, B)| < \frac{c}{r_{AB}^2} \quad \text{and} \quad |D_2 g(A, B)| < \frac{c'}{r_{AB}^3}, \tag{47}$$

where c and c' are positive constants, independent of the position of A and B. The assumption under which properties (47) were deduced were, however, restrictive, for Zaremba assumed, for the surface S, that the coordinate $\zeta(\xi, \eta)$, mentioned already on p. 234, has continuous third derivatives.

We now define the Green's Function for the mixed boundary problem: by *Green's Function of the second kind* we mean a function $G(A, B)$ of the pair of points A and B in the interior of Ω, which satisfies the same condition as Green's Function of the first kind, and the following condition.

If the point A tends to an arbitrary point P of S, and the point B is located inside Ω, then the derivative at A, in the direction of the normal at P, tends to the boundary value satisfying the relation

$$\lim_{A \to P} \left[\frac{dG(A, B)}{dn_P} \right] + a(P) G(P, B) = 0. \tag{48}$$

This implies that $g(A, B)$, harmonic at all points A of Ω, satisfies the boundary condition of the mixed problem

$$\lim_{A \to P} \left[\frac{dg(A, B)}{dn_P} \right] + a(P) g(P, B) = \frac{d\left(\dfrac{1}{r_{PB}}\right)}{dn_P} + a(P) \frac{1}{r_{PB}}. \tag{49}$$

Thus the determination of $g(A, B)$ is a particular case of the mixed problem investigated before, and it reduces to the solution of the integral equation

$$-2\pi\psi(P, B)+\iint\limits_{S}\left[\frac{\cos\nu_{PQ}}{r_{PQ}^2}+a(P)\frac{1}{r_{PQ}}\right]\psi(Q, B)\,d\sigma_Q$$

$$=\frac{d\left(\dfrac{1}{r_{PB}}\right)}{dn_P}+a(P)\frac{1}{r_{PB}}, \qquad (50)$$

where B plays the rôle of a constant parameter.

Assume that the integral equation (59) has the unique solution $\psi(P, B)$; then the Green's Function exists, and its regular component $g(A, B)$ can be represented in the form of the potential of surface distribution

$$g(A, B)=\iint\limits_{S}\frac{\psi(P, B)}{r_{AB}}\,d\sigma_P. \qquad (51)$$

This case occurs, for instance, when $a(P) \leqq 0$. It can also be proved that the derived Green's Function is symmetric, i.e. $G(A, B) = G(B, A)$.

The author has estimated [46] the inifinities of this Green's Function and its derivative using the properties of the kernel of the integral equation (50); the following inequalities were established,

$$|g(A, B)| < \frac{c_1}{r_{AB}} \quad \text{and} \quad |Dg(A, B)| < \frac{c_2}{r_{AB}^2} \qquad (52)$$

which are analogous to those for the first Green's Function. Assumptions necessary for the derivation of inequality (52) were also strong, for it was assumed for the surface S that the function $\zeta(\xi, \eta)$ (p. 235) has continuous third derivatives in the neighbourhood of every point P of S.

We now proceed to prove the inequality for $g(A, B)$, assuming Liapunov conditions for the surface S. These assumptions are considerably weaker than the previous ones, since the Liapunov conditions are equivalent to the assumption that the function $\zeta(\xi, \eta)$ has first derivatives which satisfy the Hölder condition.

We first prove the following lemma concerning integrals appearing in equation (50); it was first proved by Liapunov; our proof is different [30].

LEMMA 1. *If $\psi(P)$ is an arbitrary bounded integrable function, defined on the surface S, which satisfies the Liapunov conditions, then functions $J_1(P)$ and $J_2(P)$ defined on S by the integrals*

$$J_1(P) = \iint_S \frac{\cos \nu_{PQ}}{r_{PQ}^2} \psi(Q)\, d\sigma_Q \quad \text{and} \quad J_2(P) = \iint_S \frac{\psi(Q)}{r_{PQ}}\, d\sigma_Q \tag{53}$$

satisfy the following Hölder conditions:

$$|J_1(P) - J_1(P_1)| \leqq k_1 M_\psi r_{PP_1}^{\Theta\kappa}$$
$$\text{and} \quad |J_2(P) - J_2(P_1)| \leqq k_2 M_\psi r_{PP_1}^{\Theta}, \tag{54}$$

where Θ is an arbitrary positive constant, smaller than unity, M_ψ denotes the upper bound of function $|\psi(P)|$ and k_1, k_2 are positive constants, depending only on Θ and the surface S.

Let δ be a sufficiently small positive number such that the sphere K of radius δ and centre at an arbitrary point P of S cuts out of this surface a part Σ located inside K, to which the second Liapunov condition is applicable. It is sufficient to prove property (54), assuming that the point P_1 in Σ so close to P that the sphere K_1 of radius $2r_{PP_1}$ and centre P lies wholly within K. Now decompose the integrals $J_1(P)$ and $J_2(P)$ into three parts

$$\begin{aligned} J_1(P) &= J_1^{\Sigma_1}(P) + J_1^{\Sigma_2}(P) + J_1^{S-\Sigma}(P), \\ J_1(P_1) &= J_1^{\Sigma_1}(P_1) + J_1^{\Sigma_2}(P_1) + J_1^{S-\Sigma}(P_1), \end{aligned} \tag{55}$$

the integration being carried out over three surfaces Σ_1, Σ_2 and $S-\Sigma$, where Σ_1 is that part of Σ lying inside K_1, Σ_2 is that part of Σ lying outside K_1, and $S-\Sigma$ is that part of S lying outside K.

According to inequality (17), we obtain

$$|J_1^{\Sigma_1}(P)| = \left|\iint\limits_{\Sigma_1} \frac{\cos \nu_{PQ}}{r_{PQ}^2} \psi(Q)\, d\sigma_Q\right| \leq 4Ck^\kappa M_\psi \iint\limits_{\Sigma_1} \frac{d\sigma_Q}{r_{PQ}^{2-\kappa}}.$$

Applying now the homothetic transformation which reduces the sphere K_1 of radius $2r_{PP_1}$ to a sphere K_1' of unit radius, we have

$$\iint\limits_{\Sigma_1} \frac{d\sigma_Q}{r_{PQ}^{2-\kappa}} = 2^\kappa r_{PP_1}^\kappa \iint\limits_{\Sigma_1'} \frac{d\sigma_Q}{r_{PQ}^{2-\kappa}}.$$

Reducing the integral on the right-hand side to the projection onto the tangent plane at the point P, and bearing in mind that $\cos\alpha > 1/2$, we infer that this integral is bounded for every point P, and hence integral $J_1^{\Sigma_1}(P)$ satisfies the inequality

$$|J_1^{\Sigma_1}(P)| \leq c_1 M_\psi r_{PP_1}^\kappa \quad (\kappa \leq 1) \tag{56}$$

c_1 being a positive constant.

Evidently an analogous inequality also holds for the integral $J_1^{\Sigma_1}(P_1)$.

We now investigate the difference between the second parts

$$J_1^{\Sigma_2}(P) - J_1^{\Sigma_2}(P_1) = \iint\limits_{\Sigma_2} \left(\frac{\cos \nu_{PQ}}{r_{PQ}^2} - \frac{\cos \nu_{P_1Q}}{r_{P_1Q}^2}\right) \psi(Q)\, d\sigma_Q$$

$$= \iint\limits_{\Sigma_2} \frac{\cos \nu_{PQ} - \cos \nu_{P_1Q}}{r_{P_1Q}^2} \psi(Q)\, d\sigma_Q +$$

$$+ \iint\limits_{\Sigma_2} \left(\frac{1}{r_{PQ}^2} - \frac{1}{r_{P_1Q}^2}\right) \cos \nu_{P_1Q} \psi(Q)\, d\sigma_Q. \tag{57}$$

Denoting by ξ_1, η_1, ζ_1 the coordinates of the point P_1, and by ξ, η, ζ the coordinates of the point Q in the part Σ_2 with respect to the system of rectangular coordinate axes, the axis $P\zeta$ being directed along the normal to the surface S, and by $\alpha_1, \beta_1, \gamma_1$ the direction cosines of the normal at P_1, we have

$$\cos \nu_{PQ} - \cos \nu_{P_1Q} = \frac{\zeta}{r_{PQ}} - \left(\alpha_1 \frac{\xi - \xi_1}{r_{P_1Q}} + \beta_1 \frac{\eta - \eta_1}{r_{P_1Q}} + \gamma_1 \frac{\zeta - \zeta_1}{r_{P_1Q}}\right).$$

Hence

$$|\cos \nu_{PQ} - \cos \nu_{P_1Q}| \leqq |\alpha_1| + |\beta_1| + \left| \frac{\zeta}{r_{PQ}} - \frac{\zeta - \zeta_1}{r_{P_1Q}} \right| + |\gamma_1 - 1|.$$

According to the Liapunov inequality and inequality (12), we now have

$$|\alpha_1| \leqq Cr^{\kappa}_{P_1P}, \quad |\beta_1| \leqq Cr^{\kappa}_{P_1P}, \quad |\gamma_1 - 1| \leqq \tfrac{1}{2}Cr^{2\kappa}_{P_1P},$$

and consequently

$$\left| \frac{\zeta}{r_{PQ}} - \frac{\zeta - \zeta_1}{r_{P_1Q}} \right| \leqq |\zeta| \frac{|r_{P_1Q} - r_{PQ}|}{r_{PQ}r_{P_1Q}} + \frac{|\zeta_1|}{r_{P_1Q}}.$$

Applying the inequalities (see p. 235)

$$\begin{gathered} |\zeta| \leqq 4Ck^{\kappa} r^{\kappa+1}_{PQ}, \quad |\zeta_1| \leqq 4Ck^{\kappa} r^{\kappa+1}_{PP_1}, \\ \frac{2}{3} \leqq \frac{r_{PQ}}{r_{P_1Q}} \leqq 2, \quad |r_{P_1Q} - r_{PQ}| \leqq r_{PP_1}, \end{gathered} \tag{58}$$

we therefore obtain

$$|\cos \nu_{PQ} - \cos \nu_{P_1Q}|$$
$$\leqq 2Cr^{\kappa}_{PP_1} + \frac{1}{2} Cr^{2\kappa}_{PP_1} + 8Ck^{\kappa} r_{PP_1} \frac{1}{r^{1-\kappa}_{PQ}} + 8Ck^{\kappa} r^{\kappa+1}_{PP_1} \frac{1}{r_{PQ}},$$

when Q is in Σ_2. This implies the inequality

$$\left| \iint\limits_{\Sigma_2} \frac{\cos \nu_{PQ} - \cos \nu_{P_1Q}}{r^2_{P_1Q}} \psi(Q)\, d\sigma_Q \right|$$
$$\leqq 4\left(2Cr^{\kappa}_{PP_1} + \frac{1}{2} Cr^{2\kappa}_{PP_1}\right) M_{\psi} \iint\limits_{\Sigma_2} \frac{d\sigma_Q}{r^2_{PQ}} +$$
$$+ 32Ck^{\kappa} M_{\psi} r_{PP_1} \iint\limits_{\Sigma_2} \frac{d\sigma_Q}{r^{3-\kappa}_{PQ}} + 32Ck^{\kappa} r^{\kappa+1}_{PP_1} M_{\psi} \iint\limits_{\Sigma_2} \frac{d\sigma_Q}{r^3_{PQ}}.$$

Projecting Σ_2 onto the tangent plane at P, it is easy to prove that the first integral on the right increases as $|\log r_{PP_1}|$ when $P_1 \to P$, the second integral increases as $1/r^{1-\kappa}_{PP_1}$ for $\kappa < 1$, while the third integral increases as $1/r_{PP_1}$, when $r_{PP_1} \to 0$. We therefore infer that the following inequality holds:

$$\left| \iint\limits_{\Sigma_2} \frac{\cos \nu_{PQ} - \cos \nu_{P_1 Q}}{r_{PQ}^2} \psi(Q)\, d\sigma_Q \right| \leqq C_2 M_\psi r_{PP_1}^{\kappa - \varepsilon}, \tag{59}$$

C_2 being a certain positive constant, and ε being positive and arbitrarily small.

Similarly, applying inequality (58) and the inequality

$$|\cos \nu_{PQ}| \leqq 4Ck^\kappa r_{PQ}^\kappa,$$

we obtain

$$\left| \iint\limits_{\Sigma_2} \left(\frac{1}{r_{PQ}^2} - \frac{1}{r_{P_1 Q}^2} \right) \cos \nu_{PQ} \psi(Q)\, d\sigma_Q \right|$$

$$\leqq 40 Ck^\kappa M_\psi \left(\frac{3}{2} \right)^\kappa r_{PP_1} \iint\limits_{\Sigma_2} \frac{d\sigma_Q}{r_{PQ}^{3-\kappa}}, \tag{60}$$

and hence the same estimate as for integral (59).

Combining the results (59) and (60) we arrive at the inequality

$$|J_1^{\Sigma_2}(P) - J_1^{\Sigma_2}(P_1)| \leqq C_1' M_\psi r_{PP_1}^{\kappa - \varepsilon}, \tag{61}$$

where C_1' is a positive constant independent of ψ.

It remains to investigate the difference between the third parts in the sum (55); let us decompose it into two terms, as in the difference (57). The second term can be estimated immediately; we have $r_{PQ} \geqq \delta$ and hence, in accordance with inequality (58), we obtain

$$\left| \iint\limits_{S-\Sigma} \left(\frac{1}{r_{PQ}^2} - \frac{1}{r_{P_1 Q}^2} \right) \cos \nu_{PQ} \psi(Q)\, d\sigma_Q \right| \leqq \frac{10}{\delta^3} |S| M_\psi r_{PP_1}, \tag{62}$$

where $|S|$ denotes the area of the surface S. To estimate the first term, we denote by a_1, b_1, c_1 the direction cosines (with respect to the system $P\xi\eta\zeta$) of the vector $\vec{r}_{P_1 Q}$, and by $\alpha_1, \beta_1, \gamma_1$ the direction cosines of the normal to the surface S at the point P_1. We then have

$$|\cos \nu_{PQ} - \cos \nu_{P_1Q}| = |a_1 \alpha_1 + b_1 \beta_1 + c_1 \gamma_1 - \cos \nu_{PQ}|$$
$$\leqq |\alpha_1| + |\beta_1| + |c_1 - \cos \nu_{PQ}| + |\gamma_1 - 1| \leqq |\alpha_1| + |\beta_1| + |\gamma_1 - 1| + |\Theta^Q|,$$

where Θ^Q is the angle between the vectors $\vec{r}_{PQ}$ and $\vec{r}_{P_1Q}$; this angle attains its maximum value at a point on the surface of the sphere K with radius δ, and we have

$$\lim_{P_1 \to P} \frac{\Theta^Q_{\max}}{r_{PP_1}} = \frac{1}{\delta}.$$

Combining this result with the properties (3) and (12), we are led to the inequality

$$|\cos \nu_{PQ} - \cos \nu_{P_1Q}| \leqq B r^{\kappa}_{PP_1} \tag{63}$$

valid for a point Q of $S - \Sigma$; therefore

$$\left| \iint\limits_{S-\Sigma} \frac{\cos \nu_{PQ} - \cos \nu_{P_1Q}}{r^2_{P_1Q}} \psi(Q)\, d\sigma_Q \right|$$
$$\leqq M_\psi B r^{\kappa}_{PP_1} 4 \iint\limits_{S-\Sigma} \frac{d\sigma_Q}{r^2_{PQ}} \leqq \frac{4ABM_\psi}{\delta^2} r^{\kappa}_{PP_1} \quad (\kappa \leqq 1), \tag{64}$$

A and B being two positive constants independent of ψ. Finally, combining inequalities (56), (61), (62) and (64) we arrive at the first inequality (54), which completes the proof. Property (54) of the second integral $J_2(P)$ can be proved in a similar way, the proof being even easier. This property will be generalized to the set $\Omega + S$ in Chapter XXII.

LEMMA 2. *There exists a positive constant K such that the inequality*

$$\iint\limits_S \left| \frac{d\left(\dfrac{1}{r_{AQ}}\right)}{dn_Q} \right| d\sigma_Q = \iint\limits_S \left| \frac{\cos \nu_{QA}}{r^2_{AQ}} \right| d\sigma_Q < K, \tag{65}$$

where ν_{QA} denotes the angle between the vector $\overrightarrow{QA}$ and the normal to the surface S at Q, is satisfied by all points A in $\Omega + S$.

To prove the lemma, observe that for an arbitrary point A inside Ω there exists a point P of S at which the distance r_{AQ} of A from a variable point Q of S attains its lower bound. The point A therefore lies on the normal to the surface S at P.

Consider now the coordinate system $Pxyz$, the axis Pz being normal to S and directed inwards; axes Px and Py lie in the tangent plane to S at P. Denote by z the coordinate of A, and ξ, η, ζ the coordinates of the point Q of S. We know (p. 235) that in a sufficiently small part Σ of the surface S surrounding P, the inequality

$$|\zeta(\xi, \eta)| \leqq 4Ck^{\varkappa} r_{PQ}^{\varkappa+1} \leqq 4Ck^{2\varkappa+1}\rho^{\varkappa+1}, \tag{66}$$

holds; here $\varrho = \sqrt{\xi^2+\eta^2}$ is the distance of P from the projection Q' of Q onto the plane Pxy. Inequality (66) indicates that there exists a small positive δ_1, independent of A, such that the circle C'_* of radius δ_1 located in the tangent plane Pxy, with centre at point P, is the projection of part C_* of surface Σ all points of which, including the boundary, satisfy the inequality

$$|\zeta(\xi, \eta)| < \tfrac{1}{2}\rho. \tag{67}$$

We assume, moreover, that δ_1 is so chosen that the cylinder with base C'_* and height δ_1 does not contain any points of S except C_*.

Observe now that in triangle AQQ' we have

$$r_{AQ} \geqq r_{AQ'} - |\zeta(\xi, \eta)| > \rho - |\zeta|, \tag{68}$$

hence for points $Q \in C_*$ we obtain the inequality

$$\frac{1}{r_{AQ}} \leqq \frac{1}{r_{AQ'}} \; \frac{1}{1-|\zeta|/r_{AQ'}} \leqq \frac{1}{r_{AQ'}} \; \frac{1}{1-|\zeta|/\rho} \leqq \frac{2}{r_{AQ'}}. \tag{69}$$

Furthermore, we have

$$\cos v_{QA} = \frac{\xi}{r_{AQ}} \cos\alpha + \frac{\eta}{r_{AQ}} \cos\beta + \frac{\zeta - z}{r_{AQ}} \cos\gamma,$$

whence

$$|\cos v_{QA}| \leqq |\cos\alpha| + |\cos\beta| + \frac{|\zeta|}{\rho} + \frac{z}{r_{AQ}},$$

where α, β, γ are the angles of the normal at Q with respect to the system $Pxyz$. Bearing in mind inequalities (13) and (16) we have

$$|\cos v_{QA}| \leqq 2Ck^{\varkappa}(2k^{\varkappa+1}+1)\rho^{\varkappa}+\frac{z}{r_{AQ}} \tag{70}$$

for points $Q \in C_*$.

To prove inequality (65) we first prove the boundedness of the integral over C_*; the investigation of the integral over the remaining part $S-C_*$ is obviously easier since the integral is bounded for any small distance $z = r_{AP}$. In view of inequalities (69) and (70) we can write

$$\iint\limits_{C_*} \frac{|\cos v_{QA}|}{r_{AQ}^2}\, d\sigma_Q$$

$$\leqq 2Ck^{\varkappa}(2k^{\varkappa+1}+1)\iint\limits_{C_*}\frac{\rho^{\varkappa}\, d\sigma_Q}{r_{AQ}^2}+8z\iint\limits_{C_*}\frac{d\sigma_Q}{r_{AQ'}^3},$$

and since $\cos\gamma > 1/2$, we have

$$\iint\limits_{C_*} \frac{|\cos v_{QA}|}{r_{AQ}^2}\, d\sigma_Q$$

$$\leqq 4Ck^{\varkappa}(2k^{\varkappa+1}+1)\iint\limits_{C_*'}\frac{d\sigma_{Q'}}{\varrho^{2-\varkappa}}+16z\iint\limits_{C_*'}\frac{d\sigma_{Q'}}{(\varrho^2+z^2)^{3/2}}. \tag{71}$$

Now taking into account the values of the integrals

$$\iint\limits_{C_*'}\frac{d\sigma_{Q'}}{\rho^{2-\varkappa}} = 2\pi\int\limits_0^{\delta_1}\frac{d\rho}{\rho^{1-\varkappa}} = \frac{2\pi}{\varkappa}\,\delta_1^{\varkappa},$$

$$\iint\limits_{C_*'}\frac{d\sigma_{Q'}}{(\rho^2+z^2)^{3/2}} = 2\pi\left(1-\frac{z}{\sqrt{\delta_1^2+z^2}}\right) \tag{72}$$

we infer that integral (71) is bounded for any small z.

To investigate the integral over the remaining part $S-C_*$; observe that when $z \geqq \delta_1/2$ we obtain

$$\iint\limits_{S-C_*} \frac{|\cos \nu_{QA}|}{r_{AQ}^2}\, d\sigma_Q \leqq 4 \iint\limits_{S-C_*} \frac{d\sigma_Q}{\delta_1^2} < \frac{4|S|}{\delta_1^2},$$

where $|S|$ is the area of S. If $z < \delta_1/2$ then $r_{AQ}/r_{PQ} > 1/2$, and consequently

$$\iint\limits_{S-C_*} \frac{|\cos \nu_{QA}|}{r_{AQ}^2}\, d\sigma_Q < 4 \iint\limits_{S-C_*} \frac{d\sigma_Q}{r_{PQ}^2} < 4 \iint\limits_{S-C_*} \frac{d\sigma_Q}{\delta_1^2} < \frac{4|S|}{\delta_1^2}.$$

The boundedness of integral (65) when A coincides with the point P of S is evident, by virtue of inequality (19). This completes the proof of the lemma.

Let us observe that in the case of a convex surface S the lemma is obvious, since then integral (65) is equal to the surface area of the sphere of unit radius, i.e. 4π for points A located inside Ω, and is equal to half this area for points A located on the surface S.

LEMMA 3. *The integral of the absolute value of the density $\psi(P, B)$ of the surface distribution from which the regular part of the Green's Function* (41) *is constructed, is bounded, i.e. it satisfies the inequality*

$$\iint\limits_S |\psi(P, B)|\, d\sigma \leqq q \tag{73}$$

for any position of the point B in the interior of the region Ω, where q is a positive constant.

This property follows from the integral equation (50) the solution of which is $\psi(P, B)$. We write this equation in the form

$$\psi(P, B) = f(P, B) + \lambda \iint\limits_S N(P, Q)\, \psi(Q, B)\, d\sigma_Q, \tag{74}$$

where

$$f(P, B) = -\frac{1}{2\pi} \frac{d}{dn_P}\left(\frac{1}{r_{PB}}\right) - \frac{1}{2\pi} a(P) \frac{1}{r_{PB}},$$
$$\lambda = -\frac{1}{2\pi}, \quad N(P, Q) = \frac{\cos \nu_{PQ}}{r_{PQ}^2} + \frac{a(P)}{r_{PQ}}, \tag{75}$$

and we consider the equation iterated $p-1$ times

$$\psi(P, B) = f_1(P, B) + \lambda^p \iint_S N_p(P, Q)\psi(Q, B)\, d\sigma_Q, \qquad (76)$$

where

$$f_1(P, B) = f(P, B) + \iint_S \Big[\sum_{j=1}^{p-1} \lambda^j N_j(P, Q)\Big] f(Q, B)\, d\sigma_Q,$$

the kernel of which N_p is bounded; this equation is equivalent to the considered equation (74). If $\lambda = -1/2\pi$ is not an eigenvalue of the kernel N_p (e.g. in the case $a \leqq 0$) then the unique solution of equation (76), and therefore of (74) as well, has the form

$$\psi(P, B) = f_1(P, B) + \lambda \iint_S \mathfrak{R}(P, Q) f_1(Q, B)\, d\sigma_Q, \qquad (77)$$

$\mathfrak{R}$ being the resolvent kernel of the kernel N_p. The considered property (73) follows at once from Lemma 2.

In fact, if integral (65) is bounded then the same is true for the integrals

$$\iint_S |f(P, B)|\, d\sigma_P \quad \text{and} \quad \iint_S |N(P, Q)|\, d\sigma_P,$$

and consequently the integral

$$\iint_S |f_1(P, B)|\, d\sigma_P$$

is bounded, and there exists a positive constant q, such that inequality (73) holds for every point $B \in \Omega$.

COROLLARY. *If $a(P)$ satisfies the Hölder condition with exponent $\kappa_1 \leqq 1$, then the solution $\psi(P, B)$ of the Fredholm equation (74) satisfies the Hölder condition with an arbitrary exponent h such that*

$$h < \min(\kappa, \kappa_1); \qquad (78)$$

moreover, in an arbitrary part Δ of the surface S satisfying the second Liapunov condition, the Hölder inequality may be transformed to the form

$$|\psi(P, B) - \psi(P_1, B)| \leqq [k_f(B) + l m_\psi(B) + l'] r_{PP_1}^h, \qquad (79)$$

where $k_f(B)$ *is the Hölder coefficient of* $|f(P,B)|$ *in* Δ *depending on* B, $m_\psi(B)$ *is the upper bound of* $|\psi(P,B)|$ *in* Δ *(it also depends on* B*), and* l, l' *are positive constants, independent of* B.

$\psi(P,B)$, as a solution of the integral equation (74) defined by formula (77), is undoubtedly a continuous function of P for any $B \in \Omega$. Hence, in view of Lemma 1, the integral on the right-hand side of equation (74) satisfies the Hőlder condition on the surface S with an exponent h which satisfies condition (78). The function

$$f(P,B) = -\frac{1}{2\pi}\cdot\frac{\cos\nu_{PB}}{r_{PB}^2} - \frac{a(P)}{2\pi}\cdot\frac{1}{r_{PB}} \tag{80}$$

also satisfies the Hölder condition with the same exponent h; this result follows from the preceding considerations concerning the integral $J_1^{S-\Sigma}$ (inequalities (62), (63) and (64)). Thus we infer that, in view of equation (68), $\psi(P,B)$ satisfies the Hölder condition (with respect to P) the exponent of which satisfies condition (78).

We now prove that the Hölder inequality for ψ on that part Δ of S can be reduced to the form (79). The first term $k_f(B)$ of the coefficient is obvious; to justify the remaining two terms it is sufficient to apply some parts of the proof of Lemma 1.

To this end, let us decompose the integral in equation (74) into two terms

$$\iint_{\Delta} N(P,Q)\psi(Q,B)\,d\sigma_Q + \iint_{S-\Delta} N(P,Q)\psi(Q,B)\,d\sigma_Q. \tag{81}$$

According to the results obtained in the investigation of the integrals $J_1^{\Sigma_1}$ and $J_1^{\Sigma_2}$ (inequalities (56) and (61)) the first term of (81) satisfies the Hölder condition with an exponent h and coefficient $lm_\psi(B)$, where $m_\psi(B)$ is the upper bound of function $|\psi(Q,B)|$ on the surface Δ, depending on B, and l is a positive constant independent of B. Finally, in accordance with the investigation of the integral $J_1^{S-\Sigma}$, the upper bound of integrals (62) and (64) depends on the integral $\iint_S |\psi|\,d\sigma$ and therefore the second term of (81) also satisfies the Hölder condition with exponent h and coefficient l', the factor of the term being the upper bound of the integral $\iint\limits_S |\psi| \, d\sigma$; thus, in view of Lemma 2, coefficient l' is a positive constant, independent of B. This completes the proof of the corollary.

With the help of this corollary we now prove the basic properties of the regular component $g(A, B)$ of Green's Function for the mixed problem.

THEOREM 3. *The regular component $g(A, B)$ of Green's Function for the mixed problem and its first derivatives have definite boundary values and for arbitrary distinct points A and B in the domain $\Omega + S$, satisfy the inequalities*

$$|g(A, B)| \leq \frac{c_1}{r_{AB}} \quad \text{and} \quad |Dg(A, B)| \leq \frac{c_2}{r_{AB}^{3-h}} \quad (h > 0), \tag{82}$$

where the constants c_1 and c_2 have definite positive values depending on S and the function $a(P)$ only.

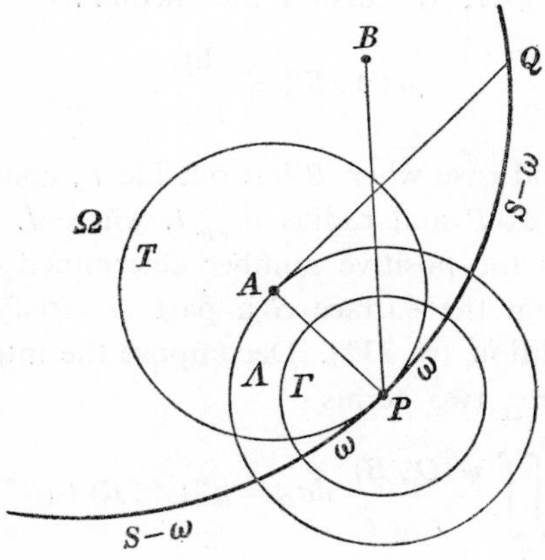

Fig. 2

Consider two arbitrary distinct points A and B in the interior of Ω. The distance r_{AQ} of A from an arbitrary point Q of the surface S is a continuous function and therefore it attains its lower bound at a point $P \in S$ (Fig. 2). Consequently, every sphere T with centre at A and radius r_{AP} is located inside Ω and it is tangent to S at P. Consider now the sphere Λ with centre at P and radius r_{AP}. We examine the two possible cases: 1) B is inside Λ or on its surface, and 2) B is outside Λ. In the first case since r_{AP} is the smallest distance from points of the surface S, $g(A, B)$ satisfies the inequality

$$|g(A, B)| = \left| \iint_S \frac{\psi(Q, B)}{r_{AQ}} d\sigma_Q \right| \leqq \frac{1}{r_{AP}} \iint_S |\psi(Q, B)| d\sigma_Q$$

and hence, in view of inequality (73), we obtain

$$|g(A, B)| \leqq \frac{q}{r_{AP}} \tag{83}$$

for every position of B. If B lies inside Λ or on its surface we have

$$\frac{r_{AP}}{r_{AB}} \geqq \frac{1}{2},$$

and, therefore $g(A, B)$ satisfies the inequality

$$|g(A, B)| \leqq \frac{2q}{r_{AB}}. \tag{84}$$

In the second case when B lies outside Γ, consider the sphere Γ with centre at P and radius $\delta r_{PB}/L$ where L is the diameter of Ω, and δ is the positive number determined on p. 251. This sphere cuts from the surface S a part ω satisfying the second Liapunov condition (p. 232). Decompose the integral expression for $g(A, B)$ into two terms

$$g(A, B) = \iint_S \frac{\psi(Q, B)}{r_{AQ}} d\sigma_Q = g^{\omega}(A, B) + g^{S-\omega}(A, B), \tag{85}$$

the integration being carried out, in the first case, over ω, and in the second, over the surface $S-\omega$ located outside Γ. In the considered case, when B lies outside Λ and Q inside the sphere Γ, we have the inequalities

$$\frac{r_{AQ}}{r_{PQ}} > \frac{1}{2} \quad \text{and} \quad \frac{r_{AB}}{r_{PB}} < 2. \tag{86}$$

Observe now that in view of inequalities (75) and (77) there exists a constant q' independent of B such that, in ω, $\psi(Q, B)$ satisfies the inequality

$$|\psi(Q, B)| < \frac{q'}{r_{QB}^2}, \tag{87}$$

and consequently the term g^{ω} satisfies the inequality

$$|g^{\omega}(A, B)| < q' \iint_{\omega} \frac{d\sigma_Q}{r_{AQ} r_{QB}^2} < 2q' \iint_{\omega} \frac{d\sigma_Q}{r_{PQ} r_{QB}^2}. \tag{88}$$

Applying now the homothetic transformation from P to the surface ω, the ratio being $L/\delta r_{PB}$, i.e. reducing Γ to the unit sphere Γ', we have

$$\iint_{\omega} \frac{d\sigma_Q}{r_{PQ} r_{QB}^2} = \frac{L}{\delta} \frac{1}{r_{PB}} \iint_{\omega'} \frac{d\sigma_{Q'}}{r_{PQ'} r_{Q'B'}^2}.$$

Since the derived integral is bounded for any P, in view of inequality (88), we obtain

$$|g^{\omega}(A, B)| < \frac{q''}{r_{PB}} < \frac{2q''}{r_{AB}}, \tag{89}$$

where q'' is a constant.

To estimate the remaining term $g^{S-\omega}$, observe that at points of $S-\omega$, we have

$$r_{AQ} > \frac{1}{2} r_{PQ} > \frac{1}{2} \frac{\delta}{L} r_{PB} > \frac{1}{4} \frac{\delta}{L} r_{AP}, \tag{90}$$

and consequently

$$|g^{S-\omega}(A, B)|$$

$$= \left| \iint_{S-\omega} \frac{\psi(Q, B)}{r_{AQ}} d\sigma_Q \right| < \frac{4L}{\delta} \cdot \frac{1}{r_{AB}} \iint_{S-\omega} |\psi| \, d\sigma < \frac{4Lq}{\delta} \cdot \frac{1}{r_{AB}}. \tag{91}$$

Combining results (84), (89) and (91), we arrive at the required estimate of the regular term of the Green's Function

$$|g(A, B)| < \frac{c_1}{r_{AB}} \tag{92}$$

for arbitrary distinct points of Ω.

We now proceed to estimate the first derivatives of $g(A, B)$. Since ψ satisfies the Hölder condition, these derivatives have definite boundary values (see corollary on p. 259). The choice of the coordinate axes is immaterial, since if the second inequality (82) is satisfied in a certain coordinate system, an inequality of the same form holds in any other system of rectangular coordinates. Select, therefore, the coordinate system the axis Pz of which is normal to surface S and the axes Px and Py are located in the tangent plane. We estimate the derivative of g in the tangent direction Px only. The estimate of the derivative in the direction Pz is simpler. To this end, first consider again the case when B lies inside sphere Λ or on its surface; then for the derivative of $g(A, B)$ with respect to the coordinate of A, we obtain the inequality

$$\left|\frac{\partial g}{\partial x}\right| = \left|\iint\limits_S \frac{x-\xi}{r_{AQ}^3}\, \psi(Q, B)\, d\sigma_Q\right| < \frac{1}{r_{AP}^2} \iint\limits_S |\psi|\, d\sigma < \frac{2q}{r_{AB}^2}. \tag{93}$$

If B lies outside Λ, then the derivatives of g are integrals which we decompose into two parts $(\partial g/\partial x)^{\omega}$ and $(\partial g/\partial x)^{S-\omega}$ over the surfaces ω and $S-\omega$, respectively. For the first part we have

$$\left(\frac{\partial g(A, B)}{\partial x}\right)^{\omega} = -\iint\limits_{\omega} \frac{x-\xi}{r_{AQ}^3}\, [\psi(Q, B) - \psi(P, B)]\, d\sigma_Q -$$

$$-\psi(P, B) \iint\limits_{\omega} \frac{x-\xi}{r_{AQ}^3}\, d\sigma_Q. \tag{94}$$

On the basis of the Hölder inequality for ψ in the form (79), we obtain

$$\left|\left(\frac{\partial g(A,B)}{\partial x}\right)^{\omega}\right| < [k_f(B)+lm_\psi(B)+l'] \iint\limits_{\omega} \frac{r_{PQ}^h}{r_{AQ}^2}\, d\sigma_Q + $$

$$+m_\psi(B)\left|\iint\limits_{\omega} \frac{(x-\xi)\, d\sigma_Q}{r_{AQ}^3}\right|. \qquad (95)$$

Observe now that the distance of $Q \in \omega$ from B satisfies the inequality

$$r_{BQ} \geqq \left(1-\frac{\delta}{L}\right) r_{BP},$$

and consequently, in view of formulae (79) and (87) there exist constants q' and q'' such that for points $Q \in \omega$,

$$k_f(B) = \frac{q'}{r_{BP}^3} \quad \text{and} \quad m_\psi(B) = \frac{q''}{r_{BP}^2}. \qquad (96)$$

Applying inequality (86) and transforming the sphere Γ homothetically from the point P, the ratio being $L/\delta r_{PB}$, we obtain

$$\iint\limits_{\omega} \frac{r_{PQ}^h}{r_{AQ}^2}\, d\sigma_Q < 4 \iint\limits_{\omega} \frac{d\sigma_Q}{r_{PQ}^{2-h}} = 4\left(\frac{\delta}{L}\right)^h r_{PB}^h \iint\limits_{\omega'} \frac{d\sigma_{Q'}}{r_{PQ'}^{2-h}}.$$

The integral on the right-hand side is absolutely convergent and has a definite upper bound for various positions of P. The integral

$$\iint\limits_{\omega} \frac{x-\xi}{r_{AQ}^3}\, d\sigma_Q$$

appearing in inequality (94) is the derivative in a tangential direction of a potential of surface distribution with constant density, and therefore it has a definite boundary value, and its absolute value has an upper bound for various positions of

A (see Theorem 10 on p. 332). Thus, in accordance with inequality (95) and formula (96), we have the inequality

$$\left|\left(\frac{\partial g(A,B)}{\partial x}\right)^{\omega}\right| < \frac{q'''}{r_{BP}^{3-h}} < \frac{2^{3-h}q'''}{r_{AB}^{3-h}}, \tag{97}$$

where q''' is a positive constant. For the remaining part in view of inequality (90), we have at once

$$\left|\left(\frac{\partial g(A,B)}{\partial x}\right)^{S-\omega}\right| = \left|\iint\limits_{S-\omega} \frac{x-\xi}{r_{AQ}^3}\,\psi(Q,B)\,d\sigma_Q\right|$$

$$< \left(\frac{4I}{\delta}\right)^2 \frac{1}{r_{AB}^2} \iint\limits_{S-\omega} |\psi|\,d\sigma \leqq \left(\frac{4L}{\delta}\right)^2 \frac{q}{r_{AB}^2}. \tag{98}$$

Combining the results (93), (97) and (98) we find that the derivative of $g(A,B)$, with respect to the variable x, satisfies the inequality

$$\left|\frac{\partial g(A,B)}{\partial x}\right| < \frac{c_2}{r_{AB}^{3-h}}, \tag{99}$$

the constant c_2 being independent of the pair of points A and B.

In a similar way we can investigate the derivatives with respect to the variable z and thus deduce an estimate which does not exceed the value (99).

The properties of the regular term of the Green's Function expressed by inequalities (74) are therefore justified. Evidently similar inequalities are also satisfied by the Green's Function itself

$$G(A,B) = \frac{1}{r_{AB}} - g(A,B).$$

Observe also that the second derivatives of $g(A,B)$ with respect to the coordinates of the point A not only exist and are continuous with respect to A and $B \in \Omega$, but they are also bounded when A lies inside Ω and B tends to an arbitrary boundary point. In fact, if P is the point of the surface S nearest to A, in view of Lemma 2 the second derivative, say with respect to x, satisfies the inequalities

$$\left|\frac{\partial^2 g(A, B)}{\partial x^2}\right| = \left|\iint\limits_S \frac{\psi(Q, B)}{r_{AQ}^3} d\sigma_Q - 3\iint\limits_S \frac{(x-\xi)^2}{r_{AQ}^5} \psi(Q, B)\, d\sigma_Q\right|$$

$$\leqq \frac{4}{r_{AP}^3}\iint\limits_S |\psi(Q, B)|\, d\sigma_Q \leqq \frac{4q}{r_{AP}^3} \qquad (100)$$

for every position of B.

A similar conclusion may be drawn for the third derivative $g(A, B)$ with respect to the point A.

The deduced properties of Green's Function are indispensable in solving boundary-value problems for more general equations of elliptic type, which will be dealt with later.

In an entirely analogous way we can estimate the derivatives of Green's Function of the first kind, expressing its regular part by a potential of surface distribution in the form (41).

§ 4. The Poisson equation

By the *Poisson equation* we mean an equation of the form

$$\Delta u(x, y, z) = f(x, y, z), \qquad (101)$$

where $f(A)$ is a known function defined at all points $A(x, y, z)$ of the region Ω bounded by a closed surface S.

Consider the problem similar to the Dirichlet problem, consisting in the determination of a function $u(x, y, z)$ continuous in the closure of Ω, satisfying equation (101) inside Ω and taking *a priori* prescribed boundary values.

It is known from potential theory (see pp. 303–309) that if the known function $f(x, y, z)$ satisfies the Hölder condition in Ω, the potential of spatial charge with density $-\frac{1}{4\pi}f(x, y, z)$, i.e. the function*

$$u_1(x, y, z) = -\frac{1}{4\pi}\iiint\limits_\Omega \frac{f(B)}{r_{AB}}\, dB \qquad (102)$$

* dB denotes the element of volume at the point B.

satisfies equation (101) at all interior points A of Ω. However, the solution (102) may not satisfy the given boundary condition. We can always assume that the required boundary values of the unknown function are zero

$$\lim_{P\to A} u(A) = 0 \quad (P\in S), \tag{103}$$

for in the case of other boundary values it is sufficient to add to the solution possessing property (103) a harmonic function with the considered boundary values, in order to obtain the required solution.

The solution of equation (101) satisfying condition (103) can at once be obtained by means of Green's Function of the first kind. For, we prove that the function

$$u(A) = -\frac{1}{4\pi}\iiint_{\Omega} G(A,B) f(B)\,dB$$

$$= -\frac{1}{4\pi}\iiint_{\Omega}\frac{1}{r_{AB}} f(B)\,dB + \frac{1}{4\pi}\iiint_{\Omega} g(A,B) f(B)\,dB \tag{104}$$

is the required solution, under the assumption that the known function $f(x, y, z)$ satisfies the Hölder condition.

In fact, the first term of the sum (104) satisfies equation (101) as a potential of spatial charge, while the second term satisfies Laplace's equation

$$\Delta \iiint_{\Omega} g(A,B) f(B)\,dB = \iiint_{\Omega} \Delta_A g(A,B) f(B)\,dB = 0$$

at all interior points A of Ω. This fact is a result of the following properties:

1) $g(A, B)$ has second derivatives and it is harmonic at all interior points A, even if A coincides with B.

2) The second derivatives are continuous with respect to B and remain bounded when A is an interior point and B tends to an arbitrary boundary point.

3) The third derivatives of $g(A, B)$ with respect to A exist and they are bounded when A is located in an arbitrary region

Ω' lying inside Ω, and B is an arbitrary point of Ω; the second derivatives of $g(A, B)$ with respect to A therefore satisfy the Lipschitz condition when $A \in \Omega'$ and $B \in \Omega$; this makes it possible to apply the theorem on differentiability of an integral with respect to a parameter.

Let us now prove that the function (104) satisfies condition (103). This is not obvious, since although $G(A, B)$ tends to zero when $A \to P$ for all positions of B, in integral (104) B is located arbitrarily near A and then Green's Function is unbounded.

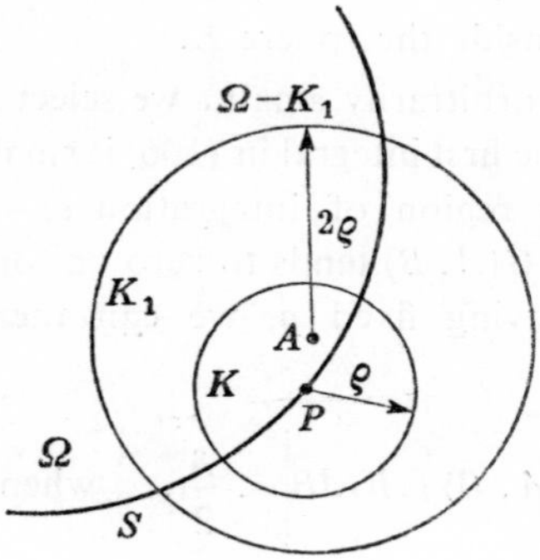

Fig. 3

We conclude the proof using the following familiar estimate for the Green's Function:

$$0 < G(A, B) < \frac{1}{r_{AB}}. \qquad (105)$$

Consider a sphere K of radius ρ with centre at an arbitrary point $P \in S$, and a sphere K_1 of radius 2ρ with centre at an arbitrary point A located inside Ω and inside K (Fig. 3). Thus, K lies inside K_1.

Decompose integral (104) into two parts

$$u(A) = -\frac{1}{4\pi} \iiint_{K_1'} G(A, B) f(B)\, dB -$$

$$-\frac{1}{4\pi} \iiint_{\Omega - K_1'} G(A, B) f(B)\, dB, \qquad (106)$$

the integration being carried out over the region K_1' which is the set of all points common to Ω and K_1, and over region $\Omega - K_1'$ which is exterior with respect to the sphere K_1. If M_f is the upper bound of $|f(B)|$ in Ω, then in accordance with estimate (105), we have the inequality

$$\left| \frac{1}{4\pi} \iiint_{K_1'} G(A, B) f(B)\, dB \right| \leq \frac{M_f}{4\pi} \int_0^{2\rho} \frac{4\pi r^2\, dr}{r} = 2M_f \rho^2 \tag{107}$$

for every point A inside the sphere K.

Thus, if for an arbitrarily small ε we select $\rho_\varepsilon = \sqrt{\varepsilon/2M_f}$, the absolute value of the first integral in (106) is smaller than $\varepsilon/2$. Since A lies outside the region of integration $\Omega - K_1'$ of the second integral (106), and $G(A, B)$ tends to zero uniformly* with respect to B in $\Omega - K$, having fixed ρ, we can therefore move A so near to P that

$$\left| \frac{1}{4\pi} \iiint_{\Omega - K'} G(A, B) f(B)\, dB \right| < \frac{\varepsilon}{2}, \quad \text{when} \quad r_{AP} < \eta_\varepsilon,$$

where η is selected in accordance with ε. Thus, we finally have

$$|u(A)| < \varepsilon, \quad \text{when} \quad r_{AP} < \eta_\varepsilon,$$

i.e. the function (106) satisfies the boundary condition (103).

Observe that the derived solution is unique. In fact, if there exist two functions satisfying Poisson's equation (101) and having the same boundary values, then their difference is a harmonic function which vanishes on the boundary of Ω; therefore it also vanishes in the interior of the region.

For the Poisson's equation (101) we now solve a problem similar to the mixed problem for the Laplace equation. Thus we seek a function $u(x, y, z)$ which satisfies the equation

$$\Delta u = f(x, y, z) \tag{108}$$

---

* This uniformity can be proved as in the proof for Green's Function on p. 273.

inside Ω, the boundary value of the derivative of which in the direction normal to the surface S satisfies the *a priori* prescribed linear relation

$$\left(\frac{du}{dn}\right)_P + a(P)\,u(P) = b(P) \tag{109}$$

at all points P on the surface S of Ω. We assume that S satisfies the Liapunov conditions and the known function $a(P)$ satisfies the Hölder condition on S. We assume, moreover, that $b = 0$, since otherwise it is sufficient to add to the solution a harmonic function v satisfying the non-homogeneous boundary condition

$$\left(\frac{dv}{dn}\right)_P + a(P)\,v(P) = b(P) \neq 0\,.$$

Consider Green's Function $G(A, B)$ of the second kind, i.e. the function satisfying the boundary condition

$$\left(\frac{dG(A, B)}{dn_P}\right) + a(P)\,G(A, B) \to 0, \quad \text{when} \quad A \to P\,. \tag{110}$$

We assume that this function exists and is unique (e.g. when $a < 0$). We prove that the function

$$u(A) = -\frac{1}{4\pi}\iiint\limits_{\Omega} G(A, B)\,f(B)\,dB \tag{111}$$

is the solution of the mixed problem, assuming that the known function $f(A)$ satisfies the Hölder condition.

By an argument similar to that of the preceding problem we establish that the function (111) satisfies Poisson's equation (101). To prove that it satisfies the boundary condition (109) in which $b = 0$, we first observe that in accordance with property (82) of the Green's Function of the second kind, the integrals

$$\begin{aligned} u(P) &= -\frac{1}{4\pi}\iiint\limits_{\Omega} G(P, B)\,f(B)\,dB\,, \\ u'(P) &= -\frac{1}{4\pi}\iiint\limits_{\Omega} G'_{x_\alpha}(P, B)\,f(B)\,dB \end{aligned} \tag{112}$$

are absolutely convergent and have definite values at all points $P \in S$. $G'_{x_\alpha}(P, B)$ denotes the limit of the derivative $G'_{x_\alpha}(A, B)$ of the Green's Function with respect to any coordinate x_α of the point $A \neq B$, when this point tends to the point $P \in S$. We prove that the integrals (112) are the limits of the integrals

$$\begin{aligned} u(A) &= -\frac{1}{4\pi} \iiint_{\Omega} G(A, B) f(B)\, dB, \\ u'(A) &= -\frac{1}{4\pi} \iiint_{\Omega} G'_{x_\alpha}(A, B) f(B)\, dB, \end{aligned} \tag{113}$$

when an interior point A tends in an arbitrary manner to a point $P \in S$. It is sufficient to prove this property for integral $u'(A)$. Therefore consider again the system of spheres in Fig. 3 and decompose the integrals $u'(A)$ and $u'(P)$ into two terms

$$\begin{aligned} u'(A) &= u'_{K'_1}(A) + u'_{\Omega - K'_1}(A), \\ u'(P) &= u'_{K'_1}(P) + u'_{\Omega - K'_1}(P), \end{aligned} \tag{114}$$

the integration being performed over the region K'_1 which constitutes the set of all points common to both K_1 and Ω, and over $\Omega - K'_1$ exterior with respect to sphere K_1. According to property (82), for any point A inside K, we have the inequality

$$|u'_{K'_1}(A)| < \frac{M_f(c_2+1)}{4\pi} \int_0^{2\rho} \frac{4\pi r^2\, dr}{r^{3-h}} = \frac{2^h M_f(c_2+1)}{h}\, \rho^h, \tag{115}$$

where M_f denotes the upper bound of $|f(A)|$ in Ω. Consequently

$$|u'_{K'_1}(A)| < \frac{\varepsilon}{3} \quad \text{and} \quad |u'_{K'_1}(P)| < \frac{\varepsilon}{3}, \tag{116}$$

if for the radius ρ of the sphere K we take the value

$$\rho_\varepsilon = \left(\frac{h\varepsilon}{3 \cdot 2^h M_f(c_2+1)} \right)^{1/h}.$$

Taking into account that A is exterior with respect to $\Omega-K_1'$ we prove that $G'_{x_\alpha}(A, B)$ tends to the value $G'_{x_\alpha}(P, B)$ uniformly with respect to B in $\Omega-K'$ when $A \in K$ tends to a point P. This property is obvious for the term $1/r_{AB}$ of the Green's Function. To prove it for the second term $g(A, B)$ which constitutes a potential of surface distribution with density $\psi(Q, B)$ we write it in the form of the sum

$$g(A, B) = \iint\limits_S \frac{\psi(Q, B)}{r_{AQ}} d\sigma_Q = g^{S_1}(A, B) + g^{S-S_1}(A, B)$$

of integrals over that part S_1 of the surface S located inside K, and the part $S-S_1$ outside K. Since B lies outside K_1, the function $\psi(Q, B)$ is bounded in S_1 and satisfies the Hölder condition with a coefficient independent of B (see inequalities (79) and (95)). It follows therefore that derivatives $g^{S_1}_{x_\alpha}(A, B)$ tend uniformly to the values $g^{S_1}_{x_\alpha}(P, B)$ when $B \in \Omega-K'$. The uniform convergence of the derivatives $g^{S-S_1}_{x_\alpha}(A, B)$ to the values $g^{S-S_1}_{x_\alpha}(P, B)$ follows from Lemma 3. These facts imply that having selected the value of ρ_ε, we can choose, for any number ε, a number η_ε such that

$$|u'_{\Omega-K_1'}(A) - u'_{\Omega-K_1'}(P)| < \frac{\varepsilon}{3}, \quad \text{when} \quad r_{AP} < \eta_\varepsilon. \tag{117}$$

Combining inequalities (116) and (117) we infer that

$$|u'(A) - u'(P)| < \varepsilon, \quad \text{when} \quad r_{AP} < \eta_\varepsilon. \tag{118}$$

These results imply that, according to the boundary property (110) of the Green's Function, the function (111) satisfies the boundary condition (109) where $b = 0$, and therefore it is the solution of the mixed problem for Poisson equation.

Let us now examine a particular case of the mixed problem, when $a = 0$, i.e. the problem analogous to the von Neumann problem. We shall determine the solution of Poisson's equation (101) which satisfies the boundary condition

$$\lim_{A \to P} \frac{du(A)}{dn_P} = 0 \tag{119}$$

at all points P of the surface S.

Since there does not exist a Green's Function satisfying the boundary condition

$$\left(\frac{dG}{dn_P}\right)_A \to 0, \quad \text{when} \quad A \to P$$

(the corresponding interior von Neumann problem has then no solution), for the interior von Neumann problem we seek a function called the *von Neumann function*

$$G^*(A, B) = \frac{1}{r_{AB}} - g^*(A, B),$$

which also is the sum of a singular part and a regular part which satisfies the boundary condition

$$\frac{dG^*(A, B)}{dn_P} \to C, \quad \text{when} \quad A \to P,$$

where C is a constant.

The function $g^*(A, B)$ is a harmonic function of the point A, which satisfies the von Neumann condition

$$\frac{dg^*(A, B)}{dn_P} \to \frac{d\left(\dfrac{1}{r_{PB}}\right)}{dn_P} - C, \quad \text{when} \quad A \to P.$$

In accordance with our previous argument, this function exists and it is unique (to within an arbitrary constant) if, and only if,

$$\iint_S \left[\frac{d\left(\dfrac{1}{r_{PB}}\right)}{dn_P} - C\right] d\sigma = 0,$$

i.e. when

$$C = \frac{4\pi}{|S|},$$

where $|S|$ is the area of the surface S. It can be shown that the von Neumann function G^* and its derivatives satisfy inequalities analogous to (82). To find now the solution of Poisson's equation (101) which satisfies the von Neumann condition (113), observe that a necessary condition for solubility of the problem is that the function $f(A)$ should satisfy the relation

$$\iiint_{\Omega} f(A)\, d\tau_A = 0 .$$

This condition is also sufficient and the solution is represented by means of the von Neumann function as follows:

$$u(A) = -\frac{1}{4\pi} \iiint_{\Omega} G^*(A, B) f(B)\, dB .$$

In fact, this function satisfies equation (95) at all interior points; it can also be proved, as before, that

$$\frac{du(A)}{dn_P} \to -\frac{1}{4\pi} \iiint_{\Omega} \frac{4\pi}{|S|} f(B)\, dB = 0, \quad \text{when} \quad A \to P .$$

The derived solution is unique to within an arbitrary constant.

§ 5. The Helmholtz equation

The (*generalized*) *Helmholtz differential equation* has the form

$$\Delta u = \lambda p(A) u + q(A), \tag{120}$$

where $p(A)$ and $q(A)$ are known functions defined in a region Ω bounded by a closed surface S, and λ is a parameter. This equation plays an important rôle in theoretical physics, namely in the theory of electric and mechanical vibrations. Equation (120) was investigated by many mathematicians at the end of the nineteenth century, namely by POINCARÉ, SCHWARTZ, STEKLOV, ZAREMBA and others. After the Fredholm discovery it became evident that the properties of the solution of the Helmholtz equation follow directly from the general theorems on the Fredholm integral equation, mainly from the theorems concerning the symmetric kernel.

Assume that the functions $p(A)$ and $q(A)$ satisfy the Hölder condition, and the surface S the Liapunov conditions. We seek a solution of equation (120) which satisfies either the boundary condition

$$u(A) \to 0, \quad \text{when} \quad A \to P, \tag{121}$$

or the mixed boundary condition

$$\frac{du(A)}{dn_P} + a(P)\,u(A) \to 0, \quad \text{when} \quad A \to P. \tag{122}$$

The cases when the boundary values are different from zero can evidently always be reduced to the preceding ones by adding a harmonic function which satisfies the appropriate boundary condition. From the solutions (104) and (111) of Poisson's equation we may state that the function $u(A)$ which at all interior points satisfies equation (120) and the boundary condition (121) or (122) also satisfies the integral equation with weak singularity

$$u(A) = -\frac{\lambda}{4\pi}\iiint\limits_{\Omega} G(A, B)\,p(B)\,u(B)\,dB - \\ -\frac{1}{4\pi}\iiint\limits_{\Omega} G(A, B)\,q(B)\,dB, \tag{123}$$

where $G(A, B)$ is the Green's Function of the first kind in the case of condition (121), and of the second kind for the mixed boundary condition (122). Conversely, a function u which constitutes a continuous solution of the integral equation (123) has first derivatives at all points of Ω and, consequently, in accordance with potential theory, it satisfies the differential equation (120) and one of the boundary conditions (121) or (122).

We now see the fundamental importance of the symmetry of the Green's Function; owing to this property the kernel of equation (123) is of Schmidt type (see Part 1, p. 152) and can be reduced to a symmetric kernel when the function $p(A)$ is positive.

Since the Green's Function is not a degenerated kernel, i.e. it is not a sum of products of functions of a single variable, it follows at once from the properties of the symmetric kernel (Part 1, p. 152) that the kernel of equation (123) has an infinite number of real eigenvalues, i.e. there exist an infinite number of values $\lambda_1, \lambda_2, \ldots, \lambda_n, \ldots$ for which the homogeneous equation

$$u(A) = -\frac{\lambda_n}{4\pi} \iiint_{\Omega} G(A, B)\, p(B)\, u(B)\, dB \tag{124}$$

has non-zero solution, and then also the equation

$$\Delta u = \lambda_n p(A) u$$

has non-zero solutions satisfying the homogeneous boundary conditions (121) or (122).

We now prove that the eigenvalues λ_n of equation (123) are negative both in the case of the Green's Function of the first kind when $p > 0$, and in the case of Green's Function of the second kind when $p > 0$ and $a(P) < 0$. In fact, applying the conclusions of Green's Theorem

$$\iiint_{\Omega} u\, \Delta u\, dA + \iint_{S} u \frac{du}{dn}\, d\sigma$$
$$= - \iiint_{\Omega} \left[\left(\frac{\partial u}{\partial x}\right)^2 + \left(\frac{\partial u}{\partial y}\right)^2 + \left(\frac{\partial u}{\partial z}\right)^2\right] dA \tag{125}$$

to the eigensolution of the equation

$$\Delta u = \lambda_n p(A) u$$

which satisfies the boundary condition $u(P) = 0$, we have

$$\lambda_n \iiint_{\Omega} p(A) u^2\, dA = - \iiint_{\Omega} \left[\left(\frac{\partial u}{\partial x}\right)^2 + \left(\frac{\partial u}{\partial y}\right)^2 + \left(\frac{\partial u}{\partial z}\right)^2\right] dA,$$

i.e. the values λ_n must be negative when $p > 0$.

Applying relation (125) to the eigensolution of the equation

$$\Delta u = \lambda_n p(A) u$$

which satisfies the boundary condition

$$\left(\frac{du}{dn}\right)_P + a(P) u(P) = 0$$

we have

$$\lambda_n \iiint_\Omega p(A) u^2 \, dA - \iint_S a(P) u^2 \, d\sigma$$

$$= - \iiint_\Omega \left[\left(\frac{\partial u}{\partial x}\right)^2 + \left(\frac{\partial u}{\partial y}\right)^2 + \left(\frac{\partial u}{\partial z}\right)^2\right] dA,$$

and therefore again $\lambda_n < 0$ when $p > 0$ and $a < 0$.

Observe that the sequence of absolute values $|\lambda_n|$ tends to infinity, since the values λ_n are the poles of a meromorphic function.

We now proceed to determine the solution u of the Helmholtz equation (120), which, at every point of S, satisfies the von Neumann condition

$$\left(\frac{du}{dn}\right)_P = 0. \tag{126}$$

According to the argument on p. 275, if this function $u(A)$ exists it satisfies the condition

$$\iiint_\Omega [\lambda p(A) u(A) + q(A)] \, dA = 0 \tag{127}$$

and the integral equation

$$u(A) = -\frac{1}{4\pi} \iiint_\Omega G^*(A, B) [\lambda p(B) u(B) + q(B)] \, dB + C, \tag{128}$$

where $G^*(A, B)$ is the von Neumann function satisfying the boundary condition

$$\lim_{A \to P} \frac{dG^*(A, B)}{dn_P} = \frac{4\pi}{|S|}, \tag{129}$$

and C is a constant. The form of equation (128) and condition (129) remains the same if the von Neumann function be completed by an arbitrary function of B. By $G^*(A, B)$ we again mean the Neumann function completed in such a way that

$$\iiint_{\Omega} G^*(A, B)\, p(A)\, dA = 0. \tag{130}$$

This is always possible if we assume that

$$\iiint_{\Omega} p(A)\, dA \neq 0. \tag{131}$$

Conversely, the function $u(A)$ satisfying the system of equations (127) and (128) is a solution of the Helmholtz equation (120) and it satisfies the boundary condition (126). Introducing expression (128) into equation (127) and taking into account relation (130) we observe that the constant C has the value

$$C = -\frac{\iiint_{\Omega} q(A)\, dA}{\lambda \iiint_{\Omega} p(A)\, dA}.$$

Thus, the solution has been reduced to the solution of the integral equation

$$u(A) = -\frac{\lambda}{4\pi} \iiint_{\Omega} G^*(A, B)\, p(B)\, u(B)\, dB - \\ -\frac{1}{4\pi} \iiint_{\Omega} G^*(A, B)\, q(B)\, dB - \frac{\iiint_{\Omega} q(A)\, dA}{\lambda \iiint_{\Omega} p(A)\, dA}. \tag{132}$$

If we assume that $-\lambda/4\pi$ is not an eigenvalue of the kernel $G^*(A, B)\, p(B)$, then the unique solution of the Fredholm equation (132) is the unique solution of the Helmholtz equation, which satisfies the Neumann boundary condition (126).

§ 6. Linear equation of elliptic type

We shall now investigate application of integral equations to boundary value problems for an elliptic type equation with three variables

$$\Delta u(A) = \sum_{j=1}^{3} F_j(A) \frac{\partial u(A)}{\partial x_j} + p(A) u(A) + q(A), \tag{133}$$

where x_1, x_2, x_3 denote the coordinates of the point A. We assume that the functions $F_j(A), p(A)$ and $q(A)$ are defined and satisfy the Hölder condition in a region Ω bounded by a surface S which as usual obeys the Liapunov conditions.

We seek a function $u(A)$ continuous in the closure of Ω, which at all points P of the boundary S of this region satisfies either the Dirichlet condition

$$\lim_{A \to P} u(A) = 0, \tag{134}$$

or the mixed condition

$$\lim_{A \to P} \left[\frac{du(A)}{dn_P} + a(P) u(A) \right] = 0. \tag{135}$$

The more general case when the right-hand sides of conditions (134) and (135) are non-zero can evidently be reduced to the considered case by adding to the solution an appropriate harmonic function.

On the basis of the argument concerning Poisson's equation (p. 267) we can state that if there exists a function $u(A)$ satisfying equation (133) and the boundary condition (134) or (135), then this function also satisfies the integro-differential equation

$$u(A) = -\frac{1}{4\pi} \iiint_{\Omega} G(A, B) \left[\sum_{j=1}^{3} F_j(B) \frac{\partial u(B)}{\partial \xi_j} + p(B) u(B) + q(B) \right] dB, \tag{136}$$

where ξ_1, ξ_2, ξ_3 denote the coordinates of the point B and $G(A, B)$ is the Green's Function of the first or second kind (assuming that the mixed problem has a unique solution).

Consider therefore the solution of equation (136). To this end we examine the system of linear integral equations

$$\begin{aligned} u(A) &= -\frac{1}{4\pi}\iiint\limits_{\Omega} G(A,B)\left[\sum_{j=1}^{3} F_j(B)u_j(B)+\right.\\ &\qquad\left. +p(B)u(B)+q(B)\right]dB \quad (i=1,2,3),\\ u_i(A) &= -\frac{1}{4\pi}\iiint\limits_{\Omega} \frac{\partial G(A,B)}{\partial x_i}\left[\sum_{j=1}^{3} F_j(B)u_j(B)+\right.\\ &\qquad\left. +p(B)u(B)+q(B)\right]dB \end{aligned} \tag{137}$$

with four unknown functions $u(A), u_1(A), u_2(A), u_3(A)$.

According to property (82) of the Green's Function equations (137) have weak singularities.

The system of integral equations (137) can be reduced in the familiar way to one Fredholm equation (see Chapter VIII). Consider, therefore, four regions $\Omega, \Omega_1, \Omega_2$ and Ω_3 displaced parallel with respect to each other and having no common points. Let A, A_1, A_2 and A_3 denote the points of these regions which correspond in the above displacement. Then the system of integral equations (137) is equivalent to one Fredholm equation

$$U(A^*) = -\frac{1}{4\pi}\iiint\limits_{D} N(A^*, B^*)\,U(B^*)\,d\tau_{B^*}+f(A^*), \tag{138}$$

where $U(A)$ is the unknown function in the domain $D = \Omega +\Omega_1+\Omega_2+\Omega_3$ and the kernel $N(A^*, B^*)$ is a known function of the pair of points of the domain D, defined by the formulae

$$\begin{aligned} N(A,B) &= G(A,B)\,p(B),\\ N(A,B_\alpha) &= G(A,B)\,F_\alpha(B),\\ N(A_\alpha,B) &= \frac{\partial G(A,B)}{\partial x_\alpha}\,p(B),\\ N(A_\alpha,B_\beta) &= \frac{\partial G(A,B)}{\partial x_\alpha}\,F_\beta(B) \quad (\alpha=1,2,3,\ \beta=1,2,3), \end{aligned} \tag{139}$$

The function $f(A^*)$ is defined in D by the formulae

$$f(A) = -\frac{1}{4\pi}\iiint\limits_{\Omega} G(A, B)\, q(B)\, dB,$$

$$f(A_\alpha) = -\frac{1}{4\pi}\iiint\limits_{\Omega} \frac{\partial G(A, B)}{\partial x_\alpha}\, q(B)\, dB \quad (\alpha = 1, 2, 3). \tag{140}$$

The integral equation (138) can, by a finite number of iterations, be reduced to an equivalent Fredholm equation with a bounded kernel.

If we assume that the number $-1/4\pi$ is not an eigenvalue of the kernel $N(A^*, B^*)$, then there exists a unique solution of equation (138) determined by the first Fredholm Theorem.

If the number $-1/4\pi$ is an eigenvalue of the kernel $N(A^*, B^*)$, then the solution is determined by the third Fredholm Theorem, provided that the function $q(A)$ satisfies the familiar necessary and sufficient conditions of orthogonality. Thus the problem may have no solution.

If $U(A^*)$ is a solution of equation (138), the solution of the system of equations (137) is given by the formulae

$$u(A) = U(A), \quad u_j(A) = U(A_j) \quad (j = 1, 2, 3).$$

These functions are defined and continuous in the set $\Omega + S$.

We see from the system of equations (137) that in view of the familiar theorem from potential theory (see p. 303) the functions $u_j(A)$ are the partial derivatives of the function $u(A)$,

$$u_j(A) = \frac{\partial u(A)}{\partial x_j} \quad (j = 1, 2, 3),$$

and therefore $u(A)$ satisfies the integro-differential equation (136).

To prove that $u(A)$ satisfies the differential equation (133), we first prove the following lemma.

LEMMA 4. *If $F(A)$ is bounded and integrable in the region Ω, then the derivatives of the potential of spatial charge expressed by the integral*

$$I(A) = \iiint\limits_{\Omega} \frac{x_j - \xi_j}{r_{AB}^3} F(B)\, dB \quad (j = 1, 2, 3) \tag{141}$$

satisfy the Hölder condition in Ω with an arbitrary exponent λ smaller than unity,

$$|I(A) - I(A_1)| < C M_F r_{AA_1}^{\lambda}, \tag{142}$$

where M_P is the upper bound of $|F|$ and C is a positive constant depending only on the surface S and the selected value of λ.

Consider two arbitrary points A and A_1 of the set $\Omega + S$. Introduce the sphere K of radius $2r_{AA_1}$, centred at the point A, and decompose the integrals $I(A)$ and $I(A_1)$ into two terms

$$\begin{aligned} I(A) &= I^{K^*}(A) + I^{\Omega - K^*}(A), \\ I(A_1) &= I^{K^*}(A_1) + I^{\Omega - K^*}(A_1), \end{aligned} \tag{143}$$

the integration being carried out over that part K^* of Ω located inside K, and over the remaining exterior part $\Omega - K^*$. Applying the homothetic transformation from the point A which reduces K to a sphere K' of unit radius, we obtain

$$\begin{aligned} |I^{K^*}(A)| &\leqq M_F \iiint\limits_{K} \frac{dB}{r_{AB}^2} \\ &= 2M_F r_{AA_1} \iiint\limits_{K'} \frac{dB'}{r_{AB'}^2} \leqq 8\pi M_F r_{AA_1} \end{aligned} \tag{144}$$

and an analogous inequality for the integral $I^{K^*}(A_1)$:

$$\begin{aligned} I^{K^*}(A_1) &\leqq M_F \iiint\limits_{K} \frac{dB}{r_{A_1 B}^2} = 2M_F r_{AA_1} \iiint\limits_{K'} \frac{dB'}{r_{A_1' B'}^2} \\ &\leqq 2M_F r_{AA_1} \int\limits_0^{3/2} 4\pi\, dr = 12\pi M_F r_{AA_1}. \end{aligned} \tag{144'}$$

We now proceed to investigate the difference between the second terms of sums (143), expressing it as follows:

$$I^{\Omega-K^*}(A)-I^{\Omega-K^*}(A_1)$$

$$=\iiint\limits_{\Omega-K^*}\frac{x_j-\bar{x}_j}{r_{AB}^3}F(B)\,dB+\iiint\limits_{\Omega-K^*}(\bar{x}_j-\xi_j)\left(\frac{1}{r_{AB}^3}-\frac{1}{r_{A_1B}^3}\right)F(B)\,dB,$$

where $\bar{x}_1, \bar{x}_2, \bar{x}_3$ are the coordinates of the point A_1.

We have the inequality

$$\left|\iiint\limits_{\Omega-K^*}\frac{x_j-\bar{x}_j}{r_{AB}^3}F(B)\,d\tau_B\right|$$

$$\leqq M_F r_{AA_1}\int\limits_{2r_{AA_1}}^{L}\frac{4\pi r^2\,dr}{r^3}=4\pi M_F r_{AA_1}\log\frac{L}{2r_{AA_1}}, \tag{145}$$

where L denotes the diameter of the region Ω.

Further, taking into account that

$$\frac{1}{2}\leqq\frac{r_{A_1B}}{r_{AB}}\leqq\frac{3}{2},$$

if $B\in\Omega-K^*$ we have

$$\left|\iiint\limits_{\Omega-K^*}(\bar{x}_j-\xi_j)\left(\frac{1}{r_{AB}^3}-\frac{1}{r_{A_1B}^3}\right)F(B)\,dB\right|$$

$$\leqq M_F\iiint\limits_{\Omega-K^*}\frac{|r_{AB}-r_{A_1B}|\,(r_{AB}^2+r_{AB}r_{A_1B}+r_{A_1B}^2)}{r_{AB}^3 r_{A_1B}^3}\,dB$$

$$<19M_F r_{AA_1}\iiint\limits_{\Omega-K^*}\frac{dB}{r_{AB}^3}<76\pi M_F r_{AA_1}\log\frac{L}{2r_{AA_1}}. \tag{146}$$

Combining the results (144), (144′), (145) and (146) we arrive at the stated inequality (142).

Observe now that the equations of the system (137) can be written in the form

$$u_j(A) = \frac{1}{4\pi} \iiint\limits_{\Omega} \frac{x_j - \xi_j}{r_{AB}^3} \left[\sum_{j=1}^{3} F_j(B) u_j(B) + \right.$$

$$\left. + p(B) u(B) + q(B) \right] dB -$$

$$- \frac{1}{4\pi} \iiint\limits_{\Omega} \frac{\partial g(A, B)}{\partial x_j} \left[\sum_{j=1}^{3} F_j(B) u_j(B) + \right.$$

$$\left. + p(B) u(B) + q(B) \right] dB. \qquad (147)$$

In view of the assumed continuity of the functions u and u_j and the above proved lemma, we may state that the first integral of the sum (147) satisfies the Hölder condition in the closure $\Omega + S$ of Ω; the second integral, in view of the known properties of the harmonic function g, has bounded derivatives in the neighbourhood of every interior point A located inside Ω. It follows therefore that the functions $u_j(A)$ satisfy the Hölder condition in the neighbourhood of every interior point A, and consequently (see Theorem on p. 271) the function $u(A)$ satisfying the integral equation (136) also satisfies the differential equation (133) at all interior points A of Ω.

The properties of the solution (111) of Poisson's equation also imply that the determined function $u(A)$ satisfies the boundary condition (134) or (135).

§ 7. Semi-linear equation of elliptic type

We now proceed to investigate an elliptic type of more general form

$$\Delta u(A) = F\left(A, u, \frac{\partial u}{\partial x_1}, \frac{\partial u}{\partial x_2}, \frac{\partial u}{\partial x_3}\right). \qquad (148)$$

We assume that the function of 2.3+1 variables

$$F(x_1, x_2, x_3, u, p_1, p_2, p_3) \qquad (149)$$

is defined in the closed bounded domain

$$[A(x_1, x_2, x_3) \in \Omega + S, \ |u| \leqq R, \quad |p_j| \leqq R] \qquad (j = 1, 2, 3) \qquad (150)$$

and that it satisfies the Hölder condition with respect to all variables in the domain (150).

We seek a function $u(x_1, x_2, x_3)$ which satisfies equation (148) at every interior point A of Ω and obeys the boundary condition

$$\lim_{A \to P} \left[\frac{du(A)}{dn_P} \right] + a(P) u(P) = 0 \qquad (151)$$

at all points P of the surface S bounding Ω. We assume as before that the function $a(P)$ defined on S satisfies the Hölder condition.

In accordance with the investigations of the Poisson's equation, the function $u(A)$, satisfying equation (148) and the boundary condition (151), also satisfies the integro-differential equation

$$u(A) = -\frac{1}{4\pi} \iiint_{\Omega} G(A, B) \times$$
$$\times F \left[B, u(B), \frac{\partial u(B)}{\partial \xi_1}, \frac{\partial u(B)}{\partial \xi_2}, \frac{\partial u(B)}{\partial \xi_3} \right] dB, \qquad (152)$$

where ξ_1, ξ_2, ξ_3 denote the coordinates of the point B.

The boundary problem for equation (148) has thus been reduced to the investigation of the integro-differential equation (152). To solve the latter, consider the system of integral equations

$$u(A)$$
$$= -\frac{1}{4\pi} \iiint_{\Omega} G(A, B) F[B, u(B), u_1(B), u_2(B), u_3(B)] \, dB,$$
$$(153)$$
$$u_j(A)$$
$$= -\frac{1}{4\pi} \iiint_{\Omega} \frac{\partial G(A, B)}{\partial x_j} F[B, u(B), u_1(B), u_2(B), u_3(B)] \, dB$$
$$(j = 1, 2, 3)$$

with four unknown functions u, u_1, u_2, u_3. The Hölder condition assumed for the function F is insufficient to solve system (153) by the classical method of successive approximations. Therefore we solve system (153) by applying Schauder's Fixed Point Theorem. Consider the space T the points of which are all systems

$$U = [u(A), u_1(A), u_2(A), u_3(A)]$$

of four real functions defined and continuous in the closure of the domain Ω.

The sum of two points $U = [u, u_1, u_2, u_3]$ and $\bar{U} = [\bar{u}, \bar{u}_1, \bar{u}_2, \bar{u}_3]$ and the product of U by a real number γ are defined by the formulae

$$\begin{aligned} U+\bar{U} &= [\bar{u}+u, \bar{u}_1+u_1, \bar{u}_2+u_2, \bar{u}_3+u_3], \\ \gamma U &= [\gamma u, \gamma u_1, \gamma u_2, \gamma u_3]. \end{aligned} \tag{154}$$

The distance $\delta(U, \bar{U})$ between two points U and $\bar{U}$ is defined by

$$\delta(U, \bar{U}) = \sup|u(A)-\bar{u}(A)| + \sum_{j=1}^{3} \sup|u_j(A)-\bar{u}_j(A)|, \tag{155}$$

while the norm of the point U is its distance from the zero point $\Theta = [0, 0, 0, 0]$:

$$\|U\| = \delta(U, \Theta) = \sup|u(A)| + \sum_{j=1}^{3} \sup|u_j(A)|. \tag{156}$$

Thus the space T is linear, metric and normed. This space is, of course, complete (see p. 196) and therefore it is a Banach space.

Consider now in the space T a bounded set E of points $U = [u(A), u_1(A), u_2(A), u_3(A)]$ which satisfy the inequalities

$$|u(A)| \leq R, \quad |u_j(A)| \leq R \quad (j = 1, 2, 3), \tag{157}$$

where R is the positive number appearing in inequalities (150). The set E is closed and convex; this follows from the considerations on p. 207

To prove the existence in E of a point $U = [u(A), u_1(A), u_2(A), u_3(A)]$ which is the solution of the system of integral equations (153), consider the functional transformation

$$
\begin{aligned}
& v(A) \\
& = -\frac{1}{4\pi}\iiint\limits_{\Omega} G(A,B)\,F[B,u(B),u_1(B),u_2(B),u_3(B)]\,dB, \\
& && (158) \\
& v_j(A) \\
& = -\frac{1}{4\pi}\iiint\limits_{\Omega} \frac{\partial G(A,B)}{\partial x_j}\,F[B,u(B),u_1(B),u_2(B),u_3(B)]\,dB \\
& \qquad (j=1,2,3),
\end{aligned}
$$

which associates with every point $U=[u,u_1,u_2,u_3]$ in the set E a point $V=[v,v_1,v_2,v_3]$ of T.

We establish a condition which ensures that the set E' of all transformed points V of the set E be a subset of E. For this purpose, applying the properties of the Green's Function

$$
|G(A,B)|<\frac{c_1'}{r_{AB}}, \qquad \left|\frac{\partial G(A,B)}{\partial x_j}\right|<\frac{c_2'}{r_{AB}^{3-h}} \tag{159}
$$

we obtain for functions (158) the inequalities

$$
\begin{aligned}
|v(A)| &< \frac{M_F c_1'}{4\pi}\iiint\limits_{\Omega}\frac{d\tau_B}{r_{AB}} < \frac{M_F c_1'}{4\pi}\int_0^L \frac{4\pi r^2\,dr}{r} = \frac{M_F c_1'}{2}L^2, \\
& && (160) \\
|v_j(A)| &< \frac{M_F c_2'}{4\pi}\iiint\limits_{\Omega}\frac{d\tau_B}{r_{AB}^{3-h}} < \frac{M_F c_2'}{4\pi}\int_0^L \frac{4\pi r^2\,dr}{r^{3-h}} = \frac{M_F c_2'}{h}L^h \\
& \qquad (j=1,2,3),
\end{aligned}
$$

where M_F denotes the upper bound of the known function $|F|$ in the domain (150), and L is the diameter of Ω. We infer now that E' is a subset of the set E if M_F and L satisfies simultaneously the two inequalities

$$
M_F L^2 \leqq \frac{2R}{c_1'} \quad \text{and} \quad M_F L^h \leqq \frac{hR}{c_2'}. \tag{161}
$$

If the diameter L is prescribed *a priori*, then conditions (161) are satisfied if the upper bound M_F satisfies the condition

$$M_F < \min\left(\frac{2R}{c_1' L^2}, \frac{hR}{c_2' L^h}\right). \tag{162}$$

If M_F is prescribed then the initial conditions are satisfied when the diameter L of Ω satisfies the condition

$$L < \min\left[\left(\frac{2R}{c_1' M_F}\right)^{1/2}, \left(\frac{hR}{c_2' M_F}\right)^{1/h}\right]. \tag{163}$$

We now prove that transformation (158) is continuous in T. Consider therefore an arbitrary sequence of points $U_\nu = [u^{(\nu)}, u_1^{(\nu)}, u_2^{(\nu)}, u_3^{(\nu)}]$ of E converging to the point $U = [u, u_1, u_2, u_3]$ of this set; thus we have

$$\delta(U_\nu, U) \to 0, \quad \text{when} \quad \nu \to \infty,$$

and consequently the functional sequences $\{u^{(\nu)}(A)\}$ and $\{u_j^{(\nu)}(A)\}$ are uniformly convergent to the functions $u(A)$ and $u_j(A)$. We prove that the transformed functions

$$\begin{aligned} v^{(\nu)}(A) &= -\frac{1}{4\pi}\iiint\limits_{\Omega} G(A, B) F[B, u^{(\nu)}, u_1^{(\nu)}, u_2^{(\nu)}, u_3^{(\nu)}]\, dB, \\ v_j^{(\nu)}(A) &= -\frac{1}{4\pi}\iiint\limits_{\Omega} \frac{\partial G(A, B)}{\partial x_j} F[B, u^{(\nu)}, u_1^{(\nu)}, u_2^{(\nu)}, u_3^{(\nu)}]\, dB \\ & \qquad (j = 1, 2, 3) \end{aligned} \tag{164}$$

tend uniformly to functions $v(A)$ and $v_j(A)$ corresponding to the limit functions $u(A)$ and $u_j(A)$ according to transformation (158). In fact, by virtue of property (159) of the Green's Function, we have

$$\begin{aligned} & |v^{(\nu)}(A) - v(A)| \\ & < \frac{c_1'}{4\pi}\iiint\limits_{\Omega} \frac{|F(B, u^{(\nu)}, u_1^{(\nu)}, u_2^{(\nu)}, u_3^{(\nu)}) - F(B, u, u_1, u_2, u_3)|}{r_{AB}}\, dB, \\ & |v_j^{(\nu)}(A) - v_j(A)| \\ & < \frac{c_2'}{4\pi}\iiint\limits_{\Omega} \frac{|F(B, u^{(\nu)}, u_1^{(\nu)}, u_2^{(\nu)}, u_3^{(\nu)}) - F(B, u, u_1, u_2, u_3)|}{r_{AB}^{3-h}}\, dB \\ & \qquad (j = 1, 2, 3). \end{aligned} \tag{165}$$

Moreover, in view of the continuity of F and the uniform convergence of the sequences $\{u^{(\nu)}\}$ and $\{u_j^{(\nu)}\}$, given $\varepsilon > 0$ we can select a positive integer N_ε, such that

$$|F(B, u^{(\nu)}, u_1^{(\nu)}, u_2^{(\nu)}, u_3^{(\nu)}) - F(B, u, u_1, u_2, u_3)| < \kappa\varepsilon, \quad \text{when} \quad \nu > N_\varepsilon,$$

where

$$\kappa = \min\left(\frac{2}{c_1' L^2}, \frac{h}{c_2' L^h}\right).$$

On the basis of inequality (160) this implies that

$$|v^{(\nu)}(A) - v(A)| < \varepsilon \quad \text{and} \quad |v_j^{(\nu)}(A) - v_j(A)| < \varepsilon, \quad \text{when} \quad \nu > N_\varepsilon,$$

and consequently the sequence of transformed points $V_\nu = [v^{(\nu)}, v_1^{(\nu)}, v_2^{(\nu)}, v_3^{(\nu)}]$ tends to point $V = [v, v_1, v_2, v_3]$ corresponding to the limit point $U = [u, u_1, u_2, u_3]$ according to transformation (158), and moreover the transformation is continuous.

It remains to prove that the set E' of the transformed points is relatively compact. To this end, it is sufficient to prove that the functions (158) are equicontinuous. We shall prove this property for the functions $v_j(A)$, which, for this purpose, we decompose in the following way:

$$v_j(A) = \frac{1}{4\pi} \iiint\limits_{\Omega} \frac{x_j - \xi_j}{r_{AB}^3} F[B, u(B), u_1(B), u_2(B), u_3(B)]\, dB +$$

$$+ \frac{1}{4\pi} \iiint\limits_{\Omega} \frac{\partial g(A, B)}{\partial x_j} F[B, u(B), u_1(B), u_2(B), u_3(B)]\, dB$$

$$= v_j^{\mathrm{I}}(A) + v_j^{\mathrm{II}}(A) \quad (j = 1, 2, 3). \quad (166)$$

The first term represents functions which in view of Lemma 4 satisfy the same Hölder condition (142), since M_F is common for all functions of the set E, and, consequently, all functions $v_j^{\mathrm{I}}(A)$ are equicontinuous, i.e. they satisfy the inequality

$$|v_j^{\mathrm{I}}(A) - v_j^{\mathrm{I}}(A_1)| < \varepsilon, \quad \text{when} \quad r_{AA_1} < \eta,$$

η depending only on ε.

To investigate the second integral $v_j^{II}(A)$ observe that $g(A,B)$ constitutes the potential (51) of surface distribution with density $\psi(P,B)$, i.e.

$$v_j^{II}(A) = \frac{1}{4\pi}\frac{\partial}{\partial x_j}\iiint_{\Omega} g(A,B)F[B,u(B),u_1(B),u_2(B),u_3(B)]\,dB = \frac{\partial}{\partial x_j}\left[\iint_S \frac{W(P)}{r_{AP}}\,d\sigma_P\right], \tag{167}$$

where

$$W(P) = \frac{1}{4\pi}\iiint_{\Omega} \psi(P,B)F[B,u(B),u_1(B),u_2(B),u_3(B)]\,dB. \tag{168}$$

Applying to integral (168) the same method as to integral (141) and taking into account property (79) of the function $\psi(P,B)$, we can prove that on S the function $W(P)$ satisfies the Hölder condition

$$|W(P)-W(P_1)| \leqq k_1 M_F r_{PP_1}^{h_1}, \tag{169}$$

where h_1 is an arbitrary positive number smaller than h and k_1 is a positive constant depending only on the surface S and h_1.

Property (169) of density $W(P)$ makes it possible to infer that the functions (167) constituting the derivatives of a potential of surface distribution with density $W(P)$ tend uniformly to their boundary values defined at all points of the surface S, and that every such function is uniformly continuous in the set $\Omega+S$.

To prove that these functions are equicontinuous, observe from investigations of the existence of the boundary values of the derivatives of a potential of surface distribution (see formulae (94) and (95)), their uniform convergence to these boundary values, and in view of the Hölder condition (169), for the investigation of the continuity of functions (167), knowledge of the upper bound of function $|F|$ only is required. For, given

$\varepsilon > 0$, we can select a surface S' located inside Ω so close to the boundary surface S that in the region Ω^* between the surfaces S and S', and on these surfaces, the inequality

$$|v_j^{\mathrm{II}}(A) - v_j^{\mathrm{II}}(A_1)| < \varepsilon, \quad \text{when} \quad r_{AA_1} < \eta_\varepsilon, \tag{170}$$

is satisfied, where η_ε depends on ε and the upper bound M_F only, and is independent of the functions u, u_1, u_2, u_3. Observe now that in region $\Omega - \Omega^*$ the function $v_j^{\mathrm{II}}(A)$ has bounded derivatives, for we have then in view of property (101), the inequality

$$\left| \iiint\limits_{\Omega} \frac{\partial^2 g(A, B)}{\partial x_i \partial x_j} F[B, u(B), u_1(B), u_2(B), u_3(B)]\, dB \right| < \frac{4q}{\inf r_{AP}} V_\Omega M_F, \tag{171}$$

where $\inf r_{AP}$ denotes the greatest lower bound of the distances of points A of $\Omega - \Omega^*$ from points P of the surface S, and V_Ω is the volume of Ω.

Hence, in region $\Omega - \Omega^*$, $v_j^{\mathrm{II}}(A)$ satisfies the Lipschitz condition with the same coefficient for all functions u, u_1, u_2, u_3. Therefore we can select for number ε a number η'_ε such that

$$|v_j^{\mathrm{II}}(A) - v_j^{\mathrm{II}}(A_1)| < \varepsilon, \quad \text{when} \quad r_{AA_1} < \eta'_\varepsilon,$$

for all points A and A_1 of Ω, and for all functions u, u_1, u_2, u_3 simultaneously. Therefore we infer that $v_j^{\mathrm{II}}(A)$ satisfies the inequality

$$|v_j^{\mathrm{II}}(A) - v_j^{\mathrm{II}}(A_1)| < \varepsilon,$$

when the distance r_{AA_1} of two arbitrary points A and A_1 from Ω is less than the smaller of the two numbers η_ε and η'_ε, independent of the point $[u, u_1, u_2, u_3]$ of E. Consequently, the functions $v_1(A)$ are equicontinuous in Ω, and since they are uniformly bounded (p. 201), the transformed set E' is relatively compact, in accordance with Arzéla's Theorem.

Thus, all conditions of Schauder's Theorem are fulfilled, and therefore (provided inequalities (161) are satisfied) there exists at least one fixed point in E with respect to transformation (158), i.e. there exists a system of functions

$$u(A), u_1(A), u_2(A), u_3(A) \tag{172}$$

continuous in $\Omega+S$, which is a solution of the system of integral equations (153).

This implies at once that the functions $u_1(A), u_2(A)$ and $u_3(A)$ are the derivatives of $u(A)$:

$$u_j(A) = \frac{\partial u(A)}{\partial x_j} \qquad (A \in \Omega,\ j = 1, 2, 3),$$

and consequently, $u(A)$ satisfies the integro-differential equation

$$u(A) = -\frac{1}{4\pi} \iiint\limits_{\Omega} G(A, B) \times$$
$$\times F\left[B, u(B), \frac{\partial u}{\partial \xi_1}, \frac{\partial u}{\partial \xi_2}, \frac{\partial u}{\partial \xi_3}\right] dB \tag{173}$$

at all points $A \in \Omega+S$.

Observe that in view of Lemma 4, the functions $u_j(A)$ satisfy the Hölder condition in every region Ω' located inside region Ω, and therefore the compound function

$$F\left[B, u(B), \frac{\partial u(B)}{\partial \xi_1}, \frac{\partial u(B)}{\partial \xi_2}, \frac{\partial u(B)}{\partial \xi_3}\right] = \Phi(B)$$

by virtue of the assumptions on function $F(B, u, p_1, p_2, p_3)$, satisfies the Hölder condition in every interior region Ω. Hence we infer that the function (173) satisfies the equation

$$\Delta u(A) = F\left[A, u(A), \frac{\partial u(A)}{\partial x_1}, \frac{\partial u(A)}{\partial x_2}, \frac{\partial u(A)}{\partial x_3}\right]$$

at every interior point A of Ω.

In accordance with inequality (173) and the investigation of integral (111), the determined function $u(A)$ satisfies the considered boundary condition (151) at every point P of the surface S.

If, for the function $P(A, u, p_1, p_2, p_3)$, we made the assumptions somewhat stronger, namely that it satisfies the Hölder condition with respect to point A and the Lipschitz condition with respect to variables u, p_1, p_2, p_3, i.e. that

$$|F(A, u, p_1, p_2, p_3) - F(\bar{A}, \bar{u}, \bar{p}_1, \bar{p}_2, \bar{p}_3)| < k\left[r_{A\bar{A}}^{\mu} + |u-\bar{u}| + |p_1-\bar{p}_1| + |p_2-\bar{p}_2| + |p_3-\bar{p}_3|\right] \quad (174)$$

in domain (150), then the considered boundary problem for equation (148) can be solved by the classical method of successive approximation.

Thus, we construct the sequence of functions

$$u^{(0)}(A), u^{(1)}(A), u^{(2)}(A), \ldots, u^{(n)}(A), \ldots \quad (175)$$

by means of the recursive relation

$$u^{(n+1)}(A) = -\frac{1}{4\pi}\iiint_{\Omega} G(A, B) \times F\left[B, u^{(n)}(B), \frac{\partial u^{(n)}(B)}{\partial \xi_1}, \frac{\partial u^{(n)}(B)}{\partial \xi_2}, \frac{\partial u^{(n)}(B)}{\partial \xi_3}\right] dB, \quad (176)$$

whence

$$\frac{\partial u^{(n+1)}(A)}{\partial x_j} = -\frac{1}{4\pi}\iiint_{\Omega} \frac{\partial G(A, B)}{\partial x_j} \times F\left[B, u^{(n)}(B), \frac{\partial u^{(n)}(B)}{\partial \xi_1}, \frac{\partial u^{(n)}(B)}{\partial \xi_2}, \frac{\partial u^{(n)}(B)}{\partial \xi_3}\right] dB. \quad (177)$$

We first observe that if the first approximation $u^{(0)}(A)$ satisfies the conditions

$$|u^{(0)}(A)| \leq R, \quad \left|\frac{\partial u^{(0)}(A)}{\partial x_j}\right| \leq R,$$

and, moreover, the upper bound M_F and diameter L of Ω satisfy inequalities (161), then, in view of property (159) of the Green's Function, all approximations of the sequence (175) satisfy, in Ω, the inequalities

$$|u^{(n)}(A)| \leq R, \quad \left|\frac{\partial u^{(n)}(A)}{\partial x_j}\right| \leq R \quad (178)$$

and the sequence (175) is defined for all n. To prove the convergence of sequence (175) we investigate the difference between successive terms. Applying condition (174) and property (159) we obtain

$$|u^{(n+1)}(A)-u^{(n)}(A)|$$
$$<\frac{c_1'}{4\pi}\iiint_{\Omega}\frac{k}{r_{AB}}\Big[|u^{(n)}(B)-u^{(n-1)}(B)|+$$
$$+\sum_{j=1}^{3}\left|\frac{\partial u^{(n)}(B)}{\partial\xi_j}-\frac{\partial u^{(n-1)}(B)}{\partial\xi_j}\right|\Big]dB,$$

$$\left|\frac{\partial u^{(n+1)}(A)}{\partial x_j}-\frac{\partial u^{(n)}(A)}{\partial x_j}\right| \tag{179}$$
$$<\frac{c_2'}{4\pi}\iiint_{\Omega}\frac{k}{r_{AB}^{3-h}}\Big[|u^{(n)}(B)-u^{(n-1)}(B)|+$$
$$+\sum_{j=1}^{3}\left|\frac{\partial u^{(n)}(B)}{\partial\xi_j}-\frac{\partial u^{(n-1)}(B)}{\partial\xi_j}\right|\Big]dB.$$

These inequalities imply the following:

$$|u^{(n+1)}(A)-u^{(n)}(A)|+\sum_{j=1}^{3}\left|\frac{\partial u^{(n+1)}(A)}{\partial x_j}-\frac{\partial u^{(n)}(A)}{\partial x_j}\right|$$
$$\leq\left(\frac{1}{2}c_1'L^2+\frac{3}{h}c_2'L^h\right)k\sup\Big[|u^{(n)}(A)-u^{(n-1)}(A)|+$$
$$+\sum_{j=1}^{3}\left|\frac{\partial u^{(n)}(A)}{\partial x_j}-\frac{\partial u^{(n-1)}(A)}{\partial x_j}\right|\Big].$$

Hence the series

$$u^{(0)}(A)+\sum_{n=0}^{\infty}[u^{(n+1)}(A)-u^{(n)}(A)],$$
$$\tag{180}$$
$$\frac{\partial u^{(0)}(A)}{\partial x_j}+\sum_{n=0}^{\infty}\left[\frac{\partial u^{(n+1)}(A)}{\partial x_j}-\frac{\partial u^{(n)}(A)}{\partial x_j}\right]$$

are absolutely and uniformly convergent in $\Omega+S$, and therefore the sequence of functions (175) tends to a differentiable function $u(A)$ which satisfies the integro-differential equation (173), provided the diameter L satisfies the condition

$$\left(\frac{1}{2}c_1' L^2+\frac{3c_2' L^h}{h}\right)k<1. \tag{181}$$

In view of a known result, the derived function $u(A) = \lim u_n(A)$ satisfies the differential equation (148) and the boundary condition (151). In a familiar way we can prove that the derived solution is unique.

The merit of the method of successive approximations is that it yields the proof of uniqueness of the solution. It has, however, the disadvantage as compared with the method based on Schauder's Theorem, that it requires a stronger condition (174) concerning the function F and the additional condition (181) concerning the diameter of Ω.

§ 8. Non-linear boundary problem

A *non-linear boundary problem* for Laplace's equation consists in the determination of a function u satisfying the Laplace equation inside a region Ω bounded by a surface S, which at every point $P\in S$ satisfies the non-linear relation

$$\frac{du}{dn_P}+a(P)\,u_P=F(P,u_P) \tag{182}$$

between the boundary values of the normal derivative and the function itself. This problem was investigated by CARLEMAN and LICHTENSTEIN [27] by the methods of classical analysis.

We shall solve this problem by the fixed point method, assuming only that the given function $F(P, u)$ defined in the closed domain

$$[P\in S, |u|\leqq R] \tag{183}$$

is continuous at every point of this domain. Concerning the function $a(P)$ we assume only that it is continuous and that the corresponding linear mixed problem has a unique solution (e.g. when $a < 0$).

As usual we seek the solution in the form of potential of surface distribution

$$u(A) = \iint\limits_S \frac{\varphi(Q)\, d\sigma_Q}{r_{AQ}} \tag{184}$$

with unknown density $\varphi(Q)$. If we demand that the function (184) satisfies the boundary condition (182) we obtain, in view of formulae (6) for the boundary values of the normal derivative, the non-linear integral equation

$$-2\pi\varphi(P) + \iint\limits_S \left[\frac{\cos \nu_{PQ}}{r_{PQ}^2} + a(P)\frac{1}{r_{PQ}}\right] \varphi(Q)\, d\sigma_Q = F\left[P, \iint\limits_S \frac{\varphi(Q)}{r_{PQ}} d\sigma_Q\right] \tag{185}$$

with unknown function $\varphi(P)$.

In accordance with the assumption, the linear equation

$$-2\pi\,\varphi(P) + \iint\limits_S \left[\frac{\cos \nu_{PQ}}{r_{PQ}^2} + \frac{a(P)}{r_{PQ}}\right] \varphi(Q)\, d\sigma_Q = f(P), \tag{186}$$

corresponding to the linear mixed problem, has a unique solution for every function $f(P)$ continuous on the surface S. According to the Liapunov conditions assumed for S, the kernel

$$N(P, Q) = \frac{\cos \nu_{PQ}}{r_{PQ}^2} + \frac{a(P)}{r_{PQ}} \tag{187}$$

of equation (186) satisfies the inequality (see (19))

$$|N(P, Q)| < \frac{k_1'}{r_{PQ}^{2-\kappa}}, \tag{188}$$

and therefore it has a weak singularity.

In view of the assumption of continuity of the function $F(P, u)$ only, equation (185) cannot be solved by the method of successive approximation, and we shall solve it using Schauder's Theorem. Consider, therefore, the space T of all functions $\varphi(P)$ continuous on the surface S. This space is a Banach space if we adopt the familiar definitions of addition, multiplication, distance and norm. In the space T we now consider set E consisting of all functions $\varphi(P)$ defined on the surface S and satisfying the inequality

$$|\varphi(P)| \leqq \frac{R}{s}, \tag{189}$$

where s denotes the upper bound of the integral

$$\iint_S \frac{d\sigma}{r_{PQ}}$$

and R is as in inequality (183).

Evidently E is complete and convex.

In view of the integral equation (185), let us now apply to points of E the transformation defined by

$$-2\pi\psi(P) + \iint_S \left[\frac{\cos\nu_{PQ}}{r_{PQ}^2} + \frac{a(P)}{r_{PQ}}\right]\psi(Q)\,d\sigma_Q = F\left[P, \iint_S \frac{\varphi(Q)}{r_{PQ}}\,d\sigma_Q\right]. \tag{190}$$

According to the assumption made with respect to the Fredholm equation (186), equation (190) associates with every point $\varphi(P)$ of R a point $\psi(P)$ of T. It follows from the form of the solution of the Fredholm equation that there exists a sufficiently large positive number, depending on the surface S and the function a, such that the solution of equation (190) satisfies the inequality

$$|\psi| < K \sup |F(P, u)|.$$

Therefore the solution ψ of equation (190) satisfies inequality (189), i.e. it belongs to the set E provided

$$\sup |F| < \frac{R}{sK}. \tag{191}$$

Under assumption (191), the set E' of all transformed points of E is a subset of E.

Transformation (190) is evidently continuous in E, for if the sequence of functions $\varphi_n(Q)$ of E tends uniformly to a function $\varphi(Q)$ of this set, then in accordance with Fredholm formulae, the sequence of the corresponding functions $\psi_n(P)$ tends uniformly to the function $\psi(P)$ of E corresponding to $\varphi(Q)$ with respect to relation (190). Further, the functions of the set E' are uniformly bounded and equi-continuous. In fact, the integrals appearing in equation (190) are functions of the point P, which are equi-continuous, for to estimate their uniform continuity it is sufficient to know a number exceeding the functions $|\varphi|$ and $|\psi|$ and the latter are uniformly bounded. This and relation (190) imply that functions ψ of the set E' are equi-continuous. Consequently, the set E' is relatively compact in T.

On the basis of the Schauder's Theorem we infer now (under the assumption (191)) that in E there exists a fixed point with respect to transformation (190), i.e. there exists a solution $\varphi(P)$ of integral equation (185). The potential of surface distribution (184) constructed by means of this function is the solution of the considered problem, since it is a harmonic function in Ω, which satisfies the boundary condition (182).

§ 9. General equation of elliptic type

The general linear partial differential equation of second order with unknown function $u(x_1, x_2, \ldots, x_n)$ of n variables has the form

$$\hat{\Psi}(u) = \sum_{\alpha,\beta=1}^{n} a_{\alpha\beta} \frac{\partial^2 u}{\partial x_\alpha \partial x_\beta} + \sum_{\alpha=1}^{n} b_\alpha \frac{\partial u}{\partial x_\alpha} + cu = f$$

$$(a_{\alpha\beta} = a_{\beta\alpha}), \qquad (192)$$

the coefficients $a_{\alpha\beta}, b_\alpha, c$ and f constituting known functions of n variables $x_1, x_2, \ldots, x_n$ defined in a bounded and measurable region Ω of n-dimensional Euclidean space, and $\hat{\Psi}$ denotes the considered functional operation over the function u.

We do not intend here to develop the complete theory of equation (192); we shall consider only certain problems which constitute an application of the theory of integral equations. First of all we assume that the quadratic form

$$\sum_{\alpha,\beta=1}^{n} a_{\alpha\beta} X_\alpha X_\beta \tag{193}$$

is complete and positive-definite, and thus equation (192) is of elliptic type in the closure of Ω.

Consider first the case when the coefficients $a_{\alpha\beta}$ are constant. Under this assumption let $a^{\alpha\beta}$ denote the elements of the inverse matrix with respect to the matrix $|a_{\alpha\beta}|$; they are therefore the quotients of the algebraic cofactors of elements $a_{\alpha\beta}$ and the determinant $\det |a_{\alpha\beta}|$. Consider the generalized Laplace equation

$$\hat{D}(u) = \sum_{\alpha,\beta=1}^{n} a_{\alpha\beta} \frac{\partial^2 u}{\partial x_\alpha \partial x_\beta} = 0 \tag{194}$$

and the function $(n > 2)$:

$$w(A, B) = \Big[\sum_{\alpha,\beta=1}^{n} a^{\alpha\beta} (x_\alpha - \xi_\alpha)(x_\beta - \xi_\beta)\Big]^{-n/2+1}, \tag{195}$$

where A denotes a point with coordinates $x_1, x_2, \ldots, x_n$ and $B \neq A$ is arbitrary, the coordinates $\xi_1, \xi_2, \ldots, \xi_n$ of which play the rôle of parameters.

We prove that *function* (195) *satisfies equation* (194) *at every point* $A \neq B$; it is called the *fundamental solution* of equation (194). This function is the counterpart of the Newtonian potential $1/r_{AB}$.

In view of the assumed property of the quadratic form (193), there exist two positive constants g_1 and g_2, such that the inequalities

$$g_1 r_{AB} < \sqrt{\sum_{\alpha,\beta=1}^{n} a^{\alpha\beta} (x_\alpha - \xi_\alpha)(x_\beta - \xi_\beta)} < g_2 r_{AB} \tag{196}$$

are satisfied, where $r_{AB}^2 = \sum_{i=1}^{n} (x_i - \xi_i)^2$ for every pair of points A and B; hence, the fundamental solution (195) satisfies the inequality $(n > 2)$

$$\frac{1}{g_2^{n-2}\, r_{AB}^{n-2}} < w(A, B) < \frac{1}{g_1^{n-2}\, r_{AB}^{n-2}}\,.$$

To prove that the function (195) satisfies equation (194) perform the operation $\hat{D}$ on the function (195). Then we have

$$w'_{x_\alpha}(A, B) = -(n-2) \frac{\sum_{i=1}^{n} a^{\alpha i}(x_i - \xi_i)}{\left[\sum_{i,k=1}^{n} a^{ik}(x_i - \xi_i)(x_k - \xi_k)\right]^{n/2}}\,,$$

$$w''_{x_\alpha x_\beta}(A, B) = -\frac{(n-2)\, a^{\alpha\beta}}{\left[\sum_{i,k=1}^{n} a^{ik}(x_i - \xi_i)(x_k - \xi_k)\right]^{n/2}} + $$

$$+ n(n-2) \frac{\sum_{i=1}^{n} a^{\alpha i}(x_i - \xi_i) \sum_{k=1}^{n} a^{k\beta}(x_k - \xi_k)}{\left[\sum_{i,k=1}^{n} a^{ik}(x_i - \xi_i)(x_k - \xi_k)\right]^{n/2+1}}\,,$$

whence

$$\hat{D}[w(A, B)] = \sum_{\alpha,\beta=1}^{n} a_{\alpha\beta}\, w''_{x_\alpha x_\beta} = \frac{-(n-2) \sum_{\alpha,\beta=1}^{n} a_{\alpha\beta}\, a^{\alpha\beta}}{\left[\sum_{i,k=1}^{n} a^{ik}(x_i - \xi_i)(x_k - \xi_k)\right]^{n/2}} +$$

$$+ \frac{n(n-2) \sum_{i,k=1}^{n} \left(\sum_{\alpha,\beta=1}^{n} a_{\alpha\beta}\, a^{\alpha i}\, a^{k\beta} \right)(x_i - \xi_i)(x_k - \xi_k)}{\left[\sum_{i,k=1}^{n} a^{ik}(x_i - \xi_i)(x_k - \xi_k)\right]^{n/2+1}} = 0\,,$$

since

$$\sum_{\alpha,\beta=1}^{n} a_{\alpha\beta}\, a^{\alpha\beta} = n\,, \qquad \sum_{\alpha,\beta=1}^{n} a_{\alpha\beta}\, a^{\alpha i}\, a^{k\beta} = a^{ik}\,.$$

Further, assuming that the coefficients $a_{\alpha\beta}$ are constant, consider the integral*

$$V(A) = \iiint\limits_{\Omega} w(A, B)\,\rho(B)\,dB \tag{197}$$

over the region Ω of n-dimensional Euclidean space. This integral constitutes the counterpart of the potential of spatial charge with density ρ and it evidently satisfies the equation

$$\hat{D}[V(A)] = 0$$

at all points A exterior with respect to region Ω.

Let us now find the equation which is satisfied by the function (197) inside Ω, first assuming that the density ρ is constant. To this end, decompose the integral (197) into two terms

$$V(A) = V^K(A) + V^{\Omega-K}(A),$$

the integration being carried out over a sphere K with centre at the point A_0, located inside Ω, and over the exterior region $\Omega - K$. Since the derivative of the function $w(A, B)$ has a weak singularity of type $1/r_{AB}^{n-1}$, the derivative of the term $V^K(A)$ with respect to a coordinate x_α of a point A inside the sphere K exists, and in view of the Green–Ostrogradski Theorem, it can be represented in the form

$$\frac{\partial V^K(A)}{\partial x_\alpha} = \rho \iiint\limits_{K} \frac{\partial w(A, B)}{\partial x_\alpha}\,dB = -\rho \iiint\limits_{K} \frac{\partial w(A, B)}{\partial \xi_\alpha}\,dB$$

$$= -\rho \iint\limits_{K'} w(A, P) \cos\nu_\alpha\, d\sigma_P,$$

where ν_α denotes the angle between the x_α-axis and the outward normal to the surface K' of the sphere K at the point P. This implies the existence of the second derivatives

$$\frac{\partial^2 V^K(A)}{\partial x_\alpha \partial x_\beta} = -\rho \iint\limits_{K'} \frac{\partial w(A, P)}{\partial x_\beta} \cos\nu_\alpha\, d\sigma_P, \tag{198}$$

---

* We preserve the symbol of triple integral for the integral over volume and of double integral for the integral over surface of an n-dimensional space; dB denotes the element of volume at the point B.

and hence the existence of the second derivatives of the function $V(A)$ at every point A inside K. At the centre A_0 of the sphere K the value of the operation $\hat{D}[V(A)]$ is the following:

$$\{\hat{D}[V(A)]\}_{A_0} = \left(\sum_{\alpha,\beta=1}^{n} a_{\alpha\beta} \frac{\partial^2 V^K(A)}{\partial x_\alpha \partial x_\beta}\right)_{A_0}$$

$$= -\frac{(n-2)\rho}{r_{A_0P}} \iint_{K'} \frac{\sum_{\alpha,\mu=1}^{n} \left(\sum_{\beta=1}^{n} a_{\alpha\beta} a^{\beta\mu} (x_\alpha^0 - \xi_\alpha)(x_\mu^0 - \xi_\mu)\right)}{\left[\sum_{\alpha,\beta=1}^{n} a^{\alpha\beta} (x_\alpha^0 - \xi_\alpha)(x_\beta^0 - \xi_\beta)\right]^{n/2}} d\sigma_P$$

$$= -(n-2)\rho \iint_{A} \left[\sum_{\alpha,\beta=1}^{n} a^{\alpha\beta} \xi_\alpha \xi_\beta\right]^{-n/2} d\sigma(\xi_1, \xi_2, \ldots, \xi_n), \tag{199}$$

where A denotes the surface of the sphere with centre at the origin of the coordinate system, and of unit radius. The value of this integral can be computed using the property of the Poisson–Weierstrass integral (see p. 366), i.e.

$$\iint_{A} \left[\sum_{\alpha,\beta=1}^{n} a^{\alpha\beta} \xi_\alpha \xi_\beta\right]^{-n/2} d\sigma(\xi_1, \xi_2, \ldots, \xi_n) = \frac{\omega_n}{\sqrt{\det |a^{\alpha\beta}|}}, \tag{200}$$

where ω_n denotes the surface area of the surface of an n-dimensional sphere of unit radius

$$\omega_n = \frac{2(\sqrt{\pi})^n}{\Gamma(n/2)}. \tag{201}$$

Consequently, equation (199) can be written in the form

$$\{\hat{D}[V(A)]\}_{A_0} = -\frac{(n-2)\omega_n}{\sqrt{\det |a^{\alpha\beta}|}} \rho. \tag{202}$$

This is the Poisson equation for a spatial charge with constant density ρ.

We prove that *the function* (197) *also satisfies an equation of the form* (202), *assuming that the density* $\rho(A)$ *satisfies in* Ω *the Hölder condition*

$$|\rho(A) - \rho(A_1)| < k r_{AA_1}^{\mu} \quad (0 < \mu \leq 1). \tag{203}$$

The proof of the existence of the first derivatives of the potential (197) can be carried out by investigating the derivatives of the improper integrals; this method is due to GEVREY [12].

To this end, consider inside the region Ω a sequence of cylinders γ_m with a common axis which is an arbitrary constant segment PP' parallel to the x_α-axis, and the radii of which tend to zero. If A denotes an arbitrary point on the segment PP', then the sequence of functions

$$V_m(A) = \iiint\limits_{\Omega-\gamma_m} w(A, B)\,\rho(B)\,dB \tag{204}$$

tends uniformly on PP' to the improper integral (197)

$$\lim V_m(A) = V(A).$$

The functions (204) have derivatives with respect to the variable x_α, namely

$$\frac{\partial V_m(A)}{\partial x_\alpha} = \iiint\limits_{\Omega-\gamma_m} \frac{\partial w(A, B)}{\partial x_\alpha}\,\rho(B)\,dB \tag{205}$$

at all points A inside PP', since the latter lies outside the region of integration $\Omega-\gamma_m$. In view of the weak singularity of the derivative $w'_{x_\alpha}(A, B)$, the integrals (205) tend uniformly on the segment PP' to the improper integral

$$\lim \frac{\partial V_m(A)}{\partial x_\alpha} = \iiint\limits_{\Omega} \frac{\partial w(A, B)}{\partial x_\alpha}\,\rho(B)\,dB.$$

On the basis of the classical theorem on uniformly convergent series of derivatives we infer that the function (197) has continuous derivatives which can be represented by the absolutely convergent improper integral

$$\frac{\partial V(A)}{\partial x_\alpha} = \iiint\limits_{\Omega} \frac{\partial w(A, B)}{\partial x_\alpha}\,\rho(B)\,dB. \tag{206}$$

However, the derivative of the function (206) cannot be determined by differentiating the integrand, since the derivative of the latter has too strong a singularity (of type $1/r^n_{AB}$) and the integral may not exist.

We apply here the method of investigation presented in our paper [43]. For this purpose introduce the function

$$\psi(A, B, z) = \Big[\sum_{\alpha,\beta=1}^{n} a^{\alpha\beta}(x_\alpha - \xi_\alpha)(x_\beta - \xi_\beta) + z^2\Big]^{-n/2+1} \tag{207}$$

and consider the integral

$$W(A, z) = \iiint\limits_{\Omega} \psi_{x_\alpha}(A, B, z)\,\rho(B)\,dB \tag{208}$$

defined in the interior of an $(n+1)$-dimensional cylinder: $A \in \Omega$ and z is real and arbitrary.

THEOREM 4. *The function* $W(A, z)$ *tends uniformly to the function* (206),

$$W(A, z) \rightrightarrows \frac{\partial V(A)}{\partial x_\alpha}, \quad \textit{when} \quad z \to 0, \tag{209}$$

provided we assume that $\rho(B)$ *is bounded and integrable.*

To prove the theorem consider a sphere K of radius R_K for the time being arbitrary, with centre at an arbitrary interior point A of the region Ω, and decompose integral (208) into the sum of two integrals

$$W(A, z) = W^{K'}(A, z) + W^{\Omega-K'}(A, z) \tag{210}$$

over the region K' equal to the product of K and Ω, and over the exterior region $\Omega - K'$. In view of the weak singularity $1/r_{AB}^{n-1}$ of the function $w'_{x_\alpha}(A, B)$ we have for every A and z

$$|W^{K'}(A, z)| < M_\rho C \int\limits_0^{R_K} \frac{\omega_n r^{n-1}\,dr}{r^{n-1}} = M_\rho C \omega_n R_K, \tag{211}$$

where C is a constant (depending on the coefficients $a_{\alpha\beta}$), ω_n denotes the area of an n-dimensional sphere of unit radius, and M_ϱ is the upper bound of the function $|\rho(B)|$.

We observe, on the basis of estimate (211), that for an arbitrary positive ε we can select a radius

$$R_K = \frac{\varepsilon}{3 M_\rho C \omega_n}, \tag{212}$$

such that

$$|W^{K'}(A, z)| < \frac{\varepsilon}{3} \tag{213}$$

at every point A of Ω and for every z. Further, we have

$$\frac{\partial V(A)}{\partial x_\alpha} = W(A, 0) = W^{K'}(A, 0) + W^{\Omega-K'}(A, 0), \tag{214}$$

whence

$$\left|\frac{\partial V(A)}{\partial x_\alpha} - W(A, z)\right|$$
$$< |W^{K'}(A, z)| + |W^{K'}(A, 0)| + |W^{\Omega-K'}(A, z) - W^{\Omega-K'}(A, 0)|.$$

Observe now that the function $W^{\Omega-K'}(A, z)$ is continuous at $z = 0$ (uniformly with respect to the point A) since A is located outside the region of integration $\Omega - K'$; consequently, having fixed the sphere K we can select $\eta(\varepsilon)$ depending only on ε, such that

$$|W^{\Omega-K'}(A, z) - W^{\Omega-K'}(A, 0)| < \frac{\varepsilon}{3}, \quad \text{when} \quad |z| < \eta(\varepsilon).$$

Finally we obtain

$$\left|\frac{\partial V(A)}{\partial x_\alpha} - W(A, z)\right| < \varepsilon, \quad \text{when} \quad |z| < \eta(\varepsilon).$$

This completes the proof.

THEOREM 5. *The function* (208) *has derivatives with respect to the coordinates of the point A inside Ω and for $z \neq 0$, which, in a sufficiently small neighbourhood of every interior point A_0, tend uniformly to the limit*

$$W'_{x_\beta}(A, z) \rightrightarrows \rho(A) \frac{\partial^2}{\partial x_\alpha \partial x_\beta} \left[\iiint_\Omega w(A, B)\, dB\right] +$$
$$+ \iiint_\Omega w''_{x_\alpha x_\beta}(A, B)[\rho(B) - \rho(A)]\, dB, \quad \textit{when} \quad z \to 0 \tag{215}$$

under the assumption that the function ρ satisfies the Hölder condition.

For $z \neq 0$ the function (208) has, at every interior point A of Ω, derivatives with respect to the coordinates of A given by the regular integral

$$W'_{x_\beta}(A, z) = \iiint_{\Omega} \psi''_{x_\alpha x_\beta}(A, B, z)\, \rho(B)\, dB. \qquad (216)$$

To prove the existence of the latter when $z \to 0$, decompose it into two terms

$$W'_{x_\beta}(A, z) = \rho(A) \frac{\partial}{\partial x_\beta} [\iiint_{\Omega} \psi'_x(A, B, z)\, dB] + \\ + \iiint_{\Omega} \psi''_{x_\alpha x_\beta}(A, B, z)[\rho(B) - \rho(A)]\, dB. \qquad (217)$$

Repeating the procedure which led to formula (198), we have

$$\iiint_{\Omega} \psi'_{x_\alpha}(A, B, z)\, dB \\ = \iiint_{\Omega - K} \psi'_{x_\alpha}(A, B, z)\, dB - \iint_{K^*} \psi(A, P, z) \cos \nu_{\xi_\alpha}\, d\sigma_P, \qquad (218)$$

where K is a sphere with centre at A_0 located wholly inside Ω, and K' denotes its surface. By virtue of relation (218), we have

$$\frac{\partial}{\partial x_\beta} [\iiint_{\Omega} \psi'_{x_\alpha}(A, B, z)\, dB] \\ = \iiint_{\Omega - K} \psi''_{x_\alpha x_\beta}(A, B, z)\, dB - \iint_{K^*} \psi'_{x_\beta}(A, P, z) \cos \nu_{\xi_\alpha}\, d\sigma_P. \qquad (219)$$

Since the centre of the sphere A_0 lies outside the domains of integration $\Omega - K$ and K^*, in view of Theorem 4 and formula (206) in which we set $\rho = 1$, we infer that derivative (219) tends uniformly in a certain neighbourhood of the point A_0 to the limit

$$\iiint_{\Omega - K} \psi''_{x_\alpha x_\beta}(A, B, 0)\, dB - \iint_{K^*} \psi'_{x_\beta}(A, P, 0) \cos \nu_{\xi_\alpha}\, d\sigma_P \\ = \frac{\partial}{\partial x_\alpha \partial x_\beta} [\iiint_{\Omega} w(A, B)\, dB], \qquad (220)$$

when $z \to 0$.

In view of the assumed Hölder condition (203), the integrand in the second term of sum (217) satisfies the inequality

$$|\psi''_{x_\alpha x_\beta}(A, B, z)[\rho(B)-\rho(A)]| < \frac{\text{const}}{r_{AB}^{n-\mu}}, \tag{221}$$

i.e. it has a weak singularity when $B \to A$ and $z \to 0$. Repeating the argument of the proof of Theorem 4, we find that the second term of the sum (217) tends uniformly to the limit

$$\iiint_\Omega w''_{x_\alpha x_\beta}(A, B)[\rho(B)-\rho(A)]\,dB, \tag{222}$$

when $z \to 0$.

Combining the determined values (220) and (222) for the limits of the two terms of the sum (217), we arrive at the statement (215) of Theorem 5.

On the basis of the classical definition of the limit of a derivative, we obtain from Theorems 4 and 5 the following corollary:

COROLLARY. *The limit* (215) *is the derivative of limit* (209), *i.e. potential* (197) *has continuous second derivatives given by the formula*

$$\frac{\partial^2 V(A)}{\partial x_\alpha \partial x_\beta} = \rho(A)\frac{\partial^2}{\partial x_\alpha \partial x_\beta}\left[\iiint_\Omega w(A, B)\,dB\right] + \iiint_\Omega w''_{x_\alpha x_\beta}(A, B)[\rho(B)-\rho(A)]\,dB \tag{223}$$

at every interior point A of Ω.

These results imply that the result of the operation $\hat{D}$ over the function $V(A)$ at an arbitrary interior point A of Ω, is given by the formula

$$\hat{D}[V(A)] = \sum_{\alpha,\beta=1}^{n} a_{\alpha\beta}\frac{\partial^2 V(A)}{\partial x_\alpha \partial x_\beta} = \rho(A)\hat{D}\left[\iiint_\Omega w(A, B)\,dB\right] + \iiint_\Omega \hat{D}_A[w(A, B)]\,.\,[\rho(B)-\rho(A)]\,dB. \tag{224}$$

Finally relation (202) and the obvious fact that $\hat{D}[w(A,B)] = 0$ at every point $A \neq B$ imply that the potential (197) with density $\rho(A)$ satisfying the Hölder condition, satisfies the Poisson equation in the form

$$\hat{D}[V(A)] = -\frac{(n-2)\,\omega_n}{\sqrt{\det|a^{\alpha\beta}|}}\,\rho(A) \tag{225}$$

at every point A inside Ω.

This result can easily be generalized to the problem when the density $\rho(A)$ satisfies the Hölder condition in a region Ω^* constituting a part of the region Ω. Namely, we have the following theorem:

THEOREM 6. *If the density of the spatial charge $\rho(A)$ is bounded and integrable in region Ω and it satisfies the Hölder condition in a measurable region Ω^* constituting a part of Ω, then the potential of spatial charge* (197) *has second derivatives satisfying the Poisson relation* (255) *at every point A of Ω^*.*

In fact, decomposing integral (197) into two parts

$$V(A) = V^{\Omega^*}(A) + V^{\Omega-\Omega^*}(A),$$

over Ω^* and the remaining region $\Omega-\Omega^*$, we have

$$\hat{D}[V^{\Omega^*}(A)] = -\frac{(n-2)\,\omega_n}{\sqrt{\det|a^{\alpha\beta}|}}\,\rho(A) \quad \text{and} \quad \hat{D}[V^{\Omega-\Omega^*}(A)] = 0$$

at every point A inside Ω^*. This completes the proof.

§ 10. Properties of the quasi-potential of an elliptic equation

We now proceed to determine the fundamental solution of the elliptic equation (192) in the general case when $a_{\alpha\beta}(x_1, x_2, \ldots$ $\ldots, x_n)$, b_α and c are functions defined in the closure of a region Ω and satisfying the Hölder condition in the form

$$\begin{aligned} |a_{\alpha\beta}(B) - a_{\alpha\beta}(B_1)| &< k r_{BB_1}^h \quad (0 < h \leqq 1), \\ |b_\alpha(B) - b_\alpha(B_1)| &< k' r_{BB_1}^h, \\ |c(B) - c(B_1)| &< k'' r_{BB_1}^h. \end{aligned} \tag{226}$$

Then the function $(n > 2)$

$$w^M(A, B) = \Big[\sum_{\alpha,\beta=1}^{n} a^{\alpha\beta}(M)(x_\alpha - \xi_\alpha)(x_\beta - \xi_\beta)\Big]^{-n/2+1}, \tag{227}$$

where $a_{\alpha\beta}$ are calculated at an arbitrary fixed point $M(\xi_1', \xi_2', \ldots$ $\ldots, \xi_n')$ of Ω, does not necessarily satisfy equation (198) at a point $A(x_1, x_2, \ldots, x_n) \neq B(\xi_1, \xi_2, \ldots, \xi_n)$. The function (227) is then called the *quasi-solution* of equation (202).

In the case $n = 2$ we can develop the theory of equation (192) in an analogous way, taking for the quasi-solution the function

$$w^M(A, B) = \log\Big[\sum_{\alpha,\beta=1}^{2} a^{\alpha\beta}(M)(x_\alpha - \xi_\alpha)(x_\beta - \xi_\beta)\Big].$$

Observe that because the equation is elliptic there exist constants g and G such that the quadratic form in (227) satisfies the inequality

$$g r_{AB} \leqq \Big[\sum_{\alpha,\beta=1}^{n} a^{\alpha\beta}(M)(x_\alpha - \xi_\alpha)(x_\beta - \xi_\beta)\Big]^{1/2} \leqq G r_{AB} \tag{228}$$

for every pair of points A and B of the closure of Ω, where r_{AB} denotes the Euclidean distance between the two points.

We prove that *the result of the operation $\hat{D}$ upon the function* (227) (*with respect to the coordinates of the point A*), *after having put $M = B$*,

$$\hat{D}_A[w^B(A, B)] = \sum_{\alpha,\beta=1}^{n} a_{\alpha\beta}(A)\frac{\partial^2 w^B(A, B)}{\partial x_\alpha \partial x_\beta} \tag{229}$$

is a function unbounded as $1/r_{AB}^{n-h}$ when $A \to B$, i.e. it has a singularity of lower order than the second derivatives of function $W^B(A, B)$.

This property follows immediately, if we transform (229) to the form

$$\hat{D}_A[w^B(A, B)] = \sum_{\alpha,\beta=1}^{n} a_{\alpha\beta}(B)\frac{\partial^2 w^B(A, B)}{\partial x_\alpha \partial x_\beta} +$$
$$+ \sum_{\alpha,\beta=1}^{n}[a_{\alpha\beta}(A) - a_{\alpha\beta}(B)]\frac{\partial^2 w^B(A, B)}{\partial x_\alpha \partial x_\beta}. \tag{230}$$

In fact, the first term of the sum vanishes, since it constitutes the result of the operation $\hat{D}$ under the assumption that the coefficients $a_{\alpha\beta}$ are constant and equal to the values of the functions $a_{\alpha\beta}(B)$ at the point B. In view of assumption (226), the second term satisfies the inequality

$$\left| \sum_{\alpha,\beta=1}^{n} [a_{\alpha\beta}(A) - a_{\alpha\beta}(B)] \frac{\partial^2 w^B(A, B)}{\partial x_\alpha \partial x_\beta} \right| < \frac{\text{const}}{r_{AB}^{n-h}},$$

and hence

$$|\hat{D}_A[w^B(A, B)]| < \frac{\text{const}}{r_{AB}^{n-h}}. \tag{231}$$

Consider now the integral

$$V(A) = \iiint_{\Omega} w^B(A, B)\rho(B)\,dB, \tag{232}$$

analogous to integral (192), where the function $W^B(A,B)$ is defined by formula (227); we call it the *quasi-potential of the spatial charge with density* $\rho(B)$. We prove that *when the density* ρ *satisfie the Hölder condition then the quasi-potential* (232) *has second derivatives inside* Ω *that satisfy an equation which is a generalization of the Poisson equation.*

Proceeding in a similar manner as for the constant coefficients, it can easily be proved that the function (232) has first derivatives representable in the form of the integral

$$\frac{\partial V(A)}{\partial x_\alpha} = \iiint_{\Omega} w_{x_\alpha}^B(A, B)\rho(B)\,dB, \tag{233}$$

where $w_{x_\alpha}^B$ denotes the derivative of the function (227) with respect to the coordinate x_α of the point A, and this integral is absolutely convergent.

To investigate the second derivatives of the function (232) we employ a method analogous to that used in deriving Poisson's equation. Suppose, therefore, that

$$\psi^M(A, B, z) = \Big[\sum_{\alpha,\beta=1}^{n} a^{\alpha\beta}(M)(x_\alpha - \xi_\alpha)(x_\beta - \xi_\beta) + z^2\Big]^{-n/2+1}, \tag{234}$$

where M is an arbitrary point of Ω, and consider the integral

$$T(A,z)=\iiint_{\Omega}\psi^{B}_{x_\alpha}(A,B,z)\,\rho(B)\,dB \tag{235}$$

defined at every point (A,z) of the cylinder; $A\in\Omega$ is arbitrary. Here we may apply Theorem 4, and the function (235) tends uniformly to the derivative of the quasi-potential (233)

$$T(A,z)\rightrightarrows\frac{\partial V(A)}{\partial x_\alpha},\qquad\text{when}\qquad z\to 0. \tag{236}$$

THEOREM 7. *If the density $\rho(B)$ and the coefficients $a^{\alpha\beta}(B)$ satisfy the Hölder condition, then the derivative of the function* (235) *with respect to the coordinates of a point A inside Ω and for $z\neq 0$ tend uniformly in a sufficiently small neighbourhood of every interior point A, to the limit*

$$T'_{x_\beta}(A,z)\rightrightarrows\left\{\frac{\partial^2}{\partial x_\alpha\,\partial x_\beta}\left[\iiint_{\Omega} w^{M}(A,B)\,\rho(B)\,dB\right]\right\}_{M=A}+$$
$$+\iiint_{\Omega}\left[\frac{\partial^2 w^{B}(A,B)}{\partial x_\alpha\,\partial x_\beta}-\left(\frac{\partial^2 w^{M}(A,B)}{\partial x_\alpha\,\partial x_\beta}\right)_{M=A}\right]\rho(B)\,dB,$$
$$\textit{when}\qquad z\to 0. \tag{237}$$

To prove the theorem observe that the function (235) has derivatives with respect to the coordinates of the point A when $z\neq 0$, and these are given by the regular integral

$$T'_{x_\beta}(A,z)=\iiint_{\Omega}\psi^{B}_{x_\alpha x_\beta}(A,B,z)\,\rho(B)\,dB. \tag{238}$$

To find the limit of this integral when $z\to 0$, we write it in the form

$$T'_{x_\beta}(A,z)=\left\{\frac{\partial}{\partial x_\beta}\left[\iiint_{\Omega}\psi^{M}_{x_\alpha}(A,B,z)\,\rho(B)\,dB\right]\right\}_{M=A}+$$
$$+\iiint_{\Omega}\left[\psi^{B}_{x_\alpha x_\beta}(A,B,z)-(\psi^{M}_{x_\alpha x_\beta}(A,B,z))_{M=A}\right]\rho(B)\,dB. \tag{239}$$

Since M is constant in the integration, the first term of this sum represents the value of the derivative of the function (208) with constant coefficients $a^{\alpha\beta}(M)$, which the derivative takes when we set $M = A$ after differentiation. Consequently, according to Theorem 5, when $z \to 0$, the first term tends uniformly in a sufficiently small neighbourhood of an interior point A_0 to the limit

$$\left\{\frac{\partial^2}{\partial x_\alpha \partial x_\beta}\left[\iiint\limits_{\Omega} w^M(A, B)\rho(B)\,dB\right]\right\}_{M=A} \tag{240}$$

which is the value taken by the second derivative of the potential in the case of constant coefficients $a^{\alpha\beta}(M)$, if after differentiation we set $M = A$.

To investigate the existence of the limit of the second term in the sum (209), observe that the second derivatives of the function (234) are given by the formulae

$$\begin{aligned} &\psi^B_{x_\alpha x_\beta}(A, B, z) \\ &\qquad = \frac{\sum\limits_{i,k=1}^{n} c_{ik}\, a^{\alpha i}(B)\, a^{\beta k}(B)(x_i-\xi_i)(x_k-\xi_k)}{\left[\sum\limits_{i,k=1}^{n} a^{ik}(B)(x_i-\xi_i)(x_k-\xi_k)+z^2\right]^{n/2+1}}, \\ &(\psi^M_{x_\alpha x_\beta}(A, B, z))_{M=A} \\ &\qquad = \frac{\sum\limits_{i,k=1}^{n} c_{ik}\, a^{\alpha i}(A)\, a^{\beta k}(A)(x_i-\xi_i)(x_k-\xi_k)}{\left[\sum\limits_{i,k=1}^{n} a^{ik}(A)(x_i-\xi_i)(x_k-\xi_k)+z^2\right]^{n/2+1}}, \end{aligned} \tag{241}$$

where c_{ik} denote certain numerical coefficients. Since, according to the assumption that the coefficients $a_{\alpha\beta}(B)$ satisfy the Hölder condition of the form (226), the functions $a^{\alpha\beta}(B)$ as rational combinations of coefficients $a_{\alpha\beta}(B)$ (with non-zero denominator) also satisfy the Hölder condition with exponent h. An elementary calculation proves that the difference between the second derivatives (241) satisfies the inequality

$$|\psi^B_{x_\alpha x_\beta}(A, B, z) - (\psi^M_{x_\alpha x_\beta}(A, B, z))_{M=A}| < \frac{\text{const}}{(gr^2_{AB}+z^2)^{(n-h)/2}}, \quad (242)$$

where g is the positive constant of inequality (228). Setting here $z = 0$ we arrive at the inequality

$$|w^B_{x_\alpha x_\beta}(A, B) - (w^M_{x_\alpha x_\beta}(A, B))_{M=A}| < \frac{\text{const}}{r^{n-h}_{AB}} \quad (243)$$

for every pair of distinct points A and B of Ω.

The differences (242) and (243) between the second derivatives have therefore a weak singularity when $B \to A$ and $z \to 0$. Repeating, therefore, the argument similar to that in the proof of Theorem 7, we infer that the second term of the sum (239) tends uniformly to the limit

$$\iiint_\Omega [w^B_{x_\alpha x_\beta}(A, B) - (w^M_{x_\alpha x_\beta}(A, B))_{M=A}] \rho(B)\, dB, \quad (244)$$

when $z \to 0$.

Combining the results concerning the existence of the limits (240) and (244), we arrive at the statement of Theorem 7, i.e. the existence of limit (237).

In view of the results (236) and (237) we obtain the following corollary:

COROLLARY. *There exist the second derivatives of the quasi-potential $V(A)$, given by the formulae*

$$\frac{\partial^2 V(A)}{\partial x_\alpha \partial x_\beta} = \left\{\frac{\partial^2}{\partial x_\alpha \partial x_\beta}\left[\iiint_\Omega w^M(A, B) \rho(B)\, dB\right]\right\}_{M=A} +$$

$$+ \iiint_\Omega \left[\frac{\partial^2 w^B(A, B)}{\partial x_\alpha \partial x_\beta} - \left(\frac{\partial^2 w^M(A, B)}{\partial x_\alpha \partial x_\beta}\right)_{M=A}\right] \rho(B)\, dB \quad (245)$$

at every interior point A of Ω.

Relation (245) implies the following result of the operation $\hat{D}$ over the quasi-potential $V(A)$:

$$\hat{D}[V(A)] = \sum_{\alpha,\beta=1}^{n} a_{\alpha\beta}(A) \frac{\partial^2 V(A)}{\partial x_\alpha \partial x_\beta}$$

$$= \{\hat{D}_A[\iint\limits_{\Omega}\int w^M(A,B)\rho(B)\,dB]\}_{M=A} +$$

$$+ \iint\limits_{\Omega}\int [\hat{D}_A[w^B(A,B)] - \{\hat{D}_A[w^M(A,B)]\}_{M=A}]\rho(B)\,dB. \quad (246)$$

Since the coefficients $a_{\alpha\beta}(A)$ of the operation $\hat{D}$ in the first term of the last part of relation (246) refer to the point A which replaces the constant point M in the functions $a^{\alpha\beta}(M)$ of the expression for $w^M(A,B)$, after differentiation, according to the preceding result, the integral

$$\iint\limits_{\Omega}\int w^M(A,B)\rho(B)\,dB$$

satisfies Poisson equation (101)

$$\{\hat{D}_A[\iint\limits_{\Omega}\int w^M(A,B)\rho(B)\,dB]\}_{M=A} = -\lambda_n(A)\rho(A),$$

where

$$\lambda_n(A) = \frac{(n-2)\omega_n}{\sqrt{\det|a^{\alpha\beta}(A)|}}.$$

On the same basis we now have

$$\{\hat{D}_A[w^M(A,B)]\}_{M=A} = 0.$$

Thus we finally conclude that the second derivatives of the quasi-potential $V(A)$ satisfy the generalized Poisson equation of the form

$$\hat{D}[V(A)] = -\lambda_n(A)\rho(A) + \iint\limits_{\Omega}\int \hat{D}_A[w^B(A,B)]\rho(B)\,dB \quad (247)$$

at every interior point A of Ω.

Similarly as for potential (197), this result can be generalized to the following theorem:

THEOREM 8. *If the density $\rho(B)$ is integrable in Ω, and satisfies the Hölder condition in a measurable region Ω^* contained in Ω, then the quasi-potential* (232) *has second derivatives at every interior point A of Ω^*, which satisfy the generalized Poisson equation* (247).

The proof is analogous to that of Theorem 6.

Observe that in view of inequality (243) the integrand in equation (247) has a weak singularity

$$|\hat{D}_A[w^B(A,B)]| < \frac{\text{const}}{r_{AB}^{n-h}} \tag{248}$$

and the integral is absolutely convergent. Inequality (248) is compatible with inequality (241) obtained before in a straightforward way.

§ 11. Determination of the fundamental solution of an elliptic equation

Having found the quasi-solution (227) of equation (149) and taking into account the proved property of the quasi-potential we now proceed to determine the fundamental solution of the complete equation

$$\hat{\Psi}(u) = \sum_{\alpha,\beta=1}^{n} a_{\alpha\beta}\frac{\partial^2 u}{\partial x_\alpha \partial x_\beta} + \sum_{\alpha=1}^{n} b_\alpha \frac{\partial u}{\partial x_\alpha} + cu = 0 \tag{249}$$

with variable coefficients, by a method announced by LEVI [26], assuming that the coefficients $a_{\alpha\beta}$ have second derivatives; this method was developed by STERNBERG [80], GEVREY [12], and GIRAUD [15] for the case of coefficients satisfying the Hölder condition.

To this end, consider an arbitrary bounded region Ω' in n-dimensional Euclidean space, containing the considered region, and extend the known functions $a_{\alpha\beta}$, b_α and c into the whole region Ω' in such a way that they satisfy the Hölder condition (226) everywhere and such that the quadratic form $\sum a_{\alpha\beta} X_\alpha X_\beta$ is positive definite.* We seek the fundamental solution of equation

* This is possible in view of the assumed ellipticity of the equation and the fulfilment of the Hölder condition by its coefficients in the closure of Ω.

(249) in the form of the sum

$$\Gamma(A,B) = w^B(A,B) + \iiint_{\Omega'} w^M(A,M)\,\Phi(M,B)\,dM \qquad (250)$$

of the known quasi-solution w and the integral of the product of this solution by an unknown function $\Phi(M,B)$, where B is treated as a constant parameter of integration. The integral in expression (250) has the form of the already examined quasi-potential of spatial charge of density $\Phi(M,B)$. If therefore this density satisfies the Hölder condition in the neighbourhood of a point A, then in view of equation (247), the result of the operation $\hat{D}$ on the integral (250) is the following:

$$\hat{D}_A\Big[\iiint_{\Omega'} w^M(A,M)\,\Phi(M,B)\,dM\Big]$$
$$= -\lambda_n(A)\,\Phi(A,B) + \iiint_{\Omega'} \hat{D}_A[w^M(A,M)]\,\Phi(M,B)\,dM. \qquad (251)$$

Consequently the result of the complete operation (192) on integral (250) is

$$\hat{\Psi}_A\Big[\iiint_{\Omega'} w^M(A,M)\,\Phi(M,B)\,dM\Big]$$
$$= -\lambda_n(A)\,\Phi(A,B) + \iiint_{\Omega'} \hat{\Psi}_A[w^M(A,M)]\,\Phi(M,B)\,dM. \qquad (252)$$

Observe that the result of the complete operation $\hat{\Psi}$ on the function $w^M(A,M)$ obtained by adding the derivatives of the first order of the function w to the result of the operation $\hat{D}$, also satisfies inequality (231). If we therefore require that the function (250) satisfy the complete equation (249) at every point A of Ω' distinct from B, then we arrive at the equation

$$\lambda_n(A)\,\Phi(A,B)$$
$$= \hat{\Psi}_A[w^B(A,B)] + \iiint_{\Omega'} \hat{\Psi}_A[w^M(A,M)]\,\Phi(M,B)\,dM. \qquad (253)$$

This is a Fredholm equation with unknown function $\Phi(A,B)$ (B is a parameter), the kernel having a weak singularity, since it satisfies an inequality of the form

$$|\hat{\Psi}_A w^M(A,M)| < \frac{\text{const}}{r_{AM}^{n-h}}; \qquad (254)$$

moreover, the function $\lambda_n(A)$ is positive in the closure of Ω'.

Assume that the arbitrary region Ω' is so chosen that the corresponding (to equality (253)) homogeneous equation has only the zero solution, and consequently the first Fredholm theorem is applicable.

Assume that the known function $\hat{\Psi}[w^B(A, B)]$ has a singularity when $A \to B$, but that the singularity is weak (in view of inequality (254)) and therefore we may introduce this function into the Fredholm formulae, regarding the point B as a constant parameter. Thus we obtain the value of the unknown function $\Phi(A, B)$ at every point A of Ω', distinct from an arbitrarily selected point B.

On the basis of integral equation (253) and the properties of its kernel, we can prove that the solution $\Phi(A, B)$ of equation (253) satisfies the Hölder condition in every neighbourhood of a point A, which does not contain the point B (see [43]). Therefore if we introduce the derived solution $\Phi(A, B)$ of equation (253) into formula (250) we obtain a function $\Gamma(A, B)$ which satisfies equation (249) at every point A of the region, distinct from B. In view of the arbitrary choice of Ω' and the extended functions $a_{\alpha\beta}(A)$, the assumption of the existence of a unique solution of the Fredholm equation (253) seems natural. This property, however, has not yet been proved. Nevertheless, a small alteration was introduced into the form of (250) of the fundamental solution, which ensures its existence for an arbitrary region Ω'. This method was given by the Italian mathematician CARLO MIRANDA [31].

We seek the fundamental solution in the form

$$\Gamma(A, B) = w^B(A, B) + \iiint\limits_{\Omega'} w^M(A, M)\,\Phi(M, B)\,dM + \sum_{\nu=1}^{p} \alpha_\nu(A)\,\beta_\nu(B)$$

and for the function $\Phi(A, B)$ we obtain the integral equation

$$\lambda_n(A)\,\Phi(A, B) = \hat{\Psi}_A\Big[w^B(A, B) + \sum_{\nu=1}^{p} \alpha_\nu(A)\,\beta_\nu(B)\Big] + \iiint\limits_{\Omega'} \hat{\Psi}_A[w^M(A, M)]\,\Phi(M, B)\,dM.$$

If the corresponding homogeneous equation has a non-zero solution, then the functions $\alpha_\nu(A)$ and $\beta_\nu(B)$ can be selected in such a way that the familiar conditions of orthogonality are satisfied, and the solution $\Phi(A, B)$ exists, on the basis of the third Fredholm Theorem.

In view of inequality (254), we infer that the solution $\Phi(A, B)$ of the integral equation (253) satisfies the following inequality with a weak singularity at the point B:

$$|\Phi(A, B)| < \frac{\text{const}}{r_{AB}^{n-h}}. \tag{255}$$

Consequently, in view of the familiar investigations from the theory of integral equations with weak singularities (Part 1, p. 79) and inequality (228), the second term of the fundamental solution (250) satisfies the inequality

$$\Big| \iiint_{\Omega'} w^M(A, M)\, \Phi(M, B)\, dM \Big| < \frac{\text{const}}{r_{AB}^{n-2-h}} \tag{256}$$

with a singularity weaker that the first term $w^B(A, B)$. This implies that the fundamental solution satisfies an inequality of the same form as the quasi-solution

$$|\Gamma(A, B)| < \frac{\text{const}}{r_{AB}^{n-2}} \tag{257}$$

for every pair of distinct points A and B.

§ 12. Properties of the generalized potential of surface distribution

The derived fundamental solution makes it possible to determine more general solutions of the elliptic equation (192), analogous to the potential of surface distribution.

DEFINITION 1. *By the generalized potential of surface distribution with density $\mu(Q)$ defined on a surface S we mean the integral*

$$U(A) = \iint_S \Gamma(A, Q)\, \mu(Q)\, d\sigma_Q. \tag{258}$$

If the function $\mu(Q)$ is bounded and integrable on the surface S, then the function (258) satisfies equation (192) at every point A of Ω, which is not located on the surface S. In view of the estimate (257), the function (258) is also defined at every point P of the surface S as an absolutely convergent improper integral

$$\begin{aligned} U(P) &= \lim_{r_\Delta \to 0} \iint_{S-\Delta} \Gamma(P, Q)\, \mu(Q)\, d\sigma_Q \\ &= \iint_S \Gamma(P, Q)\, \mu(Q)\, d\sigma_Q, \end{aligned} \tag{259}$$

where r_Δ denotes the diameter of that part Δ of S which contains the point P. In a way entirely analogous to the classical potential theory, we can prove that the value (259) is the limit of the function (258) when the point A tends in an arbitrary way to the point P

$$\lim_{A \to P} U(A) = U(P). \tag{260}$$

The properties of the potential (258) and the generalized potential of spatial charge were investigated by STERNBERG [80], GEVREY [12], GIRAUD [16], and the author (see Part 1).

The first derivatives of potential (258) defined at every point $A \in \Omega$, not located on the surface S, by the integral

$$U_{x_\nu}(A) = \iint_S \Gamma_{x_\nu}(A, Q)\, \mu(Q)\, d\sigma_Q,$$

can have no limit when A tends to a point P of the surface S, in view of the too strong singularity of the derivatives, estimated by the inequality

$$|\Gamma_{x_\nu}(A, Q)| < \frac{\text{const}}{r_{AQ}^{n-1}}.$$

However, a certain linear combination of the derivatives of the potential (158), called the *transversal derivative* of the potential, has a definite limit when A tends to a point P on S, the density $\mu(Q)$ being continuous, similar to the normal derivative of the potential of the Laplace equation. Namely, by the *transversal derivative* of the potential (258) at an interior point $A \in \Omega$ with respect to a point P of S, we mean the expression

$$\frac{dU(A)}{dT_P} = \sum_{\alpha,\beta=1}^{n} a_{\alpha\beta}(A)\cos(N_P, x_\beta)\frac{\partial U(A)}{\partial x_\alpha}, \tag{261}$$

where (N_p, x_β) denotes the angle between the inward normal at the point P of the surface S and the x_β-axis. Relation (261) implies that the vector with components

$$t_\alpha = \sum_{\beta=1}^{n} a_{\alpha\beta}(A)\cos(N_P, x_\beta) \quad (\alpha = 1, 2, \ldots, n), \tag{262}$$

called the *transversal vector*, has direction conjugate to the direction of the normal to S at the point P with respect to the quadratics

$$\sum_{\alpha,\beta=1}^{n} a_{\alpha\beta}(A) X_\alpha X_\beta = \text{const.}$$

This direction is called the *transversal direction* or the *direction of the conormal.* Observe that the transversal derivative (261) differs by a factor from the derivative of $U(A)$ in the transversal direction, for we have for this derivative

$$\frac{dU(A)}{dt_P} = \sum_{\alpha=1}^{n}\left(\frac{t_\alpha}{\sum_{\nu=1}^{n} t_\nu^2}\right)\frac{\partial U(A)}{\partial x_\alpha}. \tag{263}$$

In the theory of boundary problems for elliptic and parabolic equations we use instead of the derivative in the transversal direction (263) the transversal derivative (261), since it simplifies calculations. When the interior point A tends to a point P of S, then the transversal derivative (261) tends to the limit defined by the following theorem:

THEOREM 9. *If an interior point A of the region Ω bounded by the surface S tends* * *to a point P of this surface, then the transversal derivative* (261) *of the potential of surface distribution tends to the limit*

$$\lim_{A\to P} \frac{dU(A)}{dT_P} = -\frac{1}{2}\lambda_n(P)\mu(P) + \iint_S \frac{d\Gamma(P,Q)}{dT_P}\mu(Q)\,d\sigma_Q, \quad (264)$$

assuming that the density μ(P) is a continuous function, and that the surface S satisfies the Liapunov conditions (see p. 231).

The transversal derivative of the fundamental solution $\Gamma(P, Q)$ at a point P of the surface is defined by the formula

$$\frac{d\Gamma(P,Q)}{dT_P} = \sum_{\alpha,\beta=1}^{n} a_{\alpha\beta}(P)\cos(N_P, x_\beta)\frac{\partial\Gamma(P,Q)}{\partial x_\alpha}, \quad (265)$$

where $x_1, x_2, \ldots, x_n$ denote the coordinates of the point P. This derivative has a weak singularity with respect to the surface integral when $Q \to P$, for it satisfies the inequality

$$\left|\frac{d\Gamma(P,Q)}{dT_P}\right| < \frac{\text{const}}{r_{PQ}^{n-1-h^*}}, \quad (265')$$

where $h^* = \min(h, \kappa)$.

PROOF. In view of formula (250), potential (258) can be written in the form

$$U(A) = \iint_S w^Q(A,Q)\mu(Q)\,d\sigma_Q + \iint_S \overline{w}(A,Q)\mu(Q)\,d\sigma_Q, \quad (266)$$

where

$$\overline{w}(A,Q) = \iiint_{\Omega'} w^M(A,M)\Phi(M,Q)\,d\sigma_M. \quad (267)$$

Setting

$$\vartheta^M(A,B) = \sqrt{\sum_{\alpha,\beta=1}^{n} a^{\alpha\beta}(M)(x_\alpha-\xi_\alpha)(x_\beta-\xi_\beta)}, \quad (268)$$

* The manner of this transition will be specified later.

we obtain, in accordance with definition (261),

$$\frac{dw^Q(A,Q)}{dT_P}$$

$$= -(n-2)\frac{\sum_{\alpha,\beta=1}^{n} a_{\alpha\beta}(A)\cos(N_P, x_\beta)\left[\sum_{\gamma=1}^{n} a^{\alpha\gamma}(Q)(x_\gamma-\xi_\gamma)\right]}{[\vartheta^Q(A,Q)]^n}$$

$$= -(n-2)\frac{r_{AQ}\cos(N_P, \overline{QA})}{[\vartheta^Q(A,Q)]^n} -$$

$$-(n-2)\sum_{\alpha,\beta=1}^{n} a_{\alpha\beta}(A)\cos(N_P, x_\beta)\times$$

$$\times\frac{\sum_{\gamma=1}^{n}[a^{\alpha\gamma}(Q)-a^{\alpha\gamma}(A)](x_\gamma-\xi_\gamma)}{[\vartheta^Q(A,Q)]^n}. \quad (269)$$

Observe now that the derivatives of the functions $w^Q(A,Q)$ and $\overline{w}(A,Q)$ with respect to coordinates of the point A satisfy, in view of inequalities (228) and (255), the inequalities

$$|w^Q_{x_\alpha}(A,Q)| < \frac{\text{const}}{r_{AQ}^{n-1}} \quad \text{and} \quad |\overline{w}_{x_\alpha}(A,Q)| < \frac{\text{const}}{r_{AQ}^{n-1-h}}. \quad (270)$$

Taking into account the Hölder inequality assumed for the coefficients $a^{\alpha\gamma}(A)$, we infer that the transversal derivative of potential (266) can be expressed as a sum of two integrals

$$\frac{dU(A)}{dT_P} = -(n-2)\iint_S \frac{r_{AQ}\cos(N_P, \overrightarrow{QA})}{[\vartheta^Q(A,Q)]^n}\mu(Q)\,d\sigma_Q +$$

$$+\iint_S \frac{F(A,P,Q)\,d\sigma_Q}{[\vartheta^Q(A,Q)]^{n-1-h}}, \quad (271)$$

where the function $F(A,P,Q)$ is bounded and integrable.

Since the second integral (271) has a weak singularity when $A = P$, it has the following boundary property:

$$\lim_{A\to P}\iint_S \frac{F(A,P,Q)\,d\sigma_Q}{[\vartheta^Q(A,Q)]^{n-1-h}} = \iint_S \frac{F(P,P,Q)\,d\sigma_Q}{[\vartheta^Q(P,Q)]^{n-1-h}}. \quad (272)$$

Let us examine the first integral (271)

$$I(A) = \iint\limits_S \frac{r_{AQ} \cos(N_P, \overrightarrow{QA})}{[\vartheta^Q(A, Q)]^n} \mu(Q)\, d\sigma_Q \tag{273}$$

which is analogous to the integral

$$\iint\limits_S r_{AQ}^{1-n} \cos(N_P, \overrightarrow{QA})\, \mu(Q)\, d\sigma_Q \tag{274}$$

familiar from classical potential theory. The boundary value of integral (274) is usually sought by comparing it with the potential of double surface distribution. This method, however, is not precise and its simplicity is of didactic value only. For integral (273) we do not use this method, not only because of the required scientific rigour, but also for principal reasons; in fact, under the assumption of the Hölder condition for the coefficients of an elliptic equation, the appropriate potential of double distribution does not exist.

Assume for the time being that the interior point A lies on the inward drawn normal to the surface A at an arbitrary point P of it, and let us decompose integral (273) into two terms

$$I(A) = I_{S_K}(A) + I_{S-S_K}(A), \tag{275}$$

the integration being carried out over that part S_K of the surface S lying inside the sphere K with centre at P and radius δ appearing in the Liapunov conditions, and over the remaining part $S - S_K$. Let us examine the difference

$$R(A) = I_{S_K}(A) - I^*_{S'_K}(A) \tag{276}$$

between the integral I_{S_K} and an integral of an analogous form

$$I^*_{S'_K}(A) = \iint\limits_{S'_K} \frac{r_{AQ'} \cos(N_P, \overrightarrow{Q'A})}{[\vartheta^P(A, Q')]^n} \mu(Q)\, d\sigma_{Q'} \tag{277}$$

over the projection S'_K of the surface S_K onto the tangent plane of the surface S at the point P; Q' denotes the projection of the point Q onto the tangent plane.

We first prove that integral (277) tends to the limit

$$\lim_{A\to P} I^*_{S'_K}(A) = \frac{1}{2}\frac{\omega_n}{\sqrt{\det|a^{\alpha\beta}(P)|}}\,\mu(P), \tag{278}$$

when A tends to the point P of S.

Consider a part $\tilde{S}'_K$ of region S'_K which contains the point P, and consider a spherical surface Λ with centre at A and unit radius; denote by $\xi'_1, \xi'_2, \ldots, \xi'_n$ the coordinates of that point of the surface Λ which corresponds to the point Q' in the central projection from A. We can now write integral (277) in the form of the sum of the following integrals

$$I^*_{S'_K}(A) = \mu(P)\iint\limits_{E(\tilde{S}'_K)} \frac{d\omega(\xi'_1, \xi'_2, \ldots, \xi'_n)}{\left[\sum\limits_{\alpha,\beta=1}^{n} a^{\alpha\beta}(P)\,\xi'_\alpha\,\xi'_\beta\right]^{n/2}} +$$

$$+\iint\limits_{E(\tilde{S}'_K)} \frac{[\mu(Q)-\mu(P)]\,d\omega(\xi'_1, \xi'_2, \ldots, \xi'_n)}{\left[\sum\limits_{\alpha,\beta=1}^{n} a^{\alpha\beta}(P)\,\xi'_\alpha\,\xi'_\beta\right]^{n/2}} +$$

$$+\iint\limits_{S'_K-\tilde{S}'_K} \frac{r_{AQ'}\cos(N_P, \overrightarrow{Q'A})}{[\vartheta^P(A, Q')]^n}\,\mu(Q)\,d\sigma_{Q'}, \tag{279}$$

where $E(\tilde{S}'_K)$ denotes the set of all points of Λ which correspond to the points of the region $\tilde{S}'_K$, and by $d\omega(\xi'_1, \xi'_2, \ldots, \xi'_n)$ an element of area of surface Λ. In view of the assumed continuity of the function $\mu(P)$ and the boundedness of the first integral over the surface Λ, given $\varepsilon > 0$, we can select a small surface $\tilde{S}'_K$ such that the absolute value of the second integral (279) be smaller than $\varepsilon/3$. Observe next that in the region $S'_K - \tilde{S}'_K$ the factor $\cos(N_p, \overrightarrow{Q'A})$ and the whole integrand in the third integral (279) tend uniformly to zero when A tends to the point P. Thus, after having fixed the region $\tilde{S}'_K$, we can select in accordance with the number ε a positive number $\eta_1(\varepsilon)$ such that the absolute value of the third integral (27) be smaller than $\varepsilon/2$ when $|AP| < \eta_1(\varepsilon)$. Observe, finally, that the set $E(\tilde{S}'_K)$ tends to a hemispherical surface when $A \to P$ and consequently we can select a number $\eta_2(\varepsilon)$ such that the first integral (279) differs from the integral (see p. 366)

$$\frac{1}{2}\mu(P)\iint\limits_{A}\frac{d\omega(\xi_1',\xi_2',\dots,\xi_n')}{\left[\sum\limits_{\alpha,\beta=1}^{n}a^{\alpha\beta}(P)\xi_\alpha'\xi_\beta'\right]^{n/2}}=\frac{\mu(P)\,\omega_n}{2\sqrt{\det|a^{\alpha\beta}(P)|}}$$

by a number, the absolute value of which is smaller than $\varepsilon/3$ when $|AP|<\eta_2(\varepsilon)$. Combining these results, we have

$$\left|I^{*}_{S_K'}(A)-\frac{\omega_n}{2\sqrt{\det|a^{\alpha\beta}(P)|}}\mu(P)\right|<\varepsilon,$$

$$\text{when}\quad |AP|<\min(\eta_1,\eta_2),\tag{280}$$

which proves the validity of the stated property (278).

We now prove that the difference (276) is continuous at a point P of the surface S, i.e. that

$$\lim_{A\to P}R(A)=R(P)=I_{S_K}(P).\tag{281}$$

Observe that integral (277) vanishes when $A=P$ and that the improper integral

$$I_{S_K}(P)=\iint\limits_{S_K}\frac{r_{PQ}\cos(N_P,\overrightarrow{QP})}{[\vartheta^{Q}(P,Q)]^{n}}\mu(Q)\,d\sigma_Q\tag{282}$$

is absolutely convergent since the integrand has a weak singularity

$$\frac{r_{PQ}\,|\cos(N_P,\overrightarrow{QP})|}{[\vartheta^{Q}(P,Q)]^{n}}<\frac{\text{const}}{r_{PQ}^{n-1-\kappa}},\tag{283}$$

where κ is the exponent in the Liapunov condition

$$\delta_{PQ}<\text{const}\,r_{PQ}^{\kappa}\tag{284}$$

for the angle between the normals at two points P and Q of the surface S.

Let us examine the difference

$$R(A)-R(P)=I_{S_K}(A)-I_{S_K}(P)-I^{*}_{S_K'}(A),\tag{285}$$

when $A \to P$. Consider therefore a sphere K_1 with centre at P and radius $\rho < \delta$, and decompose each integral (285) into two parts

$$\begin{aligned} I_{S_K}(A) &= I_{S_{K_1}}(A) + I_{S_K - S_{K_1}}(A), \\ I_{S_K}(P) &= I_{S_{K_1}}(P) + I_{S_K - S_{K_1}}(P), \\ I^*_{S'_K}(A) &= I^*_{S'_{K_1}}(A) + I^*_{S'_K - S'_{K_1}}(A), \end{aligned} \tag{286}$$

the integration being carried out over the surface S_{K_1} lying inside the sphere K_1, over the surface $S_K - S_{K_1}$ and over the projections of these surfaces onto the tangent plane at P.

The integral $I_{S_{K_1}}(P)$ containing function (283) with a weak singularity tends to zero when the radius ρ of the sphere K_1 tends to zero and it is evident that given $\varepsilon > 0$, we can find a radius $\rho_1(\varepsilon)$ depending only on ε, such that

$$|I_{S_{K_1}}(P)| < \frac{\varepsilon}{4}, \quad \text{when} \quad \rho \leqq \rho_1. \tag{287}$$

We now prove that we can choose a radius $\rho_2(\varepsilon)$, such that

$$|I_{S_{K_1}}(A) - I^*_{S'_{K_1}}(A)| < \frac{\varepsilon}{4}, \quad \text{when} \quad \rho \leqq \rho_2, \tag{288}$$

for any position of the point A. An elementary calculation leads to the inequalities

$$\frac{\sqrt{4r^2_{PQ'}/r^2_{QQ'}+1}-1}{\sqrt{4r^2_{PQ'}/r^2_{QQ'}+1}+1} \leqq \frac{r^2_{AQ}}{r^2_{AQ'}} \leqq \frac{\sqrt{4r^2_{PQ'}/r^2_{QQ'}+1}+1}{\sqrt{4r^2_{PQ'}/r^2_{QQ'}+1}-1}, \tag{289}$$

whence in view of the inequality

$$r_{QQ'} \leqq \text{const}\, r^{\kappa+1}_{PQ'} \tag{290}$$

following from Liapunov's condition (284) we infer the existence of a positive constant $\chi < 1$ such that the inequalities

$$0 < \chi \leqq \frac{r_{AQ}}{r_{AQ'}} \leqq \frac{1}{\chi} \tag{291}$$

hold for any point $Q \in S_{K_1}$ and for any point A on the normal at P. Moreover, in view of inequalities (226), (228), (290) and (291), we have

$$|r_{AQ}\cos(N_P, \overrightarrow{QA}) - r_{AQ'}\cos(N_P, \overrightarrow{Q'A})| = r_{QQ'} < \text{const}\, r_{PQ'}^{\kappa+1} \quad (292)$$

and

$$| \vartheta^Q(A, Q)]^{-n} - [\vartheta^P(A, Q')]^{-n}|$$
$$< \tfrac{1}{2}n(g\chi r_{AQ})^{-n-2}[k_a r_{PQ}^h n^2 r_{AQ}^2 + nM_a r_{QQ'}(r_{AQ}+r_{AQ'})], \quad (293)$$

where M_a denotes the upper bound of the collection of functions $|a^{\alpha\beta}(A)|$ and K_a their Hölder coefficient.

We assume moreover that as before the surface S_K is sufficiently small so that the cosine $\gamma(Q)$ of the angle between the normal at Q of S and normal at point P satisfies the inequality

$$\gamma(Q) \geqq \tfrac{1}{2}. \quad (294)$$

The above inequalities imply the result

$$|I_{S_{K_1}}(A) - \overset{*}{I}_{S'_{K_1}}(A)|$$
$$< \iint_{S_{K_1}} \frac{r_{QQ'}|\mu(Q)|\, d\sigma_Q}{[\vartheta^Q(A, Q)]^n} +$$
$$+ \iint_{S_{K_1}} \frac{r_{AQ'}\cos(N_P, \overrightarrow{Q'A})}{[\vartheta^P(A, Q')]^n}\left(\frac{1}{\gamma(Q)} - 1\right)|\mu(Q)|\, d\sigma'_{Q'} +$$
$$+ \iint_{S_{K_1}} |[\vartheta^Q(A, Q)]^{-n} - [\vartheta^P(A, Q')]^{-n}|\, r_{AQ'}\cos(N_P, \overrightarrow{Q'A}) \times$$
$$\times |\mu(Q)|\, d\sigma_Q$$
$$< \text{const}.\sup|\mu(Q)|\left[\iint_{S'_{K_1}} \frac{d\sigma'_{Q'}}{r_{PQ'}^{n-1-\kappa_1}} + \iint_{S'_{K_1}} \frac{d\sigma'_{Q'}}{r_{PQ}^{n-1-h}}\right] +$$
$$+ \sup\left|\frac{1}{\gamma(Q)} - 1\right| \sup|\mu(Q)| \iint_{S'_{K_1}} \frac{r_{AQ'}\cos(N_P, \overrightarrow{Q'A})}{[\vartheta^P(A, Q')]^n}\, d\sigma'_{Q'}. \quad (295)$$

The first and the second integrals containing functions with weak singularities tend to zero when the radius ρ of the sphere K_1 tends to zero. The third integral can be reduced to an integral over the surface of the unit sphere Λ and it is bounded when $A \to P$. Since $\gamma(Q) \to 1$ when $Q \to P$, there exists $\rho_2(\varepsilon)$ depending only on ε, such that inequality (288) holds for any position of the point A.

Assuming that K_1 has radius $\rho = \min[\rho_1(\varepsilon), \rho_2(\varepsilon)]$, observe that the integral $I_{S_K - S_{K_1}}(A)$ is continuous at P_1, since the latter is located outside its region of integration; consequently there exists a number $\eta_1(\varepsilon)$ depending only on ε, such that

$$|I_{S_K - S_{K_1}}(A) - I_{S_K - S_{K_1}}(P)| < \frac{\varepsilon}{4}, \quad \text{when} \quad |AP| < \eta_1(\varepsilon). \tag{296}$$

In view of the factor $\cos(N_p, \overline{Q'A})$ tending uniformly to zero when $A \to P$, $Q' \in S'_K - S'_{K_1}$, there exists $\eta_2(\varepsilon)$ depending only on ε, such that

$$|\overset{*}{I}_{S'_K - S'_{K_1}}(A)| < \frac{\varepsilon}{4}, \quad \text{when} \quad |AP| < \eta_2(\varepsilon). \tag{297}$$

Combining inequalities (287), (288), (296) and (297) we may state that difference (285) satisfies the inequality

$$|R(A) - R(P)| < \varepsilon, \quad \text{when} \quad |AP| < \min(\eta_1, \eta_2). \tag{298}$$

Consequently, in view of (278), we obtain

$$\lim_{A \to P} I_{S_K}(A) = \lim_{A \to P} \overset{*}{I}_{S'_K}(A) + I_{S_K}(P)$$

$$= \frac{\omega_n}{2\sqrt{\det|a^{\alpha\beta}(P)|}}\mu(P) + \iint\limits_{S_K} \frac{r_{PQ}\cos(N_P, \overrightarrow{QP})}{[\vartheta^Q(P, Q)]^n}\mu(Q)\, d\sigma_Q. \tag{299}$$

In view of the continuity at the point P of the integral $I_{S-S_K}(A)$ extended to the exterior part of the surface S, these results imply directly the boundary property of integral (273):

$$\lim_{A\to P} I(A) = \frac{\omega_n}{2\sqrt{\det|a^{\alpha\beta}(P)|}}\,\mu(P) + \iint\limits_S \frac{r_{PQ}\cos(N_P, \overrightarrow{QP})}{[\vartheta^Q(P,Q)]^n}\,\mu(Q)\,d\sigma_Q. \qquad (300)$$

This property and relations (269) and (271) lead to the boundary property of the transversal derivative of the potential of surface distribution

$$\lim_{A\to P}\frac{dU(A)}{dT_P} = -\frac{1}{2}\lambda_n(P)\,\mu(P) + \iint\limits_S \frac{d\Gamma(P,Q)}{dT_P}\,\mu(Q)\,d\sigma_Q, \qquad (301)$$

in agreement with statement (264) of Theorem 9.

We have assumed in the above argument that the point A tends to P along the normal. It is easily observed that this transition is uniform, since the choice of radius $\rho(\varepsilon)$ and numbers $\eta_1(\varepsilon)$ and $\eta_2(\varepsilon)$ is independent of the points A and P.

Assume now that A tends to the point P of the surface S along an arbitrary arc located inside Ω. Let P_1 denote the point of the surface S nearest from A. The transversal derivative of the potential U at the point A with respect to P_1 is given by the formula

$$\frac{dU(A)}{dT_{P_1}} = \sum_{\alpha,\beta=1}^{n} a_{\alpha\beta}(A)\cos(N_{P_1}, x_\beta)\,U_{x_\alpha}(A), \qquad (302)$$

and therefore the difference between the transversal derivatives at A with respect to the points P and P_1 is the following:

$$\frac{dU(A)}{dT_P} - \frac{dU(A)}{dT_{P_1}} = \sum_{\alpha,\beta=1}^{n} a_{\alpha\beta}(A)\left[\cos(N_P, x_\beta) - \cos(N_{P_1}, x_\beta)\right]U_{x_\alpha}(A). \qquad (303)$$

According to the Liapunov condition, the difference between the cosines in this relation satisfies the inequality

$$|\cos(N_P, x_\beta) - \cos(N_{P_1}, x_\beta)| < \mathrm{const}\,.\, r_{PP_1}^{\varkappa}.$$

Further, the derivatives of the potential of surface distribution satisfy the inequalities

$$|U_{x_\alpha}(A)| < \text{const.} \iint\limits_S \frac{d\sigma_Q}{r_{AQ}^{n-1}},$$

and it is known that this integral is unbounded as $|\log r_{AP_1}|$ when $A \to P_1$. It follows therefore that the difference (303) tends to zero as the distance PP_1 tends to zero, provided that

$$r_{PP_1}^{\kappa} \log r_{AP_1} \to 0, \quad \text{when} \quad r_{PP_1} \to 0. \tag{304}$$

Since A is located on the normal at P_1 and expression (302) tends uniformly to a limit when $A \to P_1$, we infer that the transversal derivative at A with respect to P tends to the same limit (301) when A tends to P along an arc satisfying condition (304). This condition requires that the distance r_{AP_1} of A from the surface S tends to zero not too rapidly compared with distance r_{PP_1}. Condition (304) is rather weak since it is even satisfied by the tangent arc to the surface S at P, with an arbitrarily large degree of tangency.

The foregoing argument implies that the integrand in (301), i.e. the transversal derivative of the fundamental solution at the point P of S, has a weak singularity with respect to the surface integral. We can verify this statement directly. To this end, set $A = P$ in formula (269) and apply the inequalities

$$|\cos(N_P, \overrightarrow{PQ})| < \text{const.} \, r_{PQ}^{\kappa}, \qquad |a^{\alpha\gamma}(Q) - a^{\alpha\gamma}(P)| < k_a r_{PQ}^{h},$$

taking into account the second inequality (270). This yields the following estimate of the considered function when $Q \to P$:

$$\left| \frac{d\Gamma(P, Q)}{dT_P} \right| < \frac{\text{const}}{r_{PQ}^{n-1-h^*}}, \tag{305}$$

where $h^* = \min(h, \kappa)$.

Consequently, the improper integral in formula (301) is absolutely convergent.

The transversal derivative is introduced into boundary problems for elliptic equations exactly in view of the weak singularity (305), since the boundary value of the normal derivative, introduced in problems concerning the Laplace equation, for an elliptic equation in general form would be expressed by an integral of a function with a strong singularity and the boundary value of this derivative does not necessarily exist under the only assumption of continuity of the density $\mu(P)$.

We now proceed to consider the problem of existence of the boundary value of the derivative of potential of surface distribution in the direction of the tangent to the surface S. Consider, therefore, a rectangular coordinate system with origin at an arbitrary point P of the surface S, the axis Px_n being the inward normal to the surface S. The axes $Px_1, Px_2, \ldots, Px_{n-1}$ are then located in the tangent plane. For the derivative of potential (258) at an interior point A in the direction of a tangent axis, say Px_1, we obtain

$$U_{x_1}(A) = \iint\limits_S \Gamma_{x_1}(A, Q)\, \mu(Q)\, d\sigma_Q \tag{306}$$

according to the rule of differentiation of a regular integral, In view of the estimates (271) the derivative of the fundamental. solution satisfies the inequality

$$|\Gamma_{x_1}(A, Q)| < \frac{\text{const}}{r_{AQ}^{n-1}}. \tag{307}$$

This singularity is strong with respect to the surface integral when $A \to Q$, and therefore the boundary value of the derivative (306) also does not necessarily exist under only the assumption of continuity of the density $\mu(Q)$. The problem of existence of the boundary value of integral (306), and its determination when the point A coincides with a point P of the surface S requires a more precise consideration and a stronger assumption for the density μ.

This is contained in the following theorem:

THEOREM 10. *If the density $\mu(Q)$ of surface distribution satisfies the Hölder condition, and the surface S the Liapunov conditions, then the derivative of the potential of surface distribution* (258), *in the direction of the tangent has the definite boundary value*

$$\lim_{A \to P} U_{x_1}(A) = \iint\limits_S \Gamma_{x_1}(P, Q)\, \mu(Q)\, d\sigma_Q, \tag{308}$$

when $A \in \Omega$ *tends to an arbitrary point* $P \in S$, *and the improper integral* (308) *of the function* $\Gamma_{x_1}(P, Q)$ *has its Cauchy principal value, i.e. it is the limit*

$$\iint_S \Gamma_{x_1}(P, Q)\,\mu(Q)\,d\sigma_Q = \lim_{r_\Pi \to 0} \iint_{S-S_\Pi} \Gamma_{x_1}(P, Q)\,\mu(Q)\,d\sigma_Q, \tag{309}$$

where S_Π *is that part of the surface S located in the neighbourhood of the point P inside a cylinder* Π *with axis* Px_n *and radius* r_Π.

We emphasize that integral (309) is conditionally convergent only, and therefore the improper integral of the absolute value $|\Gamma_{x_1}(P, Q)\,\mu(Q)|$ does not necessarily exist.

We first decompose the potential into two terms (266), and on the basis of the estimate (270) for the weak singularities of the derivatives of function $\overline{w}(A, Q)$, we at once obtain the boundary property of the derivative of the second term

$$\lim_{A \to P} \iint_S \overline{w}_{x_1}(A, Q)\,\mu(Q)\,d\sigma_Q = \iint_S \overline{w}_{x_1}(P, Q)\,\mu(Q)\,d\sigma_Q. \tag{310}$$

It is thus sufficient to investigate the derivative of the first term

$$V_{x_1}(A) = \iint_S w^Q_{x_1}(A, Q)\,\mu(Q)\,d\sigma_Q, \tag{311}$$

when $A \to P$. Assume for the time being that the interior point A of Ω is located on the normal Px_n to surface S at an arbitrary point P. As before, we decompose integral (311) into two terms

$$V_{x_1}(A) = V_{x_1}^{S_W}(A) + V_{x_1}^{S-S_W}(A); \tag{312}$$

the first integral being carried out over a part S_W of the surface S located in the neighbourhood of the point P, inside a cylinder W with axis Px_n and a sufficiently small radius $\delta' < \delta$ (independent of P), such that the surface S satisfies the assumption stated in the Liapunov conditions; the second integration is over the remaining part $S-S_W$ and this term is evidently continuous at P, i.e. we have

$$\lim_{A \to P} V_{x_1}^{S-S_W}(A) = V_{x_1}^{S-S_W}(P). \tag{313}$$

It is therefore sufficient to investigate the first term of the sum (312). To this end, introduce the auxiliary integral

$$J(A) = \iint_{S'_W} w^P_{x_1}(A, Q')\,\mu(P)\,d\sigma'_{Q'} \tag{314}$$

over the projection S'_W of the surface S_W onto the tangent plane $x_n = 0$; Q' denotes the projection of the point $Q(\xi_1, \xi_2, \ldots, \xi_n)$ of S onto this plane.

Taking into account the equality of the derivatives

$$w^P_{x_1}(A, Q') = -w^P_{\xi_1}(A, Q')$$

and applying the Green–Ostrogradski Theorem, we obtain

$$J(A) = -\mu(P) \int_{C'_W} w^P(A, Q') \cos\alpha_1\, dl'_{Q'}, \tag{315}$$

where C'_W denotes the boundary of the region S'_W, and α_1 is the angle between the normal at point Q' of the boundary and the Px_1-axis. It is readily observed that the integral (315) tends to the value

$$\lim_{A\to P} J(A) = -\mu(P) \int_{C'_W} w^P(P, Q') \cos\alpha_1\, dl'_{Q'} = 0, \tag{316}$$

when A tends to a point P of the surface S. The limit (316) is also the Cauchy principal value of the improper integral (314) when $A = P$, for we have

$$\iint_{S'_W - S'_\Pi} w^P_{x_1}(P, Q')\,\mu(P)\,d\sigma'_{Q'}$$

$$= (n-2)\,\mu(P) \iint_{S'_W - S'_\Pi} \Big[\sum_{\alpha,\beta=1}^{n-1} a^{\alpha\beta}(P)\,\xi_\alpha \xi_\beta\Big]^{-n/2} \sum_{\beta=1}^{n-1} a^{1\beta}(P)\,\xi_\beta\, d\sigma_{Q'} = 0,$$

where S'_Π denotes the section by the tangent plane $x_n = 0$ of the cylinder Π with axis Px_n and radius r_Π, located inside cylinder W. This implies that

$$\lim_{A\to P} J(A) = \lim_{r_\Pi\to 0} \iint_{S'_W S - '_\Pi} w^P_{x_1}(P, Q')\,\mu(P)\,d\sigma_{Q'} = 0. \tag{317}$$

Knowing already properties of integral (314), consider the difference between it and the first term of (312)

$$R(A) = V_{x_1}^{S_W}(A) - J(A)$$

$$= \iint_{S_W} \left[w_{x_1}^{Q}(A, Q) \frac{\mu(Q)}{\gamma(Q)} - w_{x_1}^{P}(A, Q')\mu(P) \right] d\sigma'_{Q'}. \qquad (318)$$

We have

$$\begin{aligned} &w_{x_1}^{Q}(A, Q) \\ &= (2-n)[\vartheta^{Q}(A, Q)]^{-n}\left[a^{1n}(Q)(x_n - \xi_n) - \sum_{\beta=1}^{n-1} a^{1\beta}(Q)\xi_\beta\right], \\ &w_{x_1}^{P}(A, Q') \\ &= (2-n)[\vartheta^{P}(A, Q')]^{-n}\left[a^{1n}(P)x_n - \sum_{\beta=1}^{n-1} a^{1\beta}(P)\xi_\beta\right], \end{aligned} \qquad (319)$$

whence

$$\begin{aligned} &|w_{x_1}^{Q}(A, Q) - w_{x_1}^{P}(A, Q')| \\ &< (2-n)\,|[\vartheta^{Q}(A, Q)]^{-n} - [\vartheta^{P}(A, Q')]^{-n}|\, M_a[r_{AQ'} + (n-1)r_{PQ'}] + \\ &\quad + (2-n)g^{-n} r_{AQ'}^{-n}[k_a r_{PQ}^{h} r_{AQ'} + M_a|\xi_n| + (n-1)k_a r_{PQ}^{h+1}]. \end{aligned} \qquad (320)$$

Taking into account the inequalities (290), (291), (293), the assumed Hölder inequality

$$|\mu(P) - \mu(Q)| < \text{const}\, r_{PQ}^{h_\mu}, \qquad (321)$$

and the inequality $1-\gamma(Q) < \text{const}\, r_{PQ}^{2\kappa}$ following from the Liapunov conditions, we infer that the integrand in (318) satisfies the inequality

$$\left| w_{x_1}^{Q}(A, Q) \frac{\mu(Q)}{\gamma(Q)} - w_{x_1}^{P}(A, Q')\mu(P) \right| < \text{const}\, \frac{r_{PQ'}^{h^*}}{r_{AQ'}^{n-1}}, \qquad (322)$$

where $h^* = \min(h, \kappa, h_\mu)$. Estimate (322) implies at once that the integral (318) is absolutely convergent to a definite limit when $A \to P$, and since the limit of (317) is zero, the limit of the first term of the sum (312) exists and it is given by the integral

$$\lim_{A \to P} V_{x_1}^{S_W}(A) = \iint\limits_{S'_W} \left[w_{x_1}^{Q}(P, Q) \frac{\mu(Q)}{\gamma(Q)} - w_{x_1}^{P}(P, Q') \mu(P) \right] d\sigma'_{Q'}. \quad (323)$$

By virtue of estimate (322), the integrand in (323) has a weak singularity and this improper integral is absolutely convergent. Bearing in mind property (317), we can write the limit (323) in the form of the Cauchy principal value of the improper integral

$$\lim_{A \to P} V_{x_1}(A) = \iint\limits_{S_W} w_{x_1}^{Q}(P, Q) \mu(Q) d\sigma_Q = \lim_{r_\Pi \to 0} \iint\limits_{S_W - S_\Pi} w_{x_1}^{Q}(P, Q) \mu(Q) d\sigma_Q. \quad (324)$$

This integral, however, is not absolutely convergent.

Combining results (310), (313) and (324), we arrive at the statement (308) of Theorem 10 with an integral in the Cauchy sense (309). Applying the remark on uniform convergence, we infer that the boundary property (308) is valid for an arbitrary transition of the point $A \in \Omega$ to an arbitrary point $P \in S$.

§ 13. Properties of the generalized potential of spatial charge

DEFINITION 2. *By the generalized potential of spatial charge with respect to the elliptic equation* (192) *we mean the following integral over the region* Ω *inside a region* Ω':

$$W(A) = \iiint\limits_{\Omega} \Gamma(A, B) \rho(B) dB. \quad (325)$$

The bounded integrable function $\rho(B)$ is called the *density* of the spatial charge.

By an argument similar to that for the quasi-potential (see p. 368) we easily prove that the potential (325) has continuous first derivatives inside region Ω given by the formula

$$W_{x_\alpha}(A) = \iiint\limits_{\Omega} \Gamma_{x_\alpha}(A, B) \rho(B) dB, \quad (326)$$

the improper integral being absolutely convergent in view of the inequality

$$|\Gamma_{x_\alpha}(A, B)| < \frac{\text{const}}{r_{AB}^{n-1}}. \tag{327}$$

The existence of the second derivatives of potential (325) requires stronger conditions for the density $\rho(A)$. We have then the following theorem:

THEOREM 11. *If the density $\rho(A)$ satisfies the Hölder condition in the region Ω, the potential of spatial charge* (325) *has continuous second derivatives at every interior point A of the region Ω, satisfying the Poisson equation in the form*

$$\hat{\Psi}[W(A)] = -\lambda_n(A)\rho(A). \tag{328}$$

To prove the theorem we write potential (325) in the form of the sum

$$W(A) = \iiint_{\Omega} w^B(A, B)\rho(B)\,dB + \\ + \iiint_{\Omega'(M)} w^M(A, M)\rho_1(M)\,dM, \tag{329}$$

where

$$\rho_1(M) = \iiint_{\Omega(B)} \Phi(M, B)\rho(B)\,dB, \tag{330}$$

and M is an arbitrary point of the region Ω'. Thus we see that the potential (325) is expressed in the form of a sum of two quasi-potentials, one with density $\rho(B)$ and the second with density (330). According to the investigations of the fundamental solution (see [43]) the density $\rho_1(M)$ given by formula (330) satisfies the Hölder condition in Ω' under the assumption of the boundedness and integrability of $\rho(B)$ only. Consequently, both terms of the sum (329) have continuous second derivatives inside Ω, which satisfy equation (247). We infer therefore that potential (325) satisfies the equation

$$\hat{\Psi}[W(A)] = -\lambda_n(A)[\rho(A) + \rho_1(A)] + \\ + \iiint_{\Omega(B)} \hat{\Psi}_A[w^B(A, B)]\rho(B)\,dB + \iiint_{\Omega'(M)} \hat{\Psi}[w^M(A, M)]\rho_1(M)\,dM.$$

Introducing here expression (330) for ρ_1 we obtain

$$\hat{\Psi}[W(A)] = -\lambda_n(A)\rho(A) + \iiint_{\Omega(B)} \{\hat{\Psi}[w^B(A,B)] - \lambda_n(A)\Phi(A,B) + $$
$$+ \iiint_{\Omega'(M)} \hat{\Psi}[w^M(A,M)]\Phi(M,B)\,dM\}\,dB.$$

This implies the statement (328) of Theorem 11, since the function Φ satisfies the integral equation (253).

To end our treatment of the general elliptic equation, observe that on the basis of the presented properties of the potential of spatial charge and the potential of surface distribution, we can solve the problem of determination of the function $u(A)$ satisfying inside Ω an equation of the form

$$\hat{\Psi}(u) = F\left(A, u, \frac{\partial u}{\partial x_1}, \frac{\partial u}{\partial x_2}, \ldots, \frac{\partial u}{\partial x_n}\right) \tag{331}$$

and at points P of the bounding surface S, the boundary condition

$$\frac{du}{dT_P} + g(P)u(P) = \Phi(P, u). \tag{332}$$

Taking into account Poisson's Equation we seek the function $u(A)$ as a solution of the integro-differential equation

$$u(A) = -\iiint_{\Omega} \Gamma(A,B)\lambda_n^{-1}(B) \times$$
$$\times F\left[B, u(B), \frac{\partial u}{\partial \xi_1}, \frac{\partial u}{\partial \xi_2}, \ldots, \frac{\partial u}{\partial \xi_n}\right] dB +$$
$$+ \iint_S \Gamma(A,Q)\varphi(Q)\,d\sigma_Q, \tag{333}$$

the right-hand side of which is a sum of a potential of spatial charge and a potential of surface distribution with an unknown density $\varphi(Q)$. Requiring that function (333) satisfies the boundary condition (332), and employing Theorem 9 on the transversal derivative, we obtain the second integral equation in the form

$$-\frac{1}{2}\lambda_n(P)\varphi(P)+$$

$$+\iint_S \left\{\frac{d}{dT_P}[\Gamma(P,Q)]+g(P)\Gamma(P,Q)\right\}\varphi(Q)\,d\sigma_Q-$$

$$-\iiint_\Omega \left\{\frac{d}{dT_P}[\Gamma(P,B)]+g(P)\Gamma(P,B)\right\}\lambda_n^{-1}(B)\times$$

$$\times F\left[B,u(B),\frac{\partial u}{\partial\xi_1},\ldots,\frac{\partial u}{\partial\xi_n}\right]dB=\Phi[P,u(P)]. \qquad (334)$$

Thus the problem has been reduced to the solution of the system of two integral equations (333) and (334) with unknown function $u(A)$ in the region Ω, and the unknown function $\varphi(P)$ on the surface S.

A complete solution of this problem by means of the Schauder topological method requires more precise considerations and will be given in Chapter XXII of Part 3.

CHAPTER XIII

APPLICATION OF INTEGRAL EQUATIONS TO THE THEORY OF EQUATIONS OF PARABOLIC TYPE

§ 1. General considerations

The law of heat conduction implies that the temperature $u(x, y, z, t)$, as function of the point $A(x, y, z)$ of the space and time t, satisfies at all points A in the interior of the conducting medium and at every instant t, the differential equation of second order of the form

$$\frac{\partial^2 u}{\partial x^2}+\frac{\partial^2 u}{\partial y^2}+\frac{\partial^2 u}{\partial z^2}-k\frac{\partial u}{\partial t}=0. \tag{1}$$

If the medium is homogeneous, the constant k, depending on the physical properties of the medium, can be reduced to unity by an appropriate selection of the unit of time. Equation (1) called the *heat conduction equation* is of *parabolic* type and plays for equations of this type the same rôle as the Laplace equation for equations of elliptic type. The characteristics of equation (1) in four-dimensional space are the planes t = const.

By the *Fourier problem of first kind*, which is naturally implied by physics, we mean the problem of determination of a function $u(A, t)$ which satisfies the heat conduction equation (1) at all points $A(x, y, z)$ inside a region Ω bounded by a surface S and at every instant $t > 0$, and which, moreover, satisfies the following conditions.

1) *The initial condition*

$$u(A, t) \to F(A), \quad \text{when} \quad t \to 0 \ (A \text{ is inside } \Omega). \tag{2}$$

2) *The boundary condition*

$$u(A, t) \to f(P, t), \quad \text{when } A \to P \ (P \text{ is on surface } S,\ t > 0) \tag{3}$$

where $F(A)$ is an *a priori* prescribed bounded and continuous function inside Ω, and $f(P, t)$ is a known function defined and continuous at all points P of the surface S and at every instant $t > 0$, or in an interval $(0, T)$. Observe that the transitions to the limit (2) and (3) are not necessarily uniform (the first with respect to A while the second with respect to t).

For physical reasons it is not required that the limits

$$\lim_{A \to P} F(A) \quad \text{and} \quad \lim_{t \to 0} f(P, t),$$

if they exist, be equal; we shall see that also mathematical reasons do not umply this condition.

The *Fourier problem of second kind* differs from the foregoing problem only in the boundary condition which now takes the form

$$\lim_{A \to P} \left(\frac{du(A, t)}{dn_P} \right) + a(P, t) \lim_{A \to P} u(A, t) = f(P, t) \qquad (t > 0). \tag{4}$$

The known functions $a(P, t)$ and $f(P, t)$ are defined at all points of the surface S and at every instant $t > 0$, or in an interval $(0, T)$. Condition (4) is analogous to the condition in the mixed problem for the Laplace equation, and from the viewpoint of physics, it expresses the influence of radiation on the surface S, under a simplifying assumption concerning the radiated energy.

Observe now that the case $a = 0$ does not require a special investigation, as was the case for the Laplace equation.

Earlier investigations (in the nineteenth century) on the Fourier problem were based mainly on the so-called *Fourier method* which consists in seeking the function in the form of a series which is the sum of products of functions of spatial point and functions of time. This method is in many cases practically expedient, but it has the principal disadvantage of not being general, since it requires certain particular assumptions concerning the boundary functions $F(A)$ and $f(P, t)$.

It was only in this century, owing to the papers of a Swedish mathematician HOLMGREN [22], extensively developed by the French mathematician GEVREY [13] and [14], that a general method was created for the Fourier problem, which is remarkable for its beauty and simplicity.

This method proceeds along the same lines in the case of the theory of the heat conduction equation as for the Laplace equation, the fundamental solution being the function of the form

$$\frac{1}{(t-\tau)^{3/2}} \exp\left[-\frac{(x-\xi)^2+(y-\eta)^2+(z-\zeta)^2}{4(t-\tau)}\right] \tag{5}$$

called the *heat potential of point* (ξ, η, ζ, τ), where ξ, η, ζ and τ are constant parameters. We can define integrals analogous to the potentials of surface and double distributions. Their properties are analogous to those in the theory of Newtonian potential and the requirement imposed by conditions (2) and (3) leads to Volterra integral equations of a rather complicated singularity. These equations can generally be investigated, and lead to the solution of the Fourier problem. This is one of the most outstanding achievements of the theory of integral equations.

§ 2. One-dimensional Fourier problem

If temperature in a conducting medium depends on one coordinate only, say x, and time t, i.e. at the considered instant it is constant in every plane perpendicular to the axis Ox, then the temperature satisfies the particular form of the heat conduction equation

$$\frac{\partial^2 u}{\partial x^2} - \frac{\partial u}{\partial t} = 0. \tag{6}$$

This is also the equation for the temperature in a conducting rod, the surface of which is isolated from the outflow or inflow of heat.

The one-dimensional Fourier problem consists in the determination of a function of two variables $u(x, t)$ which satisfies equation (6) at every point inside the strip

$$a < x < b, \qquad t > 0 \tag{7}$$

and, moreover, it obeys the following conditions.

1) *The initial condition*

$$u(x, t) \to F(x), \quad \text{when } t \to 0 \ (a < x < b). \tag{8}$$

2) *The boundary conditions*

$$\begin{aligned} u(x, t) &\to f_1(t), \quad \text{when } x \to a, \\ u(x, t) &\to f_2(t), \quad \text{when } x \to b \end{aligned} \quad (t > 0), \tag{9}$$

where $P(x)$ is a known continuous and bounded function in the interval (a, b), and $f_1(t)$ and $f_2(t)$ are known continuous and bounded functions for $t > 0$. We emphasize that the transitions to the limit (8) and (9) are not necessarily uniform, and the functions $P(x), f_1(t)$ and $f_2(t)$ may have no limits when $x \to a$ or $t \to 0$.

According to the Holmgren method, we solve this problem using the fundamental solution of equation (6)

$$\Theta(x, t; \xi, \tau) = \frac{1}{\sqrt{t-\tau}} \exp\left[-\frac{(x-\xi)^2}{4(t-\tau)}\right] \quad (t > \tau) \tag{10}$$

called the *heat potential of the point* (ξ, τ). The function (10) tends to zero when $t \to \tau$ and x is arbitrary but distinct from ξ; however, the function is unbounded when $t \to \tau$ and $x \to \xi$ simultaneously. Before proceeding to the determination of the solution satisfying the boundary conditions (9) we find a function which satisfies equation (6) in the region (7) and the initial condition (8) only. This is the so-called *Poisson–Weierstrass integral*

$$v(x, t) = \int_{-\infty}^{\infty} \frac{\varphi(\xi)}{\sqrt{t}} \exp\left[-\frac{(x-\xi)^2}{4t}\right] d\xi, \tag{11}$$

where the function $\varphi(\xi)$ is defined over the whole axis Ox. The function (11) satisfies equation (6) for $t > 0$; further, we now prove that without solving integral equations we can easily select the function $\varphi(\xi)$ in such a way that integral (11) satisfies the initial condition (8). Setting

$$\xi = x + 2s\sqrt{t}$$

we can express integral (11) in the form

$$v(x, t) = \int_{-\infty}^{\infty} 2\varphi(x+2s\sqrt{t})e^{-s^2}\,ds. \tag{12}$$

Assuming that $\varphi(\xi)$ is bounded in the interval $(-\infty, +\infty)$, integrable in any part of it and, moreover, that it is continuous at the point $\xi = x$, we find the limit of integral (12) when $t \to 0$. To this end, we decompose integral (12) into the sum of three terms

$$v(x, t) = \int_{-\infty}^{-T} + \int_{-T}^{+T} + \int_{+T}^{+\infty} \tag{13}$$

writing $T = 1/\sqrt[4]{t}$. We observe that the first and third terms evidently tend to zero as $t \to 0$, while the second term can be written in the form

$$2\int_{-T}^{T} [\varphi(x+2s\sqrt{t})-\varphi(x)]\,e^{-s^2}\,ds+2\varphi(x)\int_{-T}^{T} e^{-s^2}\,ds. \tag{14}$$

Since in the interval of integration we have

$$|2s\sqrt{t}| \leqq 2\sqrt[4]{t},$$

in view of the assumed continuity of $\varphi(\xi)$ at the point x, the first integral in (14) tends to zero when $t \to 0$, while the second term tends to the value $2\sqrt{\pi}\varphi(x)$. We finally conclude that the function (11) tends to the limit

$$\lim_{t\to 0} v(x, t) = 2\sqrt{\pi}\,\varphi(x). \tag{15}$$

It is now sufficient to assume that

$$\varphi(x) = \begin{cases} \dfrac{1}{2\sqrt{\pi}}\,F(x), & \text{when} \quad a < x < b, \\ 0, & \text{when} \quad x < a \text{ or } x > b, \end{cases} \tag{16}$$

in order to obtain the function

$$v(x, t) = \frac{1}{2\sqrt{\pi}} \int_a^b \frac{F(\xi)}{\sqrt{t}} e^{-(x-\xi)^2/4t} d\xi, \tag{17}$$

satisfying the conduction equation (6) for $t > 0$ and the initial condition (8):

$$\lim_{t \to 0} v(x, t) = F(x) \quad (a < x < b).$$

To derive now the solution of equation (6) which satisfies not only the initial condition (8), but also the boundary conditions (9), consider the integral

$$w(x, t) = \int_0^t \left(\frac{\partial \Theta(x, t; \xi, \tau)}{\partial \xi} \right)_{\xi = a} \psi(r) \, d\tau$$

$$= \frac{1}{2} \int_0^t \frac{x-a}{(t-\tau)^{3/2}} \exp\left[-\frac{(x-a)^2}{4(t-\tau)} \right] \psi(\tau) \, d\tau, \tag{18}$$

which by analogy may be called *the heat potential of double surface distribution* with density $\psi(\tau)$ distributed over a line segment perpendicular to the axis Ox, with extremities $(a, 0)$ and (a, t).

If we assume that $\psi(\tau)$ is bounded and integrable in every interval $(0, T)$, then the function (18) satisfies the heat conduction equation at all points (x, t) such that $x \neq a$, $t > 0$; moreover, it is evident that for $x \neq a$, the function (18) tends to zero when t tends to zero

$$\lim_{t \to 0} w(x, t) = 0 \quad (x \neq a). \tag{19}$$

Assuming that $\psi(\tau)$ is continuous in every closed interval $[0, T]$, we now find the limit to which the function (18) tends when x tends to a from the right or from the left, and $t > 0$. Assuming first that $x > a$, and setting

$$\frac{x-a}{2\sqrt{t-\tau}} = s,$$

we obtain

$$w(x, t) = \int_{\frac{x-a}{2\sqrt{t}}}^{\infty} 2\psi\left[t - \frac{(x-a)^2}{4s^2}\right] e^{-s^2}\, ds. \tag{20}$$

We may always assume that the difference $x-a$ is so small that

$$\frac{x-a}{2\sqrt{t}} < \sqrt{x-a}.$$

Now decompose integral (20) into two parts

$$w(x, t) = \int_{\frac{x-a}{2\sqrt{t}}}^{\sqrt{x-a}} + \int_{\sqrt{x-a}}^{\infty}. \tag{21}$$

The first part obviously tends to zero when $x \to a$ for a constant $t > 0$, while the second part can be written in the form

$$\int_{\sqrt{x-a}}^{\infty} 2\left\{\psi\left[t - \frac{(x-a)^2}{4s^2}\right] - \psi(t)\right\} e^{-s^2}\, ds + 2\psi(t) \int_{\sqrt{x-a}}^{\infty} e^{-s^2}\, ds. \tag{22}$$

In the interval of integration, we have

$$\frac{(x-a)^2}{4s^2} \leqq \frac{x-a}{4},$$

and consequently, in view of the continuity of $\psi(\tau)$, the first term of sum (22) tends to zero when $x \to a$ and the second term then tends to the value $\sqrt{\pi}\,\psi(\tau)$; thus we infer that the right limit of the function (10) at $x = a$ is the following:

$$\lim_{x \to a+0} w(x, t) = \sqrt{\pi}\,\psi(t). \tag{23}$$

Similarly for the left limit we have

$$\lim_{x \to a-0} w(x, t) = -\sqrt{\pi}\,\psi(t). \tag{23'}$$

The heat potential of the double surface distribution (18) has therefore a discontinuity analogous to the discontinuity of the Newtonian potential.

Properties (23) and (23′) will be employed in solving the boundary problem. First observe that property (23) of integral (18) makes it possible to solve directly, without using an integral equation, the simplified Fourier problem of finding a function $u(x, t)$ satisfying the conduction equation (6) at every point of the region $x > a$, $t > 0$, and the following boundary and initial conditions:

$$\begin{aligned} &\lim_{t\to 0} u(x, t) = 0 \qquad (x > a), \\ &\lim_{x\to 0} u(x, t) = f(t) \qquad (t > 0), \end{aligned} \tag{24}$$

where $f(t)$ is a known function continuous in the interval $(0, \infty)$. For, according to properties (19) and (23) of the integral (18), the solution of this simplified Fourier problem is given by the integral

$$w(x, t) = \frac{1}{2\sqrt{\pi}} \int_0^t \frac{x-a}{(t-\tau)^{3/2}} \exp\left[-\frac{(x-a)^2}{4(t-\tau)}\right] f(\tau)\, d\tau . \tag{25}$$

We now proceed to solve the Fourier problem with conditions (8) and (9).

Thus we seek a function $u(x, t)$, satisfying equation (6) inside the strip (7) and conditions (8) and (9) on its boundary, in the form of the sum of three integrals

$$\begin{aligned} u(x, t) = &\int_a^b \frac{\varphi(\xi)}{\sqrt{t}} \exp\left[-\frac{(x-\xi)^2}{4t}\right] d\xi + \\ &+\frac{1}{2}\int_0^t \frac{x-a}{(t-\tau)^{3/2}} \exp\left[-\frac{(x-a)^2}{4(t-\tau)}\right] \psi_1(\tau)\, d\tau + \\ &+\frac{1}{2}\int_0^t \frac{x-b}{(t-\tau)^{3/2}} \exp\left[-\frac{(x-b)^2}{4(t-\tau)}\right] \psi_2(\tau)\, d\tau . \end{aligned} \tag{26}$$

The first integral is the Poisson–Weierstrass integral along the segment (a, b) of the axis Ox; the remaining two are heat potentials of double distribution along the segments with ends $(a, 0)$ and (a, t), and $(b, 0)$ and (b, t), respectively, located on the semi-infinite straight lines bounding the strip (7) (Fig. 4). The functions φ, ψ_1 and ψ_2 should be chosen so that the function (26) satisfies the initial condition (8) and the boundary conditions (9). Since

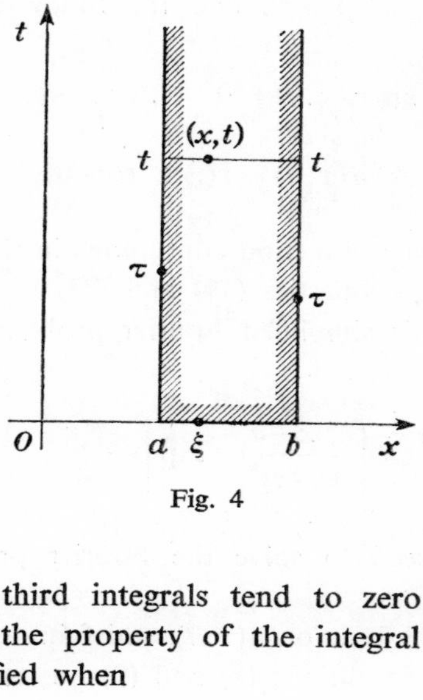

Fig. 4

the second and third integrals tend to zero when $t \to 0$, in accordance with the property of the integral (17), the initial condition is satisfied when

$$\varphi(\xi) = \frac{1}{2\sqrt{\pi}} F(\xi).$$

Now on the basis of properties (23) and (23′) of the integral (18) we may state that the function (26) satisfies the boundary conditions

$$\begin{aligned} &\lim_{x \to a} u(x, t) = f_1(t) \quad (t > 0), \\ &\lim_{x \to b} u(x, t) = f_2(t) \quad (t > 0) \end{aligned} \tag{27}$$

if, and only if, the unknown functions ψ_1 and ψ_2 satisfy the following system of two Volterra integral equations:

$$\sqrt{\pi}\,\psi_1(t)+\frac{a-b}{2}\int_0^t \frac{\psi_2(\tau)}{(t-\tau)^{3/2}}\exp\left[-\frac{(a-b)^2}{4(t-\tau)}\right]d\tau$$

$$=f_1(t)-\frac{1}{2\sqrt{\pi}}\int_a^b \frac{F(\xi)}{2\sqrt{t}}\exp\left[-\frac{(a-\xi)^2}{4t}\right]d\xi, \qquad (28_1)$$

$$-\sqrt{\pi}\,\psi_2(t)+\frac{b-a}{2}\int_0^t \frac{\psi_1(\tau)}{(t-\tau)^{3/2}}\exp\left[-\frac{(a-b)^2}{4(t-\tau)}\right]d\tau$$

$$=f_2(t)-\frac{1}{2\sqrt{\pi}}\int_a^b \frac{F(\xi)}{\sqrt{t}}\exp\left[-\frac{(b-\xi)^2}{4t}\right]d\xi. \qquad (28_2)$$

The kernels of equations (28) are defined and continuous for every value $t-\tau > 0$ and owing to the exponential factor they tend to zero when $t-\tau \to 0$, i.e. in accordance with the investigations on the system of Volterra equations (p. 182) the system of integral equations (28) has a unique and continuous solution $\psi_1(t), \psi_2(t)$ defined for any value $t > 0$. The functions $\psi_1(t)$, $\psi_2(t)$ can be expressed in the form of sums of absolutely and uniformly convergent series. Introducing the determined functions $\psi_1(t)$ and $\psi_2(t)$ into formula (26), we obtain the required solution $u(x, t)$ of the heat conduction equation, which satisfies the imposed conditions (8) and (9). It can be proved [24] that the derived solution is unique.

§ 3. Three-dimensional Fourier problem

We now investigate the solution of the Fourier problem for a region Ω of three-dimensional space, bounded by a closed surface S satisfying the Liapunov conditions (p. 231). We consider the initial condition (2) and the mixed boundary condition

$$\lim_{A\to P}\frac{du(A,t)}{dn_P}+a(P,t)\lim_{A\to P}u(A,t)=f(P,t) \qquad (29)$$

for $0 < t \leqq T$. The case of the first boundary condition (3) can be examined by means of the potential of double surface distribution. We assume that the known functions $a(P, t)$ and $f(P, t)$ are defined and continuous with respect to the pair of variables P and t at every point P of the surface S in the interval $0 < t \leqq T$. These functions may have no limits but are bounded when $t \to 0$. The considerations include the case $a = 0$ as well. Bearing in mind the fundamental solution (5) of the heat conduction equation in space, we seek the solution of the Fourier problem in the form of the sum of the heat potential of surface distribution

$$u_1(A, t) = \int_0^t \iint_S \frac{1}{(t-\tau)^{3/2}} \exp\left[-\frac{r_{AQ}^2}{4(t-\tau)}\right] \varphi(Q, \tau)\, d\sigma_Q\, d\tau \quad (30)$$

over the curved surface of a four-dimensional cylinder with base Ω and generators parallel to the axis of time, and the Poisson-Weierstrass integral

$$u_2(A, t) = \iiint_\Omega \frac{\psi(B)}{t^{3/2}} \exp\left[-\frac{r_{AB}^2}{4t}\right] dB. \quad (31)$$

As in case of the one-dimensional problem, it can be proved that if $\psi(B)$ is bounded and continuous in Ω, the function (31) has the following boundary property:

$$\lim_{t\to 0} u_2(A, t) = (2\sqrt{\pi})^3\, \psi(A) \quad (32)$$

at every point A inside Ω (see the more general theorem on p. 364).

Since integral (30) tends to zero when $t \to 0$, it is sufficient to substitute

$$\psi(A) = \frac{1}{(2\sqrt{\pi})^3} F(A), \quad (33)$$

in order that the sum of integrals (30) and (31) satisfies the initial condition (2).

Observe that transition to the limit of $F(A)$ is uniform in every closed region Ω^* contained in Ω.

The normal derivative to the surface S has the boundary property analogous to that of the derivative of the Newtonian surface distribution potential, i.e. it can be proved that under the assumption of continuity of $\varphi(Q, \tau)$ defined in the domain $[Q \in S, 0 \leqq \tau \leqq T]$, we have (see [25])

$$\lim_{A \to P} \frac{du_1(A, t)}{dn_P}$$

$$= -4\pi\sqrt{\pi}\,\varphi(P, t) +$$

$$+\frac{1}{2}\int_0^t \iint_S \frac{r_{QP}\cos\nu_{PQ}}{(t-\tau)^{5/2}} \exp\left[-\frac{r_{PQ}^2}{4(t-\tau)}\right]\varphi(Q, \tau)\, d\sigma_Q\, d\tau$$

$$= -4\pi\sqrt{\pi}\,\varphi(P, t) +$$

$$+8\iint_S \frac{\cos\nu_{PQ}}{r_{PQ}^2}\left[\int_{\frac{r_{PQ}}{2\sqrt{t}}}^{\infty} q^2 e^{-q^2} \varphi\left(Q, t-\frac{r_{PQ}^2}{4q^2}\right) dq\right] d\sigma_Q \tag{34}$$

at every point P of the surface S in the interval $0 < t \leqq T$. ν_{PQ} denotes here the angle between the vector $\overrightarrow{PQ}$ and the inward drawn normal to the surface S at P.

Since, in accordance with the Liapunov condition (3), p. 232, we have the inequality

$$|\cos\nu_{PQ}| < k r_{PQ}^{\kappa} \quad (0 < \kappa \leqq 1), \tag{35}$$

the integral in expression (34) is absolutely convergent.

If we require that the function

$$u(A, t) = u_1(A, t) + u_2(A, t)$$

satisfies the boundary condition (29) at every point P of S in the interval $0 < t \leqq T$, then for the unknown function $\varphi(P, t)$ we obtain the integral equation

$$\varphi(P, t) = \lambda \int_0^t \iint_S N(P, t; Q, \tau)\,\varphi(Q, \tau)\, d\sigma_Q\, d\tau + f^*(P, t), \tag{36}$$

where

$$N(P,t;Q,\tau) = \frac{1}{2}\cdot\frac{r_{PQ}\cos\nu_{PQ}}{(t-\tau)^{5/2}}\exp\left[-\frac{r_{PQ}^2}{4(t-\tau)}\right] + \\ + \frac{a(P,t)}{(t-\tau)^{3/2}}\exp\left[-\frac{r_{PQ}^2}{4(t-\tau)}\right], \quad (37)$$

$$f^*(P,t) = +\frac{1}{4\pi\sqrt{\pi}}\left[-f(P,t)+\lim_{A\to P}\frac{du_2(A,t)}{dn_P}+ \right. \\ \left. + a(P,t)\lim_{A\to P} u_2(A,t)\right] \quad (38)$$

and $\lambda = 1/4\pi\sqrt{\pi}, P\in S, Q\in S, P \neq Q$ and $0 < \tau < t \leqq T$.

The integral equation (36) is of Volterra type, which we know to be easier to investigate than the Fredholm equation. Equation (36), however, is a Volterra equation, the kernel (37) of which has a complicated singularity for $r_{PQ} \to 0$ and $t \to \tau$ and consequently the proof of convergence for any $|\lambda|$ and t of the series representing the solution of equation (36) is difficult. This is the reason for the fact that the solution of equation (36) and of an analogous equation for the first Fourier problem, was not fully investigated for a long time after the papers of Hölder and Gevrey. Only in 1936 MÜNTZ [36] proved the convergence for any $|\lambda|$ and t of the series representing the solution of the integral equation in the case of the two-dimensional Fourier problem, but under the stronger assumption that the boundary line has curvature. In 1938 TIKHONOV [82] investigated this problem for a three-dimensional region under weaker assumptions. MIKHLIN in his monograph [30] on integral equations examined the convergence of the considered solution, but only for a convex surface S and not for all values of the parameter λ. The present author proved [51] the convergence of the solution of the integral equation for the Fourier problem in n-dimensional space for all values of the parameter λ and time t, under the weaker assumption that the surface bounding the region satisfies the Liapunov condition. The method used is entirely different from those of the mentioned authors. This method is applied below to the investigation of the solution of the integral equation (36) for the three-dimensional Fourier problem in a simpler way than in the above quoted paper.

To this end, we deduce a certain estimate of the singular kernel (37) in which the singularities with respect to the variables t and τ and the spatial variables P and Q are separated. Let us therefore write the terms of kernel (37) as follows:

$$\begin{aligned} &\frac{r_{PQ}\cos\nu_{PQ}}{2(t-\tau)^{5/2}}\exp\left[-\frac{r_{PQ}^2}{4(t-\tau)}\right] \\ &\quad = \left[\frac{r_{PQ}^2}{4(t-\tau)}\right]^{5/2-\mu}\frac{2^{4-2\mu}}{(t-\tau)^{\mu}}\cdot\frac{\cos\nu_{PQ}}{r_{PQ}^{4-2\mu}}\exp\left[-\frac{r_{PQ}^2}{4(t-\tau)}\right], \\ &\frac{a(P,t)}{(t-\tau)^{3/2}}\exp\left[-\frac{r_{PQ}^2}{4(t-\tau)}\right] \\ &\quad = \left[\frac{r_{PQ}^2}{4(t-\tau)}\right]^{3/2-\mu}\frac{2^{3-2\mu}}{(t-\tau)^{\mu}}\cdot\frac{a(P,t)}{r_{PQ}^{3-2\mu}}\exp\left[-\frac{r_{PQ}^2}{4(t-\tau)}\right], \end{aligned} \tag{39}$$

μ being an arbitrary constant in the interval (0,1).

Observe now that e^q satisfies the inequality

$$q^m e^{-q} \leqq m^m e^{-m} \tag{40}$$

in the interval $0 \leqq q \leqq \infty$, where m is an arbitrary positive number. In view of inequality (35) we now infer that there exists a positive constant C, such that the singular kernel (37) satisfies the inequality

$$|N(P,t;Q,\tau)| < \frac{C}{(t-\tau)^{\mu}}\cdot\frac{1}{r_{PQ}^{4-2\mu-\kappa}}. \tag{41}$$

Thus both singularities in this estimate are weak with respect to the integrals in equation (36), provided that the constant μ is selected from the interval

$$1-\frac{\kappa}{2} < \mu < 1. \tag{42}$$

In fact, then we have simultaneously

$$\mu < 1 \quad \text{and} \quad 4 - 2\mu - \kappa < 2.$$

To simplify the calculations, set

$$\mu = 1 - \frac{1}{2}\theta\kappa, \tag{42'}$$

where $0 < \theta < 1$. Then estimate (41) takes the form

$$|N(P, t; Q, \tau)| < \frac{C}{(t-\tau)^{1-\theta\kappa/2}} \cdot \frac{1}{r_{PQ}^{2-(1-\theta)\kappa}}. \tag{41'}$$

Thus we have succeeded in estimate (41) in separating the singularities with respect to the variable t and the point P, which had before been involved. This separation of the singularities makes it possible to investigate the convergence of the solution of the integral equation (36).

The only solution of the integral equation (36) is given by the formula

$$\varphi(P, t) = f^*(P, t) + \lambda \int_0^t \iint_{S_{(Q)}} \mathfrak{N}(P, t; Q, \tau) f^*(Q, \tau)\, d\sigma_Q\, d\tau, \tag{43}$$

where the resolvent kernel $\mathfrak{N}$ of the kernel N is the sum of the series

$$\mathfrak{N}(P, t; Q, \tau) = \sum_{n=0}^{\infty} \lambda^n N_n(P, t; Q, \tau) \quad (N_0 = N), \tag{44}$$

and the iterated kernels are given by the recursive formula

$$N_n(P, t; Q, \tau)$$

$$= \int_\tau^t \iint_{S_{(R)}} N(P, t; R, \beta) N_{n-1}(R, \beta; Q, \tau)\, d\sigma_R\, d\beta \quad (N_0 = N). \tag{45}$$

With the help of the relation

$$\int_\tau^t \frac{d\beta}{(t-\beta)^{1-\theta\kappa/2}(\beta-\tau)^\gamma} = \frac{1}{(t-\tau)^{\gamma-\theta\kappa/2}} \int_0^1 \frac{ds}{(1-s)^{1-\theta\kappa/2}}$$

$$(\gamma < 1),$$

estimate (41′), and the inequality

$$\iint\limits_S \frac{d\sigma_Q}{r_{PR}^{\alpha}\, r_{RQ}^{\beta}} < \frac{\text{const}}{r_{PQ}^{\alpha+\beta-2}} \qquad (\alpha+\beta > 2)$$

well known from the theory of integral equations with weak singularity (Part 1, p. 81), we infer that every iteration (45) of the kernel N lowers the exponent of the difference $t-\tau$ by the $\theta\mu/2$, and the exponent of distance r_{PQ} by $(1-\theta)\mu$. This implies that the iterated kernels (45) are certainly bounded, beginning from the index n_0 equal to the greater of the two numbers

$$n_0' = E\left[\frac{2}{(1-\theta)\kappa}\right] \quad \text{and} \quad n_0'' = E\left[\frac{2}{\theta\kappa}\right]. \tag{46}$$

Denote by g the upper bound of the absolute value of the kernel N_{n_0}, $|N_{n_0}| < g$, and let us determine the bounds of the following iterated kernels. According to relation (45) and inequality (41′), we have

$$|N_{n_0+1}(P, t; Q, \tau)|$$
$$< g \int\limits_{\tau}^{t} \frac{d\beta}{(t-\beta)^{1-\theta\kappa/2}} \iint\limits_S \frac{d\sigma_R}{r_{PR}^{2-(1-)\theta\kappa}} \leqq \frac{2gg_1}{\theta\kappa}(t-\tau)^{\theta\kappa/2}, \tag{47}$$

where g_1 denotes the upper bound on the surface S of the integral

$$\iint\limits_S \frac{C\, d\sigma_R}{r_{PR}^{2-(1-\theta)\kappa}}. \tag{48}$$

In general we expect that the iterated kernel $N_{n_0+\nu}$ satisfies the inequality

$$|N_{n_0+\nu}| < \frac{2gg_1^{\nu}}{\theta\kappa} \cdot \frac{(t-\tau)^{\nu\theta\kappa/2}}{k_\nu}, \tag{49}$$

the constant k_ν is to be determined in terms of ν in such a way that if inequality (49) holds then in view of relation (45) and the familiar property of the Euler beta integral, the next kernel $N_{n_0+\nu+1}$ satisfies the inequality

$$|N_{n_0+\nu+1}| < \frac{2gg_1^{\nu+1}}{\theta\kappa} \cdot \frac{(t-\tau)^{(\nu+1)\theta\kappa/2}}{k_\nu} \int_0^1 \frac{s^{\nu\theta\kappa/2}\, ds}{(1-s)^{1-\theta\kappa/2}}$$

$$= \frac{2gg_1^{\nu+1}}{\theta\kappa} \cdot \frac{(t-\tau)^{(\nu+1)\theta\kappa/2}}{k_\nu} \cdot \frac{\Gamma(\nu\theta\kappa/2+1)\,\Gamma(\theta\kappa/2)}{\Gamma[(\nu+1)\,\theta\kappa/2+1]}. \tag{50}$$

Hence we have the recursive formula

$$k_{\nu+1} = k_\nu \frac{(\nu+1)\,\Gamma[(\nu+1)\,\theta\kappa/2]}{\nu\Gamma(\nu\theta\kappa/2)\,\Gamma(\theta\kappa/2)},$$

and by induction we infer that all kernels of order $n > n_0$ satisfy the inequality

$$|N_{n_0+\nu}(P, t; Q, \tau)| < \frac{2g}{\theta\kappa} \cdot \frac{[g_1\,\Gamma(\theta\kappa/2)\,(t-\tau)^{\theta\kappa/2}]^\nu}{\nu\Gamma(\nu\theta\kappa/2)}. \tag{51}$$

Owing to the presence of the function $\Gamma(\nu\theta\kappa/2)$ in the denominator, this at once implies the fundamental result that *the series* (44) *representing the resolvent kernel is absolutely convergent for an arbitrarily large value of the product* $|\lambda(t-\tau)|$ *and hence formula* (43) *represents a continuous solution* φ *of the integral equation* (36) *for any value of* $|\lambda|$ *and for any* $t > 0$.

Introducing the derived function into formula (30) we obtain the required solution

$$u(A, t) = u_1(A, t) + u_2(A, t)$$

of the Fourier problem at any instant $0 < t < T$.

Remark. The applicability of formula (43) to the function $f^*(P, t)$ defined by relation (38) requires an additional justification. In fact, assuming only the continuity of the given function $F(A)$, even in the set $\Omega + S$ the spatial derivatives of the Poisson–Weierstrass integral

$$u_2(A,t) = \frac{1}{(2\sqrt{\pi})^3} \iiint\limits_{\Omega} \frac{F(B)}{t^{3/2}} \exp\left(-\frac{r_{AB}^2}{4t}\right) dv_B \tag{52}$$

can have no limit when $t \to 0$, and consequently, $f^*(P,t)$ continuous in the domain $[P \in S, 0 < t \leqq T]$ can be unbounded when $t \to 0$. In view of the inequality

$$\left| \frac{r_{AB}}{t^{5/2}} \exp\left(-\frac{r_{AB}^2}{4t}\right) \right| < \frac{\text{const}}{t^\alpha} \cdot \frac{1}{r_{AB}^{4-2\alpha}},$$

following from expansion (39), we infer that $f^*(P,t)$ satisfies the inequality

$$|f^*(P,t)| < \frac{\text{const}}{t^\alpha}, \tag{53}$$

when $1/2 < \alpha < 1$ and if we assume that $F(A)$ is continuous and bounded in the open set Ω. In view of the weak singularity in estimate (53), formula (43) of Volterra is thus applicable to the function $f^*(P,t)$. The derived solution (43) of the integral equation (38) is a continuous function in the domain $[P \in S, 0 < t \leqq T]$ which also satisfies an inequality of the form (53). Thus the sum of functions (30) and (52) satisfies the conditions of the Fourier problem.

§ 4. The Green's Function and more general Fourier problems

As for the Laplace equation, by the *Green's Function of the first kind with respect to the heat conduction equation*

$$\Delta u - \frac{\partial u}{\partial t} = 0 \tag{54}$$

in a region Ω, we mean a function $G(A, t; B, \tau)$ of the pair of interior points A and B of the region Ω and a pair of arbitrary values of t and τ such that $t > \tau$, which satisfies the following conditions:

1. *G is the difference between two functions*

$$G(A,t;B,\tau) = (t-\tau)^{-3/2}\exp\left[-\frac{r_{AB}^2}{4(t-\tau)}\right] - g(A,t;B,\tau), \quad (55)$$

the first being the fundamental solution having a singularity for $t \to \tau$ and $A \to B$, while the second satisfies equation (54) at every interior point A of Ω for $t > \tau$, and for a fixed point B inside Ω, and, moreover, it satisfies the condition

$$\lim_{t\to\tau} g(A,t;B,\tau) = 0 \quad (56)$$

even when A coincides with B.

2. *G satisfies the boundary condition*

$$\lim_{A\to B} G(A,t;B,\tau) = 0, \quad (57)$$

when $t > \tau$ and B is an arbitrary point inside the region.

By the *Green's Function of the second kind with respect to the conduction equation* we mean a function $G(A, t; B, \tau)$ of the pair of interior points A and B of Ω and a pair of numerical variables t and τ in the interval $(0, T)$, where $\tau < t$ which satisfies a condition identical to the first condition for the Green's Function of first kind, and the boundary condition

$$\lim_{A\to P}\left[\frac{dG(A,t;B,\tau)}{dn_P} + a(P,t)G(A,t;B,\tau)\right] = 0, \quad (58)$$

where $B \in \Omega$, $0 < \tau < t < T$, and $a(P, t)$ is a bounded and continuous function in the domain $[P \in S, 0 < t \leqq T]$; the interval $(0, T)$ may be infinite.

The term $g(A, t; B, \tau)$ of the first or second Green's Function, although regular inside its domain, is unbounded when $t \to \tau$ and A and B tend to the same point P of the surface S. It can be shown that the unboundedness is estimated by the following inequality with separated singularities:

$$|g(A,t;B,\tau)| < \frac{\text{const}}{(t-\tau)^{\mu}} \cdot \frac{1}{r_{AB}^{n-2\mu}}, \quad (59)$$

μ being an arbitrary number inside the interval $(1-\kappa/2, 1)$ (see [55]).

The above conditions imply that the regular term $g(A, t; B, \tau)$ of the Green's Function is a solution of either the first Fourier problem defined by the conditions

$$\begin{aligned}&\lim_{A\to P} g(A, t; B, \tau) = \frac{1}{(t-\tau)^{3/2}} \exp\left[-\frac{r_{PB}^2}{4(t-\tau)}\right],\\&\lim_{t\to\tau} g(A, t; B, \tau) = 0 \quad (t > \tau,\ B \text{ inside } \Omega),\end{aligned} \tag{60}$$

or the second Fourier problem defined by the conditions

$$\begin{aligned}&\lim_{A\to P}\left[\frac{dg(A, t; B, \tau)}{dn_P} + a(P, t)\, g(A, t; B, \tau)\right]\\&\quad = \frac{d}{dn_P}\left\{\frac{1}{(t-\tau)^{3/2}} \exp\left[-\frac{r_{PB}^2}{4(t-\tau)}\right]\right\} +\\&\qquad + \frac{a(P)}{(t-\tau)^{3/2}} \exp\left[-\frac{r_{PB}^2}{4(t-\tau)}\right],\\&\lim_{t\to\tau} g(A, t; B, \tau) = 0 \quad (0 < \tau < t \leqq T).\end{aligned} \tag{61}$$

In accordance with the preceding argument, the Green's Function for the conduction equation in the region Ω exists and it is uniquely defined.

Consider now the more general heat conduction equation

$$\Delta u - \frac{\partial u}{\partial t} = f(A, t), \tag{62}$$

where $f(A, t)$ is a known function in the region Ω for $t > 0$. This equation governs the temperature in a conducting medium in presence of spatial sources of heat energy.

As for the Poisson equation, we can prove that if $f(A, t)$ satisfies the Hölder condition with respect to A in the region Ω and it is continuous with respect to variable t, then the following integral, called the *heat potential of spatial charge*

$$u(A,t) = -\frac{1}{(2\sqrt{\pi})^3}\int_0^t \iiint_{\Omega} \frac{f(B,\tau)}{(t-\tau)^{3/2}} \exp\left(-\frac{r_{AB}^2}{4(t-\tau)}\right) dB\, d\tau$$

$$= -\frac{4}{(2\sqrt{\pi})^3}\iiint_{\Omega} \frac{dB}{r_{AB}}\left[\int_{\frac{r_{AB}}{2\sqrt{t}}}^{\infty} f\left(B, t-\frac{r_{AB}^2}{4q^2}\right) e^{-q^2} dq\right] \quad (63)$$

satisfies equation (62) at every interior point A of Ω, and for every value $t > 0$ (see the more general solution on p. 379).

We now proceed to determine the function $u(A, t)$ which satisfies equation (62) in region Ω, where $t > 0$, and the conditions of the Fourier problem

$$\begin{aligned} &\lim_{A\to P} u(A,t) = 0 \quad (t > 0), \\ &\lim_{t\to 0} u(A,t) = 0 \quad (A \in \Omega) \end{aligned} \quad (64)$$

or

$$\begin{aligned} &\lim_{A\to P}\left(\frac{du(A,t)}{dn_P} + a(P)u(A,t)\right) = 0 \quad (0 < t \leq T), \\ &\lim_{t\to 0} u(A,t) = 0 \quad (A \in \Omega). \end{aligned} \quad (65)$$

The solution of the more general problem when the right-hand sides of relation (64) or (65) are non-vanishing functions can evidently be obtained by adding to the solution satisfying conditions (64) or (65) a solution of the homogeneous equation satisfying more general initial and boundary conditions.

It is readily observed, using the properties of integral (63) and the Green's Function, that the solution satisfying condition (64) or (65) is the integral

$$u(A,t) = -\frac{1}{(2\sqrt{\pi})^3}\int_0^t \iiint_{\Omega} \frac{G(A,t;B,\tau)}{(t-\tau)^{3/2}} f(B,\tau) \times$$

$$\times \exp\left(-\frac{r_{AB}^2}{4(t-\tau)}\right) dB\, d\tau. \quad (66)$$

A rigorous proof is analogous to that on p. 269 (see also [24], vol. I) and is based on the estimate (59).

Consider now the equation

$$\Delta u - \frac{\partial u}{\partial t} = p(A, t)u + q(A, t) \tag{67}$$

analogous to the Helmholtz equation (p. 275). The functions $p(A, t)$ and $q(A, t)$ are defined in the domain $[A \in \Omega, 0 \leqq t \leqq T]$, satisfy the Hölder condition with respect to the point A, and are continuous with respect to the pair of variables A and t.

In view of the properties of integral (66), we see that the determination of the function $u(A, t)$ satisfying the generalized equation (67) inside Ω where $t > 0$, and, moreover, the boundary-initial condition (64) or (65), is reduced to the solution of the singular integral Volterra equation

$$u(A, t) = -\frac{1}{(2\sqrt{\pi})^3} \int_0^t \iiint_\Omega \frac{G(A, t; B, \tau)}{(t-\tau)^{3/2}} p(B, \tau) \times$$
$$\times \exp\left(-\frac{r_{AB}^2}{4(t-\tau)}\right) u(B, \tau)\, dB\, d\tau + F(A, t), \tag{68}$$

$F(A, t)$ being known.

Equation (68) can be solved, as before by expanding as a series.

A generalization of the above problem consists in the determination of the function $u(A, t)$ satisfying the heat conduction equation in the form

$$\Delta u - \frac{\partial u}{\partial t} = F(A, t, u)$$

in the interior of the domain $[\Omega, (0, T)]$, the non-linear boundary condition

$$\frac{du}{dn_P} = \Phi(P, t, u_p)$$

at every point P of the surface S for $0 < t \leqq T$, and, as usual, the initial condition

$$\lim_{t \to 0} u(A, t) = f(A) \quad (A \in \Omega).$$

This problem can be solved using the properties of heat potentials and the Schauder Fixed Point Theorem assuming only the continuity of the known function $\Phi(P, t, u)$ and the Hölder condition for function $F(A, t, u)$. This problem constitutes a particular case of a problem dealt with in Chapter XXII.

§ 5. More general equation of parabolic type (general remarks)

We now determine the fundamental solution of the parabolic equation in the so-called normal form

$$\hat{\Psi}(u) = \sum_{\alpha,\beta=1}^{n} a_{\alpha\beta}(x_1, x_2, \ldots, x_n; t) \frac{\partial^2 u}{\partial x_\alpha \partial x_\beta} +$$

$$+ \sum_{\alpha=1}^{n} b_\alpha(x_1, x_2, \ldots, x_n; t) \frac{\partial u}{\partial x_\alpha} +$$

$$+ c(x_1, x_2, \ldots, x_n; t) u - \frac{\partial u}{\partial t} = 0, \qquad (69)$$

coefficients $a_{\alpha\beta}$, b_α and c being known functions of $n+1$ variables $x_1, x_2, \ldots, x_n$ and t, defined in the closed, bounded and measurable region Ω in n-dimensional Euclidean space and in the interval $0 \leqq t \leqq T$. We assume that the quadratic form

$$\sum_{\alpha,\beta=1}^{n} a_{\alpha\beta} X_\alpha X_\beta \qquad (70)$$

is positive definite in the closed domain $[\Omega, (0, T)]$.

The first idea of determining the fundamental solution of equation (69) in a way similar to the case of the elliptic equation, was announced by GIRAUD [15]. Subsequently DRESSEL [6] investigated in detail the fundamental solution of equation (1) under the stronger assumption that the coefficients $a_{\alpha\beta}$ have second derivatives satisfying the Hölder condition. The author recently investigated and determined [44] the fundamental solution of equation (69) under an assumption considerably weaker, namely that the coefficients $a_{\alpha\beta}$, b_α and c satisfy the Hölder condition only. Below we discuss the more important parts of these investigations.

Consider, therefore, the function

$$w^{M,\tau}(A,t;B,\tau) = (t-\tau)^{-n/2}\exp\left(-\frac{\vartheta^{M,\tau}(A,B)}{4(t-\tau)}\right), \tag{71}$$

where

$$\vartheta^{M,\tau}(A,B) = \sum_{\alpha,\beta=1}^{n} a^{\alpha\beta}(M,\tau)(x_\alpha-\xi_\alpha)(x_\beta-\xi_\beta), \tag{72}$$

and $a^{\alpha\beta}(M,\tau)$ are the elements of the inverse matrix of the matrix $\|a_{\alpha\beta}(M,\tau)\|$, i.e. they are quotients of the algebraic cofactors of the elements $a_{\alpha\beta}(M,\tau)$ by the determinant of their matrix $\det|a_{\alpha\beta}(M,\tau)|$. Function (71) is defined and continuous for every pair of points $A(x_1, x_2, \ldots, x_n)$ and $B(\xi_1, \xi_2, \ldots, \xi_n)$ (not necessarily distinct) of the closed region Ω and for every pair of distinct numbers t and τ, $\tau < t$, belonging to interval $(0, T)$; M denotes an arbitrary fixed point of Ω. According to the assumption on the quadratic form (70), there exist two positive constants g and G, such that the function (72) satisfies the inequalities

$$g r_{AB}^2 < \vartheta^{M,\tau}(A,B) < G r_{AB}^2 \tag{73}$$

in the considered domain, r_{AB} denoting the Cartesian distance between the points A and B. If the coefficients $a_{\alpha\beta}$ were constant, (71) would constitute the fundamental solution of the equation

$$\sum_{\alpha,\beta=1}^{n} a_{\alpha\beta}\frac{\partial^2 u}{\partial x_\alpha \partial x_\beta} - \frac{\partial u}{\partial t} = 0, \tag{74}$$

when $\tau < t$. If the coefficients $a_{\alpha\beta}$ are variable, then (71) may not satisfy equation (74). It is called the *quasi-solution* of equation (74).

§ 6. Properties of the Poisson–Weierstrass integral and the quasi-potential with respect to the general parabolic equation

We now present a few theorems expressing the properties of some integrals constructed by means of the function (71).

THEOREM 1. *If the functions $a_{\alpha\beta}(A, t)$ and $\rho(A, t)$ are continuous with respect to the variables $x_1, x_2, \ldots, x_n, t$ in the closed domain*

$$[A \in \Omega, 0 \leqq t \leqq T], \tag{75}$$

then the following volume integral, called the generalized Poisson–Weierstrass integral,

$$J(A, t, \tau) = \iiint_{\Omega} w^{B,\tau}(A, t; B, \tau)\, \rho(B, \tau)\, dB, \tag{76}$$

is regular and continuous for $0 \leqq \tau < t \leqq T$, and tends uniformly to the limit

$$\lim_{\tau \to t} J(A, t, \tau) = \frac{(2\sqrt{\pi})^n}{\sqrt{\det |a^{\alpha\beta}(A, t)|}}\, \rho(A, t) \tag{77}$$

at every point A of every closed region Ω^* located in the interior of Ω, when $0 \leqq t \leqq T$.

Proof. Consider first the case when the function ρ and coefficients $a_{\alpha\beta}$ are constant. Then, by means of the change of variables

$$\zeta_\nu = \sum_{\alpha=1}^{n} C_\alpha^\nu (\xi_\alpha - x_\alpha),$$

which reduces the quadratic form $\vartheta(A, B)$ to the canonical form

$$\vartheta(A, B) = \sum_{\nu=1}^{n} \zeta_\nu^2,$$

we obtain

$$J(A, t, \tau)$$
$$= \rho \iiint_{\Omega'} (t-\tau)^{-n/2} \exp\left[-\frac{\sum_\nu \zeta_\nu^2}{4(t-\tau)}\right] \frac{D(\xi_1, \xi_2, \ldots, \xi_n)}{D(\zeta_1, \zeta_2, \ldots, \zeta_n)}\, dv_B, \tag{78}$$

where Ω' denotes the region of variables $\zeta_1, \zeta_2, \ldots, \zeta_n$ corresponding to Ω. We have

$$[\det|C_\alpha^\nu|]^2 = \det|\sum_{\nu=1}^{n} C_\alpha^\nu C_\beta^\nu| = \det|a^{\alpha\beta}|,$$

hence

$$\left|\frac{D(\xi_1, \xi_2, \ldots, \xi_n)}{D(\zeta_1, \zeta_2, \ldots, \zeta_n)}\right| = \frac{1}{|\det|C_\alpha^\nu||} = \frac{1}{\sqrt{\det|a^{\alpha\beta}|}}.$$

Consider now in the Euclidean space of variables $\zeta_1, \zeta_2, \ldots$ $\ldots, \zeta_n$, the sphere K with centre at $(0, 0, \ldots, 0)$ and radius R, contained in the interior of Ω'. Decompose integral (78) into two parts

$$J(A, t, \tau) = J^K(A, t, \tau) + J^{\Omega'-K}(A, t, \tau)$$

over the sphere K and the exterior region $\Omega' - K$. Then we obtain

$$J^K(A, t, \tau) = \frac{\rho\omega_n (t-\tau)^{-n/2}}{\sqrt{\det|a^{\alpha\beta}|}} \int_0^R \exp\left[-\frac{r^2}{4(t-\tau)}\right] r^{n-1} dr$$

$$= \frac{2^{n-1}\omega_n}{\sqrt{\det|a^{\alpha\beta}|}} \rho \int_0^{\frac{R^2}{4(t-\tau)}} q^{n/2-1} e^{-q} dq, \tag{79}$$

where ω_n denotes the surface area of an n-dimensional sphere of unit radius:

$$\omega_n = \frac{2(\sqrt{\pi})^n}{\Gamma(n/2)}.$$

From formula (79) we obtain the limit

$$\lim_{\tau\to t} J^K(A, t, \tau) = \frac{(2\sqrt{\pi})^n}{\sqrt{\det|a^{\alpha\beta}|}} \rho. \tag{80}$$

In the exterior region $\Omega' - K$, the integrand in (78) tends uniformly to zero when $\tau \to t$, and therefore integral $J^{\Omega'-K}$ also tends to zero, and we arrive at the boundary property

$$\lim_{\tau\to t} J(A, t, \tau) = \frac{2(\sqrt{\pi})^n}{\sqrt{\det|a^{\alpha\beta}|}}\,\rho\,. \tag{81}$$

The derived result makes it possible to determine the value of integral (200) in the theory of elliptic equation on p. 303. For, consider the Poisson–Weierstrass integral in the form

$$I(t) = \iiint\limits_K t^{-n/2} \exp\left[-\frac{\sum\limits_{\alpha,\beta=1}^{n} a^{\alpha\beta}\xi_\alpha\xi_\beta}{4t}\right] dv(\xi_1, \xi_2, \ldots, \xi_n) \qquad (\alpha)$$

over the sphere K of unit radius, the centre of which is the origin of the rectangular coordinate system $\xi_1, \xi_2, \ldots, \xi_n$. According to property (81), we have

$$\lim_{t\to 0} I(t) = \frac{(2\sqrt{\pi})^n}{\sqrt{\det|a^{\alpha\beta}|}}\,. \qquad (\beta)$$

Let us now find this limit in another way, writing

$$I(t) = \int\limits_0^1 t^{-n/2}\left[\iint\limits_A \exp\left(-\frac{r^2}{4t}\sum_{\alpha,\beta=1}^{n} a^{\alpha\beta}\xi'_\alpha\xi'_\beta\right)d\omega\right] r^{n-1}\,dr,$$

where ξ'_α are the coordinates of points of the surface Λ of K. Further, substituting $\vartheta = \sum\limits_{\alpha,\beta=1}^{n} a^{\alpha\beta}\xi'_\alpha\xi'_\beta$ we have

$$I(t) = 2^{n-1}\iint\limits_A \vartheta^{-n/2}\Big[\int\limits_0^{\theta/4t} q^{n/2-1}e^{-q}\,dq\Big]\,d\omega\,.$$

Hence

$$\lim_{t\to 0} I(t) = 2^{n-1}\Gamma(\tfrac{1}{2}n)\iint\limits_A \vartheta^{-n/2}\,d\omega\,. \qquad (\gamma)$$

Comparing this boundary value with the value (β) we are led to the relation

$$\iint\limits_A\Big[\sum_{\alpha,\beta=1}^{n} a^{\alpha\beta}\xi'_\alpha\xi'_\beta\Big]^{-n/2} d\omega(\xi'_1, \xi'_2, \ldots, \xi'_n) = \frac{\omega_n}{\sqrt{\det|a^{\alpha\beta}|}}, \qquad (\delta)$$

employed in the theory of elliptic equation.

If $\rho(A, t)$ and the coefficients $a_{\alpha\beta}(A, t)$ are variable, then we write

$$J(A, t, \tau) = \rho(A, \tau) \iiint_{\Omega} w^{A,t}(A, t; B, \tau)\, dB +$$

$$+\rho(A, \tau) \iiint_{\Omega} [w^{B,\tau}(A, t; B, \tau) - w^{A,t}(A, t; B, \tau)]\, dB +$$

$$+ \iiint_{\Omega} w^{B,\tau}(A, t; B, \tau)[\rho(B, \tau) - \rho(A, \tau)]\, dB = J_1 + J_2 + J_3. \quad (82)$$

For the first of the above integrals, the coefficients $a^{\alpha\beta}$ at point (A, t) have definite values and therefore this integral, in accordance with (81), tends to the limit

$$\lim_{\tau \to t} J_1 = \frac{(2\sqrt{\pi})^n}{\sqrt{\det |a^{\alpha\beta}(A, t)|}}\, \rho(A, t). \quad (83)$$

To investigate the second integral (82), observe that the difference in the integrand satisfies the inequality

$$|w^{B,\tau}(A, t; B, \tau) - w^{A,t}(A, t; B, \tau)| < n^2 r_{AB}^2 (t-\tau)^{-n/2-1} \times$$

$$\times \sup |a^{\alpha\beta}(B, \tau) - a^{\alpha\beta}(A, t)| \exp\left[-\frac{g r_{AB}^2}{4(t-\tau)}\right], \quad (84)$$

where g is the positive number appearing in inequality (73). Decompose integral J_2 into the sum of two integrals $J_2 = J_2^K + J_2^{\Omega-K}$ over the sphere K with centre at A and radius R_K located inside Ω, and over the exterior region $\Omega - K$. Proceeding as in the case of integral (82), we obtain

$$|J_2^K| < 2M_\rho n^3 (2\sqrt{\pi})^n g^{-n/2-1} \sup_{(K)} |a^{\alpha\beta}(B, \tau) - a^{\alpha\beta}(A, t)|, \quad (85)$$

where M_ϱ is the upper bound of $|\rho(A, t)|$.

In view of the assumed continuity of the coefficients $a_{\alpha\beta}(A, t)$ and the property of the quadratic form (70), the functions $a^{\alpha\beta}(A, t)$ are continuous with respect to the variables $x_1, x_2, \ldots, x_n; t$ in the closed domain $[A \in \Omega, 0 \leq t \leq T]$, and consequently, given

$\varepsilon > 0$, we can select a radius $R_K(\varepsilon)$ of the sphere K, and a number $\eta(\varepsilon)$, such that the inequality

$$\sup_{(K)} |a^{\alpha\beta}(B,\tau) - a^{\alpha\beta}(A,t)| < \frac{g^{n/2+1}}{2^{n+2} n^3 (\sqrt{\pi})^n M_\rho} \varepsilon \qquad (86)$$

is satisfied when $A \in K$, $B \in K$, $t-\tau < \eta(\varepsilon)$.

Furthermore, observe that when A is the centre of K, and B lies in the exterior region $\Omega - K$, then $w^{B,\tau}$ and $w^{A,t}$ tend uniformly to zero when $\tau \to t$. Consequently, having fixed the radius $R_K(\varepsilon)$ of K, we can select a number $\eta'(\varepsilon)$, such that

$$|J^{\Omega-K}| < \tfrac{1}{2}\varepsilon, \qquad t-\tau < \eta'(\varepsilon).$$

Thus, finally we have

$$|J_2(A,t,\tau)| < \varepsilon, \quad \text{when} \quad t-\tau < \min(\eta, \eta').$$

An easier investigation of the third integral (82) proves in an analogous way that this integral also tends to zero when $\tau \to t$. Combining these results we arrive at the statement (77) of Theorem 1.

Observe that transition to the limit is uniform with respect to A in an arbitrary closed region Ω^* contained in Ω.

DEFINITION 1. *By the quasi-potential of spatial charge with density $\rho(A,t)$ we mean the integral*

$$V(A,t) = \int_0^t \iiint_\Omega w^{B,\tau}(A,t;B,\tau)\,\rho(B,\tau)\,dB\,d\tau. \qquad (87)$$

Formula (71) indicates that the integrand $w^{B,\tau}(A,t;B,\tau)$ and all its derivatives with respect to the coordinates of A are regular when $A = B$ and $\tau < t$, as distinct from the case of the quasi-solution of the elliptic equation. Thus the spatial integral in formula (87) and all its derivatives exist and are regular when $\tau < t$. On the other hand, the integral is unbounded when $\tau \to t$, $A = B$ and the existence of the integral with respect to the variable τ requires an investigation.

To prove the existence of the improper integral (87), we find an estimate for function $w^{B,\tau}$, with separated singularities, the procedure being analogous to that in estimating functions (39). Thus, we write

$$w^{M,\tau}(A,t;B,\tau)$$
$$=\frac{1}{(t-\tau)^{\mu}}\cdot\frac{2^{n-2\mu}}{(\vartheta^{M,\tau})^{n/2-\mu}}\left[\frac{\vartheta^{M,\tau}}{4(t-\tau)}\right]^{n/2-\mu}\exp\left[-\frac{\vartheta^{M,\tau}(A,B)}{4(t-\tau)}\right] \quad (88)$$

and making use of inequality (73), we infer that the function (88) satisfies the inequality

$$|w^{M,\tau}(A,t;B,\tau)|<\frac{\text{const}}{(t-\tau)^{\mu}}\cdot\frac{1}{r_{AB}^{n-2\mu}} \quad (89)$$

with separated singularities, for arbitrary points M and $A \neq B$ of Ω and for $0 \leqq \tau < t \leqq T$. Selecting the constant μ from the interior of the interval $(0, 1)$, we see that the singularities (89) are weak when $\tau \to t$ and $A \to B$, and consequently this implies the existence of the improper integral (78) when $A \in \Omega$, $0 \leqq t \leqq T$; this integral is absolutely convergent in the sense

$$V(A,t)=\lim_{\varepsilon\to 0}\int_{0}^{t-\varepsilon}\iiint_{\Omega} w^{B,\tau}(A,t;B,\tau)\,\rho(B,\tau)\,dB\,d\tau \quad (89')$$

assuming that the functions $a_{\alpha\beta}$ and $\rho(A, t)$ are bounded and integrable. Observe that in estimate (89) the singularity for $\tau \to t$ is weakened at the expense of introducing a weak spatial singularity.

The existence of the first spatial derivatives of the function (87) is described by the following theorem.

THEOREM 2. *If the coefficients* $a_{\alpha\beta}(A, t)$ *are continuous functions and the density* $\rho(A, t)$ *is bounded and integrable in the domain* $[\Omega, (0, T)]$, *then the quasi-potential* (87) *has continuous first spatial derivatives in the interior of* $[\Omega, (0, T)]$; *they are given by the formula*

$$V_{x_\alpha}(A,t)=\int_{0}^{t}\iiint_{\Omega} w_{x_\alpha}^{B,\tau}(A,t;B,\tau)\,\rho(B,\tau)\,dB\,d\tau\,. \quad (90)$$

the integral being absolutely convergent.

Proof. By means of a decomposition analogous to (88) we find that the spatial derivatives of $w^{M,\tau}$ satisfy the inequality

$$|w^{M,\tau}_{x_\alpha}(A, t; B, \tau)| < \frac{\text{const}}{(t-\tau)^\mu} \cdot \frac{1}{r_{AB}^{n+1-2\mu}}. \tag{91}$$

The singularities in this estimate are still weak when we select μ from the interval (1/2, 1), and therefore the improper integral (90) is absolutely and uniformly convergent. To prove that this integral represents the derivative of $V(A, t)$, we write this function in the form

$$V(A, t) = \int_0^t J(A, t, \tau)\, d\tau, \tag{92}$$

introducing the function

$$J(A, t, \tau) = \iiint_\Omega w^{B,\tau}(A, t; B, \tau)\, \rho(B, \tau)\, dB \tag{93}$$

which is continuous with respect to A and satisfies the inequality

$$|J(A, t, \tau)| < \frac{\text{const}}{(t-\tau)^\mu}.$$

$w^{B,\tau}(A, t; B, \tau)$ has derivatives with respect to the coordinates of A which are obviously continuous and bounded with respect to the pair of points A and B of Ω, when the parameters t and τ, $\tau < t$, are fixed in the interval $(0, T)$. Thus the function (93) has derivatives with respect to the coordinates of point $A(x_1, x_2, \ldots, x_n)$ in Ω, of the form

$$J_{x_\alpha}(A, t, \tau) = \iiint_\Omega w^{B,\tau}_{x_\alpha}(A, t; B, \tau)\, \rho(B, \tau)\, dB; \tag{94}$$

they are continuous when $\tau < t$. According to estimate (91), the derivatives (94) satisfy the inequality with a weak singularity

$$|J_{x_\alpha}(A, t, \tau)| < \frac{\text{const}}{(t-\tau)^\mu} \quad (\tfrac{1}{2} < \mu < 1), \tag{95}$$

and therefore the improper integral

$$V^*(A, t) = \int_0^t J_{x_\alpha}(A, t, \tau)\, d\tau \tag{96}$$

exists and is absolutely convergent. To prove that integral (96) represents the derivative of function (92), consider the difference

$$\delta = \frac{V(A_1, t) - V(A, t)}{\Delta x_\alpha} - V^*(A, t)$$

$$= \int_0^t \left[\frac{J(A_1, t, \tau) - J(A, t, \tau)}{\Delta x_\alpha} - J_{x_\alpha}(A, t, \tau) \right] d\tau$$

$$= \int_0^t [J_{x_\alpha}(A', t, \tau) - J_{x_\alpha}(A, t, \tau)] \, d\tau, \qquad (97)$$

where A' denotes an interior point of the segment AA_1 parallel to the x_α-axis and having measure Δx_α; according to inequality (95), given $\varepsilon > 0$ there corresponds a number $t_\varepsilon < t$, such that

$$\int_{t_\varepsilon}^t |J_{x_\alpha}(A, t, \tau)| \, d\tau < \frac{\varepsilon}{3} \qquad (98)$$

for every point $A \in \Omega$. Now decompose the difference (97) into three terms

$$\delta = \int_0^{t_\varepsilon} [J_{x_\alpha}(A', t, \tau) - J_{x_\alpha}(A, t, \tau)] \, d\tau +$$
$$+ \int_{t_\varepsilon}^t J_{x_\alpha}(A', t, \tau) \, d\tau - \int_{t_\varepsilon}^t J_{x_\alpha}(A, t, \tau) \, d\tau$$

and observe that the derivative $J_{x_\alpha}(A, t, \tau)$ is a uniformly continuous function of the point A with respect to the variable τ in the interval $(0, t_\varepsilon)$. Consequently, having fixed the value of t_ε, we can select a number $\eta(\varepsilon)$ independent of ε, such that

$$|J_{x_\alpha}(A', t, \tau) - J_{x_\alpha}(A, t, \tau)| < \frac{\varepsilon}{3t_\varepsilon},$$
$$\text{when} \quad |\Delta x_\alpha| < \eta(\varepsilon), \; 0 < \tau < t_\varepsilon .$$

Finally, we therefore have

$$|\delta| < \varepsilon, \quad \text{when} \quad |\Delta x_\alpha| < \eta(\varepsilon),$$

in agreement with the statement (90) of Theorem 2.

Let us now investigate the existence of the second spatial derivatives of the quasi-potential (87). By means of a decomposition analogous to (88) we can prove that the second derivatives of the quasi-solution with respect to the coordinates of the point $A(x_1, x_2, \ldots, x_n)$ satisfy the inequality

$$|w^{M,\tau}_{x_\alpha x_\beta}(A, t; B, \tau)| < \frac{\text{const}}{(t-\tau)^\mu} \cdot \frac{1}{r_{AB}^{n+2-2\mu}} \tag{99}$$

for arbitrary points M and $A \neq B$ of Ω and for $0 \leqq \tau < t \leqq T$; μ is an arbitrary positive number. We observe that, for every choice of the constant μ in the interval (0, 1), the right-hand side of inequality (99) has a strong spatial singularity ($n+2-2\mu > n$). If, however, we selected the exponent μ in such a way that $n+2-2\mu < n$, then the singularity with respect to the variable t would be too strong. Therefore the investigation of the second derivatives of the quasi-potential requires different assumptions and more precise methods than the investigation of the first derivatives.

THEOREM 3. *If the coefficients $a_{\alpha\beta}(A, t)$ and the density $\rho(A, t)$ are continuous functions of the variables $x_1, x_2, x_3, \ldots, x_n$; t in the closed domain $[A \in \Omega, 0 \leqq t \leqq T]$ and, moreover, they satisfy the Hölder condition with respect to the spatial variables*

$$\begin{aligned} |a_{\alpha\beta}(A, t) - a_{\alpha\beta}(A_1, t)| &< \text{const}\, r^h_{AA_1} \quad (0 < h \leqq 1), \\ |\rho(A, t) - \rho(A_1, t)| &< \text{const}\, r^\delta_{AA_1} \quad (0 < \delta \leqq 1), \end{aligned} \tag{100}$$

then the quasi-potential (87) *has continuous second derivatives at all interior points $A \in \Omega$ for $0 < t \leqq T$, given by the formula*

$$V_{x_\alpha x_\beta}(A, t) = \int_0^t \iint_\Omega \int w^{B,\tau}_{x_\alpha x_\beta}(A, t; B, \tau)\, \rho(B, \tau)\, dB\, d\tau, \tag{101}$$

where the spatial integral is regular for $\tau < t$ and the improper integral with respect to variable τ is convergent in a sufficiently small neighbourhood of every interior point A.

Consider the derivative of the quasi-potential in the form

$$V_{x_\alpha}(A, t) = \int_0^t J_{x_\alpha}(A, t, \tau)\, d\tau \tag{102}$$

and write the derivative of function (93) in the form

$$J_{x_\alpha}(A,t,\tau) = \iiint\limits_{\Omega} w_{x_\alpha}^{B,\tau}(A,t;B,\tau)\,\rho(B,\tau)\,dB$$

$$= \rho(M,\tau)\iiint\limits_{\Omega} w_{x_\alpha}^{M,\tau}(A,t;B,\tau)\,dB +$$

$$+\rho(M,\tau)\iiint\limits_{\Omega}[w_{x_\alpha}^{B,\tau}(A,t;B,\tau)-w_{x_\alpha}^{M,\tau}(A,t;B,\tau)]\,dB +$$

$$+\iiint\limits_{\Omega} w_{x_\alpha}^{B,\tau}(A,t;B,\tau)[\rho(B,\tau)-\rho(M,\tau)]\,dB, \qquad (103)$$

where M is an arbitrary fixed point of Ω. Consider a sphere K inside Ω, containing the point A, with a constant centre A_0. Decomposing the first integral on the right-hand side of relation (103) into two integrals over the sphere K and the exterior region $\Omega - K$, and applying Green's Theorem to the integral over K, we obtain

$$J_{x_\alpha}(A,t,\tau) = \rho(M,\tau)\Big[-\iint\limits_{K^*} w^{M,\tau}(A,t;P,\tau)\cos\nu_\alpha\,d\sigma_P +$$

$$+\iiint\limits_{\Omega-K} w_{x_\alpha}^{M,\tau}(A,t;B,\tau)\,dB\Big] +$$

$$+\rho(M,\tau)\iiint\limits_{\Omega}[w_{x_\alpha}^{B,\tau}(A,t;B,\tau)-w_{x_\alpha}^{M,\tau}(A,t;B,\tau)]\,dB +$$

$$+\iiint\limits_{\Omega} w_{x_\alpha}^{B,\tau}(A,t;B,\tau)[\rho(B,\tau)-\rho(M,\tau)]\,dB, \qquad (104)$$

where K^* denotes the surface of the sphere K and ν_α the angle between the normal at the point P of the surface K^* and the x_α-axis. The integrals in expression (104) are regular when $\tau < t$ and the function (104) has continuous derivatives with respect to the spatial coordinates when $\tau < t$:

$$J_{x_\alpha x_\beta}(A,t,\tau) = \iiint\limits_{\Omega} w_{x_\alpha x_\beta}^{B,\tau}(A,t;B,\tau)\,\rho(B,\tau)\,dB$$

$$= \rho(A,\tau)\Big[-\iint\limits_{K^*} w_{x_\beta}^{M,\tau}(A,t;P,\tau)\cos\nu_\alpha\,d\sigma_P +$$

$$+\iiint\limits_{\Omega-K} w_{x_\alpha x_\beta}^{M,\tau}(A,t;B,\tau)\,dB\Big]_{M=A} +$$

$$+\rho(A,\tau)\iiint\limits_{\Omega}\{w_{x_\alpha x_\beta}^{B,\tau}(A,t;B,\tau)-[w_{x_\alpha x_\beta}^{M,\tau}(A,t;B,\tau)]_{M=A}\}\,dB +$$

$$+\iiint\limits_{\Omega} w_{x_\alpha x_\beta}^{B,\tau}(A,t;B,\tau)[\rho(B,\tau)-\rho(A,\tau)]\,dB, \qquad (105)$$

these have been derived by setting $M = A$ after differentiating the sum (104) with respect to x_β. If A is fixed inside K, then the sum of the first two integrals on the right-hand side of relation (105) is bounded and, moreover, tends to zero when $\tau \to t$. The last integral J_3, in accordance with inequality (99) and the Hölder condition (100), satisfies the inequality

$$|I_3| < \frac{k'}{(t-\tau)^\mu} \iiint\limits_{\Omega} \frac{dv_B}{r^{n+2-2\mu-\delta}} < \frac{k''}{(t-\tau)^\mu}, \tag{106}$$

where k'' is a positive constant independent of A, and μ is such that

$$1 - \frac{\delta}{2} < \mu < 1. \tag{107}$$

It remains to examine the second last integral (105). Consider, therefore, the following expression for the second derivative of $w^{B,\tau}$:

$$w^{B,\tau}_{x_\alpha x_\beta}(A, t; B, \tau) = \frac{1}{4}(t-\tau)^{-n/2-2} \exp\left[-\frac{\vartheta^{B,\tau}(A, B)}{4(t-\tau)}\right] \times$$
$$\times\left[-2(t-\tau)\, a^{\alpha\beta}(B, \tau) + \right.$$
$$\left. + \sum_{\gamma=1}^{n} a^{\alpha\gamma}(B, \tau)(x_\gamma - \xi_\gamma) \sum_{\gamma=1}^{n} a^{\beta\gamma}(B, \tau)(x_\gamma - \xi_\gamma)\right]. \tag{108}$$

Observe that the coefficients $a^{\alpha\beta}(A, t)$ are rational combinations of the functions $a_{\alpha\beta}(A, t)$ with a non-vanishing divisor $\det|a_{\alpha\beta}|$ and, consequently, these coefficients also satisfy the Hölder condition

$$|a^{\alpha\beta}(A, t) - a^{\alpha\beta}(B, t)| < k_1 r^h_{AB}. \tag{109}$$

Taking into account inequality (73), it follows that the difference between the second derivatives (108) satisfies the inequality

$$|w^{B,\tau}_{x_\alpha x_\beta}(A, t; B, \tau) - [w^{M,\tau}_{x_\alpha x_\beta}(A, t; B, \tau)]_{M=A}|$$
$$< \frac{1}{4} k_1 (t-\tau)^{-n/2-1} \exp\left[-\frac{g r^2_{AB}}{4(t-\tau)}\right] \times$$
$$\times\left[2 + \frac{5}{2} M_a n^2 \frac{r^2_{AB}}{t-\tau} + \frac{1}{4} n^4 M^2_a \frac{r^4_{AB}}{(t-\tau)}\right] r^h_{AB}, \tag{110}$$

where M_a denotes the upper bound of the collection of functions $|a^{\alpha\beta}(A, t)|$. An argument analogous to that for the function (88) leads to the conclusion that, in view of inequality (110), the difference between the second derivatives satisfies the inequality

$$|w^{B,\tau}_{x_\alpha x_\beta}(A, t; B, \tau) - [w^{M,\tau}_{x_\alpha x_\beta}(A, t; B, \tau)]_{M=A}|$$

$$< \frac{\text{const}}{(t-\tau)^\mu} \cdot \frac{1}{r_{AB}^{n+2-2\mu-h}}, \qquad (111)$$

if $t > \tau$ and $A \neq B$. The singularities in this estimate are weak if the exponent μ is chosen such that

$$1 - \frac{h}{2} < \mu < 1. \qquad (112)$$

According to the derived inequality (111), the second last integral satisfies an inequality similar to (106) and we can thus state that the sum of integrals (105), representing the second integral of J, satisfies the inequality with a weak singularity

$$|J_{x_\alpha x_\beta}(A, t, \tau)| < \frac{C_A}{(t-\tau)^\mu}, \qquad (113)$$

μ being selected simultaneously from the intervals

$$\left(1 - \frac{h}{2}, 1\right) \quad \text{and} \quad \left(1 - \frac{\delta}{2}, 1\right) \qquad (114)$$

and the constant C_A is fixed in a sufficiently small neighbourhood of the point A inside Ω.

Using inequality (113) and repeating the argument for the first derivative (90), we infer the existence of the second derivative of the quasi-potential defined by formula (101). This completes the proof.

THEOREM 4. *If the coefficients $a_{\alpha\beta}(A, t)$ and the density $\rho(A, t)$ satisfy the conditions stated in Theorem 3, then the quasi-potential (87) has a derivative with respect to t given by the formula*

$$V_t(A, t) = \frac{(2\sqrt{\pi})^n}{\sqrt{\det |a^{\alpha\beta}(A, t)|}} \rho(A, t) +$$

$$+ \int_0^t \iiint_\Omega \sum_{\alpha,\beta=1}^n a_{\alpha\beta}(B, \tau) w^{B,\tau}_{x_\alpha x_\beta}(A, t; B, \tau) \rho(B, \tau) \, dB \, d\tau, \tag{115}$$

at any interior point A of Ω, and for $0 < t < T$.

We use formulae (92) and (93) for the quasi-potential and assume that

$$J(A, t, t) = \lim_{\tau \to t} J(A, t, \tau) = \frac{(2\sqrt{\pi})^n}{\sqrt{\det |a^{\alpha\beta}(A, t)|}} \rho(A, t), \tag{116}$$

in accordance with Theorem 1. Under this assumption, $J(A, t, \tau)$ is continuous in the closed domain $[0 \leqq t \leqq T, 0 \leqq \tau \leqq t]$ when A is a fixed point inside Ω. Assuming now that $0 < \tau < t < T$ and that A is an interior point of Ω, we can say that $J(A, t, \tau)$, defined by the regular integral (92), has a continuous derivative with respect to the variable t

$$J_t(A, t, \tau) = \iiint_\Omega w^{B,\tau}_t(A, t; B, \tau) \rho(B, \tau) \, dB, \tag{117}$$

since it is easy to verify that the conditions of differentiability of a regular integral are satisfied.

Observe now that $w^{B,\tau}$ is an exact solution of the equation

$$\sum_{\alpha,\beta=1}^n a_{\alpha\beta}(B, \tau) \frac{\partial^2 u}{\partial x_\alpha \partial x_\beta} - \frac{\partial u}{\partial t} = 0, \tag{118}$$

as in the case of constant coefficients, and hence the derivative (117) can be written in the form

$$J_t(A, t, \tau) = \iiint_\Omega \sum_{\alpha,\beta=1}^n a_{\alpha\beta}(B, \tau) w^{B,\tau}_{x_\alpha x_\beta}(A, t; B, \tau) \rho(B, \tau) dB. \tag{119}$$

Integral (119) is the sum of integrals of the same form as (105) estimated by inequality (113) and therefore integral (119) satisfies the following inequality with a weak singularity

$$|J_t(A, t, \tau)| < \frac{C'_A}{(t-\tau)^{\mu}}, \tag{120}$$

where μ is selected simultaneously from the intervals (114), and the positive constant C'_A has a fixed value in a sufficiently small neighbourhood of an interior point A.

We now prove that the properties of $J(A, t, \tau)$ are sufficient to deduce the derivative of the integral

$$V(A, t) = \int_0^t J(A, t, \tau)\, d\tau \tag{121}$$

in the form

$$V_t(A, t) = J(A, t, t) + \int_0^t J_t(A, t, \tau)\, d\tau \tag{122}$$

in accordance with the classical rule. Consider, for this purpose the ratio

$$\frac{V(A, t+\Delta t) - V(A, t)}{\Delta t}$$

$$= \frac{1}{\Delta t} \int_t^{t+\Delta t} J(A, t+\Delta t, \tau)\, d\tau + \int_0^t J_t(A, t_1, \tau)\, d\tau, \tag{123}$$

where t_1 lies between t and $t+\Delta t$. Assume first that $\Delta t > 0$. The first term of the right-hand side of relation (123) tends to the limit (116) when $\Delta t \to 0$. To investigate the second term, consider the difference

$$D = \int_0^t J_t(A, t, \tau)\, d\tau - \int_0^t J_t(A, t_1, \tau)\, d\tau. \tag{124}$$

According to property (120), given $\varepsilon > 0$, we can find a positive number

$$s_\varepsilon = \left[\frac{(1-\mu)\varepsilon}{5C'_A}\right]^{\frac{1}{1-\mu}}, \tag{125}$$

such that

$$\left|\int_{t-s_\varepsilon}^{t} J_t(A, t, \tau)\, d\tau\right| < \frac{\varepsilon}{5} \tag{126}$$

for every t in the interval $(0, T)$. Now decompose the difference D as follows:

$$D = \int_0^{t-s_\varepsilon} [J_t(A, t, \tau) - J_t(A, t_1, \tau)]\, d\tau + \int_{t-s_\varepsilon}^{t} J_t(A, t, \tau)\, d\tau -$$

$$- \int_{t_1-s_\varepsilon}^{t_1} J_t(A, t_1, \tau)\, d\tau + \int_t^{t_1} J_t(A, t_1, \tau)\, d\tau - \int_{t-s_\varepsilon}^{t_1-s_\varepsilon} J_t(A, t_1, \tau)\, d\tau. \tag{127}$$

Having s_ε given by formula (125) we can now choose a positive number $\eta(\varepsilon)$, such that

$$|J_t(A, t, \tau) - J_t(A, t_1, \tau)| < \frac{\varepsilon}{5T}, \tag{128}$$

when $t_1 - t < \eta(\varepsilon)$ for any τ in the interval $(0, t-s_\varepsilon)$. Moreover, in view of inequality (120) we have

$$\left|\int_t^{t_1} J_t(A, t_1, \tau)\, d\tau\right| < \frac{\varepsilon}{5}, \quad \text{when} \quad t_1 - t < s_\varepsilon,$$

$$\left|\int_{t-s_\varepsilon}^{t_1-s_\varepsilon} J_t(A, t_1, \tau)\, d\tau\right| < \frac{\varepsilon}{5}, \quad \text{when} \quad t_1 - t < s_\varepsilon. \tag{129}$$

Hence we infer that

$$|D| < \varepsilon, \quad \text{when} \quad \Delta t < \min[\eta(\varepsilon), s_\varepsilon].$$

In a similar way we can investigate the case $\Delta t < 0$, thus justifying relation (122). Substituting the values (116) and (119) to formula (122) we arrive at statement (115) of Theorem 4.

THEOREM 5. *If coefficients* $a_{\alpha\beta}(A,t)$ *and the density* $\rho(A,t)$ *satisfy the conditions of Theorem* 3, *then the derivatives of the quasi-potential* (87) *satisfy the equation*

$$\sum_{\alpha,\beta=1}^{n} a_{\alpha\beta}(A,t)\, V_{x_\alpha x_\beta}(A,t) - V_t(A,t)$$

$$= -\frac{(2\sqrt{\pi})^n}{\sqrt{\det|a^{\alpha\beta}(A,t)|}}\rho(A,t) + \int_0^t \iiint_{\Omega} \sum_{\alpha,\beta=1}^{n} [a_{\alpha\beta}(A,t) -$$

$$- a_{\alpha\beta}(B,\tau)]\, w^{B,\tau}_{x_\alpha x_\beta}(A,t;B,\tau)\,\rho(B,\tau)\,dB\,d\tau \qquad (130)$$

at every interior point A *of* Ω *and inside the interval* $0 < t < T$. *It is emphasized that the spatial integral is regular, the integral with respect to* t *is improper, but has a weak singularity.*

The validity of relations (130) follows at once from formulae (101) and (115) for the derivatives of the quasi-potential.

In the particular case of constant coefficients $a_{\alpha\beta}$, equation (130) is reduced to the Poisson equation

$$\sum_{\alpha,\beta=1}^{n} a_{\alpha\beta} V_{x_\alpha x_\beta}(A,t) - V_t(A,t) = -\frac{(2\sqrt{\pi})^n}{\sqrt{\det|a^{\alpha\beta}|}}\rho(A,t). \qquad (131)$$

If the density $\rho(A,t)$ is integrable in the whole region Ω, but it satisfies the Hölder condition with respect to the spatial variables in a part Ω^* of region Ω only, then Theorems 3, 4 and 5 remain true in the interior of Ω^*. To prove this property it is sufficient to decompose integral (87) into two parts over the regions Ω^* and $\Omega - \Omega^*$, and to observe that the part over $\Omega - \Omega^*$ has derivatives of all orders inside region Ω^*.

§ 7. Determination of the fundamental solution of the parabolic equation

As in the case of the solution of the elliptic equation we seek the fundamental solution of the parabolic equation (69) in the form of the sum

$$\Gamma(A,t;B,\tau) = w^{B,\tau}(A,t;B,\tau) +$$

$$+ \int_\tau^t \iiint_{\Omega'(Z)} w^{Z,\zeta}(A,t;Z,\zeta)\,\Phi(Z,\zeta;B,\tau)\,dZ\,d\zeta \qquad (132)$$

where B and τ play the rôle of parameters, Φ denotes the unknown function, and Ω' an arbitrary bounded, measurable region containing Ω and its boundary. The coefficients $a_{\alpha\beta}(A, t)$ appearing in expression (132) are extended into Ω in an arbitrary manner but must be continuous and satisfy both the Hölder condition (100) with respect to the spatial variables, and condition (73).*

Assume now that the coefficients $b_\alpha(A, t)$, $c(A, t)$ in equation (69) are continuous with respect to the variables (A, t) and that they satisfy the Hölder condition

$$\begin{aligned} |b_\alpha(A, t) - b_\alpha(A_1, t)| &\leq \text{const}\, r^h_{AA_1}, \\ |c(A, t) - c(A_1, t)| &\leq \text{const}\, r^h_{AA_1}. \end{aligned} \tag{132'}$$

These coefficients are now extended into Ω', applying properties (132').

The integral term in sum (132) has the form of a quasi-potential with density Φ. Consequently, requiring that the function (132) satisfies the parabolic equation (69) with respect to the variables A and t inside domain $[A \in \Omega', 0 < t < T]$, applying the preceding rules on differentiation of the quasi-potential and equation (130), we arrive at the integral equation

$$\hat{\Psi}_{A,t}[w^{B,\tau}(A, t; B, \tau)] - \frac{(2\sqrt{\pi})^n}{\sqrt{\det |a^{\alpha\beta}(A, t)|}} \Phi(A, t; B, \tau) +$$

$$+ \int_\tau^t \iiint_{\Omega'(Z)} \hat{\Psi}_{A,t}[w^{Z,\zeta}(A, t; Z, \zeta)] \Phi(Z, \zeta; B, \tau)\, dZ\, d\zeta = 0 \tag{133}$$

with the unknown function Φ, assuming that the latter satisfies the Hölder condition in a sufficiently small neighbourhood of A not containing the fixed point B. We remind the reader that $\hat{\Psi}_{A,t}$ denotes the differential operation defined by formula (69). In the integral equation (133), the point B fixed arbitrarily in Ω', and τ in the interval $(0, T)$, play the rôle of parameters.

---

* This extension is not necessary, since we can set $\Omega' = \Omega$ in formula (132).

The integral equation (133) has the form of the singular Volterra equation

$$\Phi(A,t;B,\tau)=f(A,t;B,\tau)+$$
$$+\lambda\int_{\tau}^{t}\iiint_{\Omega'(Z)}N(A,t;Z,\zeta)\,\Phi(Z,\zeta;B,\tau)\,dZ\,d\zeta, \qquad (134)$$

the kernel N and the function f being defined by the formulae

$$N(A,t;Z,\zeta)=\sqrt{\det|a^{\alpha\beta}(A,t)|}\,\hat{\Psi}_{A,t}[w^{Z,\zeta}(A,t;Z,\zeta)],$$
$$f(A,t;B,\tau)=\lambda N(A,t;B,\tau) \quad (\lambda=(2\sqrt{\pi})^{-n}). \qquad (135)$$

According to the previous investigations, the result of the operation $\hat{\Psi}$ can be written in the form

$$\hat{\Psi}_{A,t}[w^{Z,\zeta}(A,t;Z,\zeta)$$
$$=\sum_{\alpha,\beta=1}^{n}[a_{\alpha\beta}(A,t)-a_{\alpha\beta}(Z,\zeta)]\,w^{Z,\zeta}_{x_\alpha x_\beta}(A,t;Z,\zeta)+$$
$$+\sum_{\alpha=1}^{n}b_\alpha(A,t)\,w^{Z,\zeta}_{x_\alpha}(A,t;Z,\zeta)+c(A,t)\,w^{Z,\zeta}(A,t;Z,\zeta). \qquad (136)$$

Investigation of the integral equation (134) has certain difficulties, in view of the complicated singularity of the kernel. To simplify the solution of this equation we assume that the coefficients $a_{\alpha\beta}(A,t)$ satisfy the Hölder condition not only with respect to the spatial variables but also with respect to the variable t

$$|a_{\alpha\beta}(A,t)-a_{\alpha\beta}(A_1,t_1)|<\text{const}\,[r^h_{AA_1}+|t-t_1|^{h'}]. \qquad (137)$$

As regards the coefficients $b_\alpha(A,t)$ and $c(A,t)$, we do not assume the validity of the Hölder condition with respect to the variable t. Taking into account the estimate (99) of the second derivatives of the quasi-solution, and estimate (91) of the first derivatives, we infer, in view of assumption (137), that kernel (135) of the integral equation (134) satisfies the following inequality with separated weak singularities:

$$|N(A,t;Z,\zeta)|<\frac{\text{const}}{(t-\zeta)^\mu}\cdot\frac{1}{r_{AZ}^{n+2-2\mu-h_1}}, \qquad (138)$$

where $h_1 = \min(h, 2h')$ and μ is arbitrarily selected from the interval $(1-\frac{1}{2}h_1, 1)$. An analogous inequality is satisfied by the function $f(A, t; B, \tau)$.

Thus, the Volterra equation (134) has a unique solution in the form

$$\Phi(A, t; B, \tau) = f(A, t; B, \tau) + \\ + \lambda \int_{\tau}^{t} \iiint_{\Omega'(Z)} \mathfrak{N}(A, t; Z, \zeta) f(Z, \zeta; B, \tau)\, dZ\, d\zeta, \qquad (139)$$

the resolvent kernel $\mathfrak{N}$ of the kernel $N(A, t; Z, \zeta)$ being the sum of the series

$$\mathfrak{N}(A, t; Z, \zeta) = N(A, t; Z, \zeta) + \sum_{\nu=1}^{\infty} \lambda^{\nu} N_{\nu}(A, t; Z, \zeta). \qquad (140)$$

The resolvent kernels N_ν are given by the recursive relation

$$N_{\nu+1}(A, t; Z, \zeta) \\ = \int_{0}^{t} \iiint_{\Omega'(\Pi)} N(A, t; \Pi, \zeta) N_{\nu}(\Pi, \zeta; Z, \zeta)\, d\Pi\, d\zeta \qquad (N_0 = N). \qquad (141)$$

Each iteration lowers the order of singularity, and according to inequality (138) the iterated kernels are certainly bounded, beginning from an index ν_0 equal to the greater of the two numbers

$$\nu_0' = \mathrm{E}\left[\frac{1}{1-\mu}\right] \quad \text{and} \quad \nu_0'' = \mathrm{E}\left[\frac{n}{h_1 - 2(1-\mu)}\right]. \qquad (142)$$

Using estimate (138) we prove analogously to the integral equation (36), that all bounded kernels satisfy the inequality

$$|N_{\nu_0+m}(A, t; Z, \zeta)| < \frac{g_1}{(1-\mu)m} \cdot \frac{[g_2 \Gamma(1-\mu)(t-\zeta)^{1-\mu}]^m}{\Gamma[m(1-\mu)]}, \qquad (143)$$

where g_1 and g_2 denote positive upper bounds of the functions

$$|N_{\nu_0}| \leq g_1 \quad \text{and} \quad \iiint_{\Omega'} \frac{C dZ}{r_{AZ}^{n+2-2\mu-h_1}} \leq g_2.$$

The denominator $\Gamma[m(1-\mu)]$ in estimate (143) ensures the absolute and uniform convergence of series (140) for every value of λ and $t-\zeta$, after having dropped out a few unbounded terms. The only solution (139) of the integral equation (134) is therefore defined and continuous at every point $A \neq B$ of Ω' and for t from the interval (τ, T).

It can easily be proved that the integral term in formula (139) obeys the estimate with a weaker singularity than the function f, and consequently, the solution Φ of the integral equation (134) satisfies inequalities of the same form as kernel N

$$|\Phi(A, t; B, \tau)| < \frac{\text{const}}{(t-\tau)^{\mu}} \cdot \frac{1}{r_{AB}^{n+2-2\mu-h_1}}, \tag{144}$$

where $1-h_1/2 < \mu < 1$, $h_1 = \min(h, 2h')$.

The derived function Φ has an important property expressed by the following theorem:

THEOREM 6. *The solution* (139) *of the integral equation* (134) *satisfies the Hölder condition*

$$|\Phi(A, t; B, \tau) - \Phi(A_1, t; B, \tau)| < \frac{\text{const}}{\inf r_{AB}^{n+3}} r_{AA_1}^{h^*} \tag{145}$$

in every closed region Ω^* located inside Ω and not containing the point B; the number h^* satisfies the condition $0 < h^* < \min(h, 2h')$, *and* $\inf r_{AB}$ *denotes the lower greatest bound of the distances of the fixed point B from the variable point A in Ω^*.*

The proof of this theorem, which is not easy, will not be given here; we refer the reader to the author's paper [44].

Using Theorem 6 and the properties of the quasi-potential expressed by Theorems 3, 4 and 5, we at once infer that the function $\Gamma(A, t; B, \tau)$, defined by formula (132), has first and second derivatives which satisfy the considered parabolic equation

$$\hat{\Psi}_{A,t}[A, t; B, \tau)] = 0$$

at every point A of Ω' distinct from B, and for $0 \leqq \tau < t < T$. The fundamental solution of the parabolic equation (69) therefore has been determined.

§ 8. Properties of the potential of spatial charge for a parabolic equation

As in the case of the potential of the elliptic equation, by the *potential of spatial charge for the parabolic equation* (69), we mean the integral

$$U(A,t)=\int_0^t\iiint_\Omega \Gamma(A,t;B,\tau)\rho(B,\tau)\,dB\,d\tau, \tag{146}$$

where the density $\rho(B,\tau)$ is a bounded and integrable function in the domain $[B\in\Omega, 0\leqq\tau\leqq T]$, and Ω is a measurable region located inside Ω'.

To prove that function (146) is defined in the domain $[A\in\Omega, 0\leqq t\leqq T]$, we write the fundamental solution in the form

$$\Gamma(A,t;B,\tau)=w^{B,\tau}(A,t;B,\tau)+\bar{w}(A,t;B,\tau), \tag{147}$$

where

$$\bar{w}(A,t;B,\tau)$$
$$=\int_\tau^t\iiint_{\Omega'} w^{Z,\zeta}(A,t;Z,\zeta)\Phi(Z,\zeta;B,\tau)\,dZ\,d\zeta. \tag{148}$$

The first term of sum (147) has a singularity estimated by inequality (89). To estimate the second term $\bar{w}$, we apply inequality (144) to the function Φ; then we obtain

$$|\bar{w}(A,t;B,\tau)|<\text{const}\int_\tau^t\frac{d\zeta}{(t-\zeta)^\mu(\zeta-\tau)^\mu}\iiint_{\Omega'(Z)}\frac{dZ}{r_{AZ}^{n-2\mu}\,r_{ZB}^{n+2-2\mu-h_1}}$$

which implies the inequality

$$|\bar{w}(A,t;B,\tau)|<\frac{\text{const}}{(t-\tau)^{2\mu-1}}\cdot\frac{1}{r_{AB}^{n+2-4\mu-h_1}}. \tag{149}$$

(Note that $1-h_1/2<\mu<1$). The singularities of estimate (149) are weaker than those for the function (89), and consequently the potential (146) is defined and continuous in the domain $[A\in\Omega', 0\leqq t\leqq T]$.

THEOREM 7. *The potential* (146) *has a first spatial derivative continuous in the domain* $[A \in \Omega, 0 < t \leqq T]$, *and given by the formula*

$$U_{x_\alpha}(A, t) = \int_0^t \iiint_{\Omega} \Gamma_{x_\alpha}(A, t; B, \tau)\, \rho(B, \tau)\, dB\, d\tau, \qquad (150)$$

under the same assumption as before that the density ρ *is a bounded, integrable function.*

According to formula (132) we can write potential (146) in the form of the sum of two quasi-potentials

$$U(A, t) = \int_0^t \iiint_{\Omega(B)} w^{B,\tau}(A, t; B, \tau)\, \rho(B, \tau)\, dB\, d\tau + \\ + \int_0^t \iiint_{\Omega'(M)} w^{Z,\zeta}(A, t; Z, \zeta)\, \rho_1(Z, \zeta)\, dZ\, d\zeta \qquad (151)$$

the first with density ρ, while the second with density ρ_1 given by the formula

$$\rho_1(Z, \zeta) = \int_0^\zeta \iiint_{\Omega(B)} \Phi(Z, \zeta; B, \tau)\, \rho(B, \tau)\, dB\, d\tau, \qquad (152)$$

Φ being defined by formula (139) and satisfying estimate (144).

It is evident that the function (152) is continuous and bounded in the domain $[\Omega', (0, T)]$, and hence, in view of Theorem 2, we infer the validity of the statement (150).

THEOREM 8. *If the density* $\rho(B, \tau)$ *is a continuous function with respect to the variables B and* τ *in the closed domain* $[\Omega, (0, T)]$, *and it satisfies the Hölder condition with respect to the spatial variables*

$$|\rho(B, \tau) - \rho(B_1, \tau)| < \text{const}\, r_{BB_1}^{\delta} \qquad (0 < \delta \leqq 1), \qquad (153)$$

then the potential (146) *has second spatial derivatives and a first derivative with respect to the variable t, which satisfy the Poisson equation*

$$\hat{\Psi}[U(A, t)] = -\frac{(2\sqrt{\pi})^n}{\sqrt{\det|a^{\alpha\beta}(A, t)|}}\, \rho(A, t) \qquad (154)$$

at every interior point of the domain $[\Omega, (0, T)]$.

Proof. Proceeding as in the proof of Theorem 6, we can prove that the function (152) satisfies the Hölder condition in the form

$$|\rho_1(Z, \zeta) - \rho_1(Z_1, \zeta)| < \text{const}\, r_{ZZ_1}^{h^*} \tag{155}$$

and here only the continuity of the function ρ is sufficient. In view of Theorems 3 and 4 on the quasi-potential, we infer that potential (151) has second spatial derivatives and a first derivative with respect to t, and subsequently we conclude in accordance with Theorem 5 that these derivatives satisfy the equation

$$\hat{\Psi}[U(A, t)] = -\frac{(2\sqrt{\pi})^n}{\sqrt{\det|a^{\alpha\beta}(A, t)|}}[\rho(A, t) + \rho_1(A, t)] +$$

$$+ \int_0^t \iiint_{\Omega(B)} \hat{\Psi}_{A,t}[w^{B,\tau}(A, t; B, \tau)]\, \rho(B, \tau)\, dB\, d\tau +$$

$$+ \int_0^t \iiint_{\Omega'(M)} \hat{\Psi}_{A,t}[w^{Z,\zeta}(A, t; Z, \zeta)]\, \rho_1(Z, \zeta)\, dZ\, d\zeta \tag{156}$$

at every interior point of the domain $[\Omega, (0, T)]$. Substituting expression (152) into formula (156) for ρ_1, we obtain

$$\hat{\Psi}[U(A, t)] = -\frac{(2\sqrt{\pi})^n}{\sqrt{\det|a^{\alpha\beta}(A, t)|}}\rho(A, t) +$$

$$+ \int_0^t \iiint_{\Omega(B)} \Big\{\hat{\Psi}_{A,t}[w^{B,\tau}(A, t; B, \tau)] -$$

$$- \frac{(2\sqrt{\pi})^n}{\sqrt{\det|a^{\alpha\beta}(A, t)|}}\Phi(A, t; B, \tau) -$$

$$- \int_\tau^t \iiint_{\Omega'(M)} \Psi_{A,t}[w^{Z,\zeta}(A, t; Z, \zeta)]\, \Phi(Z, \zeta; B, \tau)\, dZ\, d\zeta\Big\} \times$$

$$\times \rho(B, \tau)\, dB\, d\tau. \tag{157}$$

Since the function Φ satisfies integral equation (133), the expression in figure brackets in equation (157) vanishes and this implies the statement (154) of Theorem 8.

§ 9. Properties of potential of surface distribution and of the Poisson–Weierstrass integral for the parabolic equation

DEFINITION 2. *By a potential of surface distribution for the parabolic equation* (69) *we mean an integral*

$$W(A,t) = \int_0^t \iint_S \Gamma(A,t;Q,\tau)\,\varphi(Q,\tau)\,d\sigma_Q\,d\tau\,, \tag{158}$$

where S is a surface in Ω', which satisfies the Liapunov conditions, and $\varphi(Q,\tau)$ is a function defined, bounded and integrable in the domain

$$[Q\in S,\ 0\leqq\tau\leqq T]. \tag{159}$$

We now state certain important properties of potential (158) without presenting their proofs (see [45]).

The function (158) satisfies the parabolic equation (69) at every point A of the region Ω' which does not lie on the surface S, and for $0 < t < T$. When the density $\varphi(Q,\tau)$ satisfies the assumption of continuity only, then the first spatial derivatives of the potential (158)

$$W_{x_\alpha}(A,t) = \int_0^t \iint_S \Gamma_{x_\alpha}(A,t;Q,\tau)\,\varphi(Q,\tau)\,d\sigma_Q\,d\tau \tag{160}$$

do not necessarily tend to definite limits when A tends to a point P of the surface S. However, as in the case of the elliptic equation, a certain linear combination of these derivatives, called the *transversal derivative*, has a limit defined by the following theorem.

THEOREM 9. *If the density $\varphi(Q,\tau)$ is a continuous function, then the transversal derivative of the potential of surface distribution at the point A inside Ω bounded by a surface S*

$$\frac{dW(A,t)}{dT_P} = \sum_{\alpha,\beta=1}^{n} a_{\alpha\beta}(A,t)\cos(N_P,x_\beta)\,W_{x_\alpha}(A,t) \tag{161}$$

has the following boundary property:

$$\lim_{A\to P}\frac{dW(A,t)}{dT_P} = -\frac{1}{2}\,\frac{(2\sqrt{\pi})^n}{\sqrt{\det|a^{\alpha\beta}(P,t)|}}\,\varphi(P,t) + \int_0^t \iint_S \frac{d}{dT_P}[\Gamma(P,t;Q,\tau)]\,\varphi(Q,\tau)\,d\sigma_Q\,d\tau\,, \tag{162}$$

where the transversal derivative of the fundamental solution in the integrand satisfies the inequality

$$\left|\frac{d}{dT_P}[\Gamma(P, t; Q, \tau)]\right| < \frac{\text{const}}{(t-\tau)^{\mu}} \cdot \frac{1}{r_{PQ}^{n+1-2\mu-\kappa_1}}, \tag{163}$$

where $\kappa_1 = \min(h, 2h', \kappa)$ *and the positive number* μ *is arbitrary in the open interval* $(1-\kappa_1/2, 1)$.

Both separated singularities in inequality (163) are weak with respect to the ordinary and surface integrals, for

$$0 < \mu < 1 \quad \text{and} \quad n+1-2\mu-\kappa_1 < n-1.$$

On the basis of the properties of the Poisson–Weierstrass integral, we can easily prove the following theorem:

THEOREM 10. *If* $\rho(B, \tau)$ *is a bounded and continuous function in the domain* $[B \in \Omega, 0 \leqq \tau \leqq T]$, *then the generalized Poisson–Weierstrass integral*

$$I(A, t, \tau) = \iiint_{\Omega} \Gamma(A, t; B, \tau)\, \rho(B, \tau)\, dv_B \tag{164}$$

satisfies equation (69) *at every interior point A of* Ω *for* $0 < t < T$ *and has the boundary property*

$$\lim_{t \to \tau} I(A, t, \tau) = \frac{(2\sqrt{\pi})^n}{\sqrt{\det|a^{\alpha\beta}(A, \tau)|}}\, \rho(A, \tau) \tag{165}$$

at every interior point $A \in \Omega$.

These properties make it possible to solve the problem of determination of a function $\mu(A, t)$ which satisfies the parabolic equation

$$\hat{\Psi}[u(A, t)] = f(A, t) \tag{166}$$

at all points inside Ω for $0 < t < T$, and which, moreover, satisfies the mixed boundary condition

$$\lim_{A \to P}\left[\frac{du(A, t)}{dT_P} + a(P, t)\, u(A, t)\right] = F(P, t), \tag{167}$$

when $0 < t \leqq T$, and the initial condition

$$\lim_{t \to 0} u(A, t) = \Phi(A) \tag{168}$$

at every point A inside Ω. The functions f, F and Φ are known; $f(A, t)$ is defined, bounded and continuous in the domain $[A \in \Omega, 0 < t < T]$ and it satisfies the Hölder condition with respect to the spatial variables; $F(P, t)$ is defined, bounded and continuous in the domain $[P \in S, 0 < t < T]$; $\Phi(A)$ is defined, bounded and continuous in the interior of Ω. We seek the solution in the form of the sum of integrals

$$u(A, t) = \int_0^t \iint_S \Gamma(A, t; Q, \tau)\, \varphi(Q, \tau)\, d\sigma_Q\, d\tau +$$

$$+ (2\sqrt{\pi})^{-n} \int_0^t \iiint_\Omega \Gamma(A, t; B, \tau) [\det |a^{\alpha\beta}(B, \tau)|]^{1/2} f(B, \tau)\, dB\, d\tau +$$

$$+ (2\sqrt{\pi})^{-n} \iiint_\Omega \Gamma(A, t; B, 0) [\det |a^{\alpha\beta}(B, 0)|]^{1/2} \Phi(B)\, dB. \quad (169)$$

In view of Poisson's equation (154), the second integral (169) ensures that the function $u(A, t)$ satisfies the considered equation (166). By virtue of property (165) of the Poisson–Weierstrass integral, the third integral (169) ensures that the initial condition (168) is satisfied. Finally, the unknown function $\varphi(Q, \tau)$ in the first integral is determined by requiring that the sum (169) satisfies the boundary condition (167). On the basis of property (162) of the transversal derivative of the potential of surface distribution, we thus obtain the following singular Volterra equation:

$$-\frac{1}{2} \frac{(2\sqrt{\pi})^n}{\sqrt{\det |a^{\alpha\beta}(P, t)|}} \varphi(P, t) +$$

$$+ \int_0^t \iint_S \left[\frac{d\Gamma(P, t; Q, \tau)}{dT_P} + a(P, t)\, \Gamma(P, t; Q, \tau) \right] \varphi(Q, \tau)\, d\sigma_Q\, d\tau -$$

$$- (2\sqrt{\pi})^{-n} \int_0^t \iiint_\Omega \left[\frac{d\Gamma(P, t; B, \tau)}{dT_P} + a(P, t)\, \Gamma(P, t; B, \tau) \right] \times$$

$$\times [\det |a^{\alpha\beta}(B, \tau)|]^{1/2} f(B, \tau)\, dB\, d\tau +$$

$$+ (2\sqrt{\pi})^{-n} \iiint_\Omega \left[\frac{d\Gamma(P, t; B, 0)}{dT_P} + a(P, t)\, \Gamma(P, t; B, 0) \right] \times$$

$$\times [\det |a^{\alpha\beta}(B, 0)|]^{1/2} \Phi(B)\, dB = F(P, t). \quad (170)$$

The kernel of the derived equation satisfies inequality (163) with weak separated singularities. Further, it can be proved that the function defined by the last integral in equation (170) is weakly unbounded as $t^{-\mu}$ where $1/2 < \mu < 1$, when $t \to 0$. Therefore, repeating the argument analogous to that in the Fourier problem for the conduction equation, we can prove that the solution of equation (170) is uniquely defined by the familiar Volterra formula. Inserting the solution φ of equation (170) into formula (169), we arrive at the required solution of the Fourier problem for equation (166).

Other properties of the potentials of spatial charge and of surface distribution for the normal parabolic equation (69), and the application of these properties to boundary problems will be presented in Chapter XXII of Part 3.

CHAPTER XIV

APPLICATION OF INTEGRAL EQUATIONS TO THE THEORY OF HYPERBOLIC TYPE EQUATIONS

§ 1. The Darboux problem

Another great success of the theory of integral equations consists in solving certain fundamental problems for partial differential equations of hyperbolic type. We shall consider here equations with two independent variables only, which when referred to characteristics, have in the case of full linearity the form

$$\frac{\partial^2 u}{\partial x\, \partial y} = a(x, y)\frac{\partial u}{\partial x} + b(x, y)\frac{\partial u}{\partial y} + c(x, y)u + f(x, y), \tag{1}$$

where $a(x, y)$, $b(x, y)$, $c(x, y)$ and $f(x, y)$ are known continuous functions in the closed region

$$0 \leqq x \leqq A, \quad 0 \leqq y \leqq B. \tag{2}$$

The *Darboux problem* consists in determining a function $u(x, y)$, continuous with its first derivatives and mixed derivative in the closed region (2), which satisfies equation (1) inside region (2) and which takes on two characteristics (say $x = 0$ and $y = 0$) *a priori* prescribed values; we require, therefore, that

$$u(x, 0) = \varphi(x) \quad \text{and} \quad u(0, y) = \psi(y), \tag{3}$$

where $\varphi(x)$ and $\psi(x)$ are known functions of the class C_1 in the intervals $[0, A]$ and $[0, B]$, respectively. Moreover, the condition $\varphi(0) = \psi(0)$ should be satisfied.

We first solve the Darboux problem for the equation

$$\frac{\partial^2 u}{\partial x\, \partial y} = F(x, y), \tag{4}$$

where $F(x, y)$ is a known continuous function in the region (2). We observe at once that such a solution is given by the function

$$u(x, y) = \varphi(x) + \psi(y) - \varphi(0) + \int_0^x \int_0^y F(\xi, \eta)\, d\xi\, d\eta \tag{5}$$

and that this is the only solution which satisfies condition (3). If now we replace in equation (5) the function F by the right-hand side of equation (1) we obtain the linear integro-differential equation

$$u(x, y) = \lambda \int_0^x \int_0^y \left[a(\xi, \eta) \frac{\partial u}{\partial \xi} + b(\xi, \eta) \frac{\partial u}{\partial \eta} + c(\xi, \eta) u(\xi, \eta) \right] d\xi\, d\eta + g(x, y) \quad (\lambda = 1), \tag{6}$$

where $g(x, y)$ is a known function, given by the formula

$$g(x, y) = \varphi(x) + \psi(y) - \varphi(0) + \int_0^x \int_0^y f(\xi, \eta)\, d\xi\, d\eta. \tag{7}$$

Evidently, a function satisfying the differential equation (1) in region (2) and condition (3), satisfies the integro-differential equation (6) and, conversely, a function satisfying equation (6) in region (2) satisfies also equation (1) and condition (3).

Equation (6) can easily be solved without any restrictions on the number A and B, by the method which we applied to the Volterra equation. We therefore seek the solution in the form of the sum of a power series in the parameter λ:

$$u(x, y) = g(x, y) + \sum_{n=1}^{\infty} \lambda^n u_n(x, y), \tag{8}$$

$$\begin{aligned} \frac{\partial u(x, y)}{\partial x} &= g'_x(x, y) + \sum_{n=1}^{\infty} \lambda^n \frac{\partial u_n(x, y)}{\partial x}, \\ \frac{\partial u(x, y)}{\partial y} &= g'_y(x, y) + \sum_{n=1}^{\infty} \lambda^n \frac{\partial u_n(x, y)}{\partial y}. \end{aligned} \tag{9}$$

Substituting series (8) and (9) into equation (6) we arrive at the recursive formula

$$u_n(x, y) = \int_0^x \int_0^y \left[a(\xi, \eta) \frac{\partial u_{n-1}}{\partial \xi} + b(\xi, \eta) \frac{\partial u_{n-1}}{\partial \eta} + \right.$$

$$\left. + c(\xi, \eta) u_{n-1}(\xi, \eta) \right] d\xi \, d\eta \qquad (10)$$

relating the successive terms of series (8), and the relation

$$u_0(x, y) = g(x, y). \qquad (11)$$

Since, by assumption, the function $g(x, y)$ has continuous first derivatives, by induction we infer that all functions $u_n(x, y)$ calculated from formula (10) are defined and have continuous derivatives in the region (2). We shall prove the uniform convergence of series (8) and (9) derived from relation (10). It is easy to prove the validity of the inequalities

$$|u_n| < 3mK^n \frac{(x+y)^{n+1}}{(n+1)!},$$

$$\left| \frac{\partial u_n}{\partial x} \right| < 3mK^n \frac{(x+y)^n}{n!}, \qquad (12)$$

$$\left| \frac{\partial u_n}{\partial y} \right| < 3mK^n \frac{(x+y)^n}{n!},$$

where m is the upper bound of the absolute values of the functions g, g'_x, g'_y and

$$K = M(2+A+B). \qquad (13)$$

In fact, if we assume that inequalities (12) are satisfied, then the recursive formula (10) yields

$$|u_{n+1}| < 3mMK^n \frac{(x+y)^{n+2}}{(n+2)!} \left[2 + \frac{x+y}{n+3} \right],$$

$$\left| \frac{\partial u_{n+1}}{\partial x} \right| < 3mMK^n \frac{(x+y)^{n+1}}{(n+1)!} \left[2 + \frac{x+y}{n+2} \right], \qquad (14)$$

$$\left| \frac{\partial u_{n+1}}{\partial y} \right| < 3mMK^n \frac{(x+y)^{n+1}}{(n+1)!} \left[2 + \frac{x+y}{n+2} \right],$$

where M denotes the greatest of the least upper bounds of the functions $|a(x,y)|$, $|b(x,y)|$ and $|c(x,y)|$ in the region (2). By induction we now infer that inequalities (12) are true for any positive integer n. Consequently the series (8) and (9) are uniformly convergent in the region (2), and therefore the sum of the series (8) is the solution of the integro-differential equations (6). This function is also a required solution of the Darboux problem. The uniqueness of the solution of equation (6) can be proved by means of the familiar, frequently applied method.

The considered Darboux problem can be generalized to the case of a non-linear hyperbolic equation of the form

$$\frac{\partial^2 u}{\partial x\,\partial y} = F\left(x, y, u, \frac{\partial u}{\partial x}, \frac{\partial u}{\partial y}\right), \tag{1'}$$

where $F(x, y, u, v, w)$ is a known function in a certain region. Assuming that this function is continuous with respect to the variables x and y and that it satisfies the Lipschitz condition with respect to variables u, v and w, we can obtain the solution by the classical method of successive approximation. The more general problem of the determination of a system of functions satisfying equations (1′) when the values of their derivatives on two lines are prescribed, has recently been solved by Z. SZMYDT in the paper [81].

§ 2. The Riemann Function

Consider a particular case of the preceding problem when $\varphi = 0$ and $\psi = 0$. Here we seek a function $u(x, y)$ which, in the region (2), satisfies the equation

$$\frac{\partial^2 u}{\partial x\,\partial y} = \lambda\left[a(x,y)\frac{\partial u}{\partial x} + b(x,y)\frac{\partial u}{\partial y} + c(x,y)u\right] + f(x,y) \tag{15}$$

and the conditions

$$u(x, 0) = 0 \quad \text{and} \quad u(0, y) = 0 \tag{16}$$

on the characteristics $x = 0$ and $y = 0$. As in the solution of Poisson's equation by means of the Green's Function (p. 268), we seek the required function in the form of an integral

$$u(x, y) = \int_0^x \int_0^y R(x, y; \xi, \eta; \lambda) f(\xi, \eta)\, d\xi\, d\eta, \tag{17}$$

where R is an unknown function of the pair of points (x, y) and (ξ, η) in the region

$$\begin{aligned} &0 \leqq x \leqq A, \quad 0 \leqq y \leqq B, \\ &0 \leqq \xi \leqq x, \quad 0 \leqq \eta \leqq y. \end{aligned} \tag{18}$$

Assuming that R has continuous derivatives $\partial R/\partial x, \partial R/\partial y$ and $\partial^2 R/\partial x \partial y$ in the region (18), we obtain from formula (17)

$$\frac{\partial u}{\partial x} = \int_0^y R(x, y; x, \eta; \lambda) f(x, \eta)\, d\eta + \\ + \int_0^x \int_0^y R'_x(x, y; \xi, \eta; \lambda) f(\xi, \eta)\, d\xi\, d\eta,$$

$$\frac{\partial u}{\partial y} = \int_0^x R(x, y; \xi, y; \lambda) f(\xi, y)\, d\xi + \\ + \int_0^x \int_0^y R'_y(x, y; \xi, \eta; \lambda) f(\xi, \eta)\, d\xi\, d\eta,$$

$$\frac{\partial^2 u}{\partial x\, \partial y} = R(x, y; x, y; \lambda) f(x, y) + \int_0^y R'_y(x, y; x, \eta; \lambda) f(x, \eta)\, d\eta + \\ + \int_0^x R'_x(x, y; \xi, y; \lambda) f(\xi, y)\, d\xi + \int_0^x \int_0^y R''_{xy}(x, y; \xi, \eta; \lambda) f(\xi, \eta)\, d\xi\, d\eta.$$

These expressions indicate that the function (17) satisfies the considered differential equation (15) in the region (2) if the unknown function R satisfies the differential equations

$$R''_{xy}(x, y; \xi, \eta; \lambda) - \lambda [a(x, y) R'_x(x, y; \xi, \eta; \lambda) + \\ + b(x, y) R'_y(x, y; \xi, \eta; \lambda) + c(x, y) R(x, y; \xi, \eta; \lambda)] = 0, \tag{19}$$

$$\begin{aligned} &R'_y(x, y; x, \eta; \lambda) - \lambda a(x, y) R(x, y; x, \eta; \lambda) = 0, \\ &R'_x(x, y; \xi, y; \lambda) - \lambda b(x, y) R(x, y; \xi, y; \lambda) = 0, \end{aligned} \tag{20}$$

and the condition

$$R(x, y; x, y; \lambda) = 1 . \tag{21}$$

Taking into account condition (21) we obtain from equations (20)

$$\begin{aligned} R(x, y; x, \eta; \lambda) &= \exp\left[\lambda \int_{\eta}^{y} a(x, t)\, dt\right], \\ R(x, y; \xi, y; \lambda) &= \exp\left[\lambda \int_{\xi}^{x} b(t, y)\, dt\right]. \end{aligned} \tag{22}$$

There is nothing to prevent us from replacing x in the first formula (22) by an arbitrary number ξ belonging to the interior of the interval $(0, A)$, and in the second formula y by an arbitrary number η from the interior of the interval $(0, B)$; consequently, the determination of the function $R(x, y; \xi, \eta; \lambda)$ consists in finding a solution of the homogeneous differential equation

$$\frac{\partial^2 R}{\partial x\, \partial y} = \lambda \left[a(x, y) \frac{\partial R}{\partial x} + b(x, y) \frac{\partial R}{\partial y} + c(x, y) R \right] \tag{23}$$

in the region $\xi \leqq x \leqq A, \eta \leqq y \leqq B$, which takes the prescribed values

$$\begin{aligned} R(\xi, y; \xi, \eta; \lambda) &= \exp\left[\lambda \int_{\eta}^{y} a(\xi, t)\, dt\right], \\ R(x, \eta; \xi, \eta; \lambda) &= \exp\left[\lambda \int_{\xi}^{x} b(t, \eta)\, dt\right] \end{aligned} \tag{24}$$

on characteristics $x = \xi$ and $y = \eta$.

Thus this problem is the Darboux problem where the variables ξ and η play the rôle of parameters.

The function $R(x, y; \xi, \eta; \lambda)$ satisfying conditions (19), (20) and (21) therefore exists in the region (18) and it is unique. This function is called the *Riemann Function* for equation (15); it depends on the coefficients a, b and c, and is analogous to the Green Function, the essential difference being that it has no singularity when $x \to \xi$ and $y \to \eta$. According to our foregoing argument, the Riemann Function R is the sum of the series

$$R(x, y; \xi, \eta; \lambda) = R_0(x, y; \xi, \eta) + \sum_{n=1}^{\infty} \lambda^n R_n(x, y; \xi, \eta) \quad (25)$$

which is absolutely and uniformly convergent for any λ, where

$$R_0(x, y; \xi, \eta) = -1 + \exp\left[\lambda \int_{\eta}^{y} a(x, t)\, dt\right] + \exp\left[\lambda \int_{\xi}^{x} b(t, y)\, dt\right],$$

$$R_n(x, y; \xi, \eta) = \int_{\xi}^{x}\int_{\eta}^{y} \left(a(s, t) \frac{\partial R_{n-1}(s, t; \xi, \eta)}{\partial s} + \right.$$

$$\left. + b(s, t) \frac{\partial R_{n-1}(s, t; \xi, \eta)}{\partial t} + c(s, t) R_{n-1}(s, t; \xi, \eta) \right) ds\, dt. \quad (26)$$

On the basis of the derived Riemann Function (25) we can therefore state that formula (17) determines the unique solution of equation (15), which satisfies conditions (16).

It is noteworthy that Riemann introduced his function R in investigating equation (15) by a different method based on the adjoint equation.

§ 3. The Cauchy problem

Consider a closed region Ω bounded by two characteristics $x = x_0$ and $y = y_0$ passing through a constant point $A_0(x_0, y_0)$, and by a line B_0C_0 (Fig. 5). The *Cauchy problem* for the equation

$$\frac{\partial^2 u}{\partial x\, \partial y} = F(x, y) \quad (27)$$

consists in the determination of a function $u(x, y)$, which is continuous with its first derivatives and the mixed derivative u_{xy} in the region Ω, satisfying equation (27) in Ω, and taking at every point $M(\xi, \eta)$ of the line B_0C_0, together with one of its derivatives, some *a priori* prescribed values. We assume that every straight line parallel to a coordinate axis cuts B_0C_0 in one point only.

Now construct through an arbitrary point $A(x, y)$ inside Ω two characteristics and consider the region ABC bounded by these characteristics and by the arc BC of the line $B_0 C_0$. Integrating both sides of equation (27) over the region ABC, we have

$$\iint_{ABC} \frac{\partial^2 u}{\partial \xi \, \partial \eta} \, d\xi \, d\eta = \iint_{ABC} F(\xi, \eta) \, d\xi \, d\eta , \tag{28}$$

where (ξ, η) denotes the variable point of integration, and the point $A(x, y)$ is regarded as constant. It follows from equation (28) that if there exists a solution of the Cauchy problem, it is determined either by the equation

$$u(A) = u(B) + \int_{BC} \varphi(\xi) \, d\xi + \iint_{ABC} F(\xi, \eta) \, d\xi \, d\eta \tag{29}$$

or by the formula

$$u(A) = u(C) + \int_{CB} \psi(\eta) \, d\eta + \iint_{ABC} F(\xi, \eta) \, d\xi \, d\eta , \tag{29'}$$

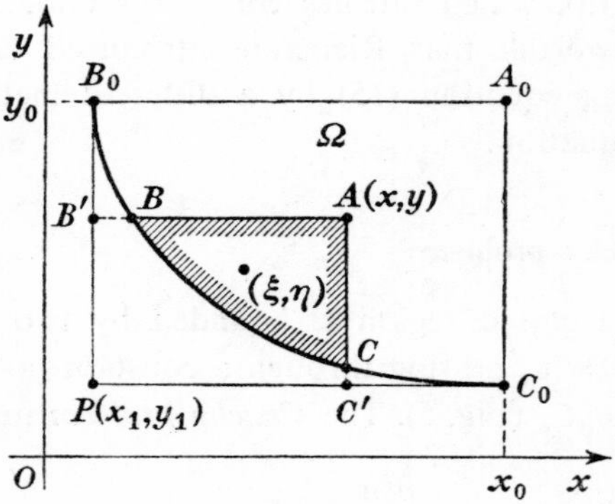

Fig. 5

where $\varphi(\xi)$ is an *a priori* prescribed value of the derivative $\partial u / \partial \xi$ at a point of the arc $B_0 C_0$ with abscissa ξ, and $\psi(\eta)$ is a prescribed value of the derivative $\partial u / \partial \eta$ at a point of the arc $B_0 C_0$ with ordinate η. The value $u(B)$ can, in view of the condition of the Cauchy problem, be regarded as a given function of the variable y

$$u(B) = f_1(y), \tag{30}$$

and the value $u(C)$ as a known function of the variable x

$$u(C) = f_2(x). \tag{30'}$$

We assume that the known functions $\varphi(x)$ and $\psi(y)$ are defined and continuous in the intervals (x_1, x_0) and (y_1, y_0) corresponding to the arc $B_0 C_0$, and that the functions $f_1(y)$ and $f_2(x)$ are defined and have continuous derivatives in these intervals.

Conversely, the functions (29) or (29′) satisfy equation (27) in Ω and the Cauchy conditions on the line $B_0 C_0$, since, as can easily be verified, the double integral in formulae (29) and (29′) is the solution of equation (27) which vanishes together with its derivatives on the line $B_0 C_0$.

Thus formula (29) or (29′) represents the unique solution of the Cauchy problem in Ω.

Let us now solve the Cauchy problem for the general equation

$$\frac{\partial^2 u}{\partial x \partial y} = \lambda \left[a(x, y) \frac{\partial u}{\partial x} + b(x, y) \frac{\partial u}{\partial y} + c(x, y) u \right] + F(x, y), \tag{31}$$

where a, b, c and F are known continuous functions in Ω.

In accordance with formula (29), we may state that the solution of equation (31) satisfying the Cauchy conditions on the line $B_0 C_0$, also satisfies the integro-differential equation

$$u(x, y) = F_1(x, y) +$$

$$+ \lambda \iint\limits_{ABC} \left[a(\xi, \eta) \frac{\partial u}{\partial \xi} + b(\xi, \eta) \frac{\partial u}{\partial \eta} + c(\xi, \eta) u(\xi, \eta) \right] d\xi\, d\eta, \tag{32}$$

F_1 being defined by the formula

$$F_1(x, y) = f_1(y) + \int\limits_{BC} \varphi(\xi)\, d\xi + \iint\limits_{ABC} F(\xi, \eta)\, d\xi\, d\eta. \tag{33}$$

Conversely, a function satisfying equation (32) also satisfies equation (31) in Ω, and the Cauchy conditions on the line $B_0 C_0$.

Thus the problem has been reduced to the solution of the integro-differential equation (32). This equation can easily be reduced to the form (6) by introducing functions $\alpha(x, y)$,

$\beta(x, y), \gamma(x, y)$ and $\Phi(x, y)$ being the continuations of the functions $a(x, y), b(x, y), c(x, y)$ and $F_1(x, y)$ into the rectangle $A_0B_0PC_0$ in such a way that

$$\begin{aligned} \alpha(x, y) &= a(x, y), \\ \beta(x, y) &= b(x, y), \\ \gamma(x, y) &= c(x, y), \\ \Phi(x, y) &= F_1(x, y), \end{aligned} \tag{34}$$

when $(x, y) \in \Omega$ and $\alpha = 0$, $\beta = 0$ and $\gamma = 0$, when (x, y) lies below the line B_0C_0. $F_1(x, y)$ is extended below the line B_0C_0 in such a way that there exist continuous derivatives Φ'_x, Φ'_y and Φ''_{xy} in the rectangle $A_0B_0PC_0$.

Under these assumptions, consider the integro-differential equation

$$U(x, y) = \Phi(x, y) + \\ + \lambda \int_{x_1}^{x} \int_{y_1}^{y} \left[\alpha(\xi, \eta) \frac{\partial U}{\partial \xi} + \beta(\xi, \eta) \frac{\partial U}{\partial \eta} + \gamma(\xi, \eta) U(\xi, \eta) \right] d\xi \, d\eta, \tag{35}$$

in which the constant coordinates x_1 and y_1 correspond to the ends of the arc B_0C_0. According to the preceding investigations, equation (35) has a unique solution defined in the rectangle $A_0B_0PC_0$ by the absolutely and uniformly convergent series

$$U(x, y) = \Phi(x, y) + \sum_{n=1}^{\infty} \lambda^n U_n(x, y), \tag{36}$$

the functions $U_n(x, y)$ being defined by the recursive formula

$$U_n(x, y) = \int_{x_1}^{x} \int_{y_1}^{y} \left[\alpha(\xi, \eta) \frac{\partial U_{n-1}}{\partial \xi} + \\ + \beta(\xi, \eta) \frac{\partial U_{n-1}}{\partial \eta} + \gamma(\xi, \eta) U_{n-1}(\xi, \eta) \right] d\xi \, d\eta \tag{37}$$

and

$$U_0(x, y) = \Phi(x, y).$$

Observe that discontinuity of the coefficients α, β and γ on the line B_0C_0 does not invalidate the applicability of these formulae.

It follows from assumptions (34) that solution $U(x, y)$ of equation (35) satisfies equation (32) at every point of the region Ω. The derived function $u(x, y) = U(x, y)$ in Ω is the required solution of the Cauchy problem for equation (31). In the familiar way we can prove that the solution of equation (32) is unique, and consequently the Cauchy solution is unique.

The solution of the Cauchy problem can also be obtained in a straightforward way by means of the Riemann Function introduced in the preceding section.

Namely, in view of equations (19), (20), and (21) satisfied by the Riemann Function, it can easily be verified that the integral

$$u^*(x, y) = \iint_{ABC} R(x, y; \xi, \eta; \lambda) F(\xi, \eta)\, d\xi\, d\eta \qquad (38)$$

satisfies equation (31) in Ω, and vanishes, together with its derivatives, on the line B_0C_0; thus, this integral is the solution of the Cauchy problem in the case of particular conditions on the line B_0C_0. To deduce the solution u for arbitrary conditions on B_0C_0, we set

$$u(x, y) = v(x, y) + w(x, y), \qquad (39)$$

where $w(x, y)$ is the solution of the equation

$$\frac{\partial^2 w}{\partial x\, \partial y} = 0$$

with the arbitrary Cauchy data

$$w(B) = f_1(y) \quad \text{and} \quad \left(\frac{\partial w}{\partial x}\right)_B = \varphi(x)$$

on the line B_0C_0; consequently, in view of formula (29)

$$w(A) = f_1(y) + \int_{BC} \varphi(\xi)\, d\xi\,.$$

Thus we obtain, for the function $v(x, y)$, the differential equation

$$\frac{\partial^2 v}{\partial x\,\partial y} = \lambda\left[a(x, y)\frac{\partial v}{\partial x} + b(x, y)\frac{\partial v}{\partial y} + c(x, y)\right] +$$

$$+\left[F(x, y) + \lambda a(x, y)\frac{\partial w}{\partial x} + \lambda b(x, y)\frac{\partial w}{\partial y} + \lambda c(x, y)\, w\right]. \tag{40}$$

According to formula (38) the integral

$$v(x, y) = \iint\limits_{ABC} R(x, y; \xi, \eta; \lambda)\left[F(\xi, \eta) + \lambda a(\xi, \eta)\frac{\partial w}{\partial \xi} + \right.$$

$$\left. + \lambda b(\xi, \eta)\frac{\partial w}{\partial \eta} + \lambda c(\xi, \eta)\, w(\xi, \eta)\right] d\xi\, d\eta \tag{41}$$

is the solution of equation (40), which satisfies the zero Cauchy conditions on B_0C_0, and therefore the function

$$u(x, y) = v(x, y) + w(x, y)$$

is the solution of equation (31), which satisfies the general Cauchy data

$$u(B) = f_1(y) \quad \text{and} \quad \left(\frac{\partial u}{\partial x}\right)_B = \varphi(x)$$

on B_0C_0.

Riemann presented a different method of solving the Cauchy problem, based on the adjoint equation (see [24]) but assuming the existence of the function R which he had not yet proved. In view of the fact that the Riemann method is based on the adjoint equation, it has the disadvantage that it requires assuming the differentiability of the coefficients, which is not necessary in the case of the above described method.

§ 4. The Picard problem

Consider a line L (line OP in Fig. 6) located in the domain bounded by two arbitrary characteristics of the equation

$$\frac{\partial^2 u}{\partial x\,\partial y} = F(x, y), \tag{42}$$

e.g. $x = 0$ and $y = 0$, and passing through their point of intersection. We assume that every line parallel in an interval to one of the characteristics, e.g. to the axis Ox, cuts L in one point only.

Consider the closed region Ω bounded by L, the characteristics Ox and the segment with ordinate PP'. The *Picard problem* for equation (42) consists in the determination of a function $u(x, y)$ continuous in Ω, which satisfies equation (42) at all points A of Ω and takes *a priori* prescribed values at points of the segment of the characteristics OP' and at points of the line L; namely, we require that

$$u(x, 0) = f(x), \quad u(B) = \varphi(y), \quad f(0) = \varphi(0), \tag{43}$$

where $f(x)$ is a known function possessing a continuous derivative in the interval $[0, p]$, and $\varphi(y)$ is a known function possessing a continuous derivative in the interval $[0, q]$.

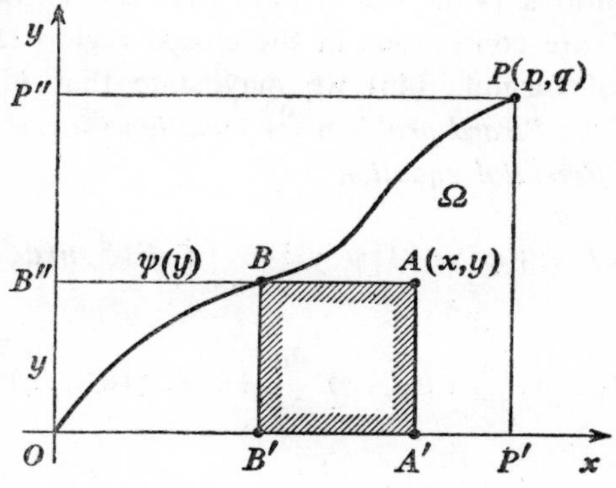

Fig. 6

Integrating equation (42) over the rectangle $ABB'A'$, we arrive at the relation

$$u(A) + u(B') - u(B) - u(A') = \iint_{ABB'A'} F(\xi, \eta)\, d\xi\, d\eta. \tag{44}$$

Thus, *if there exists a solution of the Picard problem for equation* (42), *it is unique and given by the formula*

$$U(x, y) = f(x) + \varphi(y) - f[\psi(y)] + \iint_{ABB'A'} F(\xi, \eta)\, d\xi\, d\eta, \tag{45}$$

where $\psi(y)$ is the abscissa of the point B of the line L, corresponding to ordinate y.

Assume that $\psi(y)$ is non-decreasing and has a continuous derivative in the interval $[0, q]$. Then, conversely, the function (45) satisfies the differential equation (42) in Ω and the Picard conditions (43) on the lines OP' and L; it is therefore, in fact, the only solution of the Picard problem.

Let us now solve the Picard problem for the general equation

$$\frac{\partial^2 u}{\partial x \, \partial y}$$

$$= \lambda \left[a(x, y) \frac{\partial u}{\partial x} + b(x, y) \frac{\partial u}{\partial x} + c(x, y) u(x, y) \right] + F(x, y), \quad (46)$$

i.e. we proceed to find the solution of this equation in Ω, which satisfies conditions (43). We assume that the known functions a, b, c and F are continuous in the closed region Ω.

In view of formula (45) we may state that *if there exists a solution of the Picard problem for equation* (46), *then it satisfies the integro-differential equation*

$$u(x, y) = f(x) + \varphi(y) - f[\psi(y)] + \iint_{ABB'A'} F(\xi, \eta) \, d\xi \, d\eta +$$

$$+ \lambda \iint_{ABB'A'} \left[a(\xi, \eta) \frac{\partial u}{\partial \xi} + b(\xi, \eta) \frac{\partial u}{\partial \eta} + c(\xi, \eta) u(\xi, \eta) \right] d\xi \, d\eta \, . \quad (47)$$

The solution of this equation can be derived by the method of successive approximation, which is equivalent to the solution in the form of a sum of a power series in the parameter λ:

$$u(x, y) = u_0(x, y) + \sum_{n=1}^{\infty} \lambda^n u_n(x, y), \quad (48)$$

where

$$u_0(x, y) = f(x) + \varphi(y) - f[\psi(y)] + \iint_{ABB'A'} F(\xi, \eta) \, d\xi \, d\eta$$

and where the terms $u_n(x, y)$ are given by the recursive formula

$$u_{n+1}(x, y) = \iint_{ABB'A'} \left[a(\xi, \eta) \frac{\partial u_n}{\partial \xi} + b(\xi, \eta) \frac{\partial u_n}{\partial \eta} + c(\xi, \eta) u_n(\xi, \eta) \right] d\xi \, d\eta .$$

It can be proved, as before, that the series (48) and the series of derivatives

$$\frac{\partial u_0}{\partial x} + \sum_{n=1}^{\infty} \lambda^n \frac{\partial u_n}{\partial x} \quad \text{and} \quad \frac{\partial u_0}{\partial y} + \sum_{n=1}^{\infty} \lambda^n \frac{\partial u_n}{\partial y}$$

are absolutely and uniformly convergent, i.e. that the sum of series (48) is the unique solution of the integro-differential equation (47) and, consequently, it is the unique solution of the considered Picard problem.

We do not present the proof since, apart from computational difficulties, it can easily be carried out.

Let us mention a modified Picard problem which consists in the determination of a function $u(x, y)$ satisfying equation (46) in Ω, taking on the characteristics Ox prescribed values $u(x, 0) = f(x)$, and satisfying at points B of L an *a priori* known linear relation

$$\alpha(y) \left(\frac{\partial u}{\partial x} \right)_B + \beta(y) \left(\frac{\partial u}{\partial y} \right)_B + \gamma(y) u_B = f(y)$$

between the value of the function and its derivative. This problem was solved by means of the Riemann Function by G. MAJCHER [28]; she reduced the problem to a Volterra integral equation.

§ 5. Vekua's method of investigation of elliptic equations

The Soviet mathematician I. N. VEKUA recently announced [83] a new method of deriving solutions of elliptic equations with analytic coefficients, based on the Riemann Function and Volterra integral equations in the complex variable.

Consider an elliptic equation

$$E(u) = \frac{\partial^2 u}{\partial x^2} + \frac{\partial^2 u}{\partial y^2} + a(x, y)\frac{\partial u}{\partial x} + b(x, y)\frac{\partial u}{\partial y} + c(x, y)u$$
$$= f(x, y). \qquad (49)$$

We assume that the functions of two real variables $a(x, y)$, $b(x, y)$, $c(x, y)$ and $f(x, y)$ are defined and continuous in a region Ω, and that they are analytic functions in this region, i.e. they can be expanded as the double series

$$\sum_{m,n=0}^{\infty} \alpha_{mn}(x-x_0)^m (y-y_0)^n$$

which are absolutely convergent in the neighbourhood of every interior point (x_0, y_0) of Ω. The known functions a, b, c and f can be extended analytically to the region of the complex variables $x = x_1 + ix_2$ and $y = y_1 + iy_2$, and then we obtain functions of two complex variables $a(x, y)$, $b(x, y)$, $c(x, y)$ and $f(x, y)$ which are holomorphic in certain regions $x \in D, y \in D'$.

Introduce now two new independent variables

$$z = x + iy, \quad \zeta = x - iy, \qquad (50)$$

which are conjugate for real values of x and y only; thus we have also

$$x = \frac{1}{2}(z+\zeta), \quad y = \frac{1}{2i}(z-\zeta). \qquad (51)$$

Consider the operators

$$\frac{\partial}{\partial z} = \frac{1}{2}\left(\frac{\partial}{\partial x} - i\frac{\partial}{\partial y}\right), \quad \frac{\zeta}{\partial \zeta} = \frac{1}{2}\left(\frac{\partial}{\partial x} + i\frac{\partial}{\partial y}\right). \qquad (52)$$

They can be applied to any differentiable function of two variables, but the result of the operation is the derivative only when the function to which the operators (52) are applied is holomorphic with respect to the two variables in a certain region.

By means of operators (52) we transform the Laplacian of the holomorphic function $u(x, y)$ to the second mixed derivative

$$\frac{\partial^2 u}{\partial x^2}+\frac{\partial^2 u}{\partial y^2}=4\frac{\partial^2 u}{\partial z\,\partial \zeta}.$$

Thus, owing to the introduction of the new complex variables (50) the elliptic equation (49) takes the form

$$\hat{F}(u)=\frac{\partial^2 u}{\partial z\,\partial \zeta}+A(z,\zeta)\frac{\partial u}{\partial z}+B(z,\zeta)\frac{\partial u}{\partial \zeta}+C(z,\zeta)u = F(z,\zeta), \qquad (53)$$

where

$$\begin{aligned} A(z,\zeta)&=\frac{1}{4}\left[a\left(\frac{z+\zeta}{2},\frac{z-\zeta}{2i}\right)+ib\left(\frac{z+\zeta}{2},\frac{z-\zeta}{2i}\right)\right],\\ B(z,\zeta)&=\frac{1}{4}\left[a\left(\frac{z+\zeta}{2},\frac{z-\zeta}{2i}\right)-ib\left(\frac{z+\zeta}{2},\frac{z-\zeta}{2i}\right)\right],\\ C(z,\zeta)&=\frac{1}{4}c\left(\frac{z+\zeta}{2},\frac{z-\zeta}{2i}\right),\\ F(z,\zeta)&=\frac{1}{4}f\left(\frac{z+\zeta}{2},\frac{z-\zeta}{2i}\right). \end{aligned} \qquad (54)$$

The functions A, B, C, and F are also holomorphic with respect to variables z and ζ in a domain $[z\in D_1, \zeta\in D_1']$, and we assume that D_1 and D_1' are simply-connected domains.

Equation (53) is formally of the same form as a hyperbolic equation and by reducing the elliptic equation (49) to this form Vekua was able to make use of the methods of investigation of hyperbolic equations in the theory of elliptic equations with analytic coefficients.

In our considerations we shall use the equation

$$\hat{F}^*(v) = \frac{\partial^2 v}{\partial z\,\partial \zeta} - \frac{\partial (Av)}{\partial z} - \frac{\partial (Bv)}{\partial \zeta} + Cv = F_1(z, \zeta), \tag{55}$$

which is called *adjoint* to equation (53). The operator $\hat{F}$ and the adjoint operator $\hat{F}^*$ have the fundamental property

$$v\hat{F}(u) - u\hat{F}^*(v) = \frac{\partial}{\partial z}\left(v\frac{\partial u}{\partial \zeta} + Auv\right) + \frac{\partial}{\partial \zeta}\left(-u\frac{\partial v}{\partial z} + Buv\right) \tag{56}$$

for two arbitrary holomorphic functions $u(z, \zeta)$ and $v(z, \zeta)$ in the domain $[D_1, D_1']$.

We now present the definition of the Riemann Function for equation (53) in accordance with the classical method, which is now more convenient and was impossible in the foregoing considerations which were based on weaker assumptions, excluding the existence of the adjoint equation. By the *Riemann Function* for the equation

$$\hat{F}(u) = 0 \quad \text{or} \quad \hat{E}(u) = 0$$

we mean the function of four complex variables $G(z, \zeta; t, \tau)$, holomorphic in the domain

$$[z \in D_1,\ \zeta \in D_1',\ t \in D_1,\ \tau \in D_1'], \tag{57}$$

which, at all points of this domain, satisfies the adjoint homogeneous equation

$$\hat{F}^*[G] = \frac{\partial^2 G}{\partial z\,\partial \zeta} - \frac{\partial (AG)}{\partial z} - \frac{\partial (BG)}{\partial \zeta} + CG = 0 \tag{58}$$

with respect to the variables z and ζ, for fixed parameters t and τ, and the following conditions:

$$\begin{aligned} G(t, \zeta; t, \tau) &= \exp\Big[\int_\tau^\zeta A(t, \eta)\, d\eta\Big], \\ G(z, \tau; t, \tau) &= \exp\Big[\int_t^z B(\xi, \tau)\, d\xi\Big]. \end{aligned} \tag{59}$$

We now write equation (58) in the form

$$\frac{\partial^2}{\partial z\,\partial \zeta}\Big[G(z,\zeta;t,\tau)-\int_\tau^\zeta A(z,\eta)\,G(z,\eta;t,\tau)\,d\eta-$$

$$-\int_t^z B(\xi,\zeta)\,G(\xi,\zeta;t,\tau)\,d\xi+$$

$$+\int_t^z\int_\tau^\zeta C(\xi,\eta)\,G(\xi,\eta;t,\tau)\,d\xi\,d\eta\Big]=0, \quad (60)$$

which leads to the integral equation

$$G(z,\zeta;t,\tau)-\int_\tau^\zeta A(z,\eta)\,G(z,\eta;t,\tau)\,d\eta-$$

$$-\int_t^z B(\xi,\zeta)\,G(\xi,\zeta;t,\tau)\,d\xi+$$

$$+\int_t^z\int_\tau^\zeta C(\xi,\eta)\,G(\xi,\eta;t,\tau)\,d\xi\,d\eta=1, \quad (61)$$

since in view of conditions (59) the expression in parenthesis on the left-hand side of equation (60) is equal to unity when $\zeta=\tau$ and $z=t$.

The integral equation (61) is of Volterra type and its solution can be obtained in the usual way by expansion as a power series, absolutely and uniformly convergent in the domain (57). Namely, the unique solution of the integral equation (61) has the form

$$G(z,\zeta;t,\tau)=1+\int_\tau^\zeta \Gamma_1(\zeta,z,\eta;t,\tau)\,d\eta+$$

$$+\int_t^z \Gamma_2(z,\zeta,\xi;t,\tau)\,d\xi+\int_t^z\int_\tau^\zeta \Gamma(z,\zeta;\xi,\eta;t,\tau)\,d\xi\,d\eta, \quad (62)$$

where Γ_1 and Γ_2 are the resolvent kernels of the kernels $A(z,\eta)$ and $B(\xi,\zeta)$ (t and τ are regarded as constant parameters) and therefore

$$\Gamma_1(\zeta,z,\eta;t,\tau)=\sum_{\nu=1}^{\infty} N_1^{(\nu)}(\zeta,z,\eta;t,\tau), \quad (63)$$

where

$$N_1^{(\nu)}(\zeta, z, \eta; t, \tau) = \int_\eta^\zeta N_1(\zeta, z, s; t, \tau) N_1^{(\nu-1)}(\zeta, z, s; t, \tau)\, ds,$$

$$N_1(\zeta, z, \eta; t, \tau) = N_1^{(1)} = A(z, \eta),$$

and

$$\Gamma_2(z, \zeta, \xi; t, \tau) = \sum_{\nu=1}^{\infty} N_2^{(\nu)}(z, \zeta, \xi; t, \tau), \tag{64}$$

where

$$N_2^{(\nu)}(z, \zeta, \xi; t, \tau) = \int_\xi^z N_2(z, \zeta, s; t, \tau) N_2^{(\nu-1)}(z, \zeta, s; t, \tau)\, ds,$$

$$N_2(z, \zeta, \xi; t, \tau) = N_2^{(1)} = B(\xi, \zeta).$$

Now, Γ is given by the formula

$$\Gamma(z, \zeta; \xi, \eta; t, \tau) = \Gamma_0(z, \zeta; \xi, \eta; t, \tau) + \int_\eta^\zeta \Gamma_1(\zeta, z, \eta_1, t, \tau) \Gamma_0(z, \eta_1; \xi, \eta, t, \tau)\, d\eta_1 + \int_\xi^z \Gamma_2(z, \zeta, \xi_1, t, \tau) \Gamma_0(\xi_1, \zeta; \xi, \eta, t, \tau)\, d\xi_1,$$

where

$$\Gamma_0(z, \zeta; \xi, \eta; t, \tau) = \sum_{\nu=1}^{\infty} N_0^{(\nu)}(z, \zeta; \xi, \eta; t, \tau),$$

$$N_0^{(\nu)}(z, \zeta; \xi, \eta; t, \tau) = \int_\xi^z \int_\eta^\zeta N_0(z, \zeta; s, \sigma) N_0^{(\nu-1)}(s, \sigma; \xi, \eta; t, \tau)\, ds\, d\sigma,$$

$$N_0^{(1)} = N_0(z, \zeta; \xi, \eta) = -C(\xi, \eta).$$

The unique solution G of equation (61) is a holomorphic function with respect to all arguments in the domain (57), which satisfies the adjoint equation (58) and conditions (59); thus it is the required Riemann Function.

Observe that conditions (59) are equivalent to the conditions

$$\begin{aligned} &\frac{\partial G}{\partial \zeta} - A(t, \zeta) G = 0, \quad \text{when} \quad z = 1, \\ &\frac{\partial G}{\partial z} - B(z, \tau) G = 0, \quad \text{when} \quad \zeta = \tau, \end{aligned} \tag{65}$$

$$G(t, \tau; t, \tau) = 1$$

or else to the conditions

$$\begin{aligned} &\frac{\partial G}{\partial \tau} + A(z, \tau) G = 0, \quad \text{when} \quad t = z, \\ &\frac{\partial G}{\partial t} + B(t, \zeta) G = 0, \quad \text{when} \quad \tau = \zeta, \end{aligned} \tag{65'}$$

$$G(z, \zeta; z, \zeta) = 1.$$

Taking into account property (58) of the Riemann Function, we obtain from identity (56) the relation

$$G(z, \zeta; t, \tau) \hat{F}(u)$$

$$= \frac{\partial}{\partial z}\left[G\left(\frac{\partial u}{\partial \zeta} + Au\right)\right] + \frac{\partial}{\partial \zeta}\left[u\left(BG - \frac{\partial G}{\partial z}\right)\right] \tag{66}$$

true for every function $u(z, \zeta)$ holomorphic in the domain $[D_1, D_1']$. This relation yields

$$\frac{\partial^2 (uG)}{\partial z \, \partial \zeta} = \frac{\partial}{\partial z}\left[u\left(\frac{\partial G}{\partial \zeta} - AG\right)\right] + \frac{\partial}{\partial \zeta}\left[u\left(\frac{\partial G}{\partial z} - BG\right)\right] +$$

$$+ G(z, \zeta; t, \tau) \hat{F}[u(z, \zeta)].$$

If in this relation we now exchange the pairs (z, ζ) and (t, τ) and integrate both sides of the new relation with respect to t in the interval (z_0, z), and with respect to τ in the interval (ζ_0, ζ), then making use of (65), we obtain

$$u(z, \zeta) = u(z_0, \zeta_0)\, G(z_0, \zeta_0; z, \zeta) +$$

$$+ \int_{z_0}^{z} G(t, \zeta_0; z, \zeta) \left[\frac{\partial u(t, \zeta_0)}{\partial t} + B(t, \zeta_0)\, u(t, \zeta_0) \right] dt +$$

$$+ \int_{\zeta_0}^{\zeta} G(z_0, \tau; z, \zeta) \left[\frac{\partial u(z_0, \tau)}{\partial \tau} + A(z_0, \tau)\, u(z_0, \tau) \right] d\tau +$$

$$+ \int_{z_0}^{z} \int_{\zeta_0}^{\zeta} G(t, \tau; z, \zeta)\, \hat{F}[u(t, \tau)]\, d\tau\, dt, \tag{67}$$

where $z_0 \in D_1$, $\zeta_0 \in D'_1$.

If in relation (67), which is true for any function $u(z, \zeta)$ holomorphic in the domain $[D_1, D'_1]$, we set $u(z, \zeta) = G(z_0, \zeta_0; z, \zeta)$, then in accordance with property (65′) of the function G, we have

$$\int_{z_0}^{z} \int_{\zeta_0}^{\zeta} G(t, \tau; z, \zeta)\, \hat{F}[G(z_0, \zeta_0; z, \zeta)]\, d\tau\, dt = 0.$$

This at once implies that

$$\hat{F}[G(z_0, \zeta_0; z, \zeta)] = 0, \tag{68}$$

i.e. the Riemann Function $G(z_0, \zeta_0; z, \zeta)$ satisfies the initial equation (53) with respect to the second pair of variables. Thus we observe that the considered Riemann Function is equal to the foregoing Riemann Function defined without the adjoint equation, provided we exchange the pairs of variables

$$G(t, \tau; z, \zeta) = R(z, \zeta; t, \tau).$$

As in the domain of real variables, it can easily be proved that the integral

$$u_0(z, \zeta) = \int_{z_0}^{z} \int_{\zeta_0}^{\zeta} G(t, \tau; z, \zeta)\, F(t, \tau)\, d\tau\, dt \tag{69}$$

is a particular solution of the equation

$$\hat{F}(u) = \frac{\partial^2 u}{\partial z\, \partial \zeta} + A\frac{\partial u}{\partial z} + B\frac{\partial u}{\partial \zeta} + Cu = F(z, \zeta). \quad (70)$$

Further, in view of relation (67), we may state that if the function $u(z, \zeta)$, holomorphic in the domain $[D_1, D_1']$, satisfies equation (70) in this domain, then it can be expressed in terms of the Riemann Function in the form

$$u(z, \zeta) = \alpha G(z_0, \zeta_0; z, \zeta) + \int_{z_0}^{z} \Phi(t)\, G(t, \zeta_0; z, \zeta)\, dt +$$

$$+ \int_{\zeta_0}^{\zeta} \Phi_1(t)\, G(z_0, \tau; z, \zeta)\, d\tau + \int_{z_0}^{z}\int_{\zeta_0}^{\zeta} G(t, \tau; z, \zeta)\, F(t, \tau)\, d\tau\, dt, \quad (71)$$

where

$$\Phi(z) = \frac{\partial u(z, \zeta_0)}{\partial z} + B(z, \zeta_0)\, u(z, \zeta_0),$$

$$\Phi_1(\zeta) = \frac{\partial u(z_0, \zeta)}{\partial \zeta} + A(z_0, \zeta)\, u(z_0, \zeta),$$

$$\alpha = u(z_0, \zeta_0).$$

Conversely, if $\Phi(z)$ and $\Phi_1(\zeta)$ are two holomorphic functions arbitrarily prescribed in regions $z \in D_1$ and $\zeta \in D_1'$, respectively, then the function $u(z, \zeta)$, given by formula (71), satisfies equation (70) in the domain $[D_1, D_1']$. Consequently formula (71) represents all holomorphic solutions of equation (70) in this domain. Setting now in formula (71) $z = x + iy$ and $\zeta = x - iy$, we obtain an expression representing all holomorphic solutions of the elliptic equation

$$\frac{\partial^2 u}{\partial x^2} + \frac{\partial^2 u}{\partial y^2} + a(x, y)\frac{\partial u}{\partial x} + b(x, y)\frac{\partial u}{\partial y} + c(x, y)\, u = f(x, y) \quad (72)$$

in the domain $[x \in D_1, y \in D_1']$.

For applications it is important to obtain all real analytic solutions of (71) in the case when $a(x, y)$, $b(x, y)$, $c(x, y)$ and $F(x, y)$ take real values for real x and y.

It can be proved that the Riemann Function $G(t, \tau; z, \zeta)$ is real when we set $\tau = \bar{t}, \zeta = \bar{z}$. * Thus taking $\Phi_1(t)$ such that

$$\overline{\Phi_1(t)} = \Phi(t),$$

we arrive at a real solution of equation (71) in the form

$$u(x, y) = \alpha G(z_0, \bar{z}_0; z, \bar{z}) + \int_{z_0}^{z} \Phi(t) G(t, \bar{z}_0, z, \bar{z})\, dt +$$

$$+ \int_{\bar{z}_0}^{\bar{z}} \Phi_1(t) G(z_0, \tau; z, \bar{z})\, d\tau + \int_{z_0}^{z} \int_{\bar{z}_0}^{\bar{z}} G(t, \tau; z, \bar{z}) F(t, \tau)\, d\tau\, dt, \quad (73)$$

where α is an arbitrary real constant. This solution can also be written in the form

$$u(x, y) = \alpha G(z_0, \bar{z}_0; z, \bar{z}) +$$

$$+ \operatorname{Re}\left[\int_{z_0}^{z} \Phi(t) G(t, \bar{z}_0; z, \bar{z})\, dt\right] + \int_{z_0}^{z} \int_{\bar{z}_0}^{\bar{z}} G(t, \tau; z, \bar{z}) F(t, \tau)\, d\tau\, dt. \quad (74)$$

Of special interest are the applications of the above results presented by Vekua in the quoted paper to the solution of boundary-value problems. They are, however, connected with singular integral equations and therefore will be considered in Part 3.

* The bar denotes the complex conjugate value.

ROMAN SIKORSKI

APPENDIX

Schauder's Fixed Point Theorem

We shall now present the proofs of the fixed point theorems in Banach spaces, which were employed in this monograph.

THEOREM 1. *Let W be a closed, compact and convex subset of the Banach space X. For an arbitrary continuous transformation f of the set W into itself, there exists a point $x \in W$ such that $f(x) = x$.*

THEOREM 2. *Let W be a closed convex subset of the Banach space X and f a continuous transformation of W into itself. If the set $f(W)$ (i.e. the set of all points $f(x)$ for which $x \in W$) is compact, then there exists a point $x \in W$ such that $f(x) = x$.*

The point x in the space X which satisfies relation $f(x) = x$ is called a *fixed point* of transformation f.

Theorem 1 was proved by SCHAUDER [77]. A remark that Theorem 1 can be stated in a somewhat more general form of Theorem 2 we owe to MAZUR [29].

The proof of Theorems 1 and 2 is based on a topological theorem on the fixed point, which for our purpose it is convenient to state in the following form.

BROUWER'S THEOREM. *Suppose that V is a closed, bounded, convex subset of n-dimensional Euclidean space. For an arbitrary continuous transformation φ of the set V into itself there exists a point $x \in V$ such that $\varphi(x) = x$.*

We adopt Brouwer's Theorem without proof, since the method of the proof is based on a special topological device and differs considerably from the methods used in this book (see [25], p. 238). We omit also the proof of certain simple geometric properties of convex sets in Euclidean space which will be of further use.

The proof of the Schauder Theorem will be preceded by a few lemmas and remarks.

We say that points $x_0, x_1, \ldots, x_n$ of a Banach space are *linearly independent* if the relation

$$\mu_0 x_0 + \mu_1 x_1 + \ldots + \mu_n x_n = 0,$$

where $\mu_0, \mu_1, \ldots, \mu_n$ are real numbers and $\mu_0 + \mu_1 + \ldots + \mu_n = 0$, occurs only when $\mu_0 = \mu_1 = \ldots = \mu_n = 0$.

Otherwise we say that the points $x_0, x_1, \ldots, x_n$ are *linearly dependent*.

If the points $x_0, x_1, \ldots, x_n$ are linearly independent, and the points $x, x_0, x_1, \ldots, x_n$ are linearly dependent, then there exist real numbers $\lambda_0, \lambda_1, \ldots, \lambda_n$, such that

$$x = \lambda_0 x_0 + \lambda_1 x_1 + \ldots + \lambda_n x_n \tag{1}$$

and $\lambda_0 + \lambda_1 + \ldots + \lambda_n = 1$. The numbers $\lambda_0, \lambda_1, \ldots, \lambda_n$ are uniquely determined.

In fact, from the linear dependence of the points $x, x_0, x_1, \ldots, x_n$ it follows that there exists a system of numbers $\mu, \mu_0, \mu_1, \ldots, \mu_n$, at least one of which does not vanish, such that

$$\mu x + \mu_0 x_0 + \mu_1 x_1 + \ldots + \mu_n x_n = 0,$$

$$\mu + \mu_0 + \mu_1 + \ldots + \mu_n = 0.$$

The coefficient μ is different from zero. For when $\mu = 0$ at least one of the numbers $\mu_0, \mu_1, \ldots, \mu_n$ is different from zero and $\mu_0 x_0 + \mu_1 x_1 + \ldots + \mu_n x_n = 0$, $\mu_0 + \mu_1 + \ldots + \mu_n = 0$, contrary to the assumption of the linear independence of the points $x_0, x_1, \ldots, x_n$.

Setting $\lambda_i = -\mu_i/\mu$ we obtain relation (1).

If at the same time relation (1) is valid and, moreover,

$$x = \lambda'_0 x_0 + \lambda'_1 x_1 + \ldots + \lambda'_n x_n \quad (\lambda'_0 + \lambda'_1 + \ldots + \lambda'_n = 0).$$

then, subtracting we have

$$(\lambda_0 - \lambda'_0) x_0 + (\lambda_1 - \lambda'_1) x_1 + \ldots + (\lambda_n - \lambda'_n) x_n = 0$$

and

$$(\lambda_0 - \lambda'_0) + (\lambda_1 - \lambda'_1) + \ldots + (\lambda_n - \lambda'_n) = 0.$$

Thus, in view of the linear independence of the points $x_0, x_1, \ldots$ $\ldots, x_n$, we have $\lambda_0 = \lambda_0', \lambda_1 = \lambda_1', \ldots, \lambda_n = \lambda_n'$ which implies that the coefficients $\lambda_0, \lambda_1, \ldots, \lambda_n$ in expansion (1) are uniquely determined.

The smallest convex set containing the considered points $x_0, x_1, \ldots, x_n$ of the Banach space X is the set of all points

$$x = \lambda_0 x_0 + \lambda_1 x_1 + \ldots + \lambda_n x_n,$$

where

$$\lambda_0 + \lambda_1 + \ldots + \lambda_n = 1 \quad \text{and} \quad \lambda_i \geqq 0 \quad \text{for} \quad i = 1, 2, \ldots, n.$$

If points $x_0, x_1, \ldots, x_n$ are linearly independent, then the smallest convex set containing these points is called the *n-dimensional simplex* with vertices $x_0, x_1, \ldots, x_n$.

We say that two n-dimensional simplexes Δ and Δ' *do not overlap* when, either they are disjoint or have $r+1$ common vertices $x_0, x_1, \ldots, x_r$ ($r \geqq 0$), and the common part $\Delta\Delta'$ of Δ and Δ' is an r-dimensional simplex with vertices $x_0, x_1, \ldots, x_r$.

LEMMA 1. *Let W_0 be the smallest convex set containing the points $\xi_0, \xi_1, \ldots, \xi_s$ of the Banach space X and let n denote the maximum number of linearly independent points among $\xi_0, \xi_1, \ldots$ $\ldots, \xi_s$. For any number $\delta > 0$ the set W_0 can be represented as a sum of a finite number of non-overlapping n-dimensional simplexes with diameter $< \delta$.*

Assume that the points $\xi_0, \xi_1, \ldots, \xi_n$ are linearly independent and that

$$\xi_j = \alpha_{j0}\xi_0 + \alpha_{j1}\xi_1 + \ldots + \alpha_{jn}\xi_n \quad (\alpha_{j0} + \alpha_{j1} + \ldots + \alpha_{jn} = 1)$$

for $n < j \leqq s$. Every point $x \in W_0$ is a linear combination of the points

$$x = \lambda_0\xi_0 + \lambda_1\xi_1 + \ldots + \lambda_n\xi_n \quad (\lambda_0 + \lambda_1 + \ldots + \lambda_n = 1). \tag{2}$$

With the point $x \in W_0$ given by (2) we associate the point $y = g(x) = (\lambda_1, \lambda_2, \ldots, \lambda_n)$ in the n-dimensional Euclidean space.

The set $V = g(W_0)$ of all points $g(x)$ where $x \in W_0$ is the smallest convex set containing the points

$$\eta_0 = (0, 0, \dots, 0) = g(\xi_0),$$
$$\eta_1 = (1, 0, \dots, 0) = g(\xi_1),$$
$$\eta_2 = (0, 1, 0, \dots, 0) = g(\xi_2),$$
$$\dots\dots\dots\dots\dots\dots$$
$$\eta_n = (0, 0, \dots, 0, 1) = g(\xi_n)$$

and the points

$$\eta_j = (\alpha_{j1}, \alpha_{j2}, \dots, \alpha_{jn}) = g(\xi_j) \quad (n < j \leqq s).$$

The transformation g is one to one, since every point $x \in W_0$ can be represented in the form (2) in only one way. The inverse transformation h associating with the point $y \in V$ a point $x \in W_0$ such that $y = g(x)$, i.e. the transformation

$$h[(\lambda_1, \lambda_2, \dots, \lambda_n)] = [1-(\lambda_1+\lambda_2+\dots+\lambda_n)]\, x_0+\lambda_1 x_1+\dots+\lambda_n x_n, \tag{3}$$

is uniformly continuous, since it is continuous and defined on a closed and bounded subset V of Euclidean space. Thus, there exists a number δ_0, such that

$$\|h(y_1)-h(y_2)\| < \delta, \quad \text{if} \quad \|y_1-y_2\| < \delta_0. \tag{4}$$

The convex set V can be represented as a sum of a finite number of non-overlaping n-dimensional simplexes $\Delta_1', \Delta_2', \dots$ $\dots, \Delta_r'$ with diameter $< \delta_0$. The sets

$$\Delta_j = h(\Delta_j') \quad (j = 1, 2, \dots, r)$$

are n-dimensional non-overlapping simplexes in the Banach space X and $W_0 = \Delta_1+\Delta_2+\dots+\Delta_r$. It follows from (4) that the diameter of each of the simplexes $\Delta_1, \Delta_2, \dots, \Delta_r$ is smaller than δ.

LEMMA 2. *Let W_0 be the smallest convex set containing the points $\xi_0, \xi_1, \dots, \xi_s$ of the Banach space X. For an arbitrary continuous transformation F of the set W_0 into itself there exists a point $x \in W_0$, such that $F(x) = x$.*

Let V, g and h have the same meaning as in the proof of Lemma 1. The continuous transformation $\varphi(y) = g\{F[h(y)]\}$ maps the closed, bounded, convex subset V on n-dimensional Euclidean space into V. It follows from the Brouwer Theorem that there exists a point $y_0 \in V$ such that $\varphi(y_0) = y_0$. The point $x_0 = h(y_0) \in W_0$ satisfies the equation $F(x_0) = x_0$.

A subset Z of the Banach space X is called *completely bounded* if, for every $\varepsilon > 0$, there exists a finite sequence of points $\xi_0, \xi_1, \ldots, \xi_s \in Z$ such that every point $x \in Z$ is distant from a point ξ_j by less than ε.

It can easily be verified that the set Z is completely bounded if and only if for every $\varepsilon > 0$ there exists a finite decomposition of the set Z, $Z = A_0 + A_1 + \ldots + A_s$ into sets A_j with diameter less than ε.

In fact, selecting from each of the sets A_j a point ξ_j, we obtain a sequence of points $\xi_0, \xi_1, \ldots, \xi_s$ such that for every $x \in Z$ the inequality $\|x - \xi_j\| < \varepsilon$ is true for some number j (namely, for such that $x \in A_j$).

Conversely, if $\xi_0, \xi_1, \ldots, \xi_s \in Z$ is a sequence of points such that every point $x \in Z$ is distant from a point ξ_j by less than $\varepsilon/3$, then defining A_j as the set of points $x \in Z$ distant from ξ_j by less then $\varepsilon/3$, we obtain a decomposition of the set Z into sets A_j $(j = 0\,1, \ldots, s)$ with diameter smaller than ε.

LEMMA 3. *In order that a subset Z of the Banach space X be relatively compact (i.e. that every infinite sequence $\{x_n\}, x_n \in Z$, has a subsequence converging to a point $x \in X$) it is necessary and sufficient that it be completely bounded**.

Assume that the set Z is completely bounded. Let $x_n \in Z$, $n = 1, 2, \ldots$, and let $Z = A_{k1} + A_{k2} + \ldots A_{km_k}$ be a decomposition of the set Z into the sum of sets with diameter $< 1/k$, $k = 1, 2, \ldots$

Since $Z = A_{11} + A_{12} + \ldots + A_{1m}$ at least one of the sets A_{1j} contains infinitely many terms of the sequence $\{x_n\}$. Thus, there exists a subsequence $\{x_{1n}\}$ of the sequence $\{x_n\}$ such that $\|x_{1n} - x_{1n'}\| < 1$ for $n, n' = 1, 2, \ldots$

* This lemma holds not only for a Banach space but also for an arbitrary complete metric space.

Continuing this procedure, we arrive at an infinite sequence of infinite sequences

$$\{x_{1n}\}, \{x_{2n}\}, \{x_{3n}\}, \ldots, \tag{5}$$

such that the sequence $\{x_{k+1,n}\}$ is a subsequence of sequence $\{x_{kn}\}$ and

$$\|x_{kn} - x_{kn'}\| < \frac{1}{k} \quad (n, n' = 1, 2, \ldots). \tag{6}$$

The sequence $\{x_{nn}\}$ is a convergent subsequence of the sequence $\{x_n\}$. It is sufficient to verify that the sequence $\{x_{nn}\}$ satisfies the Cauchy condition. In fact, for $n, n' > k$ the terms x_{nn} and $x_{n'n'}$ appear in the sequence $\{x_{nn}\}$ and therefore, in view of (6), $||x_{nn} - x_{n'n'}|| < 1/k$ for $n, n' > k$.

From the assumption that Z is completely bounded, it follows that it is relatively compact.

Assume now that Z is not completely bounded. Consequently there exists $\varepsilon > 0$ such that for every finite sequence of points $\xi_1, \xi_2, \ldots, \xi_s \in Z$ there exists a point $x \in Z$ whose distance from every point ξ_j is greater than ε.

Let x_1 be an arbitrary point of the set Z. Thus, there exists a point $x_2 \in Z$ such that $||x_1 - x_2|| > \varepsilon$ and, moreover, there exists a point $x_3 \in Z$ such that $||x_1 - x_3|| > \varepsilon$ and $||x_2 - x_3|| > \varepsilon$.

Continuing this procedure, we arrive at an infinite sequence $\{x_n\}$, $x_n \in Z$, such that

$$\|x_n - x_m\| \geqq \varepsilon \quad \text{for} \quad n \neq m. \tag{7}$$

The sequence $\{x_n\}$ cannot contain any convergent subsequence (since a convergent subsequence would satisfy the Cauchy condition which contradicts (7)); consequently, Z is not relatively compact.

Proof of Theorem 1. Let f and W satisfy the assumptions of Theorem 1. It is sufficient to prove that for any number $\varepsilon > 0$ there exists a point $\bar{x} \in W$ such that

$$\|f(\bar{x}) - \bar{x}\| < \varepsilon. \tag{8}$$

In fact, taking $\varepsilon = 1/n$, $n = 1, 2, \ldots$, we infer that there exists a sequence $\{x_n\}$, $x_n \in W$, with the property that

$$\|f(x_n) - x_n\| < 1/n \quad (n = 1, 2, \ldots). \tag{9}$$

Since W is compact, the sequence $\{x_n\}$ contains a convergent subsequence $x_{mn} \to x$. It follows from (9) that

$$\|f(x) - x\| = \lim_{n \to \infty} \|f(x_{mn}) - x_{mn}\| = 0,$$

i.e. $f(x) = x$.

To prove (8), denote by $\omega(\delta)$ the oscillation of the transformation f, i.e.

$$\omega(\delta) = \sup_{\|x - x'\| < \delta} \|f(x) - f(x')\|.$$

Since f is continuous on the closed compact set W, it is uniformly continuous, i.e.

$$\omega(\delta) \to 0, \quad \text{when} \quad \delta \to 0.$$

Therefore, for a given $\varepsilon > 0$, there exists a number $\delta > 0$, such that

$$2\omega(\delta) + 3\delta < \varepsilon. \tag{10}$$

For this number $\delta > 0$ there exists, in view of Lemma 3, a finite sequence of points $\xi_0, \xi_1, \ldots, \xi_s \in W_0$ such that every point of the set W is distant from a point ξ_j by less than δ. Let W denote the smallest convex set containing all points $\xi_0, \xi_1, \ldots, \xi_s$. It follows from Lemma 1 that W_0 can be represented as a sum of a finite number of non-overlapping n-dimensional simplexes $W_0 = \Delta_1 + \Delta_2 + \ldots + \Delta_r$ with diameter smaller than δ.

Let $x_1, x_2, \ldots, x_m$ be the sequence consisting of all vertices of all simplexes Δ_j and p_j a number such that $\|\xi_{p_j} - f(x_j)\| < \delta$. Assume that $F(x_j) = \xi_{p_j}$. The transformation F defined so far for points $x_1, \ldots, x_m$ only, is now continued simplectically into the whole set W_0, i.e. if $x \in W_0$ belongs to the simplex Δ_j with vertices $x_{j_0}, x_{j_1}, \ldots, x_{j_n}$, i.e. if

$$x = \lambda_0 x_{j_0} + \lambda_1 x_{j_1} + \ldots + \lambda_n x_{j_n},$$

$$\lambda_0 + \lambda_1 + \ldots + \lambda_n = 1, \quad \lambda_j \geqq 0,$$

the value of the transformation F at the point x is the point

$$F(x) = \lambda_0 F(x_{j_0}) + \lambda_1 F(x_{j_1}) + \ldots + \lambda_n F(x_{j_n})$$
$$= \lambda_0 \xi_{p_{j_0}} + \lambda_1 \xi_{p_{j_1}} + \ldots + \lambda_n \xi_{p_{j_n}} \in W_0 . \tag{11}$$

From the definition of transformation F, it follows that

$$\|F(x_j) - f(x_j)\| < \delta \quad (j = 1, 2, \ldots, m). \tag{12}$$

Since F is a continuous transformation of the set W_0 into itself, it follows from Lemma 2 that there exists a point $x \in W_0$ such that $F(\bar{x}) = \bar{x}$.

The point $\bar{x}$ satisfies inequality (8). In fact, let Δ denote one of the simplexes $\Delta_1, \Delta_2, \ldots, \Delta_r$ containing the point $\bar{x}$. Let the points $\bar{x}_0, \bar{x}_1, \ldots, \bar{x}_n$ be the vertices of the simplex Δ. We have

$$\|f(\bar{x}) - \bar{x}\| = \|f(\bar{x}) - F(\bar{x})\|$$
$$\leqq \|f(\bar{x}) - f(\bar{x}_0)\| + \|f(\bar{x}_0) - F(\bar{x}_0)\| + \|F(\bar{x}_0) - F(\bar{x})\| .$$

Since the points $\bar{x}$ and $\bar{x}_0$ belong to the simplex Δ with diameter $< \delta$, we have $\|\bar{x} - \bar{x}_0\| < \delta$. Consequently, $\|f(\bar{x}) - f(\bar{x}_0)\| \leqq \omega(\delta)$.

It follows from (12) that $\|f(\bar{x}_0) - F(\bar{x}_0)\| < \delta$. Since

$$\bar{x} = \lambda_0 \bar{x}_0 + \lambda_1 \bar{x}_1 + \ldots + \lambda_n \bar{x}_n ,$$
$$\lambda_0 + \lambda_1 + \ldots + \lambda_n = 1, \qquad \lambda_j \geqq 0,$$

we have from definition (11)

$$F(\bar{x}) = \lambda_0 F(\bar{x}_0) + \lambda_1 F(\bar{x}_1) + \ldots + \lambda_n F(\bar{x}_n) =$$
$$= F(\bar{x}_0) + \lambda_1 [F(\bar{x}_1) - F(\bar{x}_0)] + \ldots + \lambda_n [F(\bar{x}_n) - F(\bar{x}_0)] .$$

Hence

$$\|F(\bar{x}) - F(\bar{x}_0)\| \leqq \lambda_1 \|F(\bar{x}_1) - F(\bar{x}_0)\| + \ldots + \lambda_n \|F(\bar{x}_n) - F(\bar{x}_0)\| .$$

From (12) and the inequality $\|\bar{x}_j - \bar{x}_0\| < \delta$ it follows that

$$\|F(\bar{x}_j) - F(\bar{x}_0)\| \leqq \|F(\bar{x}_j) - f(\bar{x}_j)\| +$$
$$+ \|f(\bar{x}_j) - f(\bar{x}_0)\| + \|f(\bar{x}_0) - F(\bar{x}_0)\| \leqq \delta + \omega(\delta) + \delta ,$$

and consequently

$$\|F(\bar{x})-F(\bar{x}_0)\| \leqq (\lambda_1+\ldots+\lambda_n)(2\delta+\omega(\delta)) \leqq 2\delta+\omega(\delta).$$

Thus finally

$$\|f(\bar{x})-\bar{x}\| \leqq \omega(\delta)+\delta+(2\delta+\omega(\delta)) < \varepsilon.$$

This completes the proof.

LEMMA 4. *The smallest closed convex set V containing the compact set Z of the Banach space X is compact* [17].

The smallest convex set containing Z is the set W_1 of all points y of the form

$$\begin{aligned} y &= \lambda_0 x_0+\lambda_1 x_1+\ldots+\lambda_n x_n, \\ \lambda_0+\lambda_1+\ldots+\lambda_n &= 1, \quad \lambda_j \geqq 0, \end{aligned} \tag{13}$$

where $x_0, x_1, \ldots, x_n \in Z$. The set V is the closure of the set W_1.

It suffices to prove (cf. Lemma 3) that V is completely bounded.

Let ε be a given positive number. Since set Z is compact, Lemma 3 implies the existence of points $\eta_1, \eta_2, \ldots, \eta_r \in Z$ such that every point of Z is distant from one of the points η_j by less than $\varepsilon/3$.

Let W_0 denote the smallest convex set containing all points $\eta_1, \eta_2, \ldots, \eta_r$. W_0 is also completely bounded (cf. Lemma 1), and consequently there exist points $\xi_1, \xi_2, \ldots, \xi_s \in W_0$ such that every point $y_0 \in W_0$ is distant from a point $\xi_1, \xi_2, \ldots, \xi_s$ by less than $\varepsilon/3$.

We now prove that every point $x \in V$ is distant from a point $\xi_1, \xi_2, \ldots, \xi_s$ by less than ε.

In fact, let $y \in W_1$ be a point of the form (13) such that $\|x-y\| < \varepsilon/3$. Further, let j_i be a positive integer such that $\|x_i-\eta_{j_i}\| < \varepsilon/3, i = 0, 1, \ldots, \eta$, and suppose that $y_0 = \lambda_0 \eta_{j_0} +\lambda_1 \eta_{j_1}+\ldots+\lambda_n \eta_{j_n} \in W_0$. Also, let p be a positive integer such that $\|y_0-\xi_p\| < \varepsilon/3$.

Since $\|y-y_0\| < \lambda_0\|x_0-\eta_{j_0}\|+\lambda_1\|x_1-\eta_{j_1}\|+\ldots+\lambda_n\|x_n-\eta_{j_n}\| \leqq (\lambda_0+\lambda_1+\ldots+\lambda_n)\varepsilon/3$, we have $\|x-\xi_p\| \leqq \|x-y\|+\|y-y_0\|+ +\|y_0-\xi_p\| < \varepsilon$. This completes the proof.

Proof of Theorem 2. Suppose that W and f satisfy the conditions of Theorem 2. The set $Z = f(W)$ is compact. Lemma 4 implies that the smallest closed convex set V containing Z is compact. Evidently V is a subset of W, for W is a closed convex set containing Z, and V is the smallest set with this property. The transformation f maps V into itself. Replacing in Theorem 1, W by V, we find that there exists a point $x \in V$ (and hence certainly $x \in W$) such that $f(x) = x$.

PART 3

Properties of the Cauchy type integrals. Boundary problems in theory of analytic functions. Linear and non-linear singular integral equations

Translated by

Z. OLESIAK

CHAPTER XV

PROPERTIES OF THE CAUCHY TYPE INTEGRALS

§ 1. Definition of a Cauchy type integral

Let an open or closed arc L, possessing at each point $t = x+iy$ (together with its end points) a continuous tangent, be given on the complex plane. This means that the arc, called *smooth*, is determined by the functions of a parameter $x(\xi), y(\xi)$ the continuous derivatives of which are not simultaneously equal to zero. Then, the length of an arbitrary part of the arc between the points $t_1(\xi)$ and $t_2(\xi)$ is defined by the formula

$$s_{12} = \int_{\xi_1}^{\xi_2} \sqrt{x'^2(\xi)+y'^2(\xi)}\, d\xi . \tag{1}$$

It is well known that the inequality

$$0 < \chi \leqq \frac{|t_1 - t_2|}{s_{12}} \leqq 1 \tag{2}$$

holds for two arbitrary points t_1, t_2 of an arc L with distinct ends, where χ is a positive constant, smaller than 1.

Let us suppose that a given complex function $\varphi(t)$ of a complex variable t is defined and integrable on a directed arc L, i.e. that the limit

$$\lim \sum_{\nu=0}^{n} \varphi(\tau_\nu)(t_{\nu+1}-t_\nu) = \int_L \varphi(t)\, dt \tag{3}$$

exists when $\max |t_{\nu+1}-t_\nu| \to 0$. Moreover, this limit is independent of the choice of successive points $t_0, t_1, \ldots, t_\nu, \ldots, t_{n+1}$ on the arc L, as well as of the choice of the points τ_ν in each part $t_\nu\, t_{\nu+1}$;

here t_0 is the origin, while t_{n+1} is the terminal point of the directed arc L.

DEFINITION. *The integral*

$$\Phi(z) = \int_L \frac{\varphi(\tau)\,d\tau}{\tau - z} \tag{4}$$

is called a Cauchy type integral.

This integral has a definite value, as a regular integral, at each point of the complex plane except the points lying on the arc L.

Definition (4) can be extended to the case when L

$$L = L_1 + L_2 + \ldots + L_p$$

is the sum of p open or closed non-intersecting arcs $L_1, L_2, \ldots, L_p$. Namely, in this case, the integral (4) represents the sum of integrals in the sense (3) extended over all the arcs $L_1, L_2, \ldots, L_p$. The function $\varphi(\tau)$ which is the integrand of (4) is called *the density*. This name is given in connection with the potentials of a simple and a double layer.

The derivative of the function (4) is given by the formula

$$\Phi'(z) = \int_L \frac{\varphi(\tau)\,d\tau}{(\tau - z)^2} \tag{5}$$

valid at each point z which does not belong to L.

Thus, if L consists of open arcs, then the function $\Phi(z)$ defined by the Cauchy type integral (4) is holomorphic in the entire region of the complex plane lying outside the arcs L. This function obviously, for $z \to \infty$, tends uniformly to zero as $1/z$.

If L is a set of contours $L_1, L_2, \ldots, L_p$, then the function (4) is sectionally holomorphic in each of the disconnected regions into which the complex plane is divided by the curves L_1, $L_2, \ldots, L_p$.

It is a well known fact (Cauchy's Theorem) that if, on a contour L, the density $\varphi(\tau)$ assumes values equal to a certain function $f(z)$ holomorphic in the region D containing the contour

L, together with its interior W, then integral (4) equals $2\pi i f(z)$ at each point z inside the region W bounded by the contour L and is equal to zero at each point z lying in the external region $D-W$.

The investigations devoted to Cauchy integrals were commenced in the nineteenth century by a Russian mathematician SOKHOTZKI (1873) and by an Italian mathematician MORERA (1889). These investigations, however, did not attract due attention. The study of Cauchy integrals was renewed much later by a Yugoslavian mathematician PLEMELJ (1908) and by a Russian PRIVALOV (1918). More intensive study of Cauchy type integrals and their applications to applied mathematics and technology have been carried on since 1937. The most important achievements are due to a Georgian mathematician N. I. MUSKHELISHVILI [33] and his collaborators, the most well-known of whom is I. N. VEKUA. The properties of Cauchy type integrals play a fundamental rôle in the theory of singular integral equations and their applications.

§ 2. The values of the Cauchy integral on the path of integration

In order to define the meaning of integral (4) in the case when $z = t$ is a point lying on the arc of integration (except its ends), let us consider a circle K with centre t and a sufficiently small radius ρ such that circle intersects the arc L only at two points t' and t'' on both sides of the point t. If the part l lying inside the circle K is excluded from the arc L, then the Cauchy type integral (4) is regular and has a definite meaning over the exterior part, under the assumption of the ordinary integrability of the function $\varphi(t)$. The limit

$$\lim_{\rho\to 0} \int_{L-l_\rho} \frac{\varphi(\tau)\,d\tau}{\tau-t} = \int_{L} \frac{\varphi(\tau)\,d\tau}{\tau-t} = \Phi(t) \qquad (6)$$

is called the *Cauchy principal value* of integral (4) at the point t on the arc L (or the *singular integral in the Cauchy sense*) when the radius ρ of the circle K tends to zero. The limit (6) may not exist when the density $\varphi(t)$ is only integrable or even continuous. On the other hand, the existence of the limit (6) at the point t is ensured when the function $\varphi(t)$, integrable on the arc L, satisfies the Hölder condition in a certain neighbourhood of an internal point t on the arc L, i.e. when it satisfies the following inequality

$$|\varphi(t)-\varphi(\tau)| < k|t-\tau|^h \quad (0 < h \leqq 1), \tag{7}$$

where τ is an arbitrary point of the arc L in a given neighbourhood of the point t, h denotes a positive constant exponent at most equal to unity, and k is a positive constant coefficient. In fact, let us decompose the integral over the arc $L-l_\rho$, outside the circle K, into the two integrals

$$\int\limits_{L-l_\rho} \frac{\varphi(\tau)\,d\tau}{\tau-t} = \int\limits_{L-l_\rho} \frac{\varphi(\tau)-\varphi(t)}{\tau-t}\,d\tau + \varphi(t)\int\limits_{L-l_\rho} \frac{d\tau}{\tau-t}. \tag{8}$$

On the basis of the assumption (7), the function under the first integral sign satisfies the inequality

$$\left|\frac{\varphi(\tau)-\varphi(t)}{\tau-t}\right| < \frac{k}{|\tau-t|^{1-h}}, \tag{9}$$

and it thus has a weak singularity for $\tau \to t$. We are thus assured of the existence of the improper absolutely convergent integral

$$\int\limits_{L} \frac{\varphi(\tau)-\varphi(t)}{\tau-t}\,d\tau.$$

The second of the integrals (8) can be expressed in the following manner:

$$\int\limits_{L-l_\rho} \frac{d\tau}{\tau-t} = [\log(\tau-t)]_a^{t'} + [\log(\tau-t)]_{t''}^{b}$$

$$= [\log(t'-t)-\log(a-t)] + [\log(b-t)-\log(t''-t)]. \tag{10}$$

For simplicity we have assumed that the line L consists of a single arc with origin a and terminal point b. In formula (10) an arbitrary branch of the logarithm is taken for the arc $\frown at$ and an arbitrary branch for the arc $\frown tb$. In order to connect the two branches of the logarithm, we assume that the branch $\log(\tau-t)$ on the arc $\frown at$ changes into the branch $\log(\tau-t)$ on the arc $\frown tb$ (with the exception of the point t) when the point τ encircles the arc $\frown t't''$ of the circle K leaving the point t on this side of the arc $\frown ab$ which corresponds to the direction of the imaginary axis with respect to the positive direction of the real axis (in Fig. 7 it denotes the left-hand side when the direction

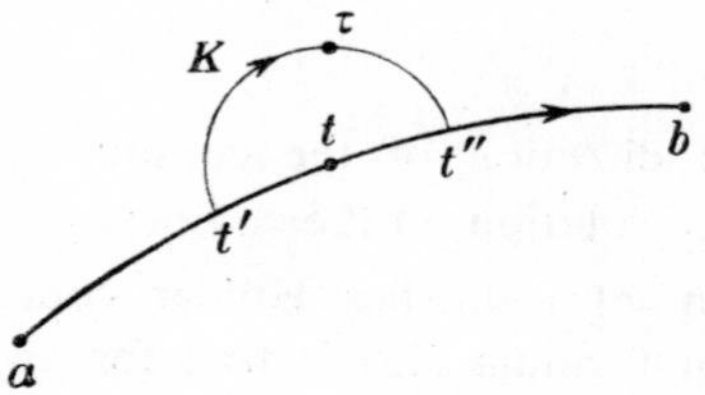

Fig. 7

of rotation from the real axis to the imaginary axis through a right angle is counterclockwise). If the radius ρ of the circle K tends to zero, we then obtain from formula (10) the limit

$$\lim_{\rho\to 0}\int\limits_{L-l_\rho}\frac{d\tau}{\tau-t} = +\pi i+\log\frac{b-t}{a-t}, \tag{11}$$

since $\log(\tau-t) = \log|\tau-t|+i\arg(\tau-t)$,and the difference between the arguments

$$\arg(t'-t)-\arg(t''-t)$$

tends to $+\pi$ as $\rho\to 0$.

Finally, under assumption (7), the improper integral in the Cauchy sense exists at the point t on the arc L and as a limit of integral (8) is expressed as follows:

$$\int\limits_L\frac{\varphi(\tau)\,d\tau}{\tau-t} = \int\limits_L\frac{\varphi(\tau)-\varphi(t)}{\tau-t}\,d\tau-\pi i\varphi(t)+\varphi(t)\log\frac{b-t}{a-t}. \tag{12}$$

It is evident that this integral is not absolutely convergent.

Formula (12) is also true when the line of integration L consists of several arcs, since the integrals over the arcs not containing the point t are regular.

As a particular case, when L is a contour (or a collection of contours) we assume that the point b in fomula (12) coincides with the point a. Thus we obtain

$$\int_L \frac{\varphi(\tau)\,d\tau}{\tau-t} = \pi i\varphi(\tau) + \int_L \frac{\varphi(\tau)-\varphi(t)}{\tau-t}\,d\tau, \qquad (13)$$

provided that the direction of the contour coincides with the positive direction of rotation on the complex plane.

If the function $\varphi(\tau)$ satisfies Hölder condition (7) on the whole line L, then formula (12) is true for any point t of this line except its end-points. For contours L formula (13) is valid at each point $t \in L$.

It is seen from formula (12) that when a point t on the arc $\frown ab$ tends to its origin a or terminal point b, then the integral (12) behaves like $\varphi(t)\log(a-t)$ or $\varphi(t)\log(b-t)$; thus it is as unbounded as the logarithm of the distance from the end-points (i.e. when $\varphi(t)$ is bounded and does not tend to zero).

As a particular case when the function $\varphi(\tau)$ is equal to zero, for example, at the origin of the arc $[\varphi(a) = 0]$, then integral (12) has a meaning at this point as an absolutely convergent integral of a weakly singular function, and it is the limit of integral (12) at the neighbouring point t on the arc L, when this point tends to the point a.

§ 3. Boundary values of the Cauchy type integral and the Plemelj formulae

We now consider the behaviour of values of the Cauchy type integral (4) at an external point z when this point tends to a point t on the line of integration L. This is expressed by the theorem:

Plemelj's Theorem. *If the density $\varphi(\tau)$ on a smooth line L satisfies the Hölder condition (7), then the value of the Cauchy integral at an external point z tends to the boundary values*

$$\begin{aligned} \lim_{z\to t} \Phi(z) &= \Phi^+(t) = \pi i \varphi(t) + \int_L \frac{\varphi(\tau)\,d\tau}{\tau - t}, \\ \lim_{z\to t} \Phi(z) &= \Phi^-(t) = -\pi i \varphi(t) + \int_L \frac{\varphi(\tau)\,d\tau}{\tau - t}, \end{aligned} \tag{14}$$

when the point z tends in an arbitrary way to the point t on the arc L (distinct from its ends). The first boundary value concerns the case when the point z tends to the point t from that side of the plane, with respect to the directed arc L, which corresponds to the half-plane $\operatorname{im} z > 0$ *with respect to the positive direction of the real axis. The second boundary value corresponds to the opposite side.*

If L is a set of positively directed contours, then the first boundary value $\varphi^+(t)$ relates to the value of the Cauchy integral inside the regions bounded by the contours L, while the second boundary value $\Phi^-(t)$ relates to the value in the outside region.

Proof. Assume, for the moment, for simplicity that the line of integration L is a single contour, and decompose the value of the Cauchy type integral (4) at the point z, which does not lie on the line L, in the following manner:

$$\Phi(z) = \int_L \frac{\varphi(\tau) - \varphi(t)}{\tau - z}\,d\tau + \varphi(t) \int_L \frac{d\tau}{\tau - z}. \tag{15}$$

It is evident that the second term in (15) is either equal to $2\pi i \varphi(t)$ or zero, depending on whether or not the point z lies inside the region bounded by the line L. Thus, it is sufficient to examine, for $z \to t$, the term

$$\Phi_1(z) = \int_L \frac{\varphi(\tau) - \varphi(t)}{\tau - z}\,d\tau. \tag{16}$$

We shall show that integral (16) tends to the value of the following improper integral

$$\Phi_1(t) = \int_L \frac{\varphi(\tau)-\varphi(t)}{\tau - t}\, d\tau \tag{17}$$

with weak singularity at the point t on the line L when the point z, in the internal or external region, tends in an arbitrary way to a point t on the line L:

$$\lim_{z\to t} \Phi_1(z) = \Phi_1(t). \tag{18}$$

We decompose integral (16) into two integrals,

$$\Phi_1(z) = \int_{t_1t_2} \frac{\varphi(\tau)-\varphi(t)}{\tau - z}\, d\tau + \int_{L-t_1t_2} \frac{\varphi(\tau)-\varphi(t)}{\tau - z}\, d\tau, \tag{19}$$

the first of which is taken over the arc $\frown t_1t_2$ which is a part of the line L containing the point t as an interior point while the second is taken over the remaining arc $L-\frown t_1t_2$. The second integral in (19) is continuous at the point t lying outside the arc of integration $L-\frown t_1t_2$. Thus, it suffices to examine the first integral in (19):

$$\Psi(z) = \int_{t_1t_2} \frac{\varphi(\tau)-\varphi(t)}{\tau - z}\, d\tau \tag{20}$$

We shall show that for this integral we get

$$\lim_{z\to t} \Psi(z) = \Psi(t) = \int_{t_1t_2} \frac{\varphi(\tau)-\varphi(t)}{\tau - t}\, d\tau \tag{21}$$

when the point z tends in an arbitrary way to the point t on the arc $\frown t_1t_2$. Here the property (21) is not only true when the point t lies inside the arc $\frown t_1t_2$, but also when it concides with one of the end-points t_1 or t_2.

First, let us assume that the point z tends to the point t on the arc $\frown t_1t_2$ along the straight line D_0 which forms an acute or right angle $\alpha \neq 0$ with the tangent at the point t. Let D_1 and

D_2 denote the lines parallel to the straight line D_0 passing through the ends of the arc t_1t_2 (Fig. 8). We assume that the arc $\frown t_1t_2$ is so small that each line D parallel to the straight line D_0 lying between the straight lines D_1 and D_2 intersects the arc $\frown t_1t_2$ at one point τ only, and that the tangent at this point of inter-

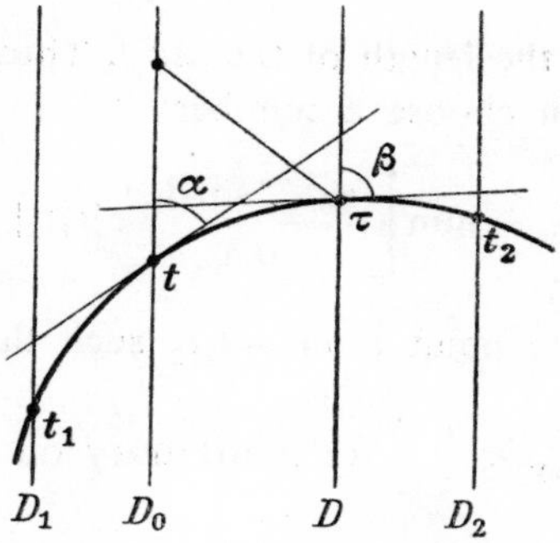

Fig. 8

section forms with the straight line D an acute angle β which in the neighbourhood of the value α is not smaller than a certain acute angle $\beta_0 \neq 0$. Hence it follows that the chord joining the point t with an arbitrary point τ of the arc $\frown t_1t_2$ forms with the straight line D_0 an acute angle which is not smaller than $\beta_0 > 0$, in such a way that

$$\frac{|z-\tau|}{|\tau-t|} \geqq \sin\beta_0 . \tag{22}$$

Property (21) will be proved in an analogous way, as in the classical theory of potential. Thus, let $l = \frown t_1' t_2'$ denote a part of the arc $\frown t_1 t_2$ containing the point t in its interior when this point is an interior point of the arc $\frown t_1t_2$. In the remaining case the point t is the common end-point of the arcs l and $\frown t_1t_2$.

We now decompose the integral (20) into the sum of two integrals,

$$\Psi(z) = \Psi^l(z) + \Psi^{t_1t_2-l}(z), \tag{23}$$

taken over the arc $l = \frown t_1' t_2'$ and over the remaining part $\frown t_1 t_2 - l$, respectively. For the first integral in the sum (23), taking into account the inequalities (2), (7), (22), we obtain

$$|\Psi^l(z)| < \frac{k}{\chi^{1-h}\sin\beta_0} \int_l \frac{d\sigma}{|\sigma - s|^{1-h}} \leqq \frac{k}{\chi^{1-h}\sin\beta_0 \,.\, h} |l|^h, \tag{23^{I}}$$

where $|l|$ denotes the length of the arc l. Thus, for an arbitrary positive ε one can choose a number

$$\lambda_\varepsilon = \min\left[\frac{\varepsilon\chi^{1-h}\sin\beta_0}{3kh}, |t_1 t_2|\right] \tag{23^{II}}$$

independent of the point t on $\frown t_1 t_2$ such that

$$|\Psi^l_{(z)}| < \frac{\varepsilon}{3} \qquad (z \text{ is arbitrary on } D_0)$$

where the length of the arc l is equal to λ_ε ($|t_1\, t_2|$ denotes the length of the arc $\frown t_1 t_2$).

Note that the point t lies outside the arc $\frown t_1 t_2 - l$ and therefore the second term in the sum (23) is continuous at this point. Thus, having established the length λ_ε of the arc l, we can let z tend to t on such a way that the second term of the sum (23) will differ from the value

$$\Psi^{t_1 t_2 - l}(t) = \int_{t_1 t_2 - l} \frac{\varphi(\tau) - \varphi(t)}{\tau - t}\, d\tau$$

by less than $\varepsilon/3$. In order to estimate this difference more accurately we express it as follows:

$$\Psi^{t_1 t_2 - l}(z) - \Psi^{t_1 t_2 - l}(t) = (z - t) \int_{t_1 t_2 - l} \frac{\varphi(\tau) - \varphi(t)}{(\tau - z)(\tau - t)}\, d\tau. \tag{23^{III}}$$

Let us assume that the point t is the centre of the arc $l = \frown t_1' t_2'$ (i.e. that the lengths of the arcs $\frown t_1' t$ and $\frown t t_2'$ are equal) when the length of the shorter of the arcs $\frown t_1 t$ and $\frown t t_2$ is not smaller than $\lambda_\varepsilon/2$ or when the lengths of the two arcs are equal. Thus, for each point $t \in \frown t_1 t_2$ the following inequality holds:

$$|\Psi^{t_1t_2-l}(z) - \Psi^{t_1t_2-l}(t)| < \frac{k|z-t|}{\chi^{2-h}\sin\beta_0} \int\limits_{t_1t_2-l} \frac{d\sigma}{|\sigma - s|^{2-h}}$$

$$< \frac{2^{1-h}k|z-t|}{\chi^{2-h}\sin\beta_0(1-h)\lambda_\varepsilon^{1-h}} \quad (h < 1). \quad (23^{\mathrm{IV}})$$

Hence we conclude that the inequality

$$|\Psi(z) - \Psi(t)|$$

$$\leqq |\Psi^l(z)| + |\Psi^l(t)| + |\Psi^{t_1t_2-l}(z) - \Psi^{t_1t_2-l}(t)| \leqq \varepsilon \quad (23^{\mathrm{V}})$$

has to be satisfied when

$$|z-t| \leqq \frac{\chi^{2-h}\sin\beta_0(1-h)\lambda_\varepsilon^{1-h}}{3\cdot 2^{1-h}k}\,\varepsilon. \quad (23^{\mathrm{VI}})$$

It is worth noting that the right-hand side of the above written inequality depends on ε and on β_0, but does not depend on the point t of the arc $\frown t_1 t_2$. This result confirms that the boundary property (21) is true when the point z tends to the point t along the straight line D_0; moreover, it tends uniformly with respect to the point $t \in \frown t_1 t_2$ for a fixed parameter $\beta_0 > 0$.

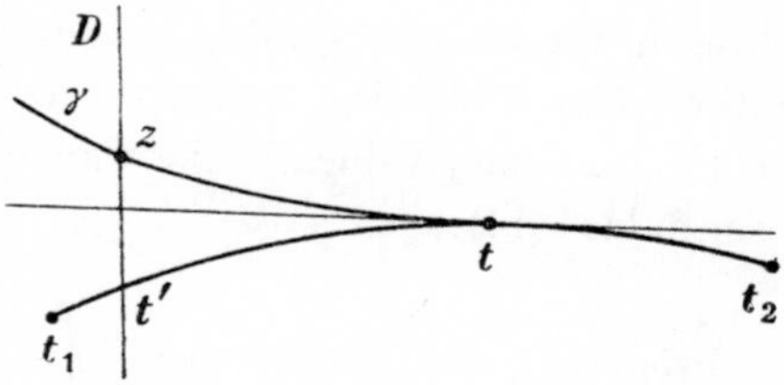

Fig. 9

Let us now assume that the point z tends to the point t along the line γ which is the tangent to the arc $\frown t_1 t_2$ at the point t (Fig. 9). We now draw the line D through *a* point $z \in \gamma$ in a sufficiently small neighbourhood of the point t, so that it forms an angle $\alpha > \beta_0$ with the tangent at the point t. Here t' denotes the point of the intersection of the straight line D with the arc $\frown t_1 t_2$. Then we have

$$\Psi(z)-\Psi(t)=[\Psi(z)-\Psi(t')]+[\Psi(t')-\Psi(t)].$$

Since $t' \to t$ when $z \to t$ and since the property (23^{V}) is independent of the choice of t, the boundary property (21) follows.

Taking into account the properties (23) and equalities (13) and (15), we deduce that the proposition (14) of the Plemelj Theorem is true for contours. Hence, it follows immediately that the boundary property (14) is true when L is a set of non-intersecting contours.

If L is a non-closed arc $\frown ab$ (or a set of such arcs), i.e. if $a \neq b$, then we complete this arc to the smooth contour $L+L'$ by the arc L' which joins points a and b but has no other points common with the arc L; next, we extend the function $\varphi(\tau)$ in an arbitrary continuous way to the arc L'. The property (14) holds for the Cauchy type integral taken over the contour $L+L'$ at each point t, distinct from the points a and b, of the arc L. Since the part of the integral extended over the complementary arc L' is regular and continuous at the point t, property (14) is true for the Cauchy type integral extended over a non-closed arc $L = ab$ *at each internal point.*

Formulae (14) are called *the Plemelj formulae* [41] and are analogous to those on the boundary values of potential of double surface distribution. The following formulae for the sum and the difference of the boundary values of the Cauchy type integral follows from formulae (14):

$$\Phi^+(t)-\Phi^-(t)=2\pi i\varphi(t), \quad \Phi^+(t)+\Phi^-(t)=2\int_L \frac{\varphi(\tau)\,d\tau}{\tau-t}. \tag{24}$$

If the density $\varphi(\tau)$ is assumed only to be continuous on the arcs L, then the Cauchy type integral

$$\Phi(z)=\int_L \frac{\varphi(\tau)\,d\tau}{\tau-t} \tag{24'}$$

may not possess a limit when a point z, external with respect to L, tends to a certain point on the arcs L. We are able to prove (see Muskhelishvili's monograph [33], p. 44) the following boundary property

$$\lim_{z', z'' \to t} [\Phi(z') - \Phi(z'')] = 2\pi i \varphi(t) \tag{24''}$$

which holds for the difference of the values of the function (24') at two points z' and z'' lying on a straight line which passes through an internal point t of the arcs L, on both sides of the point at equal distances from it ($|z'-t| = |z''-t|$). Moreover, it is assumed that the vector $\overrightarrow{z'z''}$ is not tangent to the line L at the point t.

§ 4. The Plemelj–Privalov Theorem

A certain regularity of the continuity of the Cauchy type integrals on the line of integration is shown by an important theorem due to PRIVALOV [1]. We first give it for contours.

The PRIVALOV THEOREM (I). *If a complex function $\varphi(\tau)$, defined on a smooth contour L, satisfies the Hölder condition*

$$|\varphi(\tau) - \varphi(\tau_1)| < k|\tau - \tau_1|^h, \tag{25}$$

then the values of the Cauchy singular integral

$$\Phi(t) = \int_L \frac{\varphi(\tau)\, d\tau}{\tau - t} \tag{26}$$

at points t of the line of integration satisfy Hölder's condition in the form

$$|\Phi(t) - \Phi(t_1)| < Ck|t - t_1|^h \quad (0 < h < 1) \tag{27}$$

where h is the same exponent as for the density (25) (*for* $h < 1$), *whereas a condition of the form*

$$|\Phi(t) - \Phi(t_1)| < C'k|t - t_1|^\theta \quad (h = 1) \tag{27'}$$

where θ denotes an arbitrary positive number smaller than 1 *(for $h = 1$). Here C and C' are certain positive constants independent of the function φ but dependent on the shape of the line L; the constant C' also depends on the choice of the constant exponent θ.*

Proof. Write, according to formula (13),

$$\Phi(t) = \pi i \varphi(t) + \Psi(t) \tag{28}$$

where

$$\Psi(t) = \int_L \frac{\varphi(\tau) - \varphi(t)}{\tau - t} \, d\tau . \tag{29}$$

Thus, it is sufficient to prove that the integral (29) with weak singularity satisfies the Hölder condition.

Let t and t_1 denote two arbitrary points on the contour L. It suffices to examine the case when $|t - t_1| \leqq \delta$, where δ is a positive constant sufficiently small such that the circle K, with centre t and radius $2|t - t_1|$, intersects the line L at two points t' and t'' only. If $|t - t_1| > \delta$, then selecting suitable constants C and C' we can always satisfy the conditions (27) or (27'). We now decompose the integral (29) into two integrals

$$\Psi(t) = \Psi^l(t) + \Psi^{L-l}(t) \tag{30}$$

over the arc $l = \frown t' t''$ lying inside the circle K and over the external part $L - l$. Similarly, we decompose the integral referring to the point t_1:

$$\Psi(t_1) = \Psi^l(t_1) + \Psi^{L-l}(t_1) . \tag{30'}$$

For the integrals over the arc l we have the inequalities

$$|\Psi^l(t)| < \int_l \frac{k\, dl_\tau}{|\tau - t|^{1-h}}, \qquad |\Psi^l(t_1)| < \int_l \frac{k\, dl_\tau}{|\tau - t_1|^{1-h}} . \tag{31}$$

In view of inequality (2), the integrals are of the same order as the radius of the circle K to the h-th power, i.e. there exists a positive constant c, depending only on the shape of the line L, only such that the following inequalities hold:

$$|\Psi^l(t)| < ck|t - t_1|^h, \qquad |\Psi^l(t_1)| < ck|t - t_1|^h . \tag{32}$$

For the difference of the integrals (30) and (30′) taken over the external arc $L-l$ we obtain the expression

$$\Psi^{L-l}(t)-\Psi^{L-l}(t_1)$$

$$=\int_{L-l}\frac{\varphi(t_1)-\varphi(t)}{\tau-t}\,dt+\int_{L-l}[\varphi(\tau)-\varphi(\tau_1)]\left[\frac{1}{\tau-t}-\frac{1}{\tau-t_1}\right]d\tau$$

$$=[\varphi(t_1)-\varphi(t)]\int_{L-l}\frac{d\tau}{\tau-t}+(t-t_1)\int_{L-l}\frac{\varphi(\tau)-\varphi(t_1)}{(\tau-t)(\tau-t_1)}\,d\tau. \tag{33}$$

It is evident that the absolute value of the first part of the last sum is less than a product of the form const $k\,|t-t_1|^h$. We now estimate the second component

$$I=(t-t_1)\int_{L-l}\frac{\varphi(\tau)-\varphi(t_1)}{(\tau-t)(\tau-t_1)}\,d\tau, \tag{34}$$

which is a regular integral, since the singular points do not belong to the line of integration $L-l$.

For points on the arc $L-l$ we obviously have

$$\frac{2}{3}\leqq\frac{|\tau-t|}{|\tau-t_1|}\leqq 2; \tag{35}$$

hence, using condition (25), we obtain

$$|I|\leqq 2^{1-h}k\,|t-t_1|\int_{L-l}\frac{dl_\tau}{|\tau-t|^{2-h}}.$$

Because of inequality (2), there exist positive constants c' and c'' depending on L such that the inequality

$$|I|\leqq c'k\,|t-t_1|\int_{c''|t-t_1|}^{\Lambda}\frac{dl_\tau}{l_\tau^{2-h}} \tag{36}$$

is satisfied; here l_τ denotes the length of the variable arc $\frown t\tau$, while Λ is the total length of the arc L. The following estimate

$$|I| < c''' k |t-t_1|^h \tag{37}$$

follows from the inequality (36) for $h < 1$, and for $h = 1$ we have the estimate

$$|I| < c''' k |t-t_1| \left|\log|t-t_1|\right| < c_1''' k |t-t_1|^\theta, \tag{37'}$$

c''' and c_1''' being certain positive constants, and the exponent θ is an arbitrarily chosen positive number smaller than 1. Combining results (32), (37) and (37′) we obtain the statement (27), (27′) of Privalov's Theorem.

In view of numerous applications in the Theory of Singular Integral Equations and the Theory of Functions of Complex Variables, Privalov's Theorem is of great importance. We particularly emphasize the behaviour of the Hölder exponent h when it is smaller than 1, and the proportionality of the Hölder coefficient in inequality (27) to the Hölder coefficient k for the density $\varphi(\tau)$.

Remark. If L is a non-closed arc $\frown ab$, then completing it to a contour $L+L_1$ by means of the arc L_1 and extending the function $\varphi(\tau)$ continuously over this arc, we draw the conclusion that the Cauchy integral along the arc L also satisfies the Hölder condition (27) or (27′), however not on the whole arc L, but on an arbitrary part $\frown a'b'$ which, with its end-points, is interior to L. In fact, it is sufficient to notice that the integral over the arc L_1 possesses a derivative at each point of the internal arc $\frown a'b'$, and hence, the integral satisfies Lipschitz condition on the arc $\frown a'b'$. It should be noted that now the constant coefficients C and C' appearing in inequalities (27) and (27′), depending on the arc $\frown a'b'$ may now be unbounded, since the end-points a' and b' tend to the corresponding end-points a and b of the arc of integration. This property will be discussed in detail in the last chapter. Here we give a certain generalization of Privalov's Theorem when the integrand depends on a parameter.

THEOREM II. *If a complex function* $\varphi(\tau, u)$ *of two variables is defined in a domain*

$$\tau \in L, \quad u \in \Pi$$

(where Π *is a certain region or a line in the complex plane) and satisfies Hölder's condition with respect to both variables,*

$$|\varphi(\tau, u) - \varphi(\tau_1, u_1)| < k_\varphi[|\tau - \tau_1|^h + |u - u_1|^\mu],$$

$0 < h < 1, 0 < \mu \leqq 1$, *then the singular generalized Cauchy type integral*

$$\Phi(t, u) = \int_L \frac{\varphi(\tau, u)\, d\tau}{\tau - t} \tag{38}$$

satisfies the inequality

$$|\Phi(t, u)| < \pi M_\varphi + C' k_\varphi \tag{39}$$

and Hölder's condition with respect to both variables, that is

$$|\Phi(t_1, u_1) - \Phi(t, u)| < C k_\varphi[|t - t_1|^h + |u - u_1|^{\mu_1}], \tag{40}$$

where $\mu_1 < \mu$ *is an arbitrary positive constant less than* μ, M_φ *denotes the upper bound of the function* $|\varphi(\tau, u)|$, C *is a positive constant depending on the line* L *and on the choice of* μ_1, *and* C' *is an upper bound of the integral* $\int_L |\tau - t|^{h-1} d\tau$.

Proof. The Hölder condition with respect to the variable t follows from the preceding theorem. In order to prove the property with respect to the variable u, we write, as before

$$\Phi(t, u) = \pi i \varphi(t, u) + \Psi(t, u)$$

where

$$\Psi(t, u) = \int_L \frac{\varphi(\tau, u) - \varphi(t, u)}{\tau - t}\, d\tau. \tag{41}$$

Hence, inequality (39) follows immediately. It suffices to examine integral (41) with respect to the parameter u. Thus we have

$$\Psi(t, u) - \Psi(t, u_1) = I$$

$$= \int_L \frac{[\varphi(\tau, u) - \varphi(t, u)] - [\varphi(\tau, u_1) - \varphi(t, u_1)]}{\tau - t}\, d\tau. \tag{42}$$

Let us decompose integral (42) into two parts,

$$I = I^l + I^{L-l},$$

taken over the part l of the arc L and the remaining part $L-l$.

We assume that the length of the arc is equal to $|u_1 - u|$ and that the point t is the point of the arc dividing it into two parts of equal length. It may always be assumed that the number $|u_1 - u|$ is smaller than the length of the contour L. Then, according to inequality (2), we obtain

$$|I^l| < 2k_\varphi \int_l \frac{dl_\tau}{|\tau - t|^{1-h}} < ck_\varphi \int_0^{1/2|u_1-u|} \frac{d\sigma}{\sigma^{1-h}}$$

$$< \frac{c}{2^h h} k_\varphi |u_1 - u|^h, \tag{43}$$

where the constant c depends only on the line L.

For the integral taken over the external part $L-l$, we obtain the obvious inequality

$$|I^{L-l}| < 2k_\varphi |u - u_1|^\mu \int_{L-l} \frac{dl_\tau}{\tau - t}. \tag{44}$$

The last integral, however, is comparable with the logarithm of the length of the arc l, and hence we have

$$|I^{L-l}| < 2k_\varphi |u - u_1|^\mu [c' \log |u - u_1| + c''] \tag{45}$$

where c' and c'' are two positive constants depending on L.

Combining inequalities (43) and (45) we obtain the statement (40) of theorem.

We remark that both of the above theorems are also valid for integrals taken over a finite set L of smooth disjoint contours.

Theorem II is also true in a particular case, important in applications, when $u = t$ and $\Pi = L$.

§ 5. Poincaré–Bertrand transformation formula for iterated singular integrals

An integral of the form

$$F(t) = \int_{L(\tau_1)} \frac{N_1(t, \tau_1)}{\tau_1 - t} \left[\int_{L(\tau)} \frac{N(\tau_1, \tau)}{\tau - \tau_1} d\tau \right] d\tau_1 \tag{46}$$

is called an *iterated singular integral*. Here L is a smooth contour in the complex plane, and $N_1(t, \tau_1)$, $N(\tau_1, \tau)$ are two prescribed functions in the domains

$$\tau_1 \in L, \quad \tau \in L, \quad t \in L,$$

satisfying the Hölder conditions

$$\begin{aligned} |N(\tau_1, \tau) - N(\tau_1', \tau')| &< \text{const}\,[|\tau_1 - \tau_1'|^{\mu} + |\tau - \tau'|^{\mu}], \\ |N_1(t, \tau_1) - N_1(t', \tau_1')| &< \text{const}\,[|t - t'|^{\mu} + |\tau_1 - \tau_1'|^{\mu}], \end{aligned} \tag{47}$$

where $0 < \mu \leqq 1$.

It is known from the preceding theorems that the first integral

$$I(\tau_1) = \int_{L(\tau)} \frac{N(\tau_1, \tau)\, d\tau}{\tau - \tau_1} \tag{48}$$

is defined and satisfies the Hölder's condition on the line L with exponent μ' and arbitrarily fixed μ:

$$|I(\tau_1) - I(\tau_1')| < \text{const}\, |\tau_1 - \tau_1'|^{\mu'}. \tag{49}$$

Hence, it again follows that the iterated integral (46)

$$F(t) = \int_{L(\tau_1)} \frac{N_1(t, \tau_1) I(\tau_1)}{\tau_1 - t} d\tau_1 \tag{50}$$

is defined and satisfies the Hölder's condition on the line L with exponent $\mu' < \mu$:

$$|F(t) - F(t')| < \text{const}\, |t - t_1|^{\mu'}. \tag{51}$$

Let us change the order of integration in expression (46), i.e. consider the integral

$$\Phi(t) = \int_{L(\tau)} \left[\int_{L(\tau_1)} \frac{N_1(t, \tau_1) N(\tau_1, \tau)}{(\tau_1 - t)(\tau - \tau_1)} d\tau_1 \right] d\tau. \tag{52}$$

We shall show that under the assumptions (47) the above integral exists. Making use of the identity

$$\frac{1}{(\tau_1-t)(\tau-\tau_1)}=\frac{1}{\tau-t}\left(\frac{1}{\tau_1-t}+\frac{1}{\tau-\tau_1}\right),$$

we may write

$$\Phi(t)=\int\limits_{L(\tau)}\frac{f(t,\tau,t)-f(t,\tau,\tau)}{\tau-t}\,d\tau, \tag{52'}$$

where

$$f(t,\tau,\theta)=\int\limits_{L(\tau_1)}\frac{N_1(t,\tau_1)\,N(\tau_1,\tau)}{\tau_1-\theta}\,d\tau_1. \tag{52''}$$

According, however, to Privalov's Theorem, the function (52″) satisfies Hölder's condition with respect to the variable θ with exponent $\mu'<\mu$. Thus the integrand in (52′), as the result of internal integration (52), satisfies the inequality

$$\left|\frac{f(t,\tau,t)-f(t,\tau,\tau)}{\tau-t}\right|<\frac{\text{const}}{|\tau-t|^{1-\mu'}}, \tag{52'''}$$

and the integral (52) is meaningful as an integral of weak singularity.

It has been proved that the integral (52) is not necessarily equal to the integral (46), i.e. the following equality holds:

$$F(t)=\Phi(t)-\pi^2 N(t,t)\,N_1(t,t). \tag{53}$$

This equality is called *Poincaré–Bertrand transformation of an iterated integral.* It was first proved by Poincaré in the case when the line of integration L is an interval of the real axis and the functions N, N_1 are holomorphic in certain regions in the neighbourhood of the line of integration. The transformation (53) was considered by POINCARÉ [70] in connection with a certain boundary problem of the ebb and flow of the tide.

Afterwards, BERTRAND [2] proved the validity of transformation (53) for a contour, also assuming that the functions $N(\tau_1,\tau)$ and $N(t,\tau_1)$ are holomorphic in a certain strip Ω containing the line of integration L. This proof, analogous to Poincaré's proof, being an excellent application of the calculus of residues, will be given below in a form somewhat simplified by the author.

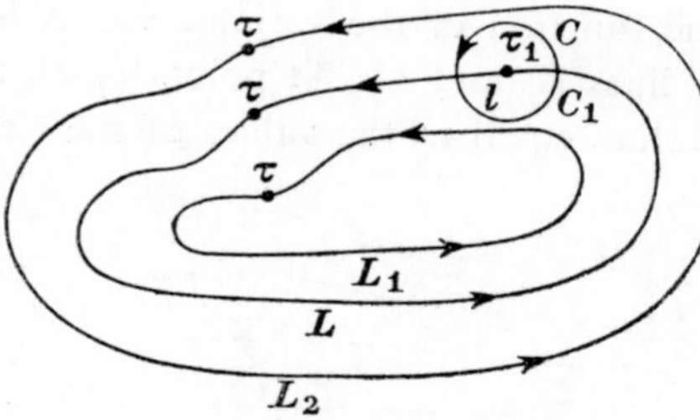

Fig. 10

Let us assume that the prescribed functions $N(\tau_1, \tau)$ and $N_1(t, \tau)$ are holomorphic in a strip Ω containing the line L. We first show that the Cauchy principal value of the first integral (48) at the point τ_1 on the line of integration L is equal to half of the sum of regular integrals taken over the contours L_1 and L_2 lying in the strip Ω on both sides of the line L (Fig. 10):

$$\int_L \frac{N(\tau_1, \tau)\, d\tau}{\tau-\tau_1} = \frac{1}{2}\int_{L_1} \frac{N(\tau_1, \tau)\, d\tau}{\tau-\tau_1} + \frac{1}{2}\int_{L_2} \frac{N(\tau_1, \tau)\, d\tau}{\tau-\tau_1}. \quad (54)$$

In fact, we have according to elementary properties of holomorphic functions

$$2\int_{L-l} \frac{N(\tau_1, \tau)\, d\tau}{\tau-\tau_1} + \int_{C+C'} \frac{N(\tau_1, \tau)\, d\tau}{\tau-\tau_1}$$
$$= \int_{L_1} \frac{N(\tau_1, \tau)\, d\tau}{\tau-\tau_1} + \int_{L_2} \frac{N(\tau_1, \tau)\, d\tau}{\tau-\tau_1}.$$

Here the semicircles C and C' of the circle with the centre at τ_1 are oppositely directed, and l denotes the arc of the line L lying inside the circle. It can readily be shown that the sum of the integrals over the semicircles C and C' tends to zero together with their radius, and hence in the limit we get equality (54).

Note that the sum of the integrals

$$\tilde{I}(\tau_1) = \frac{1}{2}\int\limits_{L_1} \frac{N(\tau_1, \tau)\,d\tau}{\tau-\tau_1} + \frac{1}{2}\int\limits_{L_2} \frac{N(\tau_1, \tau)\,d\tau}{\tau-\tau_1} \tag{55}$$

is a holomorphic function of the variable τ_1 inside of the strip bounded by the lines L_1 and L_2. At points τ_1 on the line L the function takes values equal to the values of the Cauchy singular

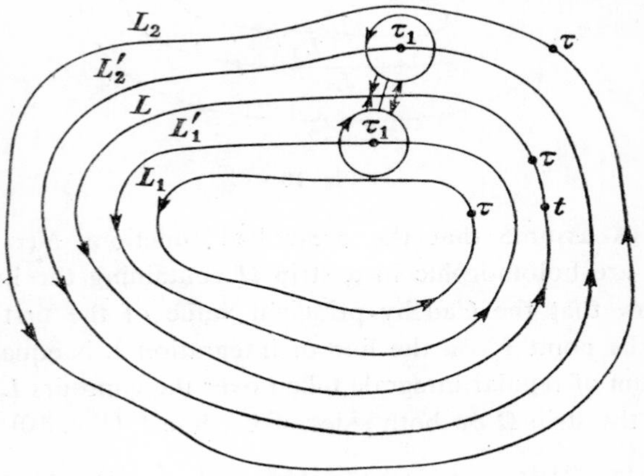

Fig. 11

integral (48). On the basis of this property the result of the second integration (46) with respect to the variable τ_1 can be represented as follows

$$F(t) = \int\limits_{L} \frac{N_1(t, \tau_1) I(\tau_1)}{\tau_1 - t}\, d\tau_1$$

$$= \frac{1}{2}\int\limits_{L'_1} \frac{N_1(t, \tau_1)\tilde{I}(\tau_1)}{\tau_1 - t}\, d\tau_1 + \frac{1}{2}\int\limits_{L'_2} \frac{N_1(t, \tau_1)\tilde{I}(\tau_1)}{\tau_1 - t}\, d\tau_1, \tag{56}$$

where L'_1 and L'_2 are contours lying on opposite sides of the line L (Fig. 11) in the strip bounded by lines L_1 and L_2, and the point t lies on the line L. Making use of equality (55) the value (56) of the singular integral can be represented in the form of the sum of integrals:

$$F(t)$$

$$=\frac{1}{4}\left[\iint\limits_{L_1L_1'}+\iint\limits_{L_1L_2'}+\iint\limits_{L_2L_1'}+\iint\limits_{L_2L_2'}\right]\frac{N_1(t,\tau_1)N(\tau_1,\tau)}{(\tau_1-t)(\tau-\tau_1)}\,d\tau_1\,d\tau. \quad (57)$$

The four iterated integrals in (57) are regular and the order of integration is irrelevant.

Applying the theorem on residues, the integral along lines L_1 and L_2 can be expressed by an integral along the line L as follows:

$$\begin{aligned}
&\int\limits_{L_1}\frac{N(\tau_1,\tau)\,d\tau}{\tau-\tau_1}=\int\limits_{L}\frac{N(\tau_1,\tau)\,d\tau}{\tau-\tau_1}-2\pi iN(\tau_1,\tau_1) \quad (\tau_1\in L_1'),\\
&\int\limits_{L_1}\frac{N(\tau_1-\tau)\,d\tau}{\tau-\tau_1}=\int\limits_{L}\frac{N(\tau_1,\tau)\,d\tau}{\tau-\tau_1} \quad (\tau_1\in L_2'),\\
&\int\limits_{L_2}\frac{N(\tau_1,\tau)\,d\tau}{\tau-\tau_1}=\int\limits_{L}\frac{N(\tau_1,\tau)\,d\tau}{\tau-\tau_1}+2\pi iN(\tau_1,\tau_1) \quad (\tau_1\in L_2'),\\
&\int\limits_{L_2}\frac{N(\tau_1,\tau)\,d\tau}{\tau-\tau_1}=\int\limits_{L}\frac{N(\tau_1,\tau)\,d\tau}{\tau-\tau_1} \quad (\tau_1\in L_1').
\end{aligned} \quad (58)$$

Substituting expressions (58) into formula (57) we obtain

$$\begin{aligned}
F(t)=\frac{1}{2}\left[\iint\limits_{L\,L_1'}+\iint\limits_{L\,L_2'}\right]&\frac{N_1(t,\tau_1)N(\tau_1,\tau)}{(\tau_1-t)(\tau-\tau_1)}\,d\tau_1\,d\tau-\\
&-\frac{1}{2}\pi i\int\limits_{L_1'}\frac{N_1(t,\tau_1)N(\tau_1,\tau)\,d\tau_1}{\tau_1-t}+\\
&+\frac{1}{2}\pi i\int\limits_{L_2'}\frac{N_1(t,\tau_1)N(\tau_1,\tau)\,d\tau}{\tau_1-t}.
\end{aligned} \quad (59)$$

Hence, again applying the theorem on residues to the difference between the integrals over lines L_1' and L_2', we obtain

$$F(t) = \int_L J(t, \tau)\, d\tau - \pi^2 N(t, t) N_1(t, t) \tag{60}$$

where we have used the notation

$$J(t, \tau) = \frac{1}{2} \int_{L_1' + L_2'} \frac{N_1(t, \tau_1) N(\tau_1, \tau)\, d\tau_1}{(\tau_1 - t)(\tau - \tau_1)}. \tag{61}$$

Thus the function defined by the integral (61) is *holomorphic* with respect to both variables t, τ in the strip between the lines L_1', L_2' and takes values equal to the internal singular integral in formula (52) when the points τ and t lie on the line L. Thus, the function (61) is bounded when the difference $\tau - t$ tends to zero, and the iterated integral is meaningful. Moreover, only the first integral with respect to the variable τ_1 is singular, while the second integral with respect to the variable τ is regular.

In view of equality (60) the relation (53) of Poincaré and Bertrand is proved for holomorphic functions.

Under less restrictive assumptions (47) for the functions N and N_1, equality (53) for iterated integrals is also true, but then, as we have seen, the function (61) obtained as the result of a change in the order of integration in unbounded when $\tau - t \to 0$ and it possesses a weak singularity estimated by inequality (52″). We omit the proof of this theorem referring the reader to an excellent monograph of MUSKHELISHVILI [33] (pp. 56-60).*

From the Poincaré transformation (53) the conclusion can be drawn that the iterated integrals

$$\int_{L(\tau_1)} \frac{N_1(t, \tau_1)}{\tau_1 - t} \left[\int_{L(\tau)} \frac{N(\tau_1, \tau)\, d\tau}{|\tau - \tau_1|^\alpha} \right] d\tau_1$$

$$= \int_{L(\tau)} \left[\int_{L(\tau_1)} \frac{N_1(t, \tau_1) N(\tau_1, \tau)}{(\tau_1 - t)|\tau - \tau_1|^\alpha}\, d\tau_1 \right] d\tau, \tag{62}$$

* The transformation of singular iterated integrals in space under less restrictive assumptions for kernels will be derived in Chapter XXI.

obtained by inversion of the order of integration, are equal when one of the integrals has a weak singularity, whereas N and N_1 also satisfy the conditions (47). In order to justify equality (62) on the basis of equality (53), it is sufficient to consider the relation

$$\int_{L(\tau)} \frac{N(\tau_1, \tau)}{|\tau-\tau_1|^\alpha}\, d\tau = \int_{L(\tau)} \frac{N'(\tau_1, \tau)}{\tau-\tau_1}\, d\tau,$$

where

$$N'(\tau_1, \tau) = N(\tau_1, \tau)\, \frac{\tau-\tau_1}{|\tau-\tau_1|^\alpha}$$

and where we have assumed that

$$N'(\tau, \tau) = \lim_{\tau_1 \to \tau} N'(\tau_1, \tau) = 0.$$

Remark 1. In the case when the functions $N(t, \tau)$ and $N_1(t, \tau)$ are defined for any real t, τ and possess a period a with respect to both variables (and satisfy the condition (47)), the Poincaré–Bertrand transformation can be written in the following form which is convenient for certain applications:

$$\int_0^a N_1(t, \tau) \cot \frac{\pi}{a}(\tau_1 - t) \left[\int_0^a N(\tau_1, \tau) \cot \frac{\pi}{a}(\tau-\tau_1)\, d\tau \right] d\tau_1$$

$$= -\pi^2 N(t, t) N_1(t, t) +$$

$$+ \int_0^a \left[\int_0^a N_1(t, \tau_1) N(\tau_1, \tau) \cot \frac{\pi}{a}(\tau_1 - t) \times \right.$$

$$\left. \times \cot \frac{\pi}{a}(\tau-\tau_1)\, d\tau_1 \right] d\tau. \qquad (62')$$

We stress the fact that integrating the right-hand side of equality (62′) with respect to the variable τ_1 we obtain a function of two variables t and τ with a weak singularity for $t-\tau \to 0$.

Remark 2. It can be shown, on the basis of the properties of the Cauchy type integral for open arcs, that the Poincaré transformation (53) is also valid for such an arc when t is an interior point.

Remark 3. Finally, it can readily be observed that the Poincaré–Bertrand transformation holds for a set L of open or closed arcs.

§ 6. Certain theorems and boundary problems for holomorphic functions

Now we shall consider certain theorems on existence of holomorphic functions with prescribed boundary values. Let us consider in the complex plane a region S^+ bounded by one or more smooth non-intersecting contours $L_0, L_1, \ldots, L_p$. We assume

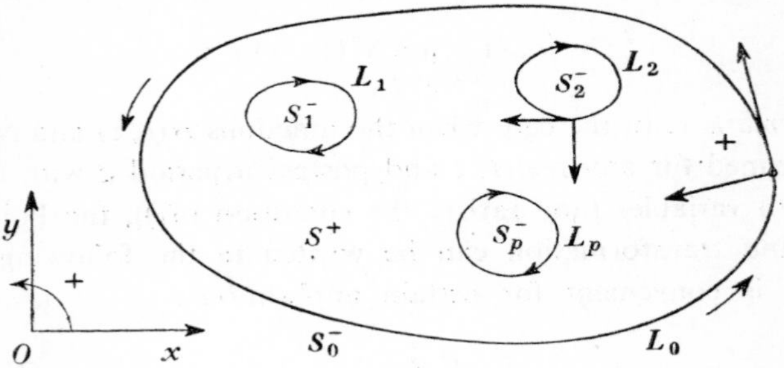

Fig. 12

that if the contour L_0 exists, it contains all the remaining ones (Fig. 12). Moreover, we assume that if the contour L_0 does not exist, then the region S^+ is an infinite region bounded by the contours

$$L_1, L_2, \ldots, L_p.$$

The direction of the contours $L_0, L_1, \ldots, L_p$ will be assumed to be such that the rotation from the positive direction of a tangent to the inward drawn normal of the region S^+ through a right angle is the same as the rotation from the real axis Ox to the imaginary axis Oy through a right angle. Thus, the direction of the contour L_0 is compatible with the positive rotation (xy), while the direction of the contours $L_1, \ldots, L_p$ is opposite. We denote by $S_1^-, \ldots, S_p^-$ the regions lying inside the contours L_1, $\ldots, L_p$, and by S_0^- the infinite region lying outside the contour

L_0, if it exists. Next, we denote by L the set of points $L_0+L_1+\ldots+L_p$. The following theorem holds:

THEOREM 1. *The values of a complex function $\varphi(\tau)$, defined and continuous on the set L, are boundary values of a function holomorphic in the region S^+, continuous in the domain S^++L, and, moreover, equal to zero at infinity in the case of the absence of the contour L_0, if and only if the equality*

$$\int_L \frac{\varphi(\tau)\,d\tau}{\tau-z}=0 \qquad (z\in S^-) \tag{63}$$

is satisfied at each interior point $z=x+iy$ of the domain

$$S^-=S_0^-+S_1^-+\ldots+S_p^- .$$

Proof. If in the region S^+ there exists a holomorphic function $\Phi(z)$ (it may be equal to zero at infinity) having the boundary values $\varphi(\tau)$, then according to the Cauchy integral formula this function is unique and at each interior point z of the region S^+ it can be expressed by the integral

$$\Phi(z)=\frac{1}{2\pi i}\int_L \frac{\varphi(\tau)\,d\tau}{\tau-z} \qquad (z\in S^+). \tag{64}$$

On the other hand, according to the properties of integrals of holomorphic functions, integral (64) is equal to zero at each point z inside the domain S^-, and hence condition (63) is necessary.

In order to show that condition (63) is also sufficient, we note that formula (64) defines the function $\Phi(z)$ holomorphic in the region S^+ and sectionally holomorphic in each of the regions $S_0^-, S_1^-, \ldots, S_p^-$. But, according to assumption (63), we have in these regions

$$\Phi(z)=0 \quad \text{for} \quad z\in S^-,$$

thus the boundary values are also equal to zero:

$$\lim_{z\to t}\Phi(z)=\Phi^-(t)=0.$$

Hence, on the basis of the property (24″), requiring only the continuity of the function $\varphi(\tau)$, we then have at each point $t \in L$ the boundary property

$$\lim_{z \to t} \Phi(z) = \Phi^+(t) = \varphi(t).$$

Thus, condition (63) is sufficient. This completes the proof of the theorem.

COROLLARY. *A necessary and sufficient condition that the values of a complex function $\varphi(\tau)$, defined and satisfying Hölder's condition on the set L be boundary values of a holomorphic function in the region S^+, continuous in the domain $S^+ + L$ (moreover, equal to zero at infinity, in the case of the absence of the contour L_0) is that the function $\varphi(t)$ satisfies at each point t of the contours L the integral equation*

$$-\pi i \varphi(t) + \int_L \frac{\varphi(\tau)\, d\tau}{\tau - t} = 0. \qquad (65)$$

In fact, condition (65) is necessary since in the case when the function $\varphi(t)$ satisfies Hölder's condition the boundary equality (65) follows from the necessary condition (63) on the basis of Plemelj's formulae (14). At the same time condition (65) is also sufficient, since when it is satisfied there exists in the region S^+ a unique holomorphic function defined by formula (64), the boundary values of which at each point $t \in L$ are the following

$$\lim_{z \to t} \Phi(z) = \Phi^+(t) = +\frac{1}{2}\varphi(t) + \frac{1}{2\pi i}\int_L \frac{\varphi(\tau)\, d\tau}{\tau - t} = \varphi(t).$$

Remark 1. In exactly the same way, we can prove that for a prescribed continuous function $\varphi(t)$ on L the equality

$$\int_L \frac{\varphi(\tau)\, d\tau}{\tau - z} = 0 \quad (z \in S^+) \qquad (66)$$

is a necessary and sufficient condition at each point of the region S^+ for the existence of a function $\Phi(z)$, sectionally holomorphic in each of the regions $S_0^-, S_1^-, \ldots, S_p^-$, equal to zero at infinity and taking the boundary values $\varphi(t)$ at each point of the boundary $L_0, \ldots, L_p$.

In the case when the given function $\varphi(t)$ satisfies the Hölder's condition on L, the above condition can be reduced, at each point $t \in L$, to the equality

$$+\pi i \varphi(t) + \int_L \frac{\varphi(\tau)\, d\tau}{\tau - t} = 0. \tag{67}$$

Remark 2. The above conditions can be generalized, in the case when instead of the requirement that $\Phi(z)$ be zero at infinity we require that $\Phi(z)$ possess a pole at infinity whose principal part is given in the form of a polynomial $g(z)$. Then, instead of the condition (66), we obtain the following

$$\int_L \frac{\varphi(\tau) - g(\tau)}{\tau - z}\, d\tau = 0 \quad \text{for} \quad z \in S^+ \tag{68}$$

or the equivalent condition

$$\int_L \frac{\varphi(\tau)\, d\tau}{\tau - z} - 2\pi i\, g(z) = 0 \tag{69}$$

for $z \in S^+$. In the case when the function $\varphi(\tau)$ satisfies Hölder condition we obtain the following equality at each point $t \in L$ instead of condition (67):

$$+\pi i \varphi(t) + \int_L \frac{\varphi(\tau)\, d\tau}{\tau - t} - g(t) = 0. \tag{70}$$

The above conditions have been investigated by Morera [32], Plemelj [41], and Privalov [71].

The following theorem, needed in the sequel, follows from previous considerations:

HARNACK'S GENERALIZED THEOREM. *If $\varphi(t)$ is a real continuous function defined on a set $L = L_0+L_1+\ldots+L_p$* (Fig. 6) *and if the function of a complex variable*

$$\Phi(z) = \int_L \frac{\varphi(\tau)\,d\tau}{\tau-z} \tag{71}$$

is equal to zero in the region S^+, then the function $\varphi(t)$ takes constant values $\varphi(t) = C_k$ $(k = 0, 1, 2, \ldots, p)$ on each of the contours $L_0, L_1, \ldots, L_p$, and, moreover $C_0 = 0$ on L_0, when L_0 exists.

If the function (71) *is equal to zero in the domain $S^- = S_0^- + S_1^- + \ldots + S_p^-$, then the function takes the same constant value $\varphi(t) = C$ at points of the contours L.*

Proof. According to Theorem 1 (Remark 1), by the assumption $\Phi(z) = 0$ for $z \in S^+$ the values of the function $\varphi(t)$ are the boundary values of the function (71), sectionally holomorphic in the regions $S_0^-, S_1^-, \ldots, S_p^-$, and moreover $\Phi(z) \to 0$ as $z \to \infty$. Since, by the assumption, the function $\varphi(t)$ takes real values only, the imaginary part of $\Phi(z)$, having boundary values equal to zero, *is equal to zero* in the regions $S_0^-, S_1^-, \ldots, S_p^-$. Hence it follows that $\Phi(z)$ is *constant* in each of the regions $S_0^-, S_1^-, \ldots$ $\ldots, S_p^-$. Thus, $\varphi(t) = C_k$ $(k = 0, 1, \ldots, p)$, and $C_0 = 0$, since $\Phi(z) \to 0$ as $z \to \infty$. The proof of the second part of the theorem is similar, moreover, the function $\varphi(t)$ takes one constant value C only, since in this case it is the boundary value of the function $\Phi(z)$, constant in the entire region S^+. This constant is equal to zero in the case when the contour L is absent.

Boundary problem. We shall determine the function $\Phi(z)$ sectionally holomorphic in the regions S^+ and S^-, formed by contours L vanishing at infinity, and such that the difference between the boundary values $\Phi^+(t)$ and $\Phi^-(t)$ at each point t of the contours L is equal to the given function $\varphi(t)$

$$\Phi^+(t) - \Phi^-(t) = \varphi(t). \tag{72}$$

The function is defined in the set L, and satisfies Hölder's condition.

By Plemelj's formulae (14) the function defined by the Cauchy type integral

$$\Phi(z) = \frac{1}{2\pi i}\int_L \frac{\varphi(\tau)\,d\tau}{\tau - z} \tag{73}$$

is a solution of the problem.

We prove that this solution is *unique*. If another solution $\Phi^*(z)$ of the given problem exists, then the difference between the solutions,

$$\Psi(z) = \Phi(z) - \Phi^*(z),$$

is a sectionally holomorphic function in the regions S^+ and S^-. It is zero at infinity and has equal boundary values,

$$\Psi^+(t) = \Psi^-(t),$$

at each point $t \in L$. We shall prove that the function $\Psi(z)$ is then holomorphic in the whole plane. It suffices to prove that $\Psi(z)$ is holomorphic in a certain neighbourhood of an arbitrary point $t \in L$. Supose we are given a circle K with centre t and radius suffi-

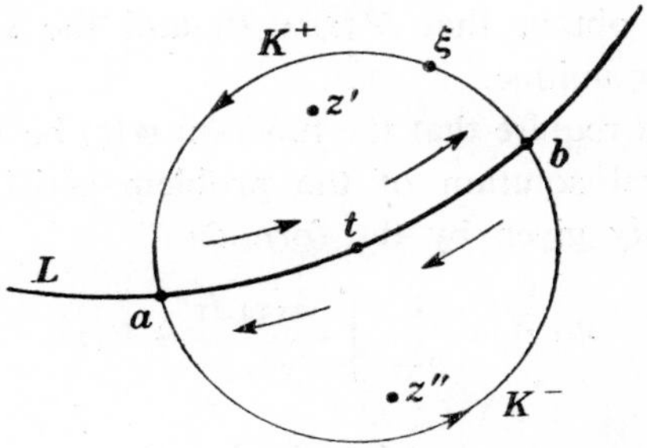

Fig. 13

ciently small such that the circle intersects the arc at two points a and b only. Denote by K^+ and K^- the parts of this circle lying in the regions S^+ and S^- divided by the line L, respectively (Fig. 13). In accordance with the Cauchy integral formula, the value of the function $\Psi(z)$ inside the region at an arbitrary point

z' common to the circle K and the region S^+, is expressed by the integral

$$\Psi(z') = \frac{1}{2\pi i}\int\limits_{K^+}\frac{\Psi(\zeta)\,d\zeta}{\zeta - z'} + \frac{1}{2\pi i}\int\limits_{ab}\frac{\Psi^+(\zeta)\,d\zeta}{\zeta - z'}. \tag{74}$$

In the same way we obtain at each point z'' inside the region common to the circle K and the domain S^- that

$$\Psi(z'') = \frac{1}{2\pi i}\int\limits_{K^-}\frac{\Psi(\zeta)\,d\zeta}{\zeta - z''} + \frac{1}{2\pi i}\int\limits_{ba}\frac{\Psi^-(\zeta)\,d\zeta}{\zeta - z''}. \tag{75}$$

In addition, we notice that the sum of the integrals (74) is equal to zero when z'' is substituted for z', while the sum of the integrals (75) is equal to zero when z' is substituted for z''. From the above considerations, it follows that the values of the function $\Psi(z)$ at each point z inside the circle K is given by the formula

$$\Psi(z) = \frac{1}{2\pi i}\int\limits_{K^+ + K^-}\frac{\Psi(\zeta)\,d\zeta}{\zeta - z}. \tag{76}$$

Thus, the function $\Psi(z)$ is holomorphic in the circle K, and hence in the entire complex plane. Since we require that $\Psi(z) \to 0$ as $z \to \infty$, we obtain that $\Psi(z) = 0$, and the solution of the problem (73) is unique.

If we do not require that the function $\Phi(z)$ be zero at infinity, then the general solution of the problem satisfying condition (73) is obviously given by the formula

$$\Phi(z) = \frac{1}{2\pi i}\int\limits_{L}\frac{\varphi(\tau)\,d\tau}{\tau - z} + P(z) \tag{77}$$

where $P(z)$ is an arbitrary function (entire, transcendental, or a polynomial).

§ 7. Inversion of the Cauchy type integral

We now solve the problem of the determination of a function $\varphi(t)$ on a set of points L such that the Cauchy type integral is equal to a prescribed function $\psi(t)$ defined, and satisfying Hölder's condition on the lines L:

$$\int_L \frac{\varphi(\tau)\,d\tau}{\tau - t} = \psi(t). \tag{78}$$

The integral equation (78) with the unknown function φ is the simplest, but most important example, of what are called *singular integral equations*. We shall systematically investigate these equations in the sequel.

We give two methods of solving equation (78). The first one is based on the Poincaré–Bertrand transformation (53). Namely, multiplying both sides of equation (78) by the factor $1/t-\theta$, we can assert that if there exists a function $\varphi(\tau)$ satisfying the Hölder's condition and equation (78) then this function also satisfies the equation

$$\int_L \frac{dt}{t-\theta}\left[\int_L \frac{\varphi(\tau)\,d\tau}{\tau - t}\right] = \int_L \frac{\psi(t)\,dt}{t-\theta}. \tag{79}$$

Thus, according to transformation (53) it also satisfies the equation

$$-\pi^2\varphi(\theta) + \int_L\left[\int_L \frac{dt}{(t-\theta)(\tau-t)}\right]\varphi(\tau)\,d\tau = \int_L \frac{\psi(t)\,dt}{t-\theta}. \tag{80}$$

However, we have the equality

$$\int_L \frac{dt}{(t-\theta)(\tau-t)} = \frac{1}{\theta - t}\left[\int_L \frac{dt}{t-\theta} - \int_L \frac{dt}{t-\tau}\right] = 0$$

and thus, if there exists a function $\varphi(t)$ satisfying equation (78) then it is unique among the class of functions satisfying Hölder's condition, and it is given by the formula

$$\varphi(\tau) = -\frac{1}{\pi^2}\int_L \frac{\psi(\theta)\,d\theta}{\theta - \tau}. \tag{81}$$

Now we prove that the function (81) satisfies equation (78). In fact this is the case, for substituting expression (81) into equation (78) and applying the Poincaré–Bertrand transformation, we obtain

$$-\frac{1}{\pi^2}\int_L \frac{d\tau}{\tau-t}\left[\frac{\psi(\theta)\,d\theta}{\theta-\tau}\right]$$

$$=\psi(t)-\frac{1}{\pi^2}\int_L\left[\int_L \frac{d\tau}{(\tau-t)(\theta-\tau)}\right]\psi\theta\,d\theta=\psi(t).$$

Thus, the function (81) is the only solution of the integral equation (78). The equations (78) and (81) may also be written as follows

$$\frac{1}{\pi i}\int_L \frac{\varphi(\tau)\,d\tau}{\tau-t}=\psi(t),\qquad \frac{1}{\pi i}\int_L \frac{\psi(t)\,dt}{t-\tau}=\varphi(\tau) \tag{82}$$

whence it is seen that these relations are reciprocal.

We also give a second method of solving the integral equation (78), or, equivalently, the first of equations (82). Let us consider the function

$$\Psi(z)=\frac{1}{\pi i}\int_L \frac{\psi(\tau)\,d\tau}{\tau-z} \tag{83}$$

holomorphic in the region S^+, taking the following boundary value at an arbitrary point $t\in L$, with respect to this region:

$$\Psi^+(t)=\psi(t)+\frac{1}{\pi i}\int_L \frac{\psi(\tau)\,d\tau}{\tau-t}. \tag{84}$$

According to the Cauchy integral formula we can write the equality

$$\int_L \frac{\Psi^+(\theta)\,d\theta}{\theta-z}=0 \tag{85}$$

which is valid at each point $z\in S^-$. Hence, assuming that the point z tends to an arbitrary point $t\in L$, we obtain, in the limit,

$$-\Psi^+(t)+\frac{1}{\pi i}\int_L \frac{\Psi^+(\theta)\,d\theta}{\theta-t}=0. \tag{86}$$

Substituting in this equation the expression on the right of (84) for $\Psi^+(t)$ we obtain

$$-\psi(t)-\frac{1}{\pi i}\int_L \frac{\psi(\tau)\,d\tau}{t-\tau}+$$

$$+\frac{1}{\pi i}\int_L \frac{d\theta}{\theta-t}\left[\psi(\theta)+\frac{1}{\pi i}\int_L \frac{\psi(\tau)\,d\tau}{\tau-\theta}\right]=0,$$

which simplifies to yield

$$\frac{1}{\pi i}\int_L \frac{d\theta}{\theta-t}\left[\frac{1}{\pi i}\int_L \frac{\psi(\tau)\,d\tau}{\tau-\theta}\right]=\psi(t). \tag{87}$$

This equality means that the function $\varphi(\tau)$ defined by the second of equalities (82) is the solution of the given integral equation.

CHAPTER XVI

HILBERT AND RIEMANN BOUNDARY PROBLEMS

§ 1. The homogeneous Hilbert problem

Let S^+ be a region bounded by a system of smooth contours $L = L_0+L_1+\ldots+L_p$ as shown in Fig. 6. The contour L_0 may be absent, S^- is the union of the regions $S_0^-, S_1^-, \ldots, S_p^-$ bounded by the contours $L_0, L_1, \ldots, L_p$.

By *the homogeneous Hilbert problem* we shall mean the problem of determination of the function $\Phi(z)$, sectionally holomorphic in the region S^+ and in the regions $S_0^-, S_1^-, \ldots, S_p^-$, whose boundary values $\Phi^+(t)$ and $\Phi^-(t)$ at each point t of the boundary L satisfy the prescribed homogeneous relation

$$\Phi^+(t) = G(t)\,\Phi^-(t) \tag{1}$$

where $G(t)$ is a given complex function defined and non-zero on L.

The problem formulated above was stated by D. HILBERT [21] who solved it by means of the theory of Fredholm's equation assuming that the regions S^+ and S^- are bounded by a single analytic contour and that the function $G(t)$ possesses second derivatives continuous with respect to the arc. Next, the problem was investigated by T. CARLEMANN [5].

In the years 1937–42, a Soviet mathematician GAKHOV showed in papers [8], [9], [10] that the solution of Hilbert's problem can be obtained directly without the use of integral equations, basing his proof on properties of Cauchy type integrals. Next, Gakhov's solution was generalized by a Georgian mathematician KHVEDELIDZE [1] in the case of multiconnected regions S^+ and S^-. This solution will be given below, assuming that there is given a function $G(t) \neq 0$ defined on L and satisfying Hölder's condition

$$|G(t)-G(t_1)| < \text{const}\,|t-t_1|^h \quad (0 < h \leqq 1). \tag{2}$$

In order to solve the problem, we notice that on account of (1) the difference between the logarithms of the boundary values of the required function $\Phi(z)$ are given, namely

$$\log \Phi^+(t) - \log \Phi^-(t) = \log G(t) \quad \text{at each point } t \in L. \tag{3}$$

If it were possible to determine certain single-valued continuous branches of the functions $\log G(t)$ on each of the contours $L_0, L_1, \ldots, L_p$, then by the boundary problem solved in the last paragraph, we could immediately determine the logarithm of the required function by the Cauchy type integral (see p. 428). Since, however, a continuous single-valued branch of the function $\log G(t)$ does not necessarily exist, the problem should be solved in a different way, shown by GAKHOV.

Let us note that if the point t performs a full rotation along the contour L_k $(k = 0, 1, \ldots, p)$ in positive direction, then any arbitrary branch of the function $\log G(t)$ changes continuously and increases by a multiple of $2\pi i$. For, we have

$$\frac{1}{2\pi i}\,[\log G(t)]_{L_k} = \frac{1}{2\pi}\,[\arg G(t)]_{L_k} = \lambda_k \tag{4}$$

where (00] L_k denotes the change in the expression in brackets, as the result of a full circuit around the contour L_k, λ_k is an integer, positive, negative or zero. The sum

$$\kappa = \lambda_0 + \lambda_1 + \lambda_2 + \ldots + \lambda_p = \frac{1}{2\pi}\sum_{k=0}^{p}\,[\arg G(t)]_{L_k} \tag{5}$$

taken over all the contours L_k will be called *the index of the function* $G(t)$, and also *the index of the Hilbert problem* (1). The notion of the index κ was introduced and widely applied by Soviet mathematicians; it plays an important rôle in the theory of Hilbert's problem, and of singular integral equations.

Let $a_1, a_2, \ldots, a_p$ be arbitrary fixed points inside the regions $S_1^-, S_2^-, \ldots, S_p^-$, respectively, and let us assume that the point $z = 0$ lies inside the region S^+. We now introduce the product

$$\Pi(z) = (z-a_1)^{\lambda_1}(z-a_2)^{\lambda_2}\ldots(z-a_p)^{\lambda_p} \tag{6}$$

where λ_k are integers defined by equalities (4); in the case when L consists only of a single contour L_0 we assume that $\Pi(z) = 1$. It follows from formulae (4), (5), (6) that the argument of the function

$$G_0(t) = t^{-\kappa}\Pi(t)G(t) \tag{7}$$

continuously varying, returns to its initial value after a full circuit of any contour L_k by the point t.

In fact, if $k \neq 0$, then the positive direction of contour L_k is in the opposite sense to that of the positive direction of the rotation (xy). Thus, when the argument of the factor $G(t)$ increases by $2\pi\lambda_k$ after a full circuit of a contour L_k, then the argument of the factor $(z-a_k)^{\lambda_k}$ increases by the opposite amount and the arguments of the remaining factors return to the initial values. If $k = 0$, then the positive direction of the contour L_0 is the same as the positive direction of the rotation (xy). In this case, after a full circuit around L_0, the argument of the factor $G(t)$ increases by $2\pi(\lambda_1+\lambda_2+\ldots+\lambda_p)$, while the argument of the factor $t^{-\kappa}$ by $-2\pi\kappa$, and the argument of the function $G_0(t)$ returns to its initial value.

Thus, a *single-valued* continuous branch of the function $\log G_0(t)$ can be chosen for each of the contours L_k ($k = 0, 1, 2, \ldots, p$). According to the assumption concerning the function $G(t)$ the function $\log G_0(t)$ satisfies Hölder's condition with the same index as $G(t)$. Let us solve an auxiliary Hilbert problem, namely, we find the function $\Psi(z)$, sectionally holomorphic in the regions S^+ and S^-, the boundary values of which satisfy the homogeneous relation

$$\Psi^+(t) = G_0(t)\Psi^-(t) \tag{8}$$

or

$$\log\Psi^+(t) - \log\Psi^-(t) = \log G_0(t). \tag{8'}$$

Since the function $\log G_0(t)$ is single-valued, taking into account the Plemelj formulae, we see that the function determined by the Cauchy type integral

$$\Gamma(z) = \frac{1}{2\pi i} \int_L \frac{\log G_0(\tau)\, d\tau}{\tau - z} \tag{9}$$

satisfies the boundary condition

$$\Gamma^+(t) - \Gamma^-(t) = \log G_0(t) \tag{9'}$$

at each point $t \in L$. Hence, the function

$$\Psi(z) = e^{\Gamma(z)} \tag{10}$$

satisfies the boundary condition (8) at each point $t \in L$. Thus, from (6) and (7) we conclude that the function X, determined by means of the formulae

$$X(z) = \begin{cases} \dfrac{1}{\Pi(z)}\, e^{\Gamma(z)} & \text{for} \quad z \in S^+, \\ z^{-\kappa} e^{\Gamma(z)} & \text{for} \quad z \in S^-, \end{cases} \tag{11}$$

is a particular solution of the homogeneous Hilbert problem, i.e. that its boundary values, for $t \in L$, satisfy the relation

$$X^+(t) = G(t)\, X^-(t). \tag{12}$$

In fact, we obtain from formulae (11) that

$$X^+(t) = \frac{1}{\Pi(z)}\, e^{\Gamma^+(t)}, \quad X^-(t) = t^{-\kappa} e^{\Gamma^-(t)}. \tag{13}$$

Since these functions are always different from zero, we write

$$\frac{X^+(t)}{X^-(t)} = \frac{t^\kappa}{\Pi(t)}\, e^{\Gamma^+(t) - \Gamma^-(t)}, \tag{14}$$

and hence, by equalities (7) and (9′), we get

$$\frac{X^+(t)}{X^-(t)} = \frac{t^\kappa}{\Pi(t)}\, G_0(t) = G(t). \tag{15}$$

We notice that by Privalov's Theorem the boundary functions $\Gamma^+(t)$ and $\Gamma^-(t)$ of function (9) satisfy Hölder's condition with the same exponent h as the function $G(t)$ does, for $h < 1$, and so the boundary values $X^+(t)$ and $X^-(t)$ of the solution (11) satisfy Hölder's condition with exponent $h < 1$.

The function X determined by formulae (11) is called *a fundamental solution* of the homogeneous Hilbert problem. This function is sectionally holomorphic in the regions $S^+, S_0^-, S_1^-, \ldots, S_p^-$ and *is different from to zero* at any interior point or on the boundary. Since, however, according to formulae (9) the function $\Gamma(z)$ tends to zero as $z \to \infty$, then the principal part of the fundamental solution (11) as $z \to \infty$ is the function $z^{-\kappa}$ of order $-\kappa$. Thus the point at infinity is a zero of order $-\kappa$ for $\kappa < 0$, is a pole of order κ for $\kappa > 0$, and is a regular point of the function $X(z)$ for $\kappa = 0$. These properties also remain valid in the case of the absence of the contour L_0 when the point at infinity lies in the region S^+, for we only have to substitute $\lambda_0 = 0$.

THEOREM. *The general solution of the homogeneous Hilbert problem is a product*

$$\Phi(z) = X(z) P(z) \tag{16}$$

of the fundamental solution (11) *by an arbitrary entire function* $P(z)$.

In fact, the product (16) satisfies the conditions of the Hilbert problem for an arbitrary entire function $P(z)$. We shall prove that the solutions determined by formula (16) are the only solutions of the Hilbert problem. Using the equalities

$$\Phi^+(t) = G(t)\Phi^-(t), \quad X^+(t) = G(t)X^-(t),$$

we obtain, for an arbitrary solution $\Phi(z)$ of the Hilbert problem, that

$$\frac{\Phi^+(t)}{X^+(t)} = \frac{\Phi^-(t)}{X^-(t)}.$$

Consequently, the function $\Phi(z)/X(z)$ does not have discontinuities when z passes along the contours L from the region

S^- into the region S^+, hence, according to what was said on page 457, it is holomorphic in the whole complex plane, i.e. it is an entire function and the statement is proved.

As a particular case, when the function $P(z)$ is a polynomial of p-th degree, the solution of the Hilbert problem (16) is a function of the order $-\kappa+p$ at infinity. Thus, it is evident that among the solutions of the Hilbert problem *the fundamental solution has the lowest order* $-\kappa$ *at infinity.*

In applications to the theory of singular integral equations a particularly important rôle is played by the solutions of the Hilbert problem which tends to zero as $z \to \infty$. Consequently, it is seen from formula (16) that when the index κ is *negative* or equal to zero, then Hilbert's problem does not possess any solutions tending to zero as $z \to \infty$, while for a positive index κ the general solution of Hilbert's problem tending to zero as $z \to \infty$, is given by the formula

$$\Phi(z) = X(z) P_{\kappa-1}(z) \tag{17}$$

where $P_{\kappa-1}(z)$ is a polynomial of degree at most $\kappa-1$. Then, there exist linearly independent solutions and equal to zero at infinity,

$$X(z), zX(z), z^2 X(z), \dots, z^{\kappa-1} X(z) \tag{18}$$

of the Hilbert problem.

DEFINITION. *The problem corresponding to the boundary conditions*

$$\Phi^+(t) = G(t)\Phi^-(t), \qquad \Psi^+(t) = [G(t)]^{-1}\Psi^-(t)$$

is called the adjoint Hilbert problem.

From the preceding, it follows that when κ is the index of the first Hilbert problem, then $-\kappa$ is the index of the adjoint problem. Also, if $X(z)$ is a fundamental solution of the first problem then $[X(z)]^{-1}$ is a fundamental solution of the second problem.

§ 2. The non-homogeneous Hilbert–Privalov problem

PRIVALOV [72] extended the homogeneous Hilbert problem to the case when the required function $\Phi(z)$ is sectionally holomorphic in the regions $S^+, S_0^-, \ldots, S_p^-$, and the boundary values of the function $\Phi^+(t)$ and $\Phi^-(t)$ satisfy the prescribed linear relation

$$\Phi^+(t) = G(t)\Phi^-(t) + g(t). \tag{19}$$

Here $G(t)$ and $g(t)$ are given functions of a complex variable defined on the set L. This problem was solved by GAKHOV [8] and generalized by KHVEDELIDZE [23].

We assume that the given functions $G(t)$ and $g(t)$ satisfy Hölder's condition with exponent h, and that $G(t) \neq 0$. To solve problem (19), we notice that

$$G(t) = \frac{X^+(t)}{X^-(t)}, \tag{20}$$

where $X(z)$ is a fundamental solution of the homogeneous problem. Substituting expression (20) into equation (19) we obtain the boundary condition of the non-homogeneous problem in an equivalent form

$$\frac{\Phi^+(t)}{X^+(t)} - \frac{\Phi^-(t)}{X^-(t)} = \frac{g(t)}{X^+(t)}. \tag{21}$$

Thus, the problem has been reduced to finding the function $\Phi(z)/X(z)$ which is such that the difference between the boundary values at points of the contours $t \in L$ is equal to a prescribed function $g(t)/X^+(t)$. Remembering what has been said on p. 458, we find that such a function is defined by a general formula

$$\frac{\Phi(z)}{X(z)} = \frac{1}{2\pi i} \int_L \frac{g(\tau)\,d\tau}{X^+(\tau)(\tau - z)} + P(z),$$

where $P(z)$ is an arbitrary entire function. Consequently, the general solution of the non-homogeneous Hilbert–Privalov problem has the following form:

$$\Phi(z)=\frac{X(z)}{2\pi i}\int_L \frac{g(\tau)\,d\tau}{X^+(\tau)(\tau-z)}+P(z)X(z). \tag{22}$$

The constant κ which is appropriate for the function $X(z)$ is also called the *index* of the non-homogeneous Hilbert problem.

In view of applications, an important rôle is played by the solutions of the Hilbert problem (19) which tend to zero as $z\to\infty$. The existence of such solutions is given by the following theorem:

THEOREM. *If the index κ of the problem is non-negative, then all solutions of the Hilbert–Privalov problem, equal to zero at infinity, are determined by the formula*

$$\Phi(z)=\frac{X(z)}{2\pi i}\int_L \frac{g(\tau)\,d\tau}{X^+(\tau)(\tau-z)}+P_{\kappa-1}(z)X(z), \tag{23}$$

where $P_{\kappa-1}(z)$ is an arbitrary polynomial of degree at most $\kappa-1$ when $\kappa>0$ or $P_{\kappa-1}=0$ for $\kappa=0$.

When the index of the problem is negative, then the solution of the Hilbert–Privalov problem, equal to zero at infinity, exists if, and only if, the following equalities hold:

$$\int_L \frac{\tau^k g(\tau)\,d\tau}{X^+(\tau)}=0 \quad (k=0,1,2,\ldots,-\kappa-1). \tag{24}$$

This solution is given by the formula

$$\Phi(z)=\frac{X(z)}{2\pi i}\int_L \frac{g(\tau)\,d\tau}{X^+(\tau)(\tau-z)}. \tag{25}$$

Proof. The first part of the theorem is obvious since the function $X(z)$ is of the order $-\kappa$ at infinity. The second part follows from the expansion as a series

$$\int_L \frac{g(\tau)\,d\tau}{X^+(\tau)(\tau-z)}=-\sum_{k=0}^{\infty}\frac{1}{z^{k+1}}\int \frac{\tau^k g(\tau)\,d\tau}{X^+(\tau)}$$

convergent for sufficiently large $|z|$.

Recently, D. SADOWSKA [76] investigated the generalized Hilbert problem for the case of an integral boundary relation.

§ 3. On a certain continuation of a function defined in a circle onto the whole plane

Let $\Phi(z)$ be a given function, holomorphic inside the interior S^+ of the circle $|z| < 1$. To each point z inside the region S^+ there corresponds an inverse point $1/\bar{z}$ † with respect to the given circle, lying in the external region S^-, and conversely. The regions S^+ and S^- are divided by the given circle. The inverse points z and $1/\bar{z}$ lie on the same ray the initial point of which is the centre $z = 0$ of the given circle. If the point z tends to a point t on the circumference of the circle L, then the inverse point $1/\bar{z}$ also tends to the same point t. In view of applications to the Riemann problem, which will be discussed in the next paragraph, we extend the function $\Phi(z)$ to the whole plane by defining a function $\Phi_*(z)$ in the region S^-. This function at any point z of S^- has the value equal to the value of the conjugate of the function Φ at the inverse point $1/z$ of the region S^+,

$$\Phi_*(z) = \overline{\Phi(1/\bar{z})}. \tag{26}$$

A function defined in the region S^- will be continued to the region S^+ by the same formula.

Relation (26) is reciprocal, i.e. we have

$$\Phi(z) = \overline{\Phi_*(1/\bar{z})} \tag{26'}$$

for $z \in S^+$ or $z \in S^-$.

If the function $\Phi(z)$ is holomorphic in the circle S^+, i.e. if it can be represented as the sum of a certain power series

$$\Phi(z) = \sum_{n=0}^{\infty} a_n z^n \quad (z \in S^+) \tag{27}$$

in the interior of S^+, then the complementary function is holomorphic in the exterior region S^-, and at each point z it is given by the sum of the Laurent series

$$\Phi_*(z) = \sum_{n=0}^{\infty} \bar{a}_n z^{-n} \quad (z \in S^-), \tag{27'}$$

and consequently, it is bounded at infinity.

† A bar over a letter or an expression denotes the complex conjugate:

$$\overline{a+ib} = a - ib.$$

Conversely, if the given function $\Phi(z)$ is holomorphic in the exterior region S^-, is bounded at infinity, and it is given by a Laurent series

$$\Phi(z) = \sum_{n=0}^{\infty} b_n z^{-n} \quad (z \in S^-),$$

then the complementary function in the region S^+ is the sum of a power series

$$\Phi_*(z) = \sum_{n=0}^{\infty} \bar{b}_n z^n \quad (z \in S^+),$$

and consequently, it is holomorphic in this region.

If a function $\Phi(z)$ has a definite boundary value $\Phi^+(t)$ at a point $t \in L$, then the complementary function $\Phi_*(z)$ also possesses a boundary value

$$\Phi_*^-(t) = \overline{\Phi^+(t)} \tag{28}$$

at the point $t \in L$. If a function $\psi(z)$ is determined in the whole plane (except in the circle L) by means of the equalities

$$\Psi(z) = \begin{cases} \Phi(z) & \text{for} \quad z \in S^+, \\ \Phi_*(z) & \text{for} \quad z \in S^-, \end{cases} \tag{29}$$

then it is sectionally holomorphic in the regions S^+ and S^-. The following relation holds for its boundary values on L:

$$\Psi^+(t) = \overline{\Psi^-(t)}. \tag{29'}$$

As a particular case when the function $\Psi(z)$ is real on a certain arc l of the circle L, we obtain from relation (29′) that the function $\Psi(z)$ is holomorphic in the whole plane with the cut $L-l$, thus, the function $\Phi_*(z)$ is the analytic continuation of the function $\Phi(z)$ through the arc l. This property is in accordance with the known Schwartz principle of reflection.

Let us now extend the meaning of the definition (26), denoting by $\Psi_*(z)$ a function connected with the function $\Psi(z)$ in the domain $S^+ + S^-$ by the equation

$$\Psi_*(z) = \overline{\Psi(1/\bar{z})}.$$

We prove that such a function is identical with the function $\Psi(z)$. In fact, if $z \in S^+$, then $1/z \in S^-$, and we have

$$\Psi_*(z) = \overline{\Psi(1/\bar{z})} = \overline{\Phi_*(1/\bar{z})} = \Phi(z).$$

On the other hand, if $z \in S^-$, then $1/\bar{z} \in S^+$, and we obtain

$$\Psi_*(z) = \overline{\Phi(1/\bar{z})} = \Phi_*(z);$$

consequently,

$$\Psi^*(z) = \Psi(z)$$

in the whole domain $S^+ + S^-$.

Two functions $F(z)$ and $\Phi(z)$ defined in a set $S^+ + S^-$ and sectionally holomorphic in the regions S^+ and S^- and which are related by an equality

$$F(z) = \overline{\Phi(1/\bar{z})} \quad \text{or} \quad \Phi(z) = \overline{F(1/\bar{z})},$$

are called *associated*; we then write in this case $F(z) = \Phi_*(z)$, or $\Phi(z) = F_*(z)$.

It is obvious that associate functions are bounded at infinity. A function Ψ determined by equalities (29) is associated with itself.

For an arbitrary given function $F(z)$ sectionally holomorphic in the regions S^+ and S^- and bounded at infinity, thus defined by certain convergent series

$$F(z) = \begin{cases} \sum_{n=0}^{\infty} a_n z^n, & z \in S^+, \\ \sum_{n=0}^{\infty} b_n z^{-n}, & z \in S^-, \end{cases}$$

there exists one and only one function $\Phi(z) = F_*(z)$ which is associated with it, and determined by the series

$$\Phi(z) = \begin{cases} \sum_{n=0}^{\infty} \bar{b}_n z^n, & z \in S^+, \\ \sum_{n=0}^{\infty} \bar{a}_n z^{-n}, & z \in S^-. \end{cases}$$

The functions $F(z)$ and $\Phi(z)$ are identical if, and only if, $a_n = \bar{b}_n$.

Let us consider a function $\Phi(z)$ defined in the domain $S^+ + S^-$ by the Cauchy type integral

$$\Phi(z) = \int_L \frac{\varphi(\tau)\, d\tau}{\tau - z}. \tag{30}$$

The associate function $\Phi_*(z)$ in the domain $S^+ + S^-$ is determined by the formula

$$\Phi_*(z) = \overline{\Phi(1/\bar{z})} = \int_L \frac{\overline{\varphi(\tau)}\, d\bar{\tau}}{\bar{\tau} - 1/z}.$$

Since we have on the circumference of the circle L

$$\tau = e^{i\theta}, \quad \bar{\tau} = e^{-i\theta}, \quad d\bar{\tau} = -ie^{-i\theta}\, d\theta = -d\tau/\tau^2,$$

it follows that, for $z \in S^+ + S^-$, we obtain

$$\Phi_*(z) = \int_L \frac{\overline{\varphi(\tau)}\, d\tau}{\tau - z} - \int_L \overline{\varphi(\tau)} \frac{d\tau}{\tau}. \tag{31}$$

§ 4. The Riemann boundary problem

The Riemann boundary problem consists of finding a function $\Phi(z) = u + iv$, holomorphic in a region S^+ bounded by a single smooth contour L, the boundary values of which at each point $t \in L$ satisfy a prescribed linear relation

$$\operatorname{re}[(a+ib)\Phi^+(t)] = a(t)u(t) - b(t)v(t) = c(t) \tag{32}$$

between the real part u and the imaginary part v of the function. Here, $a(t), b(t), c(t)$ are the given real, continuous functions defined at each point $t \in L$.

This problem was first studied by HILBERT [21] who reduced it to the problem of solving a certain singular integral equation.

We shall show, according to MUSKHELISHVILI (see [33], p. 100) that in the case when S^+ is a circular region, the Riemann problem can be solved directly by reducing it to the Hilbert problem studied in the preceding paragraph. The case when a simply connected region S^+ is not a circle may be reduced to the previous one by means of conformal mapping.

Thus, let us assume that S^+ is a circular region $|z| < 1$, bounded by the unit circle L. Moreover, we assume that the given functions $a(t), b(t), c(t)$ satisfy Hölder's condition, and that $a^2+b^2 \neq 0$. Let us write the boundary condition (32) of the Riemann problem as follows:

$$2\,\mathrm{re}\left[(a+ib)\,\Phi^+(t)\right] = (a+ib)\,\Phi^+(t)+(a-ib)\,\overline{\Phi^+(t)} = 2c \qquad (t\in L). \tag{33}$$

Introducing the complementary function $\Phi_*(z)$ determined in the region S^- by formula (26) its boundary value is given by formula (28), thus condition (33) of the Riemann problem may be written in the form

$$\Phi^+(t) = -\frac{a-ib}{a+ib}\,\Phi_*^-(t)+\frac{2c}{a+ib} \tag{34}$$

of a relation between the boundary values of the holomorphic functions $\Phi(z)$ and $\Phi_*(z)$ in the regions S^+ and S^-. Condition (34) has the same form as condition (19) of Hilbert's problem, solved in the preceding paragraph by means of formula (22). We emphasize that on account of relation (26) the complementary function Φ_* should be *bounded* at infinity.

Thus, we can assert that if a function $\Phi(z)$, holomorphic in the circle S^+, is a solution of the Riemann problem (33), then the function $F(z)$, defined in the set $S^+ + S^-$ by the formulae

$$F(z) = \begin{cases} \Phi(z) & \text{for} \quad z\in S^+, \\ \Phi_*(z) & \text{for} \quad z\in S^-, \end{cases}$$

i.e. the function associated with itself

$$F(z) = F_*(z), \qquad z\in S^+ + S^-,$$

is a certain solution of Hilbert's problem (34), bounded at infinity.

Conversely, each solution $F(z)$ of Hilbert's problem, with the boundary condition $(a+ib)F^+(t)+(a-ib)F^-(t) = 2c$, and associated with itself $[F(z) = F_*(z)]$, gives a solution of the Riemann problem (33) in the circle S^+. Since, according to the results of §1 and §2, we know all the solutions of the Hilbert problem, and hence we can obtain all the solutions of the required Riemann problem. For, selecting from the set of all solutions of Hilbert's problem (35) those functions $\Phi(z)$ which are self-associated $[\Phi_*(z) = \Phi(z)]$, we obtain the set of all solutions of the Riemann problem in the circle S^+.

We note that the set of all solutions of Hilbert's problem is a set of such pairs of functions holomorphic in the regions S^+ and S^- which are such that each function in the region S^+ is associated with one function in the region S^- only. Hence, it follows that the solution of the Riemann problem is obtained only from these solutions of the corresponding Hilbert problem which are associated with themselves.

Let $\Psi(z)$ be an arbitrary solution of the Hilbert's problem (34) defined in the set $S^+ + S^-$ and bounded as $z \to \infty$; thus the relation

$$(a+ib)\,\Psi^+(t)+(a-ib)\,\Psi^-(t) = 2c \tag{35}$$

holds at each point $t \in L$. The function $\Phi(z) = \Psi(z)$, obtained in such a way, may not be a solution of the Riemann problem, since the function $\Psi(z)$ is not necessarily associated with itself, i.e. the equality

$$\Psi(z) = \Psi_*(z) = \overline{\Psi(1/\bar{z})}$$

may not be satisfied.

However, when we know a function $\Psi(z)$ satisfying the boundary condition of Hilbert's problem (35) and which is bounded at infinity, then certain solutions of the Riemann problem can readily be obtained for the circle. In fact, let $\Psi_*(z)$ denote the function associated with the given function $\Phi(z)$, i.e. let

$$\Psi_*(z) = \overline{\Psi(1/\bar{z})} \tag{36}$$

for $z \in S^+ + S^-$. Hence, it follows that the function $\Psi_*(z)$, sectionally holomorphic in the regions S^+ and S^-, satisfies the boundary condition

$$(a-ib)\,\Psi_*^-(t)+(a+ib)\,\Psi_*^+(t)=2c. \tag{37}$$

It follows from relations (35) and (37) that the function

$$\Omega(z)=\tfrac{1}{2}[\Psi(z)+\Psi_*(z)] \tag{38}$$

(obviously associated with itself), is a solution of the Riemann problem in the region S^+. In fact, on account of equalities (35), (36), (37) we can assert that the boundary values $\Omega^+(t)$ of the function (38) satisfy either relation (33) or (32), i.e. we have at each point on the circumference of the circle L:

$$\text{re}\,[(a+ib)\,\Omega^+(t)]=c. \tag{39}$$

In the investigation of the existence of solutions of the Riemann problem, an important rôle is played by a certain integer κ called *the index* of this problem.

DEFINITION. *The index of the Riemann problem* (32) *is that integer κ which is the index of the corresponding Hilbert problem expressed by the boundary condition* (34).

According to (4) we have

$$\kappa=\frac{1}{2\pi i}\left[\log\frac{a-ib}{a+ib}\right]_L=\frac{1}{2\pi}\arg\left[\frac{a-ib}{a+ib}\right]_L, \tag{40}$$

and hence it follows that

$$\kappa=\frac{1}{\pi i}\,[\log(a-ib)]_L=\frac{1}{\pi}\,[\arg(a-ib)]_L. \tag{41}$$

Here, the positive direction of the circle L is the same as the positive rotation on the complex plane. From formula (41) we conclude that the index of the Riemann problem is always an *even* integer, positive, negative, or equal to zero.

The following four theorems provide solutions of the homogeneous and non-homogeneous Riemann problem.

THEOREM 1. *If the index* κ *is non-negative, then the homogeneous Riemann problem has* $\kappa+1$ *linearly independent solutions. All the solutions are given by the formula*

$$\Phi(z) = X(z)(C_0 z^{\kappa} + C_1 z^{\kappa-1} + \ldots + C_{\kappa}), \tag{42}$$

where $X(z)$ *is a fundamental solution of the Hilbert problem* (34), *and* $C_0, C_1, \ldots, C_{\kappa}$ *are constants satisfying the conditions*

$$C_{\kappa} = \bar{C}_{\kappa-k} \quad (k = 0, 1, 2, \ldots, \kappa). \tag{42}$$

Proof. Since there is only a single contour, i.e. the circle L, we substitute $\Pi = 1$ in formulae (11) and introduce an arbitrary constant $C \neq 0$ to obtain the formulae

$$X(z) = \begin{cases} Ce^{\Gamma(z)} & \text{for} \quad z \in S^+, \\ Cz^{-\kappa} e^{\Gamma(z)} & \text{for} \quad z \in S^- \end{cases} \tag{43}$$

($z = 0$ being the centre of the circle L), where (see (34))

$$\Gamma(z) = \frac{1}{2\pi i} \int_L \frac{\log[t^{-\kappa} G(t)]}{t-z} \, dt = \frac{1}{2\pi} \int_L \frac{E(t)\, dt}{t-z}. \tag{44}$$

Here

$$E(t) = \arg\left[-t^{-\kappa} \frac{a-ib}{a+ib} \right] \tag{45}$$

is a continuous real variable function satisfying Hölder's condition on L. From formula (31) we obtain that the function (44) is determined in the regions S^+ and S^- as follows

$$\Gamma_*(z) = \frac{1}{2\pi} \int_L \frac{E(t)\, dt}{t-z} - i\alpha, \tag{46}$$

where α denotes the following real constant:

$$\alpha = \frac{1}{2\pi i} \int_L \frac{E(t)\, dt}{t} = \frac{1}{2\pi} \int_0^{2\pi} E(e^{i\theta})\, d\theta. \tag{47}$$

Hence, we have

$$X_*(z) = \bar{C}e^{\Gamma_*(z)} = \bar{C}e^{-i\alpha}\, e^{\Gamma(z)} \quad \text{for} \quad z \in S^-, \tag{48}$$

and

$$X_*(z) = \bar{C}z^\kappa\, e^{\Gamma_*(z)} = \bar{C}e^{-i\alpha}\, z^\kappa\, e^{\Gamma(z)} \quad \text{for} \quad z \in S^+. \tag{48'}$$

Thus, at each point z of the complex plane except the points on the circumference of the circle L, the following relation holds between the fundamental solution $X(z)$ and its associate function:

$$X_*(z) = z^\kappa\, X(z) \tag{49}$$

provided that

$$C = e^{-i\alpha/2}. \tag{49'}$$

It is a known fact that for the given case $\kappa \geqq 0$ all the solutions of the homogeneous Hilbert problem

$$\Phi^+(t) = -\frac{a-ib}{a+ib}\, \Phi^-(t),$$

bounded at infinity, are determined by the formula

$$\Phi(z) = P(z)\, X(z), \tag{50}$$

where

$$P(z) = C_0\, z^\kappa + C_1\, z^{\kappa-1} + \ldots + C_\kappa \tag{51}$$

is an arbitrary polynomial of degree at most κ. The function (50) is also a solution of the homogeneous Riemann problem,

$$(a+ib)\,\Phi^+(t) + (a-ib)\,\Phi^-(t) = 0 \tag{52}$$

in the region S^+, if and only if the identity $\Phi_*(z) = \Phi(z)$ holds, i.e. if the relation

$$X_*(z)\, P_*(z) = X(z)\, P(z) \tag{53}$$

is satisfied.

Since

$$P_*(z) = \overline{P(1/\bar{z})}, \qquad X_*(z) = z^\kappa\, X(z),$$

condition (53) is satisfied, if and only if, the coefficients of the polynomial $P(z)$ satisfy the equalities

$$C_k = \overline{C}_{\kappa-k} \quad (k = 0, 1, 2, \ldots, \kappa). \tag{54}$$

Finally, we see that in the case $\kappa \geqq 0$, all the solutions of the homogeneous Riemann problem are determined by formula (42), where the fundamental solution is given by formulae (43), (44), (45), (47) while the coefficients of the polynomial $P(z)$ satisfy conditions (54) only.

If the coefficients of the polynomial $P(z)$ are written in the form

$$C_k = C_k' + iC_k'' \quad (k = 0, 1, 2, \ldots, \kappa/2),$$

then we have

$$C_k = C_{\kappa-k}' - iC_{\kappa-k}'' \quad (k = \kappa/2+1, \ldots, \kappa).$$

Thus, the general solution of the Riemann problem contains $\kappa+1$ real arbitrary constants, since the coefficient $C_{\kappa/2}$ has to be real.

THEOREM 2. *If the index κ is negative, i.e. if $\kappa \leqq -2$, then the homogeneous Riemann problem does not possess a solution different from zero.*

The statement of the theorem follows immediately from the fact that in the case $\kappa < 0$ there does not exist a solution of the corresponding Hilbert problem bounded at infinity.

We shall now discuss a solution of the non-homogeneous Riemann problem. Thus, if we know a certain particular solution $\Phi_1(z)$ of this problem, then the difference between an arbitrary solution $\Phi(z)$ of the non-homogeneous problem and the particular solution $\Phi_1(z)$ obviously satisfies the boundary condition of the homogeneous problem. Hence, we draw the conclusion that in order to obtain the general solution of the non-homogeneous Riemann problem in the case $\kappa \geqq 0$, it is sufficient to add to its particular solution the general solution of the homogeneous problem.

The following two theorems deal with the non-homogeneous Riemann problem.

THEOREM 3. *If the index κ is non-negative, then the general solution of the non-homogeneous Riemann problem is expressed by the formula*

$$\Phi(z)=\tfrac{1}{2}[\Psi(z)+\Psi_*(z)]+X(z)P(z), \tag{55}$$

where the function $\Psi(z)$ is defined by

$$\Psi(z)=\frac{1}{\pi i}X(z)\int_L\frac{c(t)\,dt}{(a+ib)X^+(t)(t-z)}. \tag{56}$$

Here, $X(z)$ is the fundamental solution (43), *and $P(z)$ denotes an arbitrary polynomial of degree κ, the coefficients of which satisfy condition* (54).

Proof. The theorem follows immediately, on account of the previous argument, from the fact that the function (56) is a particular solution of the Hilbert problem (35) connected with the given Riemann problem, equal to zero at infinity. We also note that the function $\Phi_*(z)$, associated with the function (56), in accordance with formulae (31) and (49), is determined by the formula

$$\Psi_*(z)=\frac{1}{\pi i}z^\kappa X(z)\times$$
$$\times\left\{\int_L\frac{t^{-\kappa}c(t)\,dt}{(a+ib)X^+(t)(t-z)}-\int_L\frac{t^{-\kappa-1}c(t)\,dt}{(a+ib)X^+(t)}\right\}. \tag{57}$$

THEOREM 4. *For a negative index, i.e. $\kappa\leqq-2$, the Riemann problem has a unique solution defined by the formula*

$$\Phi(z)=\frac{1}{\pi i}X(z)\int_L\frac{c(t)\,dt}{(a+ib)X^+(t)(t-z)}, \tag{58}$$

if and only if the given functions a, b, c satisfy the following equalities

$$\int_0^{2\pi}e^{i(\kappa/2+k)\theta}\,\Omega(\theta)\,c(e^{i\theta})\,d\theta=0 \quad (k=1,2,\dots,-\kappa-1), \tag{59}$$

where

$$\Omega(\theta) = \frac{1}{\sqrt{a^2(t)+b^2(t)}} \exp\left\{-\frac{1}{4\pi}\int_0^{2\pi} E(t_1)\cot\frac{\theta_1-\theta}{2}\,d\theta_1\right\}, \tag{60}$$

$t = e^{i\theta}$, $t_1 = e^{i\theta_1}$, *and the function E is defined by formula* (45).

Proof. According to what was discussed in §2, the Hilbert problem (35) corresponding to the given Riemann problem (32) has, in the case $\kappa < 0$, a unique solution, bounded at infinity (not necessarily equal to zero), determined by the formula

$$\Psi(z) = \frac{1}{\pi i} X(z) \int_L \frac{c(t)\,dt}{(a+ib)X^+(t)(t-z)} \tag{61}$$

when the following necessary and sufficient conditions are satisfied:

$$\int_L \frac{t^k g(t)\,dt}{X^+(t)} = 0 \quad (k = 0, 1, 2, \dots, -\kappa-2).$$

In the given case these conditions take the form

$$\int_L \frac{t^k c(t)\,dt}{[a(t)+ib(t)]X^+(t)} = 0. \tag{62}$$

We transform these conditions, using formula (44), to the form

$$\Gamma^+(t) = \frac{i}{2}E(t) + \frac{1}{2\pi}\int_L \frac{E(\tau)\,d\tau}{\tau - t}$$

$$= \frac{i}{2}E(t) + \frac{1}{4\pi}\int_0^{2\pi} E(e^{i\theta_1})\cot\frac{\theta_1-\theta}{2}\,d\theta_1 + \frac{i}{4\pi}\int_0^{2\pi} E(e^{i\theta_1})\,d\theta_1.$$

Hence we obtain

$$X^+(t)$$

$$= \pm t^{-\kappa/2}\sqrt{-\frac{a(t)-ib(t)}{a(t)-ib(t)}}\exp\left\{\frac{1}{4\pi}\int_0^{2\pi} E(e^{i\theta_1})\cot\frac{\theta_1-\theta}{2}\,d\theta_1\right\}.$$

Substituting this expression in conditions (62) we obtain the conditions in the form (59).

In the given case, owing to the existence of one solution (61) of the Hilbert problem, bounded at infinity, the associate function is identical with function (61), $\Psi(z) = \Psi_*(z)$. Thus the solution (61) inside the circle L is, at the same time, the unique solution of the Riemann problem, provided that conditions (59) are satisfied.

Finally, we consider the Riemann problem when S^+ is an arbitrary region bounded by a contour L. By the use of a conformal mapping, assuming that angle between the tangent to the contour L and a constant direction satisfies Hölder's condition, the problem is reduced to the problem for a circle. Let $z = \omega(\zeta)$ and $\zeta = \rho(z)$ be the functions mapping the region S^+ of the variable z into the circle $|\zeta| < 1$ in the plane of the variable ζ with the circumference Λ ($|\zeta| = 1$). It is a fact known from the theory of conformal mappings that, owing to the assumption about the boundary L, the functions $\omega(\zeta)$, $\rho(z)$ and their derivatives $\omega'(\zeta)$, $\rho'(z)$ have definite boundary values on the circle Λ or on the contour L; moreover, if σ and s denote the arc coordinates of the corresponding points on Λ and L, then the continuous derivatives $d\sigma/ds$ and $ds/d\sigma$ both exist.

It follows that if $\varphi(t)$ is an arbitrary function on L satisfying Hölder's condition, then the function $\varphi[\omega(\tau)]$ expressed in terms of a point τ on Λ also satisfies Hölder's condition with the same exponent. Thus, if the condition of the Riemann problem for the region S^+ is expressed by the equality

$$\operatorname{re}[(a+ib)\Phi^+(t)] = au - bv = c\,,$$

where $a(t), b(t), c(t)$ are the functions given on L and satisfying Hölder's condition, then the corresponding condition for the circumference of the circle is expressed by the equality

$$a(\omega(\tau))\,u - b(\omega(\tau))\,v = c(\omega(\tau))$$

where the coefficients satisfy, with respect to the new variable τ, Hölder's condition with the same index as before. Knowing the solution of the Riemann problem for a circle, we thus obtain the solution of the Riemann problem for the region S^+. Moreover, the index of the problem will have the same value as for the circle, namely

$$\kappa = \frac{1}{\pi i}\,[\log(a-ib)]_L = \frac{1}{\pi}\,[\arg(a-ib)]_L .$$

§ 5. The Hilbert boundary problem for an arbitrary system of contours

The Hilbert problem, solved in §3 for a certain particular system of contours, can be solved in the same way for an arbitrary finite system of contours. This solution was recently given by W. Żakowski [93]. For the sake of simplicity, let us consider a system of Jordan contours composed of k "sets" of contours $[L_\alpha^{(1)}, L_\alpha^{(2)}, \dots, L_\alpha^{p_\alpha}]$ ($\alpha = 1, 2, \dots, k$), enclosed by one set of contours $[L_{(0)}^1, L_0^{(2)}, \dots, L_0^{(p_0)}]$ (see Fig. 14). An arbitrary contour $L_\alpha^{(\beta)}$ of the set of index $\alpha > 0$ contains all contours of this set with an upper index less than β and only these contours. An arbitrary contour $L_0^{(\beta)}$ of the set with index 0 contains all contours of this set with an upper index less than β and all sets with lower indices $1, 2, \dots, k$. We assume that neither of the above two systems of contours has common points and that all these contours are smooth. It can easily be noted that an arbitrary system of contours on a plane is always a certain combination of the systems shown in Fig. 8. The ordering of contours into certain sets is most convenient for solving the corresponding boundary Hilbert problem. Let us denote by $S_1^{(1)}, \dots, S_k^{(1)}$ the regions bounded by the contours $L_1^{(1)}, L_2^{(1)}, \dots, L_k^{(1)}$, respectively; by $S_0^{(1)}$ the region bounded by the contours $L_1^{(p_1)}, L_2^{(p_2)}, \dots, L_k^{(p_k)}, L_0^{(1)}$; by $S_\alpha^{(\beta)}$ the regions bounded by the contours $L_\alpha^{(\beta)}$ and $L_\alpha^{(\beta-1)}$ ($\alpha > 0, \beta > 1$); finally, by S_{ext} an infinite region lying outside the contours $L_0^{(p_0)}$. We assume for each line $L_\alpha^{(\beta)}$ an arbitrarily defined positive direction which does not depend on the directions of the other contours. Each contour with a chosen positive direction possesses two sides: positive and negative. For, we assume that the positive and negative side of each contour is situated with respect to the

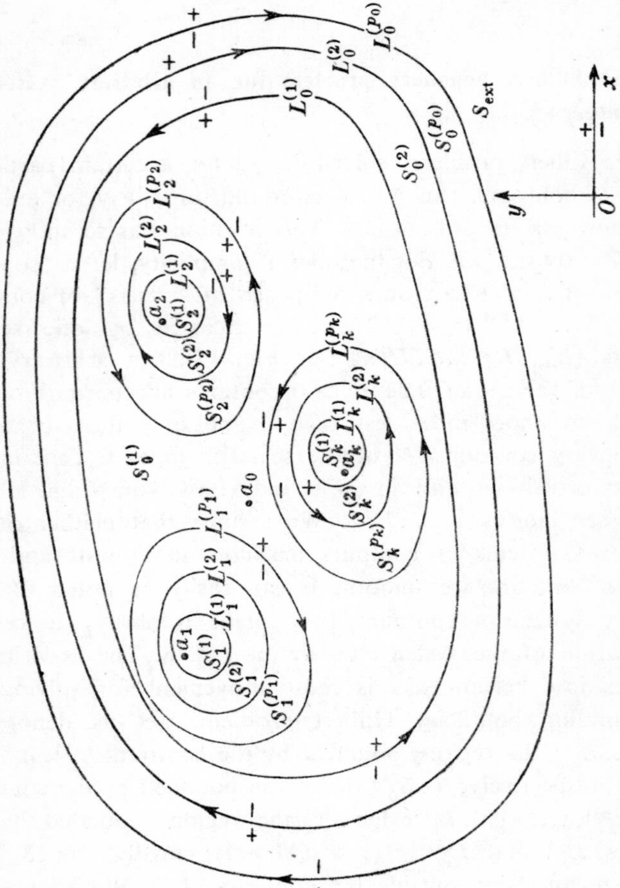
S_{ext}
$L_0^{(1)}$
$L_0^{(2)}$
$L_0^{(p_0)}$
$S_0^{(1)}$
$S_0^{(2)}$
$S_0^{(p_0)}$
a_0
a_1
$S_1^{(1)}$
$L_1^{(1)}$
$S_1^{(2)}$
$L_1^{(2)}$
$S_1^{(p_1)}$
$L_1^{(p_1)}$
a_2
$S_2^{(1)}$
$L_2^{(1)}$
$S_2^{(2)}$
$L_2^{(2)}$
$S_2^{(p_2)}$
$L_2^{(p_2)}$
a_k
$S_k^{(1)}$
$L_k^{(1)}$
$S_k^{(2)}$
$L_k^{(2)}$
$S_k^{(p_k)}$
$L_k^{(p_k)}$
x
y
O

Fig. 14

positive direction of the contour as the half-planes $\operatorname{im} z > 0$ and $\operatorname{im} z < 0$ with respect to the positive direction of the real axis (Fig. 8). As a contrast to the contours considered previously (Fig. 4), the signs $\pm$ may now be different for the sides belonging to the interior of the same region $S_\alpha^{(\beta)}$. Exactly as before, the Hilbert problem for a system of lines $L_\alpha^{(\beta)}$ in Fig. 8 consists in finding a function $\Phi(z)$, sectionally holomorphic in each of the regions $S_\alpha^{(\beta)}$, S_{ext}. The boundary values of the function $\Phi^+(t)$ and $\Phi^-(t)$ corresponding to the sides of each of the contours satisfy the prescribed linear relation

$$\Phi^+(t) = G(t)\Phi^-(t) + g(t) \tag{63}$$

at each point t of the set of points L which is the sum of all the contours $L_\alpha^{(\beta)}$. It is assumed, as before, that the given complex functions $G(t)$ and $g(t)$ defined on $L = \sum L_\alpha^{(\beta)}$ satisfy the Hölder condition,

$$|G(t) - G(t_1)| < \text{const}\,|t - t_1|^h,$$

$$|g(t) - g(t_1)| < \text{const}\,|t - t_1|^h,$$

and that the function $G(t)$ is everywhere different from zero.

First, we find the so called fundamental solution $X(z)$ of the homogeneous problem

$$X^+(t) = G(t)X^-(t). \tag{63'}$$

For this purpose, in the interior of each of the regions $S_\alpha^{(1)}$, we choose a single point a_α $(\alpha = 0, 1, 2, \ldots, k)$ and we attach to each contour $L_\alpha^{(\beta)}$ an integer

$$\lambda_\alpha^{(\beta)} = \frac{1}{2\pi i}[\log G(t)]_{L_\alpha^{(\beta)}} \qquad (\beta = 1, 2, \ldots, p_\alpha). \tag{64}$$

The increment of an arbitrarily chosen branch of the function $\log G(t)$ on a contour $L_\alpha^{(\beta)}$ concerns the full circuit in the positive direction along this line $L_\alpha^{(\beta)}$. Exactly as before, in order to make the function $\log G(t)$ continuous on each of the contours $L_\alpha^{(\beta)}$, we introduce an auxiliary function $G_0(t)$ defined on the contours $L_\alpha^{(\beta)}$ by the formulae

$$G_0(t) = (t - a_\alpha)^{-\varepsilon_\alpha^{(\beta)}\lambda_\alpha^{(\beta)}} G(t) \qquad \text{for} \qquad t \in L_\alpha^{(\beta)}, \tag{65}$$

where $\varepsilon_\alpha^{(\beta)} = +1$ when the direction of the contour is compatible with the positive rotation on the complex plane, while $\varepsilon_\alpha^{(\beta)} = -1$ otherwise. We now introduce the following function for each index $\alpha = 0, 1, 2, \ldots, k$

$$X_\alpha(z) = \begin{cases} \Psi_\alpha(z) & \text{for } z \in S_\alpha^{(1)} \ (\alpha > 0) \text{ or } z \in \tilde{S}_0^1 \ (\alpha = 0), \\ \Psi_\alpha(z)(z-a_\alpha)^{-\lambda_\alpha^{(1)}} & \text{for } z \in S_\alpha^{(2)}, \\ \cdots\cdots\cdots\cdots & \\ \Psi_\alpha(z)(z-a_\alpha)^{-\sum\limits_{\beta=1}^{\gamma-1} \lambda_\alpha^{(\beta)}} & \text{for } z \in S_\alpha^{(\gamma)}, \\ \cdots\cdots\cdots\cdots & \\ \Psi_\alpha(z)(z-a_\alpha)^{-\sum\limits_{\beta=1}^{p_\alpha} \lambda_\alpha^{(\beta)}} & \text{for } z \in S_{\alpha,\mathrm{ext}} \end{cases} \tag{66}$$

where $\tilde{S}_0^1$ denotes a simply-connected region bounded by the contour $L_0^{(1)}$, and $S_{\alpha,\mathrm{ext}}$ denotes the whole part of the plane lying outside the contour $L_\alpha^{(p_\alpha)}$, while the functions $\Psi_\alpha(z)$ are determined by the formulae

$$\Psi_\alpha(z) = \exp\left[\frac{1}{2\pi i} \sum_{\beta=1}^{p_\alpha} \int\limits_{L_\alpha^{(\beta)}} \frac{\log G_0(\tau)}{\tau - z}\, d\tau\right]. \tag{67}$$

Here, $\log G_0(\tau)$ is a continuous function on each of the contours $L_\alpha^{(\beta)}$ satisfying Hölder's condition with exponent h. Applying Plemelj's formulae, we obtain exactly as in Section 2 that the function

$$X(z) = \prod_{\alpha=0}^{k} X_\alpha(z) \tag{68}$$

is a solution of the homogeneous Hilbert problem, i.e. that its boundary values satisfy the homogeneous condition (63′) at each point $t \in L$. The integer

$$\kappa = \sum_{\alpha=1}^{k} \sum_{\beta=1}^{p_\alpha} \lambda_\alpha^{(\beta)} = \frac{1}{2\pi} \sum_{\alpha=1}^{k} \sum_{\beta=1}^{p_\alpha} [\arg G(t)]_{L_\alpha^{(\beta)}} \tag{69}$$

(independent of the ordering of the contours) is called the *index* of the given Hilbert problem. This number is equal to the order of the solution (68) at infinity, since we have

$$\lim_{z\to\infty} z^{\kappa} X(z) = 1.$$

The solution (68) is called *fundamental* and possesses the lowest order κ at infinity. It is readily seen that any other solution of the homogeneous problem can be expressed as the product of a fundamental solution and a certain entire function. Reasoning as in Section 2 we draw the conclusion that the general solution of Hilbert's problem (63) for an arbitrary system of contours is defined by the formula

$$\Phi(z) = \frac{X(z)}{2\pi i} \int_L \frac{g(\tau)\,d\tau}{X^+(\tau)(\tau - z)} + X(z) P(z), \tag{70}$$

where $P(z)$ is an arbitrary entire function. If $\kappa \geqq 0$, then we obtain all the solutions equal to zero at infinity by substituting an arbitrary polynomial of degree at most $\kappa-1$ instead of $P(z)$, or substituting $P = 0$ when $\kappa = 0$. If $\kappa < 0$, then a necessary and sufficient condition that a solution equal to zero at infinity exists is that the function $g(\tau)$ satisfies the equality

$$\int_L \frac{\tau^j g(\tau)\,d\tau}{X^+(\tau)} = 0 \tag{71}$$

(for $j = 0, 1, \ldots, -\kappa-1$). This solution is unique and determined by formula (70) when we substitute $P = 0$. It can be shown that the result (68) is compatible with formula (11) given by GAKHOV (see ŻAKOWSKI [93]).

The result (70) obtained for an arbitrary system of contours is important since it directly allows us to investigate singular integral equations for an arbitrary system of contours.

We also note that the Poincaré–Bertrand transformation (see p. 446) as well as the formula on the inversion of the Cauchy type integral (see p. 428) remain valid for the considered arbitrary system of contours.

CHAPTER XVII

LINEAR SINGULAR INTEGRAL EQUATIONS

§ 1. Historical remarks

Integral equations containing integrals in the sense of the Cauchy principal value, with integrands having a singularity in the domain of integration will be called *singular integral equations*. Such equations require different and much more intricate methods of investigation than those discussed in Part 1 for weakly-singular equations. Singular integral equations were introduced in the first decade of the present century in connection with two quite different problems: HILBERT [21] encountered these equations in a certain boundary problem of the theory of analytic functions, whereas POINCARÉ [70] in the general theory of tides. Next, papers dealing with singular integral equations we mention those of BERTRAND [2], NOETHER [40] and CARLEMANN [5]. The theory of singular integral equations was systematically developed in the third and fourth decade of this century due to a French mathematician GIRAUD [17] and Soviet mathematicians, MUSKHELISHVILI and VEKUA and their numerous collaborators.

The investigations of MUSKHELISHVILI and VEKUA, based on the properties of Cauchy type integrals and Hilbert's problem, brought a number of interesting and important results in the theory of analytic functions, and partial differential equations, as well as in problems of aerodynamics and the theory of elasticity. These investigations are presented in an excellent monograph of MUSKHELISHVILI [33].

§ 2. The Poincaré method of investigation of singular integral equations

POINCARÉ [70], investigating a boundary problem in the theory of tides (which will be considered in the next paragraph) arrived at the singular integral equation of the second kind with real variables. This equation is of the form

$$\varphi(s)+\lambda\int_0^a F(s,\sigma)\cot\frac{\pi}{a}(\sigma-s)\,\varphi(\sigma)\,d\sigma=f(s),\tag{1}$$

where $f(s)$ and $F(s,\sigma)$ are given continuous functions of period a, and the integral is taken in the sense of the Cauchy principal value. It can easily be shown that equation (1) is equivalent to the equation

$$\varphi(t)+\lambda\int_L\frac{K(t,\tau)}{\tau-t}\,\varphi(\tau)\,d\tau=f(t)\tag{2}$$

with an integral of the form previously investigated, and t,τ are complex variables. We assume that L is the circumference of a circle with radius $a/2\pi$ and centre at the point $z=0$. Let t and τ denote the points of the circumference of the circle L corresponding to the arguments $2\pi s/a$ and $2\pi\,\sigma/a$. Then we have

$$t=\frac{a}{2\pi}e^{2\pi is/a},\qquad\tau=\frac{a}{2\pi}e^{2\pi i\sigma/a},$$

$$\frac{d\tau}{\tau-t}=\frac{2\pi i}{a}\cdot\frac{e^{2\pi i\sigma/a}\,d\sigma}{e^{2\pi i\sigma/a}-e^{2\pi is/a}}=\frac{\pi}{a}\cot\frac{\pi}{a}(\sigma-s)\,d\sigma+\frac{\pi i}{a}\,d\sigma,$$

whence

$$\cot\frac{\pi}{a}(\sigma-s)\,d\sigma=\frac{a}{\pi}\,\frac{d\tau}{\tau-t}-\frac{a}{2\pi}\cdot\frac{d\tau}{\tau}\tag{2'}$$

and the equation (1) takes the form (2). Conversely, equation (2) can be reduced to the form (1).

A kernel of the form

$$\cot \frac{\pi}{a}(\sigma - s)$$

is called *the Hilbert kernel.* A kernel of the form

$$\frac{1}{\tau - t}$$

will be called *the Cauchy kernel.*

The Poincaré method consists in the reduction of equations (1) or (2) to the regular or weakly-singular Fredholm equations, by means of the transformation (53) (p. 446) of the iterated integral derived for this purpose by POINCARÉ. POINCARÉ assumed that the curve L, as well as the complex functions $f(t)$, $K(t, \tau)$ are analytic. This method, however, can be applied for less restrictive assumptions, namely, that the complex functions $f(t)$, $K(t, \tau)$ determined in the set $t \in L$ or $t, \tau \in L$ satisfy the Hölder conditions

$$\begin{aligned} |f(t) - f(t_1)| &< \text{const}\, |t - t_1|^{\mu}, \\ |K(t, \tau) - K(t_1, \tau_1)| &< \text{const}\, [|t - t_1|^{\mu} + |\tau - \tau_1|^{\mu}], \end{aligned} \tag{3}$$

where $0 < \mu \leqq 1$. For the sake of generality we assume that L is a finite set of smooth non-intersecting contours on the complex plane.

The left-hand side of integral equation (2) represents a certain functional operation over an arbitrary complex function $\varphi(t)$. This operation, dependent on the parameter λ, will be denoted by the symbol

$$\mathbf{K}_{\lambda}\varphi = \varphi(t) + \lambda \int_L \frac{K(t, \tau)}{\tau - t}\, \varphi(\tau)\, d\tau . \tag{4}$$

If the function $\varphi(\tau)$ satisfies Hölder's condition with exponent $\mu < 1$ then on account of Privalov's Theorem (p. 439), we obtain that the result of the operation (4) is a function of the variable t determined on L and satisfying Hölder's condition with the same exponent. Thus, the operation $\mathbf{K}_{-\lambda}$ with the parameter

$-\lambda$ can again be applied to the result of the operation (4) over the function φ. We then have

$$\mathbf{K}_{-\lambda}[\mathbf{K}_{\lambda}\varphi] = \varphi(t) = \lambda \int\limits_{L} \frac{K(t,\tau)}{\tau-t}\,\varphi(\tau)\,d\tau -$$

$$-\lambda \int\limits_{L} \frac{K(t,\tau)}{\tau-t}\left[\varphi(\tau)+\lambda\int\limits_{L}\frac{K(\tau,\theta)}{\theta-\tau}\,\varphi(\theta)\,d\theta\right]d\tau. \quad (5)$$

Applying the Poincaré–Bertrand transformation (53) and interchanging the symbols τ and θ we obtain

$$\mathbf{K}_{-\lambda}[\mathbf{K}_{\lambda}\varphi] = [1+\pi^2\lambda^2 K^2(t,t)]\,\varphi(t) -$$

$$-\lambda^2 \int\limits_{L}\left[\int\limits_{L}\frac{K(t,\theta)\,K(\theta,\tau)}{(\theta-t)(\tau-\theta)}\,d\theta\right]\varphi(\tau)\,d\tau. \qquad (6)$$

It is a fundamental result that the obtained iterated kernel

$$K_1(t,\tau) = \int\limits_{L}\frac{K(t,\theta)\,K(\theta,\tau)}{(\theta-t)(\tau-\theta)}\,d\theta \qquad (7)$$

is *weakly-singular*, since (according to our argument on p. 446) it satisfies the inequality

$$|K_1(t,\tau)| < \frac{\text{const}}{|t-\tau|^{1-\mu'}} \qquad (\mu' < \mu). \qquad (8)$$

The obtained result allows us to transform the prescribed singular integral equation (2) of the second kind into a weakly-singular equation. For, we can assert that if the function $\varphi(t)$, satisfying Hölder's condition, satisfies the equation (2), then it also satisfies the equation

$$\mathbf{K}_{-\lambda}[\mathbf{K}_{\lambda}\varphi] = \mathbf{K}_{-\lambda}[f(t)].$$

Thus, on account of equality (6) it satisfies the weakly-singular equation

$$[1+\pi^2\lambda^2 K^2(t,t)]\,\varphi(t) - \lambda^2 \int\limits_{L} K_1(t,\tau)\,\varphi(\tau)\,d\tau$$

$$= f(t) - \lambda\int\limits_{L}\frac{f(\tau)\,d\tau}{\tau-t}. \qquad (9)$$

If we assume that

$$1+\pi^2\lambda^2 K^2(t,t)\neq 0,$$

then we can apply to equation (9) the theory of the Fredholm weakly-singular equation studied in Part 1 (pp. 79-96). If this is the case, equation (9) is equivalent to an equation, iterated a sufficient number of times, with a bounded kernel. All three theorems of Fredholm can be applied to this equation. If we assume that the homogeneous equation

$$[1+\pi^2\lambda^2 K^2(t,t)]\,\varphi(t)=\lambda^2\int_L K_1(t,\tau)\,\varphi(\tau)\,d\tau \tag{10}$$

does not possess solutions with norm different from zero, then equation (9) has the only one solution $\psi(t)$ determined by Fredholm's First Theorem. Thus, there exists a unique function $\psi(t)$ which is continuous and satisfies equation (9):

$$[1+\pi\lambda^2 K^2(t,t)]\,\psi(t)-\lambda^2\int_L K_1(t,\tau)\,\psi(\tau)\,d\tau = f(t)-\lambda\int_L \frac{f(\tau)\,d\tau}{\tau-t}. \tag{11}$$

We prove that the function $\psi(t)$ is also the solution (obviously unique) of the initial equation (2). For this purpose, we prove first a more general lemma which we shall use in the sequel.

LEMMA 1. *If a complex function $f(t,u)$, defined in the domain $t\in L$, $u\in\Pi$ (where Π is a certain curve or region in the complex plane) satisfies Hölder's condition with respect to both variables,*

$$|f(t,u)-f(t_1,u_1)|<k_f[|t-t_1|^\mu+|u-u_1|^\mu]\quad(0<\mu\leqq 1), \tag{12}$$

then the function

$$\Psi(t,\tau,u)=\frac{f(t,u)-f(\tau,u)}{t-\tau} \tag{13}$$

is expressed in the form

$$\Psi(t,\tau,u)=\frac{\Psi^*(t,\tau,u)}{|t-\tau|^{1-\alpha}} \tag{13^{I}}$$

where the bounded function Ψ^* satisfies Hölder's condition with respect to each of the variables t,τ,u with the exponent $\mu-\alpha$. Here α is an arbitrary positive number less than μ.

Proof. By formulae (13) and (13′), the function Ψ^* can be expressed in the form

$$\Psi^*(t,\tau,u)=\frac{f(t,u)-f(\tau,u)}{|t-\tau|^{\alpha}}\cdot\frac{|t-\tau|}{t-\tau}. \tag{13^{II}}$$

For the moment we fix the variable $u\in\Pi$ and we prove the properties of the function Ψ^* with respect to the variables t and τ. Due to the symmetry of the function Ψ^* with respect to the variables t and τ, it suffices to prove the above property with respect to the variable t, assuming that the point t lies in a sufficiently small neighbourhood of the point τ on the one side of this point, for example, when it follows τ along the positive direction of the arc L. Since we have

$$\frac{|t-\tau|}{t-\tau}=e^{-i\vartheta(t,\tau)}, \tag{13^{III}}$$

where $\vartheta(t,\tau)$ is the angle formed between the vector $t-\tau$ and the axis Ox, and the point t lies on the one side only, then the ratio (13^{III}) satisfies the Lipschitz condition. It is sufficient to examine the function

$$\psi(t,\tau,u)=\frac{f(t,u)-f(\tau,u)}{|t-\tau|^{\alpha}} \tag{13^{IV}}$$

with respect to the variable t, fixing for the moment the variables τ and u. Then we obtain

$$\begin{aligned}&|\psi(t_1,\tau,u)-\psi(t,\tau,u)|\\&<\frac{|f(t_1,u)-f(t,u)|}{|t_1-\tau|^{\alpha}}+|f(t,u)-f(\tau,u)|\,\frac{||t_1-\tau|^{\alpha}-|t-\tau|^{\alpha}|}{|t_1-\tau|^{\alpha}.|t-\tau|^{\alpha}}\end{aligned} \tag{13^{V}}$$

where we assume, without loss of generality, that the point t lies between the point τ and $t_1\in L$ and that the points t, t_1 lie in such a small neighbourhood of the point τ that $|t_1-\tau|>|t-\tau|$. Let us first assume that $|t_1-t|\leqq|t-\tau|$; then we have

$$\begin{aligned}&|\psi(t_1,\tau,u)-\psi(t,\tau,u)|\\&<k_f|t-t_1|^{\mu-\alpha}+k_f|t-\tau|^{\mu-\alpha}\left[\left(1+\frac{|t-t_1|}{|t-\tau|}\right)^{\alpha}-1\right]\\&<k_f|t-t_1|^{\mu-\alpha}+\alpha k_f|t-\tau|^{\mu-\alpha-1}|t-t_1|<k_f(\alpha+1)|t-t_1|^{\mu-\alpha}.\end{aligned}$$

In the second case, for $|t_1 - t| > |t - \tau|$, we obtain, according to (13^{IV}),

$$\begin{aligned} &|\psi(t, \tau, u)| < k_f |t-\tau|^{\mu-\alpha} < k_f |t-t_1|^{\mu-\alpha}, \\ &|\psi(t_1, \tau, u)| < 2k_f |t-t_1|^{\mu-\alpha}. \end{aligned} \tag{13^{VI}}$$

Finally, there exists a positive constant k_ψ independent of τ and u, such that for an arbitrary difference $t - t_1$ we have

$$|\psi(t_1, \tau, u) - \psi(t, \tau, u)| < k_\psi |t-t_1|^{\mu-\alpha}. \tag{13^{VII}}$$

In view of symmetry, this inequality is also valid with respect to the variable τ.

In order to prove the validity of Hölder's inequality with respect to the parameter u, we obtain immediately from formula (13^{IV}) the inequality

$$|\psi(t, \tau, u) - \psi(t, \tau, u_1)| < \frac{2k_f |u-u_1|^\mu}{|t-\tau|^\alpha},$$

where $u \in \Pi$, $u_1 \in \Pi$. Hence, in the case $|u-u_1| \leqq |t-\tau|$ the inequality

$$|\psi(t, \tau, u_1) - \psi(t, \tau, u)| < 2k_f |u-u_1|^{\mu-\alpha} \tag{13^{VIII}}$$

holds, while for $|u - u_1| > |t - \tau|$ the same inequality is valid on account of inequality (13^{VI}).

Combining the proved inequalities (13^{VII}) and (13^{VIII}), we obtain the statement of the lemma.

Let us now return to equation (11). The kernel (7), according to the argument on p. 446, may be expressed in the form

$$K_1(t, \tau) = \frac{\omega(t, \tau, t) - \omega(t, \tau, \tau)}{\tau - t},$$

where the function $\omega(t, \tau, \rho)$ is determined by the formula

$$\omega(t, \tau, \rho) = \int_L \frac{K(t, \theta) K(\theta, \tau)}{\theta - \rho}\, d\theta \quad (\rho \in L),$$

and on the basis of Theorem II on p. 443, it satisfies Hölder's condition with an arbitrary positive exponent μ' less than μ

(see assumption (3)). Thus, the function K_1 may be written in the form

$$K_1(t,\tau) = \frac{\omega^*(t,\tau)}{|\tau - t|^{1-\alpha}}, \qquad (13^{\mathrm{IX}})$$

where, according to the previous lemma, the bounded function ω^* satisfies Hölder's condition

$$|\omega^*(t,\tau) - \omega^*(t_1,\tau_1)| < \text{const}\,[|t-t_1|^{\mu'-\alpha} + |\tau-\tau_1|^{\mu'-\alpha}]; \qquad (13^{\mathrm{X}})$$

here, α is an arbitrary positive fixed number less than μ'.

Using properties (13^{IX}) and (13^{X}) of the function K_1 and the continuity of the solution ψ of equation (11) we prove the following lemma:

LEMMA 2. *The integral of a weakly-singular function*

$$I(t) = \int_L K_1(t,\tau)\psi(\tau)\,d\tau = \int_L \frac{\omega^*(t,\tau)}{|t-\tau|^{1-\alpha}}\psi(\tau)\,d\tau, \qquad (13^{\mathrm{XI}})$$

where ψ is a bounded, integrable function, satisfies Hölder's condition with exponent $\frac{1}{2}\mu'$ ($\mu' < \mu$).

Proof. The proof will be analogous to that applied several times in Part 2. Thus, we write

$$I(t) - I(t_1) = \int_L \frac{\omega^*(t,\tau) - \omega^*(t_1,\tau)}{|t-\tau|^{1-\alpha}}\psi(\tau)\,d\tau +$$

$$+ \int_L \omega^*(t_1,\tau)\frac{|t_1-\tau|^{1-\alpha} - |t-\tau|^{1-\alpha}}{|t-\tau|^{1-\alpha}|t_1-\tau|^{1-\alpha}}\psi(\tau)\,d\tau.$$

The first integral, denoted by J_1, obviously satisfies the inequality

$$|J_1| < \text{const}\sup|\psi|\,.\,|t-t_1|^{\mu'-\alpha}.$$

The second integral, J_2, satisfies the inequality

$$|J_2| < \sup|\psi|\,.\,|t-t_1|^{1-\alpha}\int_L \frac{d\tau}{|t-\tau|^{1-\alpha}|t_1-\tau|^{1-\alpha}}.$$

The estimate of the last integral is well known from the theory of weakly-singular integral equations, namely, we obtain

$$\int_L \frac{d\tau}{|t-\tau|^{1-\alpha}|t_1-\tau|^{1-\alpha}} < \begin{cases} \dfrac{\text{const}}{|t-t_1|^{1-2\alpha}} & \text{for} \quad \alpha < \frac{1}{2}, \\ \text{const} & \text{for} \quad \alpha > \frac{1}{2}, \end{cases}$$

and finally, in the case $\alpha = 1/2$, the integral is comparable with the function $|\log|t-t_1||$. Owing to the arbitrary choice of the exponent $\alpha < \mu$, we conclude that integral (13^{XI}) satisfies Hölder's condition with exponent $\mu'/2$:

$$|I(t)-I(t_1)| < \text{const} \sup|\psi| \,.\, |t-t_1|^{\mu'/2} \qquad (\mu' < \mu). \qquad (13^{\mathrm{XII}})$$

Using lemma 2, we can draw the conclusion that the solution $\psi(t)$ of equation (11) satisfies Hölder's condition with exponent $\mu'/2$, namely

$$|\psi(t)-\psi(t_1)| < \text{const}\, |t-t_1|^{\mu'/2}.$$

We can perform operation (4) on this function, getting

$$\varphi_1(t) = \mathbf{K}_\lambda[\psi(t)] - f(t) \qquad (14)$$

which also satisfies Hölder's condition. Performing on the obtained function (14) the operation $\mathbf{K}_{-\lambda}$, we obtain

$$\mathbf{K}_{-\lambda}\varphi_1 = \mathbf{K}_{-\lambda}[\mathbf{K}_\lambda(\psi) - f] = 0, \qquad (15)$$

since equation (15), by equalities (5) and (6), is equivalent to equation (9).

Note that the homogeneous integral equation

$$\mathbf{K}_{-\lambda}\omega = 0 \qquad (15')$$

possesses the zero solution $\omega = 0$ only, since the function ω satisfying equation (15′) also satisfies the equation

$$\mathbf{K}_\lambda[\mathbf{K}_{-\lambda}\omega] = 0,$$

which being equivalent to equation (10), possesses, by assumption, only the zero solution. Hence, on account of equality (15), which now is satisfied, we conclude that the solution $\psi(t)$ of equation

(11) satisfies the equation

$$\mathbf{K}_{\lambda}(\psi) - f(t) = 0$$

and, what is the same thing, the initial equation (2).

In the examined case the transformed equation (9) is completely equivalent to the given singular equation (2).

In the case when the homogeneous equation (10) possesses solution with norm different from zero, we cannot assert that each solution of the transformed equation (9) is a solution of the given equation (2), although the solutions of this equation, if they exist, can all be found among the solutions of the transformed equation (9).

On the other hand, we can assert that if the transformed equation (9) does not possess solutions, then the same is true for the initial equation (2).

Thus, the Poincaré method does not afford the complete investigation of the singular integral equations. The complete solution of these equations was given by VEKUA whose method, based on the theory of the Hilbert problem, will be discussed later.

The case of a constant coefficient. Making use of the above method, we solve a singular integral equation with constant coefficients

$$\varphi(t) + \lambda \int_L \frac{\varphi(\tau)\, d\tau}{\tau - t} = f(t). \tag{16}$$

On account of the identity given on p. 446, we obtain

$$K_1(t, \tau) = \int_L \frac{d\theta}{(\theta - t)(\tau - \theta)} = 0.$$

Thus, the transformed equation (9) takes the form

$$(1 + \pi^2 \lambda^2)\, \varphi(t) = f(t) - \lambda \int_L \frac{f(\tau)\, d\tau}{\tau - t}.$$

Hence we obtain the only solution of equation (16) in the form

$$\varphi(t)=\frac{1}{1+\pi^2\lambda^2}\left[f(t)-\lambda\int_L\frac{f(\tau)\,d\tau}{\tau-t}\right], \tag{16'}$$

provided $1+\pi^2\lambda^2\neq 0$.

Singular equation of the first kind. A singular equation of the first kind takes the form

$$\int_L\frac{K(t,\tau)}{\tau-t}\,\varphi(\tau)\,d\tau=f(t), \tag{17}$$

where the functions $K(t,\tau)$, and $f(t)$ determined in the domains $[t\in L, \tau\in L]$ or $(t\in L)$ satisfy the assumption (3). We shall show that equation (17) can easily be reduced to the equivalent Fredholm equation of the second kind. This was not the case in dealing with the ordinary integral equations of the first kind, the investigation of which offered other difficulties compared with investigation of equations of the second kind (see Part 1, p. 154). Let us note that if the function $\varphi(\tau)$, satisfying Hölder's condition, satisfies equation (17) then, consequently, the equation

$$\int_L\frac{dt}{t-\theta}\left[\int_L\frac{K(t,\tau)}{\tau-t}\,\varphi(\tau)\,d\tau\right]=\int_L\frac{f(t)\,dt}{t-\theta}\qquad(\theta\in L) \tag{18}$$

holds, and hence applying the Poincaré-Bertrand transformation formula, we obtain

$$-\pi^2K(\theta,\theta)\,\varphi(\theta)+\int_L K_1(\theta,\tau)\,\varphi(\tau)\,d\tau=\int_L\frac{f(t)\,dt}{t-\theta}, \tag{19}$$

where

$$K_1(\theta,\tau)=\int_L\frac{K(t,\tau)\,dt}{(t-\theta)(\tau-t)}. \tag{20}$$

The obtained equation (19), under the assumption that $K(\theta,\theta)\neq 0$ on L, is a Fredholm equation of the second kind with the kernel (20), which, as we know, can be expressed in the form

$$K_1(\theta, \tau) = \frac{\omega^*(\theta, \tau)}{|\theta-\tau|^{1-\alpha}}$$

and thus, it is weakly singular. We recall that α is an arbitrary number smaller than μ, and the function ω^* satisfies Hölder's condition with exponent $\mu-\alpha$. We know from the preceding paragraphs that each solution φ of the Fredholm equation (19) satisfies Hölder's condition with exponent $\mu'/2$, and consequently, that this solution also satisfies equation (18).

In accordance with the investigations on the inversion of the Cauchy type integral (p. 459), the equation

$$\int_L \frac{h(t)\,dt}{t-\theta} = 0$$

possesses only the solution $h(t) = 0$ in the domain of functions satisfying the Hölder condition. Hence, conversely, the function φ satisfying equation (18) also satisfies the initial equation (17). Thus, equation (17) is completely equivalent to the transformed equation (19).

In this way, the existence and the form of the solutions of equation (19) are determined by the First and Third Theorems of Fredholm applied to the weakly-singular equation (19). The solution of equation (17) can also be obtained by using the method of Vekua derived in §6.

DEFINITION. *The singular kernel*

$$\frac{K(t, \tau)}{\tau-t} \tag{20'}$$

is said to be closed when the integral equation

$$\int_L \frac{K(t, \tau)}{\tau-t}\,\varphi(\tau)\,d\tau = 0$$

has only the zero solution $\varphi = 0$ *in the set of functions satisfying Hölder's condition.*

A necessary and sufficient condition for kernel (20′) to be closed is that the homogeneous, weakly-singular integral equation corresponding to equation (19) possesses the zero solution only.

An example of a closed kernel is the function

$$\frac{\text{const}}{\tau - t}.$$

§ 3. On the dominant equation of a singular equation

Before the derivation of the Vekua method, we consider the properties of the dominant equation and some general properties of singular equations which following Soviet mathematicians can be written in the form

$$\mathbf{K}\varphi = A(t)\varphi(t) + \frac{1}{\pi i}\int\limits_L \frac{K(t,\tau)\varphi(\tau)\,d\tau}{\tau - t} = f(t); \tag{21}$$

K is a symbol of a functional operation performed over the unknown function φ determined by the left-hand side of equation (21). We assume that: (i) L is an arbitrary set of a finite number of smooth, closed, non-intersecting curves $L_0, L_1, \ldots, L_p$ in the complex plane, (ii) the given functions $A(t), f(t)$, and $K(t,\tau)$ are determined for $t \in L, \tau \in L$ and satisfy Hölder's conditions

$$\begin{gathered} |A(t) - A(t_1)| < \text{const}\,|t - t_1|^{\mu}, \\ |f(t) - f(t_1)| < \text{const}\,|t - t_1|^{\mu}, \\ |K(t,\tau) - K(t_1,\tau_1)| < \text{const}\,[|t - t_1|^{\mu} + |\tau - \tau_1|^{\mu}] \end{gathered} \tag{22}$$

$(0 < \mu \leqq 1)$, (iii) the integral in equation (21) has its Cauchy principal value.

In order to determine the dominant equation of the singular equation (21), we write the left-hand side of the equation in the following manner;

$$\mathbf{K}\varphi = A(t)\varphi(t) + \frac{K(t,t)}{\pi i}\int\limits_L \frac{\varphi(\tau)\,d\tau}{\tau - t} + \\ + \int\limits_L \frac{K(t,\tau) - K(t,t)}{\tau - t}\varphi(\tau)\,d\tau = f(t). \tag{23}$$

The second of the above integrals, on account of the assumed property (22), concerns the weak singularity. Thus, the equation

$$\mathbf{K}^{\circ}\varphi = A(t)\varphi(t) + \frac{K(t,t)}{\pi i}\int_L \frac{\varphi(\tau)\,d\tau}{\tau - t} = f(t) \tag{24}$$

is called *the dominant equation* of the singular equation (21) or (23). It contains the singular part of the given equation (23).

This equation plays an important rôle, since the analysis of the complete equation (23) is based on the investigation of the dominant equation. The operation $\mathbf{K}^{\circ}\varphi$, defined by formula (24), is called *the dominant part of the operation* $\mathbf{K}\varphi$.

I. VEKUA [84] investigated and solved the dominant equation (24) showing that its solution is equivalent to the solution of a certain Hilbert problem already discussed in the preceding paragraphs. Let us assume that the contours $L_0, L_1, \ldots, L_p$ (arbitrarily ordered) bound the regions $S_\alpha^{(\beta)}$ (see Fig. 7), and consider the function $\Phi(z)$ determined by the Cauchy type integral

$$\Phi(z) = \frac{1}{2\pi i}\int_L \frac{\varphi(\tau)\,d\tau}{\tau - z} \tag{25}$$

in the domain $\sum\limits_{\alpha,\beta} S_\alpha^{(\beta)} + S_{\text{ext}}$. If the function $\varphi(\tau)$ determined on the set of points $L = L_0 + L_1 + \ldots + L_p$ satisfies Hölder's condition and is the solution of the integral equation (24), then on account of the Plemelj formulae, the function (25) has at each point $t \in L$ the boundary values

$$\begin{aligned} \Phi^+(t) &= \frac{1}{2}\varphi(t) + \frac{1}{2\pi i}\int_L \frac{\varphi(\tau)\,d\tau}{\tau - t}, \\ \Phi^-(t) &= -\frac{1}{2}\varphi(t) + \frac{1}{2\pi i}\int_L \frac{\varphi(\tau)\,d\tau}{\tau - t}, \end{aligned} \tag{26}$$

which at each point $t \in L$ also satisfy the condition of the Hilbert problem

$$(A+B)\Phi^+(t) - (A-B)\Phi^-(t) = f(t), \tag{27}$$

where

$$B(t) = K(t, t).$$

Moreover, function (25) *is equal to zero at infinity*. Conversely, if the function $\Phi(z)$ is a solution of the Hilbert problem (27) and equal to zero at infinity, then the function

$$\varphi(t) = \Phi^{+}(t) - \Phi^{-}(t) \tag{28}$$

is a solution of the integral equation (24).

In fact, the function $\Phi(z)$, having the given discontinuity of the boundary values (28) on L and being zero at infinity, is unique and can be represented by formula (25) (see the problem on p. 456). Hence, formulae (26) follow, and consequently (28) satisfies the integral equation (24).

Thus, the determination of the solution of the integral equation (24) is completely equivalent to the determination of the solution of the Hilbert problem (27) equal to zero at infinity.

The index of the corresponding Hilbert problem (27), which is the following integer

$$\kappa = \sum_{\nu=0}^{p} \frac{1}{2\pi i}\left[\log \frac{A-B}{A+B}\right]_{L_\nu} = \sum_{\nu=0}^{p} \frac{1}{2\pi}\left[\arg \frac{A-B}{A+B}\right]_{L_\nu}, \tag{29}$$

will be called *the index* κ of the integral equation (24). Here *we assume that the both functions* $A-B$ *and* $A+B$ *are always different from zero on* L.

In principle, the existence of the solutions of the integral equation (24) depends on the index κ. For, we have the following two theorems relating them to the homogeneous and non-homogeneous dominant equation (24). We recall that by the solution of the singular integral equation for a contour we shall always mean the solution belonging to the set of functions satisfying Hölder's condition.

THEOREM 1. *If* $\kappa > 0$, *then the homogeneous dominant equation* $\mathrm{K}^{\circ}\varphi = 0$ *has exactly* κ *linearly independent solutions, while, if* $\kappa \leqq 0$, *then the above homogeneous equation has no solution different from zero.*

Proof. The validity of the theorem follows from the theorem on p. 466 on the solution of the homogeneous Hilbert problem. For, if $X(z)$ denotes the fundamental solution of the Hilbert problem (27) which is obtained by the substitution in formulae (11) on p. 465

$$G(t) = \frac{A(t)-B(t)}{A(t)+B(t)}, \tag{30}$$

then, in the case $\kappa > 0$, there exist exactly κ linearly independent solutions of the Hilbert problem, connected with equation (24), equal to zero at infinity, and having the form

$$\Phi_\nu(z) = z^\nu X(z) \quad (\nu = 0, 1, 2, \ldots, \kappa-1). \tag{31}$$

Thus, for $\kappa > 0$, there exist exactly κ linearly independent solutions of the dominant equation (24):

$$\varphi_\nu(t) = \Phi_\nu^+(t) - \Phi_\nu^-(t) = t^\nu [X^+(t) - X^-(t)]$$
$$= \frac{t^\nu}{\Pi(t)} e^{\Gamma^+(t)} - t^{\nu-\kappa} e^{\Gamma^-(t)} \quad (\nu = 0, 1, \ldots, \kappa-1). \tag{32}$$

We recall that $\Gamma^\pm(t)$ are the boundary values of the Cauchy type integral (9) (p. 465) where the function $G_0(t)$ is connected with the function $G(t)$ by formulae (6) and (7) on p. 464.

The general solution of the homogeneous equation (24) is an arbitrary linear combination of solutions (32):

$$\varphi(t) = \sum_{\nu=0}^{\kappa-1} C_\nu \varphi_\nu(t).$$

The second part of the theorem, for $\kappa \leqq 0$, follows immediately from the argument on p. 467.

THEOREM 2. *If the index κ is non-negative, then the non-homogeneous dominant equation*

$$\mathrm{K}^\circ \varphi = f(t)$$

has, for an arbitrary $f(t)$, a solution linearly dependent on κ arbitrary constants, satisfying the Hölder condition; if the index κ is negative ($\kappa \leqq -1$), then the above equation has a solution if, and only if, the right-hand side $f(t)$ is orthogonal to some $-\kappa$ linearly independent functions. Then the solution is unique.

Proof. In the first case, $\kappa \geqq 0$, the theorem follows immediately from the theorem on p. 469 on the existence of the general solution of the Hilbert problem. The solution is equal to zero at infinity and is determined by formula (23). Hence, we obtain, on account of Plemelj's formulae, that the general solution of the integral equation (24) takes the form

$$\varphi(t) = \frac{X^+(t)+X^-(t)}{2[A(t)+B(t)]X^+(t)} f(t) + \\ + \frac{X^+(t)-X^-(t)}{2\pi i} \int_L \frac{f(\tau)\,d\tau}{[A(\tau)+B(\tau)]X^+(\tau)(\tau-t)} + \\ + [X^+(t)-X^-(t)]P_{\kappa-1}(t), \tag{33}$$

where $P_{\kappa-1}(t)$ denotes an arbitrary polynomial of degree at most $\kappa-1$ for $\kappa \geqq 1$, and 0 for $\kappa = 0$. In the second case, $\kappa < 0$, on the basis of the same theorem, there exists a unique solution of equation (24), determined by formula (33) with the substitution $P_{\kappa-1} = 0$, if, and only if, the function $f(t)$ satisfies the following conditions of orthogonality:

$$\int_L \frac{\tau^k f(\tau)\,d\tau}{[A(\tau)+B(\tau)]X^+(\tau)} = 0 \quad (k = 0, 1, 2, \ldots, -\kappa-1). \tag{34}$$

DEFINITION *The equation*

$$\mathbf{K}^{\circ\prime}\psi = A(t)\psi(t) - \frac{1}{\pi i}\int_L \frac{B(\tau)\psi(\tau)\,d\tau}{\tau - t} = \tilde{f}(t), \tag{35}$$

obtained by interchanging the variables t, τ in the integrand is called the associate equation of the dominant equation (24); *the form of the right-hand side is irrelevant in this case.*

We see that here we have taken the definition of the associate equation which is different from that for the Fredholm equations discussed in Part 1, where the kernel in an associate equation was obtained not only by interchanging the variables in the kernel of a given equation, but also by taking the complex conjugate.

We show that equation (35) can also be solved by reduction to the Hilbert problem.

Namely, let us consider the function

$$\Psi(z)=\frac{1}{2\pi i}\int_L \frac{B(\tau)\psi(\tau)\,d\tau}{\tau-z}. \tag{36}$$

Thus, if $\psi(\tau)$ is an arbitrary solution of the integral equation (35) satisfying Hölder's condition, then the boundary values of function (36), sectionally holomorphic in the regions $S_\alpha^{(\beta)}, +S_{\text{ext}}$ and equal to zero at infinity, are

$$\Psi^+(t)=\frac{1}{2}B(t)\psi(t)+\frac{1}{2\pi i}\int_L \frac{B(\tau)\psi(\tau)\,d\tau}{\tau-t},$$

$$\Psi^-(t)=-\frac{1}{2}B(t)\psi(t)+\frac{1}{2\pi i}\int_L \frac{B(\tau)\psi(\tau)\,d\tau}{\tau-t}, \tag{37}$$

hence, the equations

$$A(t)\psi(t)=\Psi^+(t)+\Psi^-(t)+\tilde{f}(t),$$

$$B(t)\psi(t)=\Psi^+(t)-\Psi^-(t) \tag{38}$$

follow. Thus, the boundary values of function (36) satisfy the relation

$$\Psi^+(t)=\frac{A(t)+B(t)}{A(t)-B(t)}\Psi^-(t)+\frac{B(t)\tilde{f}(t)}{A(t)-B(t)} \tag{39}$$

at each point $t\in L$. In this way, function (36) is a solution of the Hilbert problem (38) equal to zero at infinity.

Conversely, if $\psi(z)$ is a solution of the Hilbert problem with the boundary condition (39), and equal to zero at infinity, then the function

$$\psi(t)=\frac{2\Psi^+(t)+\tilde{f}(t)}{A(t)+B(t)}=\frac{2\Psi^-(t)+\tilde{f}(t)}{A(t)-B(t)} \tag{40}$$

is a solution of the integral equation (35). Thus, all solutions of the integral equation (35) can be obtained by the determination of the solutions of the Hilbert problem (39) equal to zero at infinity. Note, that the homogeneous Hilbert problem corresponding to relation (39) for $\tilde{f} = 0$ is adjoint with the homogeneous problem (27) (for $f = 0$). Hence its index κ' is equal to the opposite value $-\kappa$ of the index of the problem (27) while the fundamental solution is the inverse $[X(z)]^{-1}$ of the fundamental solution of the problem (27). Thus, we may state the following theorem, the proof of which is obvious:

THEOREM 3. *If* $\kappa' = -\kappa \geqq 0$, *then the non-homogeneous equation* $\mathbf{K}^{\circ\prime}\psi = \tilde{f}$, *which is the associate of the dominant equation, possesses the general solution*

$$\psi(t) = \frac{A(t)\tilde{f}(t)}{A^2(t)-B^2(t)} + \frac{[X^+(t)]^{-1}}{\pi i[A(t)+B(t)]}\int_L \frac{X^+(\tau)B(\tau)\tilde{f}(\tau)\,d\tau}{[A(\tau)-B(\tau)](\tau-t)} + \\ + \frac{2[X^+(t)]^{-1}}{A(t)+B(t)}P_{\kappa'-1}(t), \qquad (41)$$

where $P_{\kappa'-1}(t)$ *is an arbitrary polynomial of degree at most* $\kappa'-1$.

If $\kappa' = -\kappa < 0$, *then equation* (41) *has a solution if and only if, the given function* $\tilde{f}(t)$ *satisfies the conditions of orthogonality*

$$\int_L \frac{X^+(\tau)B(\tau)\tilde{f}(\tau)\tau^k\,d\tau}{A(\tau)-B(\tau)} = 0 \quad (k = 0, 1, 2, \ldots, -\kappa'-1).$$

This solution is then unique and determined by formula (41) *where* $P_{\kappa'-1} = 0$.

In the case when the equation adjoint to the dominant equation is homogeneous ($\tilde{f} = 0$), *the equation possesses only the zero solution for* $\kappa' = -\kappa \leqq 0$, *and the general solution of the form*

$$\psi(t) = \frac{2[X^+(t)]^{-1}}{A(t)+B(t)}P_{\kappa'-1}(t) \quad \textit{for} \quad \kappa' > 0.$$

§ 4. General properties of a singular equation

Suppose we are given a singular equation of the form already considered

$$\mathbf{K}\varphi = A(t)\varphi(t) + \frac{1}{\pi i}\int_L \frac{K(t,\tau)}{\tau - t}\varphi(\tau)\,d\tau = f(t). \qquad (42)$$

We assume that the functions $A(t), K(t, \tau), f(t)$ satisfy (22), and furthermore, we assume that

$$A^2(t) - B^2(t) \neq 0 \quad [B(t) = K(t, t)] \tag{43}$$

at each point $t \in L$. We say then that equation (42) is of *normal type*. We do not exclude the case when $A(t) \equiv 0$, provided that then $B(t) \neq 0$ everywhere.

DEFINITION. *The index of the dominant equation* (24), *i.e. the number*

$$\kappa = \frac{1}{2\pi} \sum_{\nu=0}^{p} \left[\arg \frac{A-B}{A+B} \right]_{L_\nu}, \tag{44}$$

will be called the index κ *of the operation* $\mathbf{K}$, *or of equation* (42).

On account of the assumption (43), the index κ is a definite integer, positive, negative or equal to zero.

In a particular case, when $B = K(t, t) = 0$ (then $A(t) \neq 0$), the index κ of the equation is equal to zero and the equation can be reduced to a weakly-singular equation

$$A(t)\varphi(t) + \frac{1}{\pi i} \int_L \frac{K(t, \tau) - K(t, t)}{\tau - t} \varphi(\tau)\, d\tau = f(t)$$

which does not require any further examination.

We now consider the properties of the operation consisting of two singular operations.

Let there be given two singular normal operations:

$$\mathbf{K}\varphi = A(t)\varphi(t) + \frac{1}{\pi i} \int_L \frac{K(t, \tau)}{\tau - t} \varphi(\tau)\, d\tau, \tag{45}$$

$$\mathbf{K}_1 \psi = A_1(t)\psi(t) + \frac{1}{\pi i} \int_L \frac{K_1(t, \tau)}{\tau - t} \psi(\tau)\, d\tau. \tag{45'}$$

The result of the operation

$$\mathbf{K}_1\mathbf{K}\varphi = \mathbf{K}_1[\mathbf{K}\varphi(t)]$$

$$= A_1(t)\left[A(t)\varphi(t)+\frac{1}{\pi i}\int_L \frac{K(t,\tau)}{\tau-t}\varphi(\tau)\,d\tau\right]+$$

$$+\frac{1}{\pi i}\int_L \frac{K_1(t,\theta)}{\theta-t}\left[A(\theta)\varphi(\theta)+\frac{1}{\pi i}\int_L \frac{K(\theta,\tau)}{\tau-\theta}\varphi(\tau)\,d\tau\right]d\theta$$

$$= A(t)A_1(t)\varphi(t)+$$

$$+\frac{1}{\pi i}\int_L \frac{A_1(t)K(t,\tau)+A(\tau)K_1(t,\tau)}{\tau-t}\varphi(\tau)\,d\tau-$$

$$-\frac{1}{\pi^2}\int_L \frac{K_1(t,\theta)}{\theta-t}\left[\int_L \frac{K(\theta,\tau)}{\tau-\theta}\varphi(\tau)\,d\tau\right]d\theta,$$

performed over an arbitrary function $\varphi(t)$ satisfying Hölder's condition, will be called *the product* of the first and the second operation and will be denoted by the symbol $\mathbf{K}_1\mathbf{K}$.

Applying to the last integral the Poincaré–Bertrand transformation (p. 446), we obtain

$$\mathbf{K}_1[\mathbf{K}\varphi] = \mathbf{K}_1\mathbf{K}\varphi = [A_1(t)A(t)+B_1(t)B(t)]\varphi(t)+$$

$$+\frac{1}{\pi i}\int_L \frac{A_1(t)K(t,\tau)+A(\tau)K_1(t,\tau)}{\tau-t}\varphi(\tau)\,d\tau-$$

$$-\frac{1}{\pi^2}\int_L\left[\int_L \frac{K_1(t,\theta)K(\theta,\tau)}{(\theta-t)(\tau-\theta)}\,d\theta\right]\varphi(\tau)\,d\tau \qquad (46)$$

where

$$B_1(t) = K_1(t,t).$$

The last integral operation is, as we know, weakly-singular.

The following important theorem follows from formula (46):

THEOREM. *The index of the product operation is equal to the sum of the indices of the component operations.*

In fact, on account of equality (44), we obtain from formula (46) the following value for the index κ^* of the operation $\mathbf{K}^*$:

$$\kappa^* = \frac{1}{2\pi} \sum_{\nu=0}^{p} \left[\arg \frac{(A-B)(A_1-B_1)}{(A+B)(A_1+B_1)} \right]_{L_\nu}$$

$$= \frac{1}{2\pi} \sum_{\nu=0}^{p} \left[\arg \frac{A-B}{A+B} \right]_{L_\nu} + \frac{1}{2\pi} \sum_{\nu=0}^{p} \left[\arg \frac{A_1-B_1}{A_1+B_1} \right]_{L_\nu} = \kappa+\kappa_1.$$

DEFINITION. *The operation* $\mathbf{K}_1$ *is called regularizing with respect to the operation* $\mathbf{K}$ *when the product of these operations is a weakly-singular operation.*

Thus, the operation $\mathbf{K}_1$ is regularizing with respect to the operation $\mathbf{K}$, if, and only if, the numerator of the integrand of the first integral on the right-hand side of equality (46) is equal to zero for $\tau = t$, i.e.

$$A_1(t)B(t)+A(t)B_1(t) = 0. \tag{47}$$

Obviously, the index of such an operation is equal to zero, and thus, the index of the regularizing operation $\mathbf{K}_1$ is equal to the opposite value of the index of the given operation $\mathbf{K}$. It is also apparent that if the operation $\mathbf{K}$ is regularizing with respect to the operation $\mathbf{K}$, then, conversely, the operation $\mathbf{K}$ is regularizing with respect to the operation $\mathbf{K}_1$.

It is seen from the condition (47) that for the given operation characterized by two functions $A(t)$ and $B(t)$ there exists an infinite number of regularizing operations. For instance, we can take as an operation the operation relating to characteristic functions

$$A_1(t) = A(t), \quad B_1(t) = -B(t).$$

We shall prove later that the notion of the regularizing operation plays a central rôle in the reduction of the singular equation to the equivalent weakly-singular equation.

We mention that the product of singular operations does not obey the commutative law, in other words, the result of the operation $\mathbf{K}_1\mathbf{K}$ may be different from the result $\mathbf{K}\mathbf{K}_1$.

On the other hand, the product of the singular operations does obey the associative law, i.e.

$$\mathbf{K}_2(\mathbf{K}_1\mathbf{K}\varphi) = (\mathbf{K}_2\mathbf{K}_1)\mathbf{K}\varphi\,.$$

§ 5. Properties of associate operations

Definition. *For a given singular operation*

$$\mathbf{K}\varphi = A(t)\varphi(t) + \frac{1}{\pi i}\int\limits_L \frac{K(t,\tau)}{\tau - t}\varphi(\tau)\,d\tau \tag{48}$$

the operation

$$\mathbf{K}'\psi = A(t)\psi(t) - \frac{1}{\pi i}\int\limits_L \frac{K(\tau,t)}{\tau - t}\psi(\tau)\,d\tau, \tag{49}$$

obtained by interchanging the variables t, τ in the kernel of the prescribed operation, will be called the associate operation.

The corresponding integral equations

$$\mathbf{K}\varphi = f(t), \quad \mathbf{K}'\psi = g(t)$$

are called associated, one to another, independently of the form of the functions f and g.

This definition is a generalization of the previous definition for the dominant equation. A consequence of the considered dominant equation is that the index κ' of the operation (49) associated with the given operation (48) is equal to the opposite value $-\kappa$ of the index of this operation.

The dominant operation of the associate operation (49) can be expressed in the form

$$\mathbf{K}'^{\circ}\psi = A(t)\psi(t) - \frac{B(t)}{\pi i}\int\limits_L \frac{\psi(\tau)\,dt}{\tau - t} \tag{50}$$

which, as a rule, is different from the operation $\mathbf{K}^{\circ\prime}$ associated with the dominant operation $\mathbf{K}^{\circ}$ and determined by formula (35). Of course, the index of the operation (50) is the same value $-\kappa$ as the index of operation (49) or operation (35).

THEOREM 1. *The integral equality*

$$\int_L \psi(t)\,\mathbf{K}[\varphi(t)]\,dt = \int_L \varphi(t)\,\mathbf{K}'[\psi(t)]\,dt \tag{51}$$

is valid for any two arbitrary functions $\varphi(t)$ *and* $\psi(t)$ *defined on* L *and satisfying Hölder's condition, and for the given associate operations* (48) *and* (49).

This equality can directly be verified by the use of the expressions (48) and (49). It can be proved that if for two singular operations $\mathbf{K}$ and $\mathbf{K}'$ equality (51) holds for each pair of functions φ and ψ determined on L and satisfying Hölder's condition, then the operations $\mathbf{K}$ and $\mathbf{K}'$ are mutually associate. The converse is also true.

THEOREM 2. *The operation* $(\mathbf{K}_1\mathbf{K})'$, *associate to the operation* $\mathbf{K}_1\mathbf{K}$ *which is the product of the singular operations* $\mathbf{K}$ *and* $\mathbf{K}_1$, *is identical with the product* $\mathbf{K}'\mathbf{K}_1'$ *of the associate operations* $\mathbf{K}_1'$ *and* $\mathbf{K}'$, *i.e.*

$$(\mathbf{K}_1\mathbf{K})' = \mathbf{K}'\mathbf{K}_1'.$$

The proof of the theorem can be obtained directly by the application of the formula to the product of two operations (46) and formula (49) for an associate operation.

§ 6. Vekua's method of solution of a singular equation

Poincaré's method, as well as the method derived later by NOETHER (see NOETHER [40]), reduce the given singular equation to the Fredholm equation with a weak singularity by means of the application of the regularizing operation. These methods, however, do not provide the complete equivalence of the transformed equation and the given one, in the sense that the solution of the resulting equation satisfies the initial one.

Vekua's method, which will be derived in this section, has the advantage in that it gives the complete solution of the problem of singular equations using the following theorem:

VEKUA'S THEOREM OF EQUIVALENCE. *Each singular integral equation*

$$\mathbf{K}\varphi = A(t)\varphi(t) + \frac{1}{\pi i}\int_L \frac{K(t,\tau)}{\tau - t}\varphi(\tau)\,d\tau = f(t), \qquad (52)$$

where the given functions $A(t)$, $K(t,\tau)$, $f(t)$ possess the properties previously indicated, is completely equivalent to a certain weakly-singular Fredholm equation.

Proof. The above theorem has been proved by VEKUA (see VEKUA [85]) by means of a regularizing operation which was the dominant operation $\mathbf{K}^{\circ\prime}$ or $\mathbf{K}^{\prime\circ}$. The properties of this operation have been investigated from the point of view of the solution of the Hilbert problem (see Theorem 3 on p. 506). Here, we consider two cases.

Case (i) $\kappa \geqq 0$. Then, there exists a singular operation $\mathbf{K}^{\circ\prime}$ (or $\mathbf{K}^{\prime\circ}$), with index $-\kappa$, regularizing operation (52) such that the singular equation $\mathbf{K}^{\circ\prime}\omega = 0$ possesses the zero solution $\omega = 0$ only. Thus each solution $\varphi(t)$ of equation (52) satisfies the equation

$$\mathbf{K}^{\circ\prime}[\mathbf{K}\varphi - f(t)] = 0 \qquad (53)$$

and conversely, each solution of equation (53) satisfies equation (52). Equation (53) is equivalent to the Fredholm equation (see p. 508) with the weakly-singular kernel

$$(A^2 - B^2)\varphi(t) + \frac{1}{\pi^2}\int_L\left[\int_L \frac{B(\theta)K(\theta,\tau)\,d\theta}{(\theta - t)(\tau - \theta)}\right]\varphi(\tau)\,d\tau$$

$$= A(t)f(t) - \frac{1}{\pi i}\int_L \frac{B(\tau)f(\tau)}{(\tau - t)}\,d\tau. \qquad (54)$$

This equation can always be reduced, by iteration, to the equivalent Fredholm equation with bounded kernel (Part 1, p. 84). On the basis of the argument on p. 495, each solution of equation (54) (if it exists) satisfies Hölder's condition, thus, it is the solution of equation (53), and consequently, the solution of the initial equation (52).

Case (ii) $\kappa < 0$. Then we introduce in equation (52) the new unknown function ψ, by the substitution

$$\varphi(t) = \mathbf{K}^{\circ\prime}\psi\,.$$

Hence we obtain the new equation

$$\mathbf{K}[\mathbf{K}^{\circ\prime}\psi] = f(t) \tag{55}$$

which can be reduced to the weakly-singular Fredholm equation

$$(A^2 - B^2)\psi(t) + \frac{1}{\pi^2}\int_L \left[\int_L \frac{K(t,\theta)B(\tau)\,d\theta}{(\theta - t)(\tau - \theta)}\right]\psi(\tau)\,d\tau = f(t). \tag{56}$$

Thus each solution ψ of equation (56), if it exists, is the solution of equation (55), and consequently, the function

$$\varphi = \mathbf{K}^{\circ\prime}\psi \tag{57}$$

is a solution of the initial equation (52). Conversely, if $\varphi(t)$ is an arbitrary solution of the given equation (52), then in our case (see p. 505) owing to the solubility of the equation

$$\mathbf{K}^{\circ\prime}\psi = f(t)$$

for an arbitrary right-hand side f, there exists a function ψ satisfying relation (57), and consequently equation (56).

The determination of the solutions of equation (52) is thus equivalent to the determination of the solutions of the weakly-singular equation (56), and Vekua's theorem is proved.

Using the above theorem we shall prove the following theorems which provide the conditions for the existence of a solution of singular equation (52).

THEOREM 1. *A necessary and sufficient condition that there exist solutions of the singular equation*

$$\mathbf{K}\varphi = f(t) \tag{58}$$

is that the given function $f(t)$ satisfies the equalities

$$\int_L f(t)\psi_j(t)\,dt = 0 \quad (j = 1, 2, \ldots, k'), \tag{59}$$

where $\psi_1, \ldots, \psi_{k'}$ is the complete system of linearly independent solutions of the homogeneous equation

$$\mathbf{K}'\psi = 0 \tag{60}$$

associated with the initial equation.

Proof. Of course, condition (59) is necessary on account of property (51) of the associate operation. In order to show that condition (59) is sufficient, we shall prove that it implies the solubility of equation (58). If $\kappa \geqq 0$, then the given equation (58) is completely equivalent to the weakly-singular Fredholm equation (53) or (54). A necessary and sufficient condition for the solubility of this equation is the system of equalities

$$\int_L \omega_j(t)\,\mathbf{K}^{\circ\prime}[f(t)]dt = 0 \quad (j = 1, 2, \ldots, q), \tag{61}$$

where $\omega_1, \omega_2, \ldots, \omega_q$ is the complete system of linearly independent solutions of the homogeneous equation associated with equation (54):

$$(\mathbf{K}^{\circ\prime}\mathbf{K}\omega)' = 0\,. \tag{62}$$

On account of Theorem 1 (p. 511), conditions (61) can be written in the equivalent form

$$\int_L f(t)\,\mathbf{K}^{\circ}[\omega_j(t)]\,dt = 0\,, \tag{61'}$$

and on the basis of Theorem 2 (p. 511), equation (62) has the equivalent form

$$\mathbf{K}'(\mathbf{K}^{\circ}\omega) = 0\,. \tag{62'}$$

Hence, it follows that the functions $\mathbf{K}^{\circ}\omega_j(t)$ $(j = 1, 2, \ldots, q)$ are the solutions of equation (60), and consequently they are certain linear combinations of the solutions $\psi_1, \ldots, \psi_{k'}$ and condition (61′) as well as (61) is satisfied.

Thus, $\varphi(t)$ is a solution of the Fredholm equation (54), and consequently, of the initial equation (58). This solution, according to the Third Fredholm Theorem, has the general form

$$\varphi(t) = \varphi_0(t) + \sum_{\nu=1}^{k} C_\nu \varphi_\nu(t)\,, \tag{63}$$

where $\varphi_0(t)$ is a certain particular solution of equation (54) determined by the Fredholm minors, $\varphi_1, \ldots, \varphi_k$ is the complete system of linearly independent solutions of the homogeneous equation connected with equation (54), and $C_1, \ldots, C_k$ are arbitrary constants. Let us consider the case $\kappa < 0$, when the solution of equation (58) is equivalent to the solution of the Fredholm equation (56). A necessary and sufficient condition for the solubility of this equation is that the system of equations

$$\int_L f(t)\gamma_j(t)\,dt = 0 \qquad (j = 1, 2, \ldots, r) \tag{64}$$

be satisfied. Here, $\gamma_1, \ldots, \gamma_r$ is the complete system of linearly independent solutions of the homogeneous equation associated with equation (55), and hence the equation

$$\mathbf{K}^\circ[\mathbf{K}'\gamma] = 0. \tag{65}$$

Since the equation $\mathbf{K}^\circ\omega = 0$, in the examined case $\kappa < 0$, possesses zero solutions only, then the solutions $\gamma_j(t)$ of equation (65) are the solutions of the equation

$$\mathbf{K}'\gamma = 0$$

associated with the given equation (58), and therefore are linear combinations of the functions $\psi_1, \ldots, \psi_{k'}$. Thus, on account of the assumption (59), equalities (64) are satisfied and equation (55) has the solution ψ; therefore the given equation (58) has the solution $\mathbf{K}^{\circ\prime}\psi$, also of the form (63).

THEOREM 2. *The difference between the number k of linearly independent solutions of the singular equation* $\mathbf{K}\varphi = 0$ *and the number k′ of linearly independent solutions of the associate equation* $\mathbf{K}'\psi = 0$ *is equal to the index* κ *of the first equation.*

Proof. It is sufficient to examine the case $\kappa > 0$, since the relation between the operations $\mathbf{K}$ and $\mathbf{K}'$ is mutual and the index of the associate operation is equal to $-\kappa$. In this case, the equation $\mathbf{K}^{\circ\prime}\varphi = 0$ does not possess any solutions different from zero, while the equation $\mathbf{K}^\circ\psi = 0$ has κ linearly independent solutions. Then, as we know, the Fredholm equation $\mathbf{K}^{\circ\prime}[\mathbf{K}\varphi] = 0$ is completely equivalent to the given equation $\mathbf{K}\varphi = 0$, and therefore the number k of its linearly independent solutions is equal to the number of the solutions of the Fredholm equation $\mathbf{K}^{\circ\prime}[\mathbf{K}\varphi] = 0$. In this way, the equation associated with the last equation, having the form $\mathbf{K}'[\mathbf{K}^\circ\psi] = 0$ and being a weakly-singular Fredholm equation, also possesses k linearly independent solutions. Thus, the equation $\mathbf{K}'\Psi = 0$ has general solution of the form

$$\Psi = c_1\psi_1 + c_2\psi_2 + \ldots + c_{k'}\psi_{k'}$$

where $\psi_1, \psi_2, \ldots, \psi_{k'}$ is the system of k' independent solutions of this equation, and $c_1, c_2, \ldots, c_{k'}$ are arbitrary constants. Therefore solving the equation

$$\mathbf{K}^\circ\psi = c_1\psi_1 + c_2\psi_2 + \ldots + c_{k'}\psi_{k'} \tag{66}$$

we obtain all the solutions of the equation $\mathbf{K}'[\mathbf{K}^\circ\psi] = 0$.

In accordance with Theorem 2 (p. 503), equation (66), for the examined case $\kappa > 0$, has general solution in the form (33), where $f(t) = c_1\psi_1 + \ldots + c_{k'}\psi_{k'}$. Thus this solution is a linear combination of $k' + \kappa$ linearly independent solutions, consequently $k = k' + \kappa$ and Theorem 2 is proved.

§ 7. The Carlemann–Vekua method

The method of solution of a singular equation

$$\mathbf{K}\varphi = A(t)\varphi(t) + \frac{1}{\pi i}\int_L \frac{K(t,\tau)}{\tau - t}\varphi(\tau)\,d\tau = f(t), \tag{67}$$

stated by Carlemann [5] and developed by Vekua, consists in the separation of the dominant part from the equation

$$\mathbf{K}\varphi = \mathbf{K}^\circ\varphi + \frac{1}{\pi i}\int_L k(t,\tau)\varphi(\tau)\,d\tau = f(t), \tag{67'}$$

where

$$k(t,\tau) = \frac{K(t,\tau) - K(t,t)}{\tau - t} = \frac{k^*(t,\tau)}{|t-\tau|^{1-\alpha}}, \tag{68}$$

and in the reduction to a weakly-singular equation by means of the application of the solution of the dominant equation. Namely, in the case $\kappa \geqq 0$, on account of Theorem 2 (p. 503), each function φ satisfying equation (67′) also satisfies the equation

$$\varphi(t) = \frac{X^+(t)-X^-(t)}{2(A+B)X^+(t)}[f(t)-\mathbf{k}\varphi(t)] + \\ + \frac{X^+(t)-X^-(t)}{2\pi i}\int_L \frac{[f(\tau)-\mathbf{k}\varphi(\tau)]\,d\tau}{[A(\tau)+B(\tau)]X^+(\tau)(\tau-t)} + \\ +[X^+(t)-X^-(t)]P_{\kappa-1}(t), \tag{69}$$

where

$$\mathbf{k}\varphi(t) = \frac{1}{\pi i}\int_L k(t,\tau)\varphi(\tau)\,d\tau, \tag{70}$$

and conversely, the solution of equation (69) is the solution of equation (67) for coefficients of the polynomial $P_{\kappa-1}$. It is readily observed that the transformed equation (69) is weakly-singular and can be solved by means of the Fredholm theory. In the case $\kappa \geqq 0$, the singular equation (67) is thus completely equivalent to the weakly-singular equation (69).

In the case $\kappa < 0$, each solution of equation (67) is the solution of equation (69) with the substitution $P_{\kappa-1} = 0$; on the other hand, however, the solution of equation (69), if it exists, satisfies the original equation (67), if, and only if, the equalities

$$\int_L \frac{t^k[f(t)-\mathbf{k}\varphi(t)]\,dt}{[A(t)+B(t)]X^+(t)} = 0 \quad (k = 0, 1, \ldots, -\kappa-1) \tag{71}$$

hold. These equalities are connected with the condition that the solution of the Hilbert problem vanishes at infinity (see p. 505).

CHAPTER XVIII

MATHEMATICAL APPLICATIONS OF THE THEORY OF SINGULAR EQUATIONS

§ 1. The Muskhelishvili problem (the modified Dirichlet problem)

Let S^+ be a multi-connected region bounded by smooth contours $L_0, L_1, \ldots, L_p$, as shown in Fig. 6. We also assume that the tangents to these contours form with a constant direction, an angle satisfying Hölder's condition. In the general case, it might not be possible to express the solution of the Dirichlet problem (see Part 2, p. 231) for a multi-connected region S^+ as a real part of a function $\Phi(z)$, holomorphic in the region S^+, i.e. there might not exist a function $\Phi(z)$, holomorphic in the region S^+, and such that the harmonic function $u(x, y)$ in the region S^+, satisfying the given boundary condition

$$\lim_{(x,y)\to t} u(x, y) = f(t) \quad \text{(a given continuous function on } L)$$

at each point $t \in L$, is a real part of this function, $u(x, y) = \operatorname{re} \Phi(z)$. Muskhelishvili stated and solved the following modified *Dirichlet problem*: to find the function $u(x, y)$, harmonic in the region S^+ and continuous in the closure $S^+ + L$, such that it can be expressed as the real part

$$u(x, y) = \operatorname{re} \Phi(z) \tag{1}$$

of a certain function $\Phi(z)$, holomorphic in the region S^+ and satisfying the boundary condition

$$\lim_{z\to t} u(z) = f(t) + a_j \tag{2}$$

at each point $t \in L_j$ ($j = 0, 1, \ldots, p$), where $f(t)$ is a real continuous function defined on the set $L = L_0 + L_1 + \ldots + L_p$, while $a_0, a_1, a_2, \ldots, a_p$ are real constants, which have to be determined, on the corresponding contours $L_0, L_1, \ldots, L_p$. In the case when the region S^+ is infinite, i.e. when the contour L_0 is absent, the boundary condition on this contour is replaced by the condition that the function $u(x, y)$ be regular at infinity.

It will be shown that the constants $a_0, a_1, \ldots, a_p$ are uniquely defined by the conditions of the problem, provided one of them is arbitrarily fixed. We assume that $a_0 = 0$; if, however, the region S^+ is infinite, then we assume that the function $u(x, y)$ is regular and equal to zero at infinity. First, we prove the following lemma:

LEMMA. *If the function $u(x, y)$, harmonic in the bounded region S^+ and continuous in $S^+ + L$, is the real part of the function $\Phi(z) = u + iv$, holomorphic in S^+, and if the function $u(x, y)$ takes the constant values a_j on L_j, and if $a_0 = 0$, then such a function is equal to zero in the region S^+, and consequently, $a_0 = a_1 = \ldots = a_p = 0$.*

In the case when the contour L_0 is absent and the region is infinite, the lemma is also valid when the condition $a_0 = 0$ is replaced by the condition that $u = 0$ at infinity.

Proof. First, assume the region S^+ to be finite and denote by a_m one of the smallest of the real constants $a_0, a_1, \ldots, a_p$. Assume that the lemma is not true, and that the function $u(x, y)$ varies in S^+. Then a_m would be the least value of the function $u(x, y)$ in $S^+ + L$ and the inequality $u(x, y) > a_m$ would be true at each point of the region S^+. Then, near the contour L_m there would exist two smooth contours L'_m and L''_m, on which the function $u(x, y)$ would assume the constant values $a_m + \varepsilon'$, $a_m + \varepsilon''$, i.e. such that $0 < \varepsilon' < \varepsilon''$. Denoting by Σ the annular region lying between the contours L'_m and L''_m, we obtain

$$\int\limits_{L'_m + L''_m} u \frac{du}{dn}\, ds = - \iint\limits_{\Sigma} \left[\left(\frac{\partial u}{\partial x}\right)^2 + \left(\frac{\partial u}{\partial y}\right)^2\right] dx\, dy \tag{3}$$

where we consider the inward drawn normals to Σ. But we have

$$\int_{L'_m} u\,\frac{du}{dn}\,ds = \int_{L'_m} u\,\frac{dv}{ds}\,ds = (a_m+\varepsilon')\int_{L'_m} dv = 0$$

and similarly

$$\int_{L''_m} u\,\frac{du}{dn}\,ds = 0\,.$$

Hence, on account of equality (3), we obtain that $\partial u/\partial x = \partial u/\partial y = 0$ at each point of the region Σ and that $u(x, y)$ is constant in Σ, and thereby in the whole region S^+. Since $u = a_0 = 0$ on L_0, in the entire region S^+ we must have $u = 0$ and $a_0 = a_1 = \ldots = a_p = 0$.

If the region S^+ is infinite, and if we assume $u(x, y)$ vanishes at infinity, then in the case when a_m, the least of the constants $a_1, a_2, \ldots, a_p$, is *negative* or equal to zero, the above argument may be repeated without modification. If $a_m > 0$, then the above argument can be applied to $-u(x, y)$. Thus, the lemma is true.

A consequence of the above lemma is that the modified Dirichlet problem possesses at most one solution. Now, we determine this solution by means of the method given by MUSKHELISHVILI [33], p. 163.

The holomorphic function $\Phi(z) = u(x, y)+iv(x, y)$, the real part of which is the required function $u(x, y)$, is sought in the form of the Cauchy type integral

$$\Phi(z) = u(x, y)+iv(x, y) = \frac{1}{\pi i}\int_L \frac{\mu(\tau)\,d\tau}{\tau-z} \tag{4}$$

where $\mu(t)$ is an unknown continuous function, real on the contours L.

Substituting $\tau-z = re^{i\theta}$, we obtain the required function in the form of the potential of a double layer

$$u(x, y) = \frac{1}{\pi}\int_L \mu(\tau)\,d\theta = \frac{1}{\pi}\int_L \frac{\cos(r, n)}{r}\,\mu(\tau)\,d\sigma \tag{5}$$

where (r, n) denotes the angle between the radius-vector $\vec{r} = \overrightarrow{\tau z}$ and the normal at the point $\tau(\sigma)$ of the contour L, inward to the region S^+. Requiring that the function (5) takes the boundary value (2) at the point $t \in L$, we obtain, on account of the property of the potential of a double layer, the equation

$$\mu(t)+\frac{1}{\pi}\int\limits_L \frac{\cos(r_{s\sigma}, n)}{r_{s\sigma}}\,\mu(t)\,d\sigma = f(t)+a(t), \tag{6}$$

or in the form

$$\mu(t)+\frac{1}{\pi}\int\limits_L \mu(\tau)\,d\theta = f(t)+a(t), \tag{6'}$$

where $a(t) = a_j$ for $t \in L_j$, θ denotes the angle between the vector $\overrightarrow{t\tau}$ and the real axis Ox, $r_{s\sigma}$ is the length of this vector, and s and σ denote the arc coordinates of the points t and τ on L.

Equation (6) or (6′) is a Fredholm equation with weakly-singular kernel of the form

$$K(t, \tau) = \frac{1}{\pi}\cdot\frac{\cos(r_{s\sigma}, n)}{r_{s\sigma}} = \frac{K_0(t, \tau)}{r_{s\sigma}^{\alpha}} \tag{7}$$

where $0 \leqq \alpha < 1$, while the bounded function $K_0(t, \tau)$ satisfies Hölder's condition with respect to both variables.

If the integral equation (6) possesses the solution $\mu(t)$, then substituting this solution in formula (4) we obtain the function $\Phi(z)$, holomorphic in S^+, the real part of which is the solution $u(x, y)$ of the Muskhelishvili problem, i.e. which satisfies the boundary value (2). Thus, let us examine, for which values of the constants a_j the integral equation (6) possesses a solution. To do this, we consider the homogeneous integral equation

$$\mu(t)+\frac{1}{\pi}\int\limits_L \mu(\tau)\,d\theta = 0 \tag{8}$$

corresponding to equation (6′). It can readily be verified that this equation has the non-zero solution

$$\mu = C_j \quad \text{for} \quad t \in L_j, \tag{9}$$

where C_j are arbitrary constants for $j = 1, 2, \ldots, p$, while $C_0 = 0$. The homogeneous equation will now be shown to have no other solutions. In fact, if $\mu_0(t)$ is an arbitrary solution of equation (8), it follows that the real part of the function

$$\Phi_0(z) = \frac{1}{\pi i} \int_L \frac{\mu_0(\tau)\, d\tau}{\tau - z} \tag{9'}$$

is equal to zero on L, and consequently

$$\operatorname{re} \Phi_0(z) = 0 \quad \text{for} \quad z \in S^+ .$$

Hence $\Phi(z) = Ai$ in the region S^+, where A is a real constant, and therefore

$$\Phi^+(t) = Ai, \quad \Phi^-(t) = \Phi^+(t) - \mu_0(t) = Ai - \mu_0(t).$$

Thus we have $\Phi^-(t) = A$ on L_j, and consequently, $\operatorname{im} \Phi(z) = A$ in the region S_j^-, whence it follows that $\Phi(z) = Ai - C_j$ in S_j^-, where C_j is a real constant. Finally, we obtain

$$\mu_0(t) = \Phi^+(t) - \Phi^-(t) = C_j \quad \text{for} \quad t \in L_j,$$

i.e. the solution of the form (9). The general solution of equation (8) is an arbitrary linear combination of the following p linearly independent solutions $\mu_1(t), \ldots, \mu_p(t)$:

$$\mu_j(t) = \begin{cases} 1 & \text{for} \quad t \in L_j, \\ 0 & \text{for} \quad t \in L_k,\ k \neq j. \end{cases} \tag{10}$$

It is seen, that the non-homogeneous equation (6′) is not always soluble. Namely, the non-homogeneous equation (6′) has a solution if, and only if (by the Third Fredholm Theorem), the constant values a_j are chosen in such a way that the known orthogonality conditions are satisfied. Since the application of this conditions, for the determination of the constants a_j, is rather complicated, Muskhelishvili devised another method of the determination. Namely, let us consider an auxilliary integral equation

$$\mu(t) + \frac{1}{\pi} \int_L \mu(\tau)\, d\theta - \int_L k(t, \tau)\, \mu(\tau)\, d\sigma = f(t) \tag{11}$$

where the real function $k(t, \tau)$ is defined in the following manner

$$k(t,\tau) = \begin{cases} \rho_j(\tau) & \text{for } t, \tau \in L_j \ (j = 1, 2, \ldots, p), \\ 0 & \text{in the remaining cases,} \end{cases} \tag{12}$$

where $\rho_j(t)$ denotes an arbitrary continuous real function, given on L_j $(j = 1, 2, \ldots, p)$ and satisfying the condition

$$\int_{L_j} \rho_j(\tau)\, d\sigma \neq 0 \tag{13}$$

(for example one can take $\rho(t) = 1$ for $t \in L$). We shall show that for this choice of the functions $\rho_j(t)$ the homogeneous equation

$$\mu(t) + \frac{1}{\pi} \int_L \mu(t)\, d\theta - \int_L k(t, \tau)\, \mu(\tau)\, d\sigma = 0 \tag{14}$$

corresponding to equation (11), possesses only the zero solution $\mu = 0$. In fact, if $\mu_0(t)$ is an arbitrary solution of equation (11), then the real part of the function

$$\Phi_0(z) = \frac{1}{\pi i} \int_L \frac{\mu(\tau)\, d\tau}{\tau - z}$$

holomorphic in S^+, has constant values on the contours L_j,

$$c_j = \int_L k(t, \tau)\, \mu_0(\tau)\, d\sigma = \int_{L_j} \rho_j(\tau)\, \mu_0(\tau)\, d\sigma \quad (j = 1, 2, \ldots, p) \tag{15}$$

and $c_0 = 0$. Hence, by the lemma, we have $\operatorname{re} \Phi_0(z) = 0$ in the region S^+, hence again, on account of the reasoning for (8), it follows that $\mu_0(\tau) = b_j$ on L_j, where b_j are certain constants and $b_0 = 0$.

Substituting these values into equation (14) we obtain

$$b_j \int_{L_j} \rho_j\, d\sigma = 0 \quad (j = 1, 2, \ldots, p).$$

Thus, according to the assumption (13), $b_j = 0$ and therefore equation (14) has the zero solution only.

In this way equation (11) has the solution $\tilde{\mu}(t)$ only determined by the First Fredholm Theorem. This solution is simultaneously the solution of the integral equation (6′) if the constants a_j take the values

$$a_j = \int_{L_j} \rho_j(\tau)\,\tilde{\mu}(\tau)\,d\sigma. \tag{16}$$

Thus the real part of the holomorphic function

$$\Phi(z) = \frac{1}{\pi i}\int_L \frac{\tilde{\mu}(\tau)\,d\tau}{\tau - z} \tag{17}$$

is the solution of the Muskhelishvili problem, i.e. it satisfies the boundary condition (2), when a_j are given by formula (16).

Note that although the kernel $k(t, \tau)$ and the function $\mu(\tau)$ depend on the choice of the function $\rho_j(\tau)$, the constant values a_j, determined by formula (16), are independent of them, since the solution of the considered problem is unique.

Two interesting corollaries follow from the above.

COROLLARY 1. *Each function $\Psi(z)$, holomorphic in a bounded region S^+, the real part of which has boundary values determined on L, is expressed in the form*

$$\Psi(z) = \frac{1}{\pi i}\int_L \frac{\mu(\tau)\,d\tau}{\tau - z} + Ci, \tag{18}$$

where $\mu(\tau)$ is a real continuous function, and C denotes a real constant.

In fact, if we set in the preceding problem

$$f(t) = [\operatorname{re}\Psi(t)]^+,$$

then the Muskhelishvili problem has the solution $u(x, y) = \operatorname{re}\Psi(z)$, and

$$a_0 = a_1 = \dots = a_p = 0.$$

Since the other solutions do not exist, it should be

$$u(x, y) = \operatorname{re}\left[\frac{1}{\pi i}\int_L \frac{\mu(\tau)\,d\tau}{\tau - z}\right],$$

where $\mu(\tau)$ is a certain continuous real function. Hence formula (18) follows.

In the case, when the region S^+ is infinite, i.e. when the contour L_0 is absent, the holomorphic function, satisfying the above conditions, bounded at infinity, is expressed as

$$\Psi(z) = \frac{1}{\pi i}\int_L \frac{\mu(\tau)\,d\tau}{\tau - z} + \Psi(\infty), \tag{18'}$$

where $\mu(\tau)$ is a real continuous function, given on L.

COROLLARY 2. *If the real part of a function $\Psi(z)$, holomorphic in S^+, assumes on L boundary values satisfying Hölder's condition, then its imaginary part will also have this property.*

In fact, according to the preceding corollary, a given function can be expressed in the form (18), and in such a way that the real function $\mu(\tau)$ satisfies an integral equation of the form (6), where $f(t) = \operatorname{re}[\Psi(t)]^+$. But, by the assumption, the function $f(t)$, and consequently the function $\mu(t)$, satisfy the Hölder condition. Thus the function $\Psi(z)$ has boundary values satisfying Hölder's condition, and the function $\operatorname{im}\Psi(z)$ will also have this property.

§ 2. The Dirichlet problem for a multi-connected region

The Muskhelishvili and Dirichlet problems in a simply connected region coincide. Now, it will be proved, that the solution of the Dirichlet problem for a multi-connected region can be obtained using the preceding solution of the Muskhelishvili problem for a multi-connected region S^+. As a matter of fact, the solution of the Dirichlet problem can be obtained directly by the method of the potential of a double layer, derived in Chapter XII, since this method can also be applied to multi-connected regions. However, the solution based on the solution of the Muskhelishvili problem is of interest, since it expresses the solution of the Dirichlet problem for a multi-connected region by means of functions of a complex variable.

Let $z_1, z_2, \ldots, z_p$ denote arbitrarily chosen points inside the regions $S_1^-, S_2^-, \ldots, S_p^-$. We write the required harmonic function $u(x, y)$ satisfying the boundary condition

$$\lim_{(x,y)\to t} u(x, y) = f(t) \quad (t \in L) \tag{19}$$

(where $f(t)$ is a continuous function on L) in the form

$$u(x, y) = U(x, y) + \sum_{k=1}^{p} A_k \log|z - z_k|, \tag{20}$$

where $U(x, y)$ denotes a new unknown harmonic function, while A_k are some real constants, not yet defined.

From the condition (19) it follows that the unknown harmonic function $U(x, y)$ satisfies the boundary condition

$$\lim_{(x,y)\to t} U(x, y) = f(t) - \sum_{k=1}^{p} A_k \log|t - z_k|. \tag{21}$$

For arbitrarily fixed values of the real coefficients A_k, the harmonic function $U(x, y)$, which is the real part of the holomorphic function in S^+ satisfying the condition (21) may not exist. On the other hand, for fixed values $A_1, \ldots, A_p$, the unique solution of the corresponding Muskhelishvili problem always exists, i.e. the harmonic function $U(x, y)$ exists which is the real part of a function $\Phi(z)$, holomorphic, in S^+, satisfying the boundary condition

$$\lim_{(x,y)\to t} U(x, y) = f(t) - \sum_{k=1}^{\infty} A_k \log|t - z_k| + a_j \tag{22}$$

where $t \in L_j$ $(j = 0, 1, \ldots, p)$, the constant $a_0 = 0$, while the real constants $a_1, a_2, \ldots, a_p$ are known.

According to the preceding paragraph, the solution $U(x, y) = \operatorname{re}\Phi(z)$ of the same problem is determined by formula (17), the constants have the values (16), where $\tilde{\mu}(\tau)$ is the only solution of the Fredholm equation (11) in which $f(t)$ is replaced by the difference

$$f(t) - \sum_{k=1}^{p} A_k \log|t - z_k|.$$

Hence, it is seen that the constants are obtained in the form

$$a_j = f_j + \sum_{k=1}^{p} \gamma_{jk} A_k \quad (j = 1, 2, \ldots, p), \tag{23}$$

where γ_{jk} are definite real constants, independent of the function $f(t)$, while the f_j are real constants which depend on the function $f(t)$ and are identically equal to zero when $f(t) = 0$.

A necessary and sufficient condition that the function given by formula (20) be the solution of the Dirichlet problem (19) is that $a_j = 0$ $(j = 0, 1, 2, \ldots, p)$, i.e. that the constants A_k should be so chosen that they satisfy the system of equations

$$\sum_{k=1}^{p} \gamma_{jk} A_k + f_j = 0 \quad (j = 1, 2, \ldots, p). \tag{24}$$

We shall show that the determinant $\det|\gamma_{jk}|$ of this system is different from zero, thus this system has a unique solution $A_1, \ldots, A_p$, under the assumption that the region S^+ is finite. In fact, if the determinant $\det|\gamma_{jk}|$ is equal to zero, then the corresponding system of homogeneous equations ($f_j = 0$) obtained in the case $f(t) \equiv 0$, has the solution $A_1, \ldots, A_p$. But, then we would obtain the function

$$u(x, y) = U(x, y) + \sum_{k=1}^{p} A_k \log|z - z_k|$$

harmonic and not identically zero* in S^+, but equal to zero on L, and this is impossible. Finally we obtain the solution of the Dirichlet problem for a multi-connected bounded region S^+ in the form (22), where the constants A_k and a_j are determined by equalities (24) and (23).

In the case of an infinite region S^+, when the contour L_0 is absent, the solution of the Dirichlet problem is somewhat different. First of all, the function $u(x, y)$ satisfying the boundary condition (19) has to be bounded, but not necessarily equal to zero, at infinity. In order to solve the problem, we first seek an auxilliary function Δ, harmonic in S^+, and satisfying the

* The sum $U + \Sigma A_k \log|z - z_k|$ cannot be zero identically unless all A_k are zero, since otherwise the function $U + iV + \Sigma A_k \log(z - z_k)$ (where V is conjugate to U) would be constant, and this is impossible, because $U + iV$ should be a single-valued function in S^+.

condition of the Dirichlet problem in the form

$$\lim_{(x,y)\to t} w(x, y) = f(t) + A, \tag{25}$$

where A is a certain constant (to be chosen in such a way that the function $w(x, y)$ is regular and equal to zero at infinity). Thus we require the function w in an analogous form

$$w(x, y) = W(x, y) + \sum_{k=1}^{p} A_k \log|z - z_k|, \tag{26}$$

where $W(x, y)$ is the solution of the Muskhelishvili problem with boundary condition

$$\lim_{(x,y)\to t} W(x, y) = f(t) + A + a_j - \sum_{k=1}^{p} A_k \log|t - z_k| \tag{27}$$

for $t \in L_j$, regular and equal to zero at infinity. This function is the real part of the holomorphic function in the form (17), equal to zero at infinity, when $\tilde{\mu}$ is the solution of the integral equation (11), while the constants a_j have values such that

$$a_j + A = \int_{L_j} \rho_j(\tau)\, \tilde{\mu}(\tau)\, d\sigma.$$

The boundary condition (25) is satisfied and the function $w(x, y)$ vanishes at infinity when the unknown constants $A, A_1, A_2, \ldots, A_p$ are determined from the following system of equations:

$$\sum_{k=1}^{p} \gamma_{jk} A_k - A + f_j = 0, \qquad \sum_{k=1}^{p} A_k = 0.$$

Similarly as above, it can be shown that this system has a unique solution, and thus there exists a harmonic function $w(x, y)$ satisfying boundary condition (25) and vanishing at infinity. Knowing the function $w(x, y)$, we obtain the function

$$u(x, y) = w(x, y) - A$$

which is harmonic in S^+, satisfies the boundary condition (19), and is bounded at infinity.

§ 3. The Poincaré boundary problem

In connection with the theory of tides, H. POINCARÉ first considered the problem of the determination of a function $u(x, y)$ harmonic in a certain plane region S^+ (simply or multi-connected) which at each point $P(s)$ of the boundary L of this region satisfies the given linear relation

$$\frac{du}{dn} + a(s)\,u(P) + b(s)\,\frac{du}{ds} = f(s). \tag{28}$$

This relation connects the boundary values of: 1) the derivative in the direction of the normal, 2) the function itself, 3) the derivative in the direction of the tangent to the contour L. The functions $a(s), b(s), f(s)$ are defined on L. Similarly, as in the classical theory, the solution of the problem will be expressed in the form of the logarithmic potential

$$u(A) = \int\limits_L \log \frac{1}{r_{s\sigma}}\,\mu(\sigma)\,d\sigma, \tag{29}$$

where μ is an unknown density. Assuming that the angle between the tangents to the contour L at the points (s) and (s_1) satisfies the condition

$$\delta(s, s_1) < \text{const}\,|s - s_1|^{\gamma} \quad (0 < \gamma \leq 1) \tag{29'}$$

and that the function $\mu(\sigma)$ satisfies Hölder's condition, we obtain that the boundary values of the derivatives in the normal and tangential directions at the point $P(s)$ (see Part 2, p. 321) become

$$\left(\frac{du}{dn}\right)_s = -\pi\mu(s) + \int\limits_L \frac{\sin\varphi_{s\sigma}}{r_{s\sigma}}\,\mu(\sigma)\,d\sigma, \tag{30}$$

$$\left(\frac{du}{ds}\right)_s = \int\limits_L \frac{\cos\varphi_{s\sigma}}{r_{s\sigma}}\,\mu(\sigma)\,d\sigma, \tag{30'}$$

where $\varphi_{s\sigma}$ denotes the angle between the vector $\overrightarrow{r_{s\sigma}}$ and the tangent, positively directed at the point $P(s)$.

The first of the integrals (30) contains a weak singularity for $s - \sigma \to 0$, the second one is singular and has a sense as the

Cauchy principal value. From the condition that the function (29) has to satisfy the boundary condition (28), we obtain that the unknown function $\mu(s)$ satisfies the singular integral equation of the form

$$-\pi\mu(s)+\int_L\left[a(s)\log\frac{1}{r_{s\sigma}}+\frac{\sin\varphi_{s\sigma}}{r_{s\sigma}}+b(s)\frac{\cos\varphi_{s\sigma}}{r_{s\sigma}}\right]\mu(\sigma)\,d\sigma=f(s) \tag{31}$$

Thus due to the tangential derivative in the boundary condition (28), there appears a singularity in the corresponding integral equation. This fact is of considerable importance in the history of mathematics.

The investigation of the singular equation (31) was a subject of one of the last, only outlined, works of POINCARÉ. POINCARÉ considered the case when $a(s) = 0$ and assumed that the functions $b(s), f(s)$ and the contour itself are analytic. He solved equation (31), reducing it by means of iteration to a regular equation.

The Poincaré problem and the integral equation (31) connected with it were investigated by a French mathematician G. BERTRAND (see BERTRAND [3]) and by the author (see POGORZELSKI [56] and [57]), but under the restrictive assumption that the functions appearing in equation (31) are analytic.

The Poincaré problem was a subject of numerous investigations of Georgian mathematicians of the MUSKHELISHVILI school (VEKUA [86], KHVEDELIDZE [23]) under much less restrictive assumptions, namely, that the functions $a(s), b(s), f(s)$ satisfy Hölder's condition and that so does the direction of the tangent to the contour L. These investigations yielded deeper results, on the basis of the general theory of singular equations.

Taking into account the above less restrictive assumptions for the given functions $a(s), b(s), f(s)$ and the contour L, equation (31) can be examined by means of the Poincaré iterative method, but this, unfortunately, does not give a complete solution. Equation (31) can be written in the form

$$\mu(s)=\lambda\int_L N(s,\sigma)\cot\frac{\pi}{l}(\sigma-s)\,\mu(\sigma)\,d\sigma-\frac{1}{\pi}f(s)\qquad\left(\lambda=\frac{1}{\pi}\right), \tag{32}$$

where l denotes the length of the contour L, and moreover, it is assumed that

$$N(s, s) = \lim_{\sigma\to s}\left[a(s)\log\frac{1}{r_{s\sigma}}+\frac{\sin\varphi_{s\sigma}}{r_{s\sigma}}+b(s)\frac{\cos\varphi_{s\sigma}}{r_{s\sigma}}\right]\times$$
$$\times\left[\cot\frac{\pi}{l}(\sigma-s)\right]^{-1}=\frac{\pi}{l}b(s). \quad (33)$$

The function $N(s, \sigma)$, satisfying the above assumptions, is periodic, and it will be proved below that it satisfies Hölder's condition with respect to both variables. In accordance with the iterative method, we note that if the function $\mu(s)$, satisfying Hölder's condition, satisfies equation (32), then it also satisfies the iterated equation

$$\mu(s)=\lambda^2\int_L N(s,\sigma)\cot\frac{\pi}{l}(\sigma-s)\times$$
$$\times\left[\int_L N(\sigma,\tau)\cot\frac{\pi}{l}(\tau-\sigma)\mu(\tau)\,d\tau\right]d\sigma+f_1(s), \quad (34)$$

where

$$f_1(s)=-\frac{1}{\pi}f(s)+\frac{1}{\pi^2}\int_L N(s,\sigma)\cot\frac{\pi}{l}(\sigma-s)f(\sigma)\,d\sigma. \quad (34')$$

We shall prove that the function $N(s, \sigma)$ satisfies the conditions of the Poincaré–Bertrand transformation (p. 446). We prove first the following lemma which is a certain generalization of Hadamard's Lemma, known in the theory of functions of a real variable.

LEMMA. *If a function $f(s, \sigma)$ of two real variables defined in a certain square*

$$0\leqq s\leqq a, \quad 0\leqq\sigma\leqq a \quad (35)$$

is equal to zero on the diagonal

$$f(s, s)=0$$

and has a partial derivative with respect to at least one variable, for example σ, satisfying Hölder's condition

$$|f'_\sigma(s,\sigma)-f'_\sigma(s_1,\sigma_1)| < k[|s-s_1|^h+|\sigma-\sigma_1|^h] \quad (0<h\leq 1), \tag{36}$$

then the function defined in the region (35) *by the formulae*

$$F(s,\sigma)=\frac{f(s,\sigma)}{\sigma-s}, \qquad F(s,s)=f'_\sigma(s,s) \tag{37}$$

satisfies Hölder's condition with respect to both variables; precisely:

$$|F(s,\sigma)-F(s_1,\sigma_1)| < \tfrac{3}{2}k[|s-s_1|^h+|\sigma-\sigma_1|^h]. \tag{38}$$

Proof. By assumption, we see that function (37) can be expressed in the following integral form

$$F(s,\sigma)=\frac{f(s,\sigma)-f(s,s)}{\sigma-s}=\int_0^1 f'_\sigma[s,s+t(\sigma-s)]\,dt. \tag{39}$$

Thus, the equalities

$$|F(s,\sigma)-F(s,\sigma_1)| < k\int_0^1 |\sigma-\sigma_1|^h t\,dt=\tfrac{1}{2}k|\sigma-\sigma_1|^h,$$

$$|F(s,\sigma)-F(s_1,\sigma)|$$

$$< k\int_0^1 [|s-s_1|^h+|s-s_1|^h(1-t)]\,dt \leq \tfrac{3}{2}k|s-s_1|^h$$

follow, which implies the proposition of the lemma.

If the functions $f(s,\sigma)$ and $f'_\sigma(s,s)$ are different from zero in the region (35), then the property of the form (38) is also true for the inverse of function (37), namely,

$$\left|\frac{1}{F(s,\sigma)}-\frac{1}{F(s_1,\sigma_1)}\right| < \frac{3k}{2[\inf|F|]^2}[|s-s_1|^h+|\sigma-\sigma_1|^h]. \tag{40}$$

Let us apply the obtained lemma to the function $N(s,\sigma)$ appearing in the integral equation (32) determined by the formula

$$N(s,\sigma)=\left[a(s)\log\frac{1}{r_{s\sigma}}+\frac{\sin\varphi_s}{r_{s\sigma}}+b(s)\frac{\cos\varphi_s}{r_{s\sigma}}\right]\times$$

$$\times\left[\cot\frac{\pi}{l}(\sigma-s)\right]^{-1} \tag{41}$$

and by formula (33). Note that we always have $r_{s\sigma} \neq 0$ for $s \neq \sigma$, as well as

$$\lim_{\sigma \to s} \frac{r_{s\sigma}}{\sigma - s} = 1,$$

and, in view of the property (29′), the functions $r_{s\sigma}$ and $\varphi_{s\sigma}$ satisfy Hölder's condition with the exponent γ in inequality (29′). Moreover, it can readily be shown that the product $r \log r$ satisfies Hölder's condition with an arbitrary exponent α less than unity, i.e. we have

$$|r \log r - r_1 \log r_1| < \text{const}\, |r - r_1|^{\alpha} \quad (0 < \alpha < 1,\ r, r_1 > 0).$$

On account of the above lemma, we can assert that the function (41) satisfies Hölder's condition with respect to both variables, for the exponent h:

$$|N(s, \sigma) - N(s_1, \sigma_1)| < \text{const}\, [|s - s_1|^h + |\sigma - \sigma_1|^h] \tag{42}$$

where h is an arbitrary positive number less than γ and not greater than the Hölder indices of the functions $a(s), b(s), f(s)$.

Owing to the property (42), we may apply to the iterated equation (34) the Poincaré–Bertrand transformation in the form (62′) (p. 451). We then obtain the following equivalent equation:

$$\left[1 + \frac{1}{l^2} b^2(s)\right] \mu(s) = \lambda^2 \int_L \left[\int_L N(s, \sigma) N(\sigma, \tau) \times \right.$$

$$\left. \times \cot \frac{\pi}{l}(\sigma - s) \cot \frac{\pi}{l}(\tau - \sigma)\, d\sigma \right] \mu(\tau)\, d\tau + f_1(s). \tag{43}$$

The kernel of this equation

$$M(s, \tau)$$

$$= \frac{l^2}{l^2 + b^2(s)} \int_L N(s, \sigma) N(\sigma, \tau) \cot \frac{\pi}{l}(\sigma - s) \cot \frac{\pi}{l}(\tau - \sigma)\, d\sigma \tag{44}$$

according to Chapter XV, §5, is weakly-singular. We verify this directly, for, we have

$$\cot\frac{\pi}{l}(\sigma-s)\cos\frac{\pi}{l}(\tau-\sigma)$$

$$=1+\cot\frac{\pi}{l}(\tau-s)\left[\cot\frac{\pi}{l}(\sigma-s)\cot\frac{\pi}{l}(\tau-\sigma)\right]$$

and hence, we obtain

$$\left[1+\frac{1}{l^2}b^2(s)\right]M(s,\tau)=\int_L N(s,\sigma)N(\sigma,\tau)\,d\sigma+$$

$$+\cot\frac{\pi}{l}(\tau-s)[f(s,\tau,s)-f(s,\tau,\tau)] \tag{45}$$

where

$$f(s,\tau,\theta)=\int_L N(s,\sigma)N(\sigma,\tau)\cot\frac{\pi}{l}(\sigma-\theta)\,d\sigma. \tag{45'}$$

According to Privalov's Theorem, this function satisfies Hölder condition with respect to the variable θ with index $h' < h$, thus the kernel (44) has a weak singularity and may be expressed in the form

$$M(s,\tau)=\frac{M^*(s,\tau)}{|s-\tau|^{1-\alpha}}, \tag{46}$$

where $0 < \alpha < h'$, while the function M^* satisfies the Hölder condition with exponent $h'-\alpha$ (see p. 495).

It follows from the classical Fredholm theory, applied to equation (43), that there exists a unique solution $\mu_0(s)$ of this equation, determined by the known formulae, provided that $\lambda^2 = 1/\pi^2$ is not an eigenvalue of the kernel (44). We prove that in this case the function $\mu_0(s)$ is also the solution of the preliminary integral equation (32) or (31).

First of all, we can assert, on account of the obvious continuity of $\mu_0(s)$, that according to equation (43), this function satisfies Hölder's condition. This follows from the fact that the function $f_1(s)$ and the integral of the weakly-singular function on the right-hand side of equality (43) satisfy the Hölder's condition.

Since $\mu_0(s)$ satisfies Hölder's condition, it follows from the Poincaré–Bertrand transformation formula that it satisfies the iterated equation (34). In order to prove that it also satisfies the preliminary equation (32) we substitute in the right-hand side of this equation $\mu_0(\sigma)$ instead of $\mu(\sigma)$, thus obtaining the function

$$\mu_1(s) = \lambda \int_L N(s,\sigma) \cot\frac{\pi}{l}(\sigma - s)\,\mu_0(\sigma)\,d\sigma - \frac{1}{\pi} f(s) \tag{47}$$

defined and satisfying Hölder's condition on L. Substituting the function $\mu_1(s)$ again instead of $\mu(\sigma)$ in the right-hand side of equation (32), we obtain, after some simplification, the function $\mu_0(s)$,

$$\mu_0(s) = \lambda \int_L N(s,\sigma) \cot\frac{\pi}{l}(\sigma - s)\,\mu_1(\sigma)\,d\sigma - \frac{1}{\pi} f(s), \tag{48}$$

since this function satisfies the iterated equation (34).

Adding equations (47) and (48) we get the equality

$$\frac{\mu_0(s)+\mu_1(s)}{2} = \lambda \int_L N(s,\sigma) \cot\frac{\pi}{l}(\sigma - s)\,\frac{\mu_0(\sigma)+\mu_1(\sigma)}{2}\,d\sigma - \frac{1}{\pi} f(s) \tag{49}$$

which shows that the function $\frac{1}{2}[\mu_0(s)+\mu_1(s)]$ is the solution of the preliminary equation (32). But, in such a case this function has also to satisfy the iterated equation (34) and (43). Since this last equation, according to the assumption, possesses the unique solution $\mu_0(s)$, we then have

$$\frac{\mu_0(s)+\mu_1(s)}{2} = \mu_0(s)$$

which implies $\mu_1 = \mu_0$ and the solution $\mu_0(s)$ of equation (43) is at the same time the only solution of the preliminary equation (31). Thus, we can assert that if $\lambda = 1/\pi^2$ is not an eigenvalue of the kernel (44), then there exists a unique solution of the Poincaré problem given by the formula

$$u(A) = \int_L \log \frac{1}{r_{A\sigma}} \mu_0(\sigma)\, d\sigma, \tag{50}$$

where $\mu_0(\sigma)$ is the unique solution of the integral equation (43).

We indicate a case, given by KHVEDELIDZE where this fact is encountered. Namely, let us assume that $a(s) \neq 0$, the function $b(s)$ has the integrable derivative, and

$$\frac{1}{2} \cdot \frac{db(s)}{ds} - c(s) \geqq 0. \tag{51}$$

Then the homogeneous Poincaré problem

$$\frac{du}{dn} + a(s)u + b(s)\frac{du}{ds} = 0$$

has no solutions different from zero. In fact, we then have

$$\iint_{S^+} \left[\left(\frac{\partial u}{\partial x}\right)^2 + \left(\frac{\partial u}{\partial y}\right)^2\right] dx\, dy$$

$$= -\int_L u \frac{du}{dn}\, ds = -\int_L \left[\frac{1}{2}\frac{db(s)}{ds} - a(s)\right] u^2\, ds < 0,$$

and we conclude that $\partial u/\partial x = \partial u/\partial y = 0$ i.e. $u = \text{const}$. It follows from the assumption $a \neq 0$ that $u = 0$. Thus, in the considered case there exists one solution of the non-homogeneous Poincaré problem.

If $\lambda^2 = 1/\pi^2$ is an eigenvalue of the kernel (44), then equation (43) and the Poincaré problem may not have a solution.

When function (34′) satisfies the known conditions of orthogonality, then the non-homogeneous equation (43) has a solution determined by the Third Fredholm Theorem. However, we cannot assert that all these solutions are then solutions of the preliminary equation (31), for then equations (43) and (31) are not completely equivalent. In this case, however, the solutions of the preliminary equation (31) exist.

If $\varphi_0(s)$ is an arbitrary solution of equation (43), then proceeding in the same way as before, we prove that the sum $\frac{1}{2}[\varphi_0(s)+\varphi_1(s)]$ is a solution of the preliminary equation (31), and consequently, we can determine the solution of the Poincaré problem in the form (50). In the case of an eigenvalue of equation (43) we thus do not obtain the complete investigation of the Poincaré problem, and therefore, in this case it is better to convert the integral equation (31), by means of the argument and formula (2′) on p. 489, into the formula

$$\varphi(t) = \int_C \frac{K(t,\tau)}{\tau - t}\,\varphi(\tau)\,d\tau + g(t) \tag{52}$$

which contains the integral over the circle C. It is known from Vekua's Theorems how to investigate such an equation, and thus we obtain the complete discussion of the Poincaré problem.

In the subsequent sections the reader will be acquainted with one more method of solution of the Poincaré problem, based on the Vekua integral formula.

§ 4. The Vekua integral formula

The Vekua integral formula [27] gives a representation of a function holomorphic in a certain region when not only the function but also its derivatives up to a certain order have given values on the boundary of the region.

We first assume that S^+ is a finite, simply connected region, bounded by a contour L, the tangent to which forms, with a constant direction, an angle satisfying Hölder's condition. Then we have the following theorem:

VEKUA'S THEOREM. *If the m-th derivative of the function $\Phi(z)$, holomorphic in the region S^+, takes a boundary value satisfying Hölder's condition, then the given function can be expressed in the region S^+ by the formula*

$$\Phi(z) = \int_L \frac{\mu(\tau)\,d\sigma}{1-z/\tau} + iC \quad (\textit{for } m = 0), \tag{53}$$

$$\Phi(z) = \int_L \mu(\tau)\left(1-\frac{z}{\tau}\right)^{m-1} \log\left(1-\frac{z}{\tau}\right) d\sigma + \int_L \mu(\tau)\,d\sigma + iC$$

$$(\textit{for } m \geqq 1), \tag{54}$$

where $\mu(\tau)$ is a real function defined on the contour L and satisfying Hölder's condition, C is a real constant, σ denotes the arc coordinate of a point $\tau \in L$, the origin of the coordinates $z = 0$ lies inside the region S^+; that branch of logarithm is chosen which is equal to zero for $z = 0$; and, finally, the function $\mu(\tau)$ and the constant C are uniquely determined for the given function $\Phi(z)$.

Proof in the case $m = 0$. We write

$$d\sigma = \tau'^{-1}\,d\tau = \bar{\tau}'\,d\tau,$$

where

$$\tau' = \frac{d\tau}{d\sigma} = \frac{dx}{d\sigma} + i\,\frac{dy}{d\sigma}, \qquad \bar{\tau}' = \frac{dx}{d\sigma} - i\,\frac{dy}{d\sigma} = \tau'^{-1}. \tag{55}$$

Then we have the following representation for formula (53):

$$\Phi(z) = \frac{1}{2\pi i}\int_L \frac{2\pi i\,\mu(\tau)\,\tau\bar{\tau}'\,d\tau}{\tau - z} + iC = \frac{1}{2\pi i}\int_L \frac{2\pi i\,\mu(\tau)\,\tau\bar{\tau}' + iC}{\tau - z}\,d\tau.$$

It is a well-known fact, however, that on account of the Cauchy integral formula, the function $\Phi(z)$ at each point $z \in S^+$ is expressed by its boundary values $\Phi^+(t)$, by the formula

$$\Phi(z) = \frac{1}{2\pi i}\int_L \frac{\Phi^+(\tau)\,d\tau}{\tau - z}.$$

Hence, by the results of § 6 of Chapter XV, we conclude that the unknown real function $\mu(\tau)$ and the real constant C should satisfy the equation

$$2\pi i\,\mu(\tau)\,\tau\bar{\tau}' + iC = \Phi^{+}(\tau) - \Omega^{-}(\tau), \tag{56}$$

where $\Omega^{-}(\tau)$ is the boundary value of a certain function, holomorphic in the external region S^{-} and equal to zero at infinity.

Let us introduce the unknown function

$$\Omega_0(z) = \Omega(z) + iC.$$

This function must have a purely imaginary value at infinity and satisfy on L the boundary condition

$$\operatorname{re}\left[\frac{\Omega_0^{-}(\tau)}{\tau\bar{\tau}'}\right] = \operatorname{re}\left[\frac{\Phi^{+}(\tau)}{\tau\bar{\tau}'}\right]$$

Thus the determination of the function $\Omega_0(z)$ is reduced to the solution of the Riemann problem for the region S^{-} with the boundary condition of the form

$$\operatorname{re}\left[(a-ib)\,\Omega_0^{-}(\tau)\right] = c(\tau), \tag{57}$$

where

$$(a-ib) = \frac{1}{\tau\bar{\tau}'} = \frac{\tau'}{\tau}, \qquad c(\tau) = \operatorname{re}\frac{\Phi^{+}(\tau)}{\tau\bar{\tau}'}.$$

According to the assumption, these functions satisfy Hölder's condition. The index of the Riemann problem in the considered case is easily seen to be zero and according to the results in Chapter XVI (§ 4) the general solution $\Omega_0(z)$ of the problem (57) is of the form

$$\Omega_0(z) = \omega(z) + A\omega_1(z), \tag{58}$$

where $\omega(z)$ is a certain particular solution of the problem (57), $\omega_1(z)$ is a particular solution of the homogeneous problem, i.e. the problem with the condition

$$\operatorname{re}\left[\frac{\tau'}{\tau}\,\omega_1^{-}(\tau)\right] = 0 \tag{59}$$

where A is a real constant. The constant A will be selected in such a way that the function $\text{re}\,\Omega_0(z)$ is zero at infinity. This is possible, since the solution of the homogeneous Riemann problem for zero index is always different from zero (together with the point at infinity).

After the determination of the function $\Omega(z)$ we obtain the function $\mu(\tau)$ by equality (58). This function obviously satisfies Hőlder's condition. From the above procedure it follows that the function $\mu(\tau)$ and the constant C are uniquely determined by the given function $\Phi(z)$.

Proof in the case $m \geqq 1$. This proof is a repetition of the proof given by VEKUA [4]. First of all we prove that if formula (54) holds, then the function $\Phi(z)$ possesses an mth derivative satisfying Hölder's condition when the real function $\mu(\tau)$ has this property. Actually, differentiating the right-hand side of formula (54) m times, we obtain the Cauchy type integral

$$\Phi^{(m)}(z) = (-1)^m (m-1)! \int\limits_L \frac{\mu(\tau)\, d\sigma}{\tau^{m-1}(\tau - z)}$$

$$= (-1)^m (m-1)! \int\limits_L \frac{\mu(\tau)\,\bar{\tau}'\, d\tau}{\tau^{m-1}(\tau - z)}. \tag{60}$$

Thus according to the Plemelj–Privalov Theorem, the derivative $\Phi^{(m)}(z)$ has a boundary value satisfying Hölder's condition at each point $t \in L$.

Before discussing the problem of the existence of the function $\mu(\tau)$ and the constant C, we first prove that they are uniquely determined for a given function $\Phi(z)$. Here it is sufficient to assume that the real function $\mu(\tau)$ is continuous. The uniqueness will be proved when we show that if the equation

$$\int\limits_L \mu(\tau)\left(1 - \frac{z}{\tau}\right)^{m-1} \log\left(1 - \frac{z}{\tau}\right) d\sigma + \int\limits_L \mu(\tau)\, d\sigma + iC = 0 \tag{61}$$

holds at each point $z \in S^+$, then $\mu(\tau) = 0$ on L, and consequently, $C = 0$. Expanding the left-hand side of equality (61) in powers of the variable z and equating to zero the successive coefficients of these powers, we obtain the equalities

$$\int_L \mu(\tau)\tau^{-k}\, d\sigma = \int_L \mu(\tau)\bar{\tau}'\tau^{-k}\, d\tau = 0 \quad (k = 0, 1, 2, \dots). \tag{62}$$

Hence it follows that the Cauchy type integral

$$\omega(z) = \frac{1}{2\pi i}\int_L \frac{\mu(\tau)\bar{\tau}'\, d\tau}{\tau - z} \tag{63}$$

is equal to zero for all $z \in S^+$. To verify this it is sufficient to expand the integrand in powers of z in a neighbourhood of the point $z = 0$. Hence we have that $\omega^+(\tau) = 0$ at each point $\tau \in L$, and therefore

$$\mu(\tau)\bar{\tau}' = \omega^-(\tau). \tag{64}$$

Let us note that, according to equality (62) for $k = 0$, the function $\omega(z)$ outside a sufficiently large circle can be expanded as a convergent series of the form

$$\omega(z) = \frac{a_{-2}}{z^2} + \frac{a_{-3}}{z^3} + \dots,$$

and hence the function

$$\omega_0(z) = \int_{z_0}^{z} \omega(z)\, dz$$

determined by the integral of function (63), holomorphic in the region S^- taken over an arbitrary arc $\frown z_0 z$ *lying in this region* (z_0 lies on L), is a holomorphic function in the external region S^+ and regular at infinity. It follows from the above that the function $\omega_0(z)$ possesses, at an arbitrary point $t \in L$, the boundary value determined by formula (see equality (64))

$$\omega_0^-(t) = \int_0^t \omega^-(t)\, d\tau = \int_0^s \mu(\tau)\, d\sigma,$$

where s denotes the length of an arc $\frown z_0 t$ on L.

In this way, the function $\omega_0^-(t)$ is real, and hence we can conclude that $\omega_0(z) = \text{const}$, in the external region S^-, consequently $\omega(z) = \omega_0'(z) = 0$ in the region S^-, and $\mu(\tau) = 0$ in view of equality (64).

We now prove the existence of the function $\mu(\tau)$ and the constant C in formula (54) when the function $\Phi(z)$ is given and its mth derivative possesses the boundary value $\Phi^{(m)}(\tau)$ satisfying Hölder's condition at each point $t \in L$. Assuming that (54) is true, we obtain the formula

$$\Phi^{(m)}(t) = (-1)^m (m-1)!\, \pi i t^{1-m} \bar{t}' \mu(t) + \\ +(-1)^m (m-1)! \int_L \frac{\mu(\tau)\, d\sigma}{\tau^{m-1}(\tau - t)} \tag{65}$$

for the boundary value of the derivative (60) at the point $t \in L$, in accordance with Plemelj's formulae (see p. 438).

Dividing both sides by $(-1)^m (m-1)\pi i \bar{t}' t^{1-m}$ and taking into account that $t'\bar{t}' = 1$, we obtain the equation

$$\mu(t) = \frac{1}{\pi i} \int_L \frac{t^{m-1}\, t' \mu(\tau)\, d\sigma}{\tau^{m-1}(\tau - t)} = \frac{t^{m-1}\, t'\, \Phi^{(m)}(t)}{(-1)^m (m-1)!\, \pi i} \tag{66}$$

and finally, the real integral equation

$$\mu(t) + \int_L \text{re}\left[\frac{t^{m-1}\, t'}{\pi i \tau^{m-1}(\tau - t)}\right] \mu(\tau)\, d\sigma \\ = \text{re}\left[\frac{t^{m-1}\, t'\, \Phi^{(m)}(t)}{(-1)^m (m-1)!\, \pi i}\right]. \tag{67}$$

We shall show that the kernel of this equation is weakly-singular. We write

$$\frac{t^{m-1}\, t'}{\pi i \tau^{m-1}(\tau - t)} = \frac{1}{\pi i} \cdot \frac{t^{m-1} - \tau^{m-1}}{\tau - t} \cdot \frac{t'}{\tau^{m-1}} + \frac{1}{\pi i} \cdot \frac{t'}{\tau - t}.$$

The first term on the right-hand side is bounded and satisfies Hölder's condition, while the second one can be expressed in the following manner

$$\frac{1}{\pi i}\cdot\frac{t'}{\tau-t}=-\frac{1}{\pi i}\cdot\frac{d}{ds}\log(\tau-t)$$

$$=-\frac{1}{\pi i}\cdot\frac{d\log r}{ds}-\frac{1}{\pi i}\cdot\frac{d\vartheta(s,\sigma)}{ds},$$

where $r=|\tau-t|$, $\vartheta(s,\sigma)=\arg(\tau-t)$. Thus we have

$$\mathrm{re}\left[\frac{1}{\pi i}\cdot\frac{t'}{\tau-t}\right]=-\frac{1}{\pi}\cdot\frac{d\vartheta(s,\sigma)}{ds}.$$

Hence, on the basis of geometric considerations, we obtain the following form of the kernel of equation (67):

$$\frac{K(t,\tau)}{|\tau-t|^{\alpha}}\qquad(0\leqq\alpha<1);$$

here the function $K(t,\tau)$ satisfies Hölder's condition with respect to both variables.

We shall show now the solubility of integral equation (67). Consider the homogeneous equation

$$\nu(t)+\int_L \mathrm{re}\left[\frac{\tau^{m-1}\tau'}{\pi i t^{m-1}(t-\tau)}\right]\nu(\tau)\,d\sigma=0 \tag{68}$$

associated with equation (67). This equation can also be written in the form

$$\mathrm{re}\left[\nu(t)-\frac{t^{1-m}}{\pi i}\int_L\frac{\tau^{m-1}\nu(\tau)\,d\tau}{\tau-t}\right]=0. \tag{68'}$$

Let us introduce an auxiliary function

$$\Omega(z)=\frac{z^{1-m}}{\pi i}\int_L\frac{\tau^{m-1}\nu(\tau)\,d\tau}{\tau-z}, \tag{69}$$

where $\nu(t)$ denotes an arbitrary continuous (real) solution of equation (68) or (68′). Thus this solution satisfies Hölder's condition. Function (69) is holomorphic in the region S^-, tends to zero at infinity as z^{-m}, and, moreover, takes purely imaginary boundary values on L, on account of equation (68′):

$$\mathrm{re}\,[\Omega^{-}(t)] = 0, \quad t \in L.$$

Hence, it follows that $\Omega(z) = 0$ in the region S^{-}, and consequently, according to the results in Chapter XV (§ 7), there exists a function $\omega(z)$ holomorphic in the region S^{+} such that

$$t^{m-1}\nu(t) = \omega^{+}(t), \quad t \in L. \tag{70}$$

Thus we have

$$\mathrm{re}\,[it^{1-m}\omega^{+}(t)] = 0, \quad t \in L,$$

and therefore the function $\omega(z)$ is a solution of the homogeneous Riemann problem $\mathrm{re}\,[(a+ib)\omega^{+}] = 0$ for $a+ib = it^{1-m}$. The index of the problem is equal to $2m-2$, and consequently, according to § 4 (p. 477) it possesses $2m-1$ linearly independent solutions. Hence we conclude that the homogeneous Fredholm equation (68) has $2m-1$ linearly independent solutions. The homogeneous equation corresponding to equation (67) has also the same number of solutions. It will be shown that the non-homogeneous equation (67) also has a solution, since it satisfies the known necessary and sufficient conditions of orthogonality, in the Third Fredholm Theorem. Actually, these conditions are expressed by the equalities

$$\int_L \nu(\tau)\,\mathrm{re}\left[\frac{\tau^{m-1}\tau'\,\Phi^{(m)}(\tau)}{(-1)^m(m-1)!\,\pi i}\right]d\sigma$$

$$= \mathrm{re}\left[\int_L \frac{\nu(\tau)\,\tau^{m-1}\tau'\,\Phi^{(m)}(\tau)\,d\sigma}{(-1)^m(m-1)!\,\pi i}\right] = 0, \tag{71}$$

where $\nu(\tau)$ is an arbitrary (real) solution of the homogeneous equation (68). In accordance with relation (70), condition (71) is equivalent to the condition

$$\mathrm{re}\left[\frac{1}{\pi i}\int_L \omega^{+}(\tau)\,\Phi^{(m)}(\tau)\,d\tau\right] = 0.$$

This condition is always satisfied, since the integrand is the boundary value of the function $\omega(z)\,\Phi^{(m)}(z)$, holomorphic in the region S^+. Thus the solubility of equation (67) is proved and its general solution takes the form

$$\mu(t) = \mu_0(t) + c_1\mu_1(t) + \ldots + c_{2m-1}\mu_{2m-1}(t), \tag{72}$$

where $\mu_1, \ldots, \mu_{2m-1}$ is a complete system of linearly independent solutions of the homogeneous equation, $c_1, \ldots, c_{2m-1}$ are arbitrary real constants, and $\mu_0(t)$ denotes a particular solution of equation (67) given by the known Fredholm integral formula, the integrand of which contains, as a factor, the right-hand side of this equation.

We further prove that the obtained solution (72) of equation (67) is also a solution of the preliminary equation (66). In fact, let us introduce the function

$$\Psi(z) = \int_L \mu(\tau)\left(1-\frac{z}{\tau}\right)^{m-1} \log\left(1-\frac{z}{\tau}\right) d\sigma + \\ + \int_L \mu(\tau)\, d\sigma + iC \quad (z \in S), \tag{73}$$

where $\mu(\tau)$ is defined by formula (72) and C is an arbitrary real constant. Then, it follows from equation (67) that

$$\operatorname{re}\left[\frac{t^{m-1}\,t'\,\Psi^{(m)}(t)}{(-1)^m(m-1)!\,\pi i}\right]^+ = \operatorname{re}\left[\frac{t^{m-1}\,t'\,\Phi^{(m)}(t)}{(-1)^m(m-1)!\,\pi i}\right]^+, \tag{74}$$

and if we let $\Psi(z) - \Phi(z) = X(z)$, then it is seen that the function $X(z)$ satisfies on L the boundary condition

$$\operatorname{re}[it^{m-1}\,t'\,X^{(m)}(t)] = 0. \tag{75}$$

This is the boundary condition of the Riemann problem for the function $X^{(m)}(z)$ with negative index $-2m$. Hence, it follows that $X^{(m)}(z) = 0$. Thus

$$\Psi^{(m)}(z) = \Phi^{(m)}(z) \tag{76}$$

and function (72) satisfies equation (66). Of course, the equality

$$\Psi(z) = \Psi(z) + Q(z) \tag{77}$$

also holds; $Q(z)$ is a certain polynomial of degree not greater than $m-1$.

It follows from the above that the functions $\mu_1, \mu_2, \dots, \mu_{2m-1}$ are the solutions of the homogeneous equation corresponding to equation (66). Let us introduce functions Ψ_j by the formulae

$$\Psi_j(z) = \int_L \mu_j(\tau)\left(1-\frac{z}{\tau}\right)^{m-1} \log\left(1-\frac{z}{\tau}\right) d\sigma + \int_L \mu_j(\tau)\, d\sigma \qquad (78)$$

$(m \geqq 1; j = 1, 2, \dots, 2m-1)$. The linear independence of the functions $\Psi_j(z)$ follows from the linear independence of the functions μ_j (with real coefficients), and conversely.

Since the functions $\mu_j(t)$ are the solutions of the homogeneous equation relating to the case $\Phi(z) = 0$, on account of equality (77) we conclude that all the functions (78) are polynomials of degree not greater than $m-1$.

Substituting in formula (73) the general solution of equation (67) we obtain

$$\Psi(z) = \Psi_0(z) + iC + c_1\Psi_1(z) + \dots + c_{2m-1}\Psi_{2m-1}(z) \qquad (79)$$

where $\Psi_0(z)$ is also determined by formula (78) when $\mu_j(\tau)$ is replaced by $\mu_0(\tau)$. It will be shown that the polynomials

$$i, \Psi_1(z), \Psi_2(z), \dots, \Psi_{2m-1}(z) \qquad (80)$$

are linearly independent. In fact,

$$Ci + c_1\Psi_1(z) + \dots + c_{2m-1}\Psi_{2m-1}(z) = 0$$

identically, then substituting $z = 0$ and taking into account that $\Psi_j(0)$ are real (see (78)), we would obtain $C = 0$, which is impossible when not all the constants $c_1, \dots, c_{2m-1}$ are zero, by linear independence of the polynomials $\Psi_1, \dots, \Psi_{2m-1}$. Hence it follows that any polynomial of degree at most $m-1$ is a certain linear combination of $2m$ polynomials (80) with real coefficients.

Applying formula (77) to the function $\Psi_0(z)$, we can assert that

$$\Phi(z) - \Psi_0(z) = Q_0(z),$$

where $Q_0(z)$ is a polynomial of degree at most $m-1$. Hence, if the given function $\Phi(z)$ is to be equal to the function $\Psi(z)$

determined by formula (73) it is necessary and sufficient to select arbitrary constants $C, c_1, c_2, \ldots, c_{2m-1}$ such that

$$Q_0(z) = iC + c_1 \Psi_1(z) + \ldots + c_2 \Psi_2(z).$$

By linear independence of polynomials (80), this is always possible in a unique manner.

Thus the proposition of Vekua's Theorem in the case $m \geqq 1$ is proved.

Remark 1. Vekua's Theorem can be proved similarly for a holomorphic function in an infinite region S^- by the substitution of t/z instead of z/t in formula (54), under the assumption that the point $z = 0$ lies in the region S^+, and that the branch of the function $\log(1-t/z)$ tends to zero for $z \to \infty$.

Remark 2. Vekua's Theorem can be generalized to a multi-connected region S^+ bounded by contours $L_0, L_1, \ldots, L_p$. Then we write

$$\Phi(z) = \frac{1}{2\pi i} \int_L \frac{\Phi^+(\tau)\, d\tau}{\tau - z} = \sum_{j=0}^{p} \Phi_j(z),$$

where

$$\Phi_j(z) = \frac{1}{2\pi i} \int_{L_j} \frac{\Phi^+(\tau)\, d\tau}{\tau - z} \qquad (j = 0, 1, 2, \ldots, p).$$

If now the derivative $\Phi^{(m)}(z)$ has on L boundary values satisfying Hölder's condition, then the Vekua integral formula can be applied to each of the functions $\Phi_j(z)$, namely, for the function $\Phi_0(z)$ in the interior region with respect to L_0, and for the function $\Phi_j(z)$ $(j = 1, \ldots, p)$ in the exterior region with respect to the contours L_j. As a result we obtain an expresssion for the function $\Phi(z)$ in the form of the sum of the integrals appearing in the Vekua formula (54).

§ 5. The Vekua boundary problem

The Vekua boundary problem is a far-reaching generalization of the Riemann boundary problem.

Let S^+ be a given region bounded by a contour L, the tangent of which satisfies the known Hölder condition. The boundary problem stated and solved by Vekua [86] and [87] consists in the determination of the function $\Phi(z)$ holomorphic in the region S^+, the derivatives of which up to and including the m-th order, possess the boundary values $\Phi^{(j)}(t)$ satisfying, at each point $t \in L$, the linear integral relation

$$\operatorname{re} \sum_{j=0}^{m} \{a_j(t)\Phi^{(j)}(t) + \int_L h_j(t,\tau)\Phi^{(j)}(\tau)\,d\sigma\} = f(t) \qquad (81)$$

($\Phi^0(t) = \Phi(t)$), where $a_j(t)$ are given complex functions defined on the contour L and satisfying Hölder's condition, $h_j(t,\tau)$ are prescribed complex functions of the form

$$h_j(t,\tau) = \frac{h_j^0(t,\tau)}{|\tau - t|^\alpha} \qquad (0 \leqq \alpha < 1),$$

where the complex functions $h_j^0(t,\tau)$ are defined for $t \in L$, $\tau \in L$, and satisfy Hölder's condition with respect to both variables.

Moreover, it will be required that the boundary value of the m-th derivative $\Phi^{(m)}(t)$, and, consequently, the derivatives of smaller orders, satisfy the Hölder condition on L. Vekua solved this boundary problem and discussed the existence of solutions, basing his argument on his integral formula derived in the preceding section. Below, we give an abbreviated version of Vekua's discussion.

Let us note that if the solution $\Phi(z)$ of Vekua's problem (81) exists, then, in accordance with the proof of Vekua's Theorem given in the preceding section, this function, in the general case $m \geqq 1$, is uniquely expressed by the formula

$$\Phi(z) = \int_L \mu(\tau)\left(1 - \frac{z}{\tau}\right)^{m-1} \log\left(1 - \frac{z}{\tau}\right) d\sigma + \int_L \mu(\tau)\,d\sigma + iC. \qquad (82)$$

Thus the unknown function $\mu(\tau)$ and the constant C should be chosen in such a way that function (82) satisfies the boundary condition (81). We use the notation

$$N_0(z,\tau) = \left(1-\frac{z}{\tau}\right)^{m-1} \log\left(1-\frac{z}{\tau}\right)+1, \tag{83}$$

$$\begin{aligned} N_j(z,\tau) &= \frac{d^j}{dz^j}\left[\left(1-\frac{z}{\tau}\right)^{m-1} \log\left(1-\frac{z}{\tau}\right)\right] \\ &= (-1)^j \frac{(m-1)(m-2)\dots(m-j)}{\tau^j}\left(1-\frac{z}{\tau}\right)^{m-j-1} \times \\ &\quad \times\left\{\log\left(1-\frac{z}{\tau}\right)+\frac{1}{m-1}+\dots+\frac{1}{m-j}\right\} \\ &\qquad (j=1,2,\dots,m-1), \end{aligned} \tag{84}$$

$$\begin{aligned} &N_m(z,\tau) \\ &= \frac{d^m}{dz^m}\left[\left(1-\frac{z}{\tau}\right)^{m-1} \log\left(1-\frac{z}{\tau}\right)\right] = \frac{(-1)^m (m-1)!}{\tau^{m-1}(\tau-z)} \end{aligned} \tag{85}$$

where $\tau \in L$, $z \in S^+$.

Assuming that the point z tends to the point $t \neq \tau$ on the contour L, we obtain the boundary values $N_j(t,\tau)$ satisfying Hölder's condition with respect to both variables, for $j < m-1$. The function $N_{m-1}(t,\tau)$ possesses at $t=\tau$ a logarithmic singularity, while the function $N_m(t,\tau)$ has a singularity of the type $(t-\tau)^{-1}$. The boundary values of function (82) and its derivatives up to and including those of order $m-1$ are determined by formulae

$$\begin{aligned} \Phi(t) &= \int_L N_0(t,\tau)\mu(\tau)\,d\sigma + iC, \\ \Phi^{(j)}(t) &= \int_L N_j(t,\tau)\mu(\tau)\,d\sigma \quad (j=1,2,\dots,m-1). \end{aligned} \tag{86}$$

By the Plemelj formula, the boundary values of the m-th derivatives are given by

$$\Phi^{(m)}(t) = (-1)^m (m-1)!\,\pi i t^{1-m} t' \mu(t) + \int_L N_m(t,\tau)\mu(\tau)\,d\sigma. \tag{87}$$

Substituting expressions (86) and (87) in condition (81) of Vekua's problem, we obtain the real integral equation

$$\mathbf{N}\mu = A(t)\,\mu(t) + \int_L N(t,\tau)\,\mu(\tau)\,d\sigma = f(t) - C\rho(t), \tag{88}$$

where

$$A(t) = \operatorname{re}\left[(-1)^m (m-1)!\,\pi i \bar{t}^{1-m} \bar{t}'\, a_m(t)\right], \tag{89}$$

$$\rho(t) = \operatorname{re}\left[ia(t) + i\int_L h_0(t,\tau)\,d\sigma\right], \tag{90}$$

$$N(t,\tau) = \sum_{j=0}^{m} \operatorname{re}\left[a_j(t)\,N_j(t,\tau) + \int_L h_j(t,\tau_1)\,N_j(\tau_1,\tau)\,d\sigma_1\right] + \\ + \operatorname{re}\left[(-1)^m (m-1)!\,\pi i h_m(t,\tau)\,\bar{\tau}^{1-m}\bar{\tau}'\right]. \tag{91}$$

The real integral equation (88) has a singular kernel of the form

$$N(t,\tau) = \frac{K(t,\tau)}{\tau - t} \tag{92}$$

where the function $K(t,\tau)$ satisfies Hölder's condition with respect to both variables. The functions $A(t)$ and $\rho(t)$ also satisfy Hölder's condition.

If equation (88), for a suitably chosen constant C, has a solution, then substituting it in formula (82) we obtain the solution of Vekua's problem.

In the particular case $m = 1$, the required function $\Phi(z)$ is of the form

$$\Phi(z) = \int_L \frac{\mu(\tau)\,d\sigma}{1 - z/\tau} + iC.$$

Then we obtain a singular integral equation for the unknown function $\mu(\tau)$. This equation is a particular case of equation (88).

Applying the general theory of integral equations previously discussed, we shall now examine equation (88).

Let us consider the dominant part of the expression $\mathbf{N}\mu$, i.e. (see p. 501)

$$\mathbf{N}^{\circ}\mu = A(t)\,\mu(t) + \frac{B(t)}{\pi i}\int_L \frac{\mu(\tau)\,d\tau}{\tau - t}. \tag{93}$$

In this case the function $A(t)$ determined by formula (89) can be also rewritten as follows:

$$A(t) = \tfrac{1}{2}(-1)^m (m-1)!\,\pi i\,[t^{1-m}\bar{t}'\,a_m(t) - \bar{t}^{1-m}t'\,\overline{a_m(t)}]. \qquad (94)$$

After some calculations the function $B(t)$ takes the form

$$B(t) = \tfrac{1}{2}(-1)^m (m-1)!\,\pi i\,[t^{1-m}\bar{t}'\,a_m(t) + \bar{t}^{1-m}t'\,\overline{a_m(t)}]. \qquad (95)$$

Hence

$$A(t)+B(t) = (-1)^m (m-1)!\,\pi i t^{1-m}\bar{t}'\,a_m(t),$$
$$A(t)-B(t) = (-1)^m (m-1)!\,\pi i \bar{t}^{1-m}t'\,\overline{a_m(t)}.$$

Thus a necessary and sufficient condition that the singular integral equation (88) be of the normal type is that

$$a_m(t) \neq 0 \quad \text{on } L. \qquad (96)$$

We now assume that this condition is satisfied. The index of equation (88), which will be called *the index of the Vekua problem,* is determined by formula

$$\kappa = \frac{1}{2\pi}\arg\left[\frac{t^{m-1}\,t'\,\overline{a_m(t)}}{\bar{t}^{m-1}\,\bar{t}'\,a_m(t)}\right]_L = 2(m+n), \qquad (97)$$

where

$$n = \frac{1}{2\pi}[\arg\overline{a_m(t)}]_L. \qquad (97')$$

In order to examine the solubility of equation (88) we consider the homogeneous equation

$$\mathbf{N}'\nu = A(t)\,\nu(t) + \int_L N(\tau, t)\,\nu(\tau)\,d\sigma = 0 \qquad (98)$$

associated with equation (88). We recall that by the theorem on p. 515 the equality

$$k - k' = \kappa$$

holds, where k and k' are the numbers of the linearly independent solutions of associate equations $\mathbf{N}\mu = 0$ and $\mathbf{N}'\nu = 0$.

A particularly important case occurs when Vekua's problem is soluble for any right-hand side $f(t)$. This is expressed in the following theorem:

THEOREM. *The Vekua problem is soluble for any right-hand side* $f(t)$ *if, and only if,* $\kappa \geqq 0$, *and moreover: either* (1) $k' = 0$, *or* (2) $k' = 1$; *furthermore, in the second case the solution* $\nu(t)$ *of the associate equation* $\mathbf{N}'\nu = 0$ *has to satisfy the condition*

$$\int_L \nu(t)\,\rho(t)\,ds \neq 0\,. \tag{99}$$

Then the Vekua problem has $\kappa+1$ *linearly independent solutions.*

Proof. First, we prove the sufficiency of the conditions. If $k' = 0$, then by the theorem on p. 513, equation (88) is soluble for an arbitrary function $f(t)$ and constant C. Then the corresponding homogeneous equation $\mathbf{N}\mu = 0$ has $k = \kappa$ linearly independent solutions. Consequently, the general solution of equation (88) for any constant C has the form

$$\mu(t) = \mu^*(t) + C\mu_0(t) + C_1\mu_1(t) + \ldots + C_\kappa\mu_\kappa(t)\,, \tag{100}$$

where $C, C_1, \ldots, C_\kappa$ are arbitrary real constants, $\mu^*(t)$ and $\mu_0(t)$ are arbitrary particular solutions of the equations $\mathbf{N}\mu = f(t)$ and $\mathbf{N}\mu = -\rho(t)$, while $\mu_1(t), \ldots, \mu_\kappa(t)$ are linearly independent solutions of the homogeneous equation $\mathbf{N}\mu = 0$.

Substituting expression (100) in formula (82) we obtain the general solution of the Vekua problem in the form

$$\Phi(z) = \Phi^*(z) + C(i+\Phi_0(z)) + C_1\Phi_1(z) + \ldots + C_\kappa\Phi_\kappa(z) \tag{101}$$

where $\Phi^*(z), \Phi_0(z), \Phi_1(z), \ldots, \Phi_\kappa(z)$ are holomorphic functions in the region S^+ related to the functions $\mu^*, \mu_0', \mu_1, \ldots, \mu_\kappa$ by formulae (78).

Since the functions $\mu_1, \mu_2, \ldots, \mu_\kappa$ are linearly independent, and since the values $\Phi_j(0)$ ($j = 0, 1, 2, \ldots, \kappa$) are real, we conclude, as on p. 546, that $i+\Phi_0(z), \Phi_1(z), \ldots, \Phi_\kappa(z)$ is a system of $\kappa+1$ independent solutions of the homogeneous Vekua problem.

Let us now consider the case when $k' = 1$ and when condition (99) is satisfied. Then equation (88) is soluble, provided the orthogonality condition

$$\int_L \nu(\tau)[f(\tau)-C\rho(\tau)]\,d\sigma = 0$$

is satisfied. This determines the value of the constant C. Now, the general solution of equation (88) will have the form

$$\mu(t) = \mu^*(t)+C_1\mu_1(t)+\ldots+C_{\kappa+1}\mu_{\kappa+1}(t) \qquad (102)$$

where $C_1, \ldots, C_{\kappa+1}$ are arbitrary real constants, while $\mu_1, \ldots, \mu_{\kappa+1}$ are linearly independent solutions of the homogeneous equation $\mathbf{N}\mu = 0$. The number of these solutions is equal to $\kappa+1$ by the relation $k-k' = \kappa$. Of course, $\kappa \geqq 0$ since κ is an even number (97).

Substituting expression (102) in formula (82) we obtain, in the considered case, the general solution of the Vekua problem in the form

$$\Phi(z) = \Phi^*(z)+C_1\Phi_1(z)+\ldots+C_{\kappa+1}\Phi_{\kappa+1}(z). \qquad (103)$$

We now prove the necessity of the conditions stated in the theorem. Let $\nu_1(t), \ldots, \nu_{k'}(t)$ be the complete system of linearly independent solutions of the equation $\mathbf{N}'\nu = 0$. We assume that these solutions are orthonormal, i.e. that

$$\int_L \nu_i\nu_j\,ds = \delta_i^j \quad \text{(Kronecker delta)}. \qquad (104)$$

Assume, that the Vekua problem is soluble for any function $f(t)$. Then the integral equation (88) must also be soluble for any function $f(t)$ and properly chosen constant C. Thus we have

$$\int_L \nu_j(t)[f(t)-C\rho(t)]\,ds = 0 \quad (j = 1, 2, \ldots, k'), \qquad (105)$$

where $f(t)$ is an arbitrary function, provided that the constant C is suitably chosen.

It has to be shown that either $k' = 0$ or $k' = 1$, and moreover in this last case equality (99) must be satisfied. Let us examine the two possibilities:

(a) all the following integrals are equal to zero:

$$\int_L \rho(t)\nu_j(t)\,ds = 0 \quad (j = 1, 2, \ldots, k'),$$

(b) at least one of them is different from zero, say

$$\int_L \rho(t) v_1(t)\, ds \neq 0.$$

The first assumption for $k' = 1$ is impossible, because then condition (105) cannot be satisfied for an arbitrary function $f(t)$, by the property (105) of the solutions $v_j(t)$. In the second case, substituting $f(t) = v_2(t)$ we would obtain from equality (105) that

$$C = 0, \qquad \int_L [v_2(t)]^2\, ds = 0,$$

and this contradicts the assumption (104). Finally, we must have either $k' = 0$ or $k' = 1$ (then inequality (99) is also satisfied). Thus the theorem is proved.

Remark. The Poincaré problem, considered previously, is a particular case of the Vekua problem. In fact, the boundary condition of the Poincaré problem

$$\frac{du}{dn} + a(s)\, u(P) + b(s) \frac{du}{ds} = f(s)$$

on account of the relations

$$\frac{du}{ds} = \frac{\partial u}{\partial x} \cos\theta + \frac{\partial u}{\partial y} \sin\theta,$$

$$\frac{du}{dn} = -\frac{\partial u}{\partial x} \sin\theta + \frac{\partial u}{\partial y} \cos\theta$$

(here θ denotes the angle between the tangent and the axis Ox) can be written in the form of a linear relation between boundary values of the partial derivatives of the function u

$$A(t) \frac{\partial u}{\partial x} + B(t) \frac{\partial u}{\partial y} + C(t)\, u = f(t), \qquad t \in L, \tag{106}$$

where $A(t), B(t), C(t)$ are functions given on L and satisfying Hölder's condition; moreover

$$A(t) + iB(t) \neq 0.$$

Thus the boundary condition (106) can be written in the form

$$\operatorname{re}[(A+iB)\Phi'(t)+C\Phi(t)]=f(t), \quad t\in L, \tag{107}$$

where $\Phi(z)$ is a function, holomorphic in the region S^+, the real part of which is the required function $u(x,y)$. The condition (107) is a particular case of the general boundary condition (81) in the Vekua problem, and consequently, the Poincaré boundary problem can be solved using Vekua's method, by means of the holomorphic function $\Phi(z)$ in the form $(m = 1)$

$$\Phi(z)=\int_L \mu(\tau)\log\left(1-\frac{z}{\tau}\right)d\sigma+\int_L \mu(\tau)\,d\sigma+iC. \tag{108}$$

The fulfilment of the boundary condition (107) leads to a singular integral equation from which the unknown function $\mu(\tau)$ can be found. This integral equation was previously considered. The Vekua problem (81) generalized to the case of a non-linear relation has been recently solved by J. WOLSKA–BOCHENEK [90].

§ 6. The Vekua method of solving boundary problems in the case of elliptic equations

Suppose we are given an elliptic equation

$$\mathbf{E}(u)=\frac{\partial^2 u}{\partial x^2}+\frac{\partial^2 u}{\partial y^2}+a(x,y)\frac{\partial u}{\partial x}+b(x,y)\frac{\partial u}{\partial y}+c(x,y)u=0 \tag{109}$$

with real coefficients, analytic in a certain region.

In Part 2, p. 405, we indicated the Vekua method of solving equation (109) which consists in the introduction of new variables

$$z=x+iy, \quad \zeta=x-iy,$$

and in the application of the properties of the Riemann function of the transformed equation

$$\frac{\partial^2 u}{\partial z\,\partial\zeta}+A(z,\zeta)\frac{\partial u}{\partial z}+B(z,\zeta)\frac{\partial u}{\partial\zeta}+C(z,\zeta)u=0. \tag{110}$$

According to Vekua's investigations, each real function $u(x, y)$, satisfying equation (109) in a certain region D, can be expressed by the formula

$$u(x, y) = \operatorname{re}\left[H_0(z)\varphi(z) + \int_0^z H(z, t)\varphi(t)\,dt\right], \tag{111}$$

where the holomorphic functions H_0 and H are defined by the formulae

$$\begin{aligned} H_0(z) &= G(z, 0; z, \bar{z}), \\ H(z, t) &= -\frac{\partial}{\partial t} G(t, 0; z, \bar{z}) + B(z, 0)\,G(t, 0; z, \bar{z}), \end{aligned} \tag{112}$$

$G(z, \zeta; t, \tau)$ being the Riemann function with respect to equation (110), $\varphi(z)$ a certain function, holomorphic in the region D, and dependent on u; moreover, it is assumed that the point $z = 0$ lies inside the region D.

VEKUA, making use of formula (111), solved some boundary problems for equation (109) (see VEKUA [88]). We give one of them, analogous to the Dirichlet problem.

Suppose we are given a simply connected region S^+ bounded by a contour L, which is such that the set $S^+ + L$ lies inside the region D. We consider the boundary problem of the determination of the function $u(x, y)$, satisfying equation (109) at each point $z = x + iy$ of the region S^+, being continuous in the set $S^+ + L$, and having the boundary values

$$u^+(t) = f(t) \qquad (t \in L) \tag{113}$$

which are equal to the prescribed real function $f(t)$, defined on L and satisfying Hölder's condition. In order to make use of the representation (111) we assume that $A(0, \zeta) = B(z, 0) = 0$, since the general case always can be reduced to this one. Thus we have

$$H(z, t) = -\frac{\partial}{\partial t} G(t, 0; z, \bar{z}). \tag{114}$$

We assume that the given function $f(t)$ satisfies the Hölder condition, and that the tangent to the contour L forms with a constant direction an angle which also satisfies Hölder's condition.

If it is assumed that the holomorphic function appearing in formula (111) has the boundary values $\varphi(t)$ satisfying Hölder's condition on the contour L, then, according to the Vekua formula (53) it can always be expressed in the form of the Cauchy type integral

$$\varphi(z)=\int_L \frac{\tau\mu(\tau)\,d\sigma}{\tau-z} \quad (z\in S^+), \tag{115}$$

where μ is a real function; moreover, it is assumed that $\varphi(0)$ is real. Substituting expression (114) in formula (111) we obtain

$$u(x,y)=\int_L K(z,\tau)\,\mu(\tau)\,d\sigma, \tag{116}$$

where

$$K(z,\tau)=\mathrm{re}\left[\frac{\tau H_0(z)}{\tau-z}+\int_0^z \frac{\tau H(z,\tau_1)}{\tau-\tau_1}\,d\tau_1\right]$$

$$=\mathrm{re}\left[\frac{\tau H_0(z)}{\tau-z}-\tau H(z,\tau)\log\left(1-\frac{z}{\tau}\right)+H^*(z,\tau)\right], \tag{117}$$

$$H^*(z,\tau)=\int_0^z \frac{t[H(z,\tau_1)-H(z,\tau)]}{\tau-\tau_1}\,d\tau_1 .$$

Assuming that an interior point z tends to an arbitrary point t on L, using the Plemelj formula for the boundary value of the Cauchy type integral, and satisfying the boundary condition (113), we obtain the integral equation

$$A(t)\,\mu(t)+\int_L K(t,\tau)\,\mu(\tau)\,d\sigma=f(t), \tag{118}$$

for the unknown function μ. Here,

$$\begin{aligned} A(t)&=\mathrm{re}\left[i\pi t\bar{t}'\,H_0(t)\right],\\ K(t,\tau)&=\mathrm{re}\left[\frac{\tau H_0(t)}{\tau-t}-\tau H(t,\tau)\log\left(1-\frac{t}{\tau}\right)+H^*(t,\tau)\right]; \end{aligned} \tag{119}$$

t' denotes the derivative with respect to the arc dt/ds. Thus we have

$$t' = e^{i\theta(t)}$$

where $\theta(t)$ denotes the angle between the tangent and the axis Ox. Hence, it follows that the function t' also satisfies Hölder's condition.

The integral equation (118) is singular and the theory discussed in the previous section can be applied. Separating the dominant part in equation (118), we obtain

$$A(t)\mu(t) + \frac{B(t)}{\pi i}\int_L \frac{\mu(\tau)\,d\tau}{\tau - t} + \int_L K_0(t,\tau)\mu(\tau)\,d\sigma = f(t), \tag{120}$$

where

$$B(t) = i\pi \operatorname{re}[t\bar{t}' H_0(t)],$$

$$K_0(t,\tau) = K(t,\tau) - \frac{t'B(t)}{\pi i(\tau - t)}.$$

It can be proved that the function K_0 possesses a weak singularity, namely

$$K_0(t,\tau) = \frac{K^*(t,\tau)}{|t-\tau|^\alpha} \qquad (0 \leqq \alpha < 1),$$

where the function K^* satisfies Hölder's condition. Further, we obtain

$$\begin{aligned} A(t) + B(t) &= i\pi t\bar{t}' H_0(t), \\ A(t) - B(t) &= -i\pi \bar{t}t' H_0(t), \end{aligned} \tag{121}$$

since $H_0(t) \neq 0$ (according to the properties of the Riemann functions). Then the integral equation (118) is of normal type, moreover its index κ is equal to zero, because

$$\kappa = \frac{1}{2\pi i}\left[\log \frac{A-B}{A+B}\right]_L = 0.$$

This property facilitates the discussion of the solubility of equation (118). Namely, equation (118) possesses a solution for an arbitrary function $f(t)$ if, and only if, the corresponding homogeneous equation

$$A(t)\mu(t)+\int_L K(t,\tau)\mu(\tau)\,d\tau=0 \tag{122}$$

has the zero solution only. We shall prove that the homogeneous equation (122) has only the zero solution when the homogeneous boundary problem $u^+(t) = 0$ has zero solution only.

In fact, if $\mu_0(t)$ is a solution of equation (122), then the function

$$u_0(x,y)=\operatorname{re}\left[H_0(z)\varphi_0(z)+\int_0^z H(z,\tau)\varphi_0(\tau)\,d\tau\right],$$

where

$$\varphi_0(z)=\int_L \frac{\tau\mu_0(\tau)\,d\sigma}{\tau-z}$$

is a continuous solution of the homogeneous problem in $S^+ + L$; thus according to the assumption we have $u_0(x,y) = 0$. Then, however, $\varphi_0(z) = 0$ in the region L, which holds provided $\mu_0(\tau) = 0$. Thus we have the theorem:

THEOREM. *If the homogeneous boundary problem for an elliptic equation* (109) *has the zero solution only, then the non-homogeneous boundary problem* (113) *for this equation is always soluble and its only solution can be expressed by formula* (116), *where the function* $\mu(t)$ *is the only solution of equation* (118).

CHAPTER XIX

NON-LINEAR SINGULAR EQUATIONS FOR CONTOURS

§ 1. Non-linear singular equations of the first kind

In view of many difficulties requiring a different approach in comparison with classical analysis, it is only recently that the theory of non-linear singular integral equations has been developed. The development of the theory is to a great extent due to modern functional analysis, namely, due to the fixed point theorems of SCHAUDER and BANACH, and, moreover, the progress in the investigation of one- and multi-dimensional singular integrals.

The equations of the form

$$\int_L \frac{K[t,\tau,\varphi(\tau)]\,d\tau}{\tau-t}=f(t), \tag{1}$$

where L is a finite set of smooth disconnected contours, $K(t,\tau,u)$ is a given complex function defined in the domain

$$t\in L, \quad \tau\in L, \quad u\in \Pi$$

(Π is a certain region in the complex plane), and $f(t)$ is a function defined on L, will be called *non-linear singular integral equations of the first kind*. The equation of the form (1) was investigated by the author [58] as early as 1924, but under the restrictive assumption that the functions K and f are holomorphic in certain strips. This assumption, owing to the property of the Poincaré transformation for holomorphic functions made it possible to apply the method of successive approximations, and in this way to prove the existence of the solution. Systems of equations of the form (1) have been considered by J. WOLSKA in her paper [89].

Now, it is possible to give the proof of the existence of the solutions of equation (1) under considerably less restrictive assumptions concerning the functions $K(t, \tau, u)$ and $f(t)$. This is due to the proof of the Poincaré transformation under less restrictive assumptions, given on p. 445, and due to the fixed point theorem given by Schauder.

To make the discussion easier, we consider a non-linear singular integral equation of the first kind, having the form

$$\int_L \frac{N(t, \tau)}{\tau - t} \varphi(\tau)\, d\tau + \lambda \int_L \frac{K[t, \tau, \varphi(\tau)]}{\tau - t}\, d\tau = f(t), \tag{2}$$

where λ is a parameter.

The given complex functions $f(t), N(t, \tau), K(t, \tau, u)$ are respectively defined in the domains:

$$t \in L, \tag{3}$$

$$t \in L, \quad \tau \in L, \tag{3'}$$

$$t \in L, \quad \tau \in L, \quad |u| \leqq R, \tag{3''}$$

where R is a given positive number, u is a complex variable. We assume that the functions satisfy the Hölder conditions

$$\begin{gathered} |f(t) - f(t_1)| < k_f |t - t_1|^\mu, \\ |N(t, \tau) - N(t_1, \tau_1)| < k_N [|t - t_1|^\mu + |\tau - \tau_1|^{\mu_1}], \\ |K(t, \tau, u) - K(t_1, \tau_1, u_1)| < k_K [|t - t_1|^\mu + |\tau - \tau_1|^{\mu_1} + |u - u_1|] \end{gathered} \tag{4}$$

where $0 < \mu < \mu_1 \leqq 1$, and k_N, k_f, k_K are positive constants.

Next we assume that the kernel $N(t, \tau)/(\tau - t)$ is closed (see p. 499).

Equation (2) can be reduced to the equivalent weakly-singular equation. Namely, if we multiply both sides of equation (2) by $1/(t - \theta)$, where $\theta \in L$, and integrate with respect to the variable

t then we can assert that the function $\varphi(t)$ satisfying Hölder's condition and equation (2) also satisfies the equation

$$\int_L \frac{dt}{t-\theta}\left[\int_L \frac{N(t,\tau)}{\tau-t}\varphi(\tau)\,d\tau\right]+\lambda\int_L \frac{dt}{t-\theta}\left[\int_L \frac{K[t,\tau,\varphi(\tau)]}{\tau-t}\,d\tau\right] = \int_L \frac{f(t)\,dt}{\tau-\theta} \tag{5}$$

at each point $\theta \in L$. Conversely, the function φ which satisfies equation (5) also satisfies the given equation (2) since, according to the property of the Cauchy type integral, the equation

$$\int_L \frac{\psi(t)\,dt}{t-\theta} = 0$$

possesses the zero solution $\psi = 0$, only.

Now, applying the Poincaré–Bertrand transformation to the iterated integrals on the left-hand side of equation (5), we obtain the equivalent equation

$$-\pi^2 N(\theta,\theta)\varphi(\theta)-\lambda\pi^2 K[\theta,\theta,\varphi(\theta)]+ + \int_L F(\theta,\tau)\varphi(\tau)\,d\tau+\lambda\int_L \Phi[\theta,\tau,\varphi(\tau)]\,d\tau = f_1(\theta) \tag{6}$$

where the functions F, Φ, f_1 are defined by the formulae

$$F(\theta,\tau) = \int_L \frac{N(t,\tau)\,dt}{(t-\theta)(\tau-t)},$$

$$\Phi(\theta,\tau,u) = \int_L \frac{K(t,\tau,u)\,dt}{(t-\theta)(\tau-t)}, \tag{7}$$

$$f_1(\theta) = \int_L \frac{f(t)\,dt}{t-\theta},$$

for $\theta \in L$, $\tau \in L$, $|u| \leq R$ $(\theta \neq \tau)$.

The transformed equation (6) is already weakly-singular. In fact, applying the decomposition

$$\frac{1}{(t-\theta)(\tau-t)} = \frac{1}{\tau-\theta}\left(\frac{1}{t-\theta}+\frac{1}{\tau-t}\right),$$

the function (7) can be expressed in the following way:

$$\begin{aligned} F(\theta,\tau) &= \frac{\omega(\theta,\tau)-\omega(\tau,\tau)}{\tau-\theta}, \\ \Phi(\theta,\tau,u) &= \frac{\Omega(\theta,\tau,u)-\Omega(\tau,\tau,u)}{\tau-\theta} \end{aligned} \tag{8}$$

where the functions ω and Ω are determined by the Cauchy type integrals

$$\omega(\theta,\tau) = \int_L \frac{N(t,\tau)}{t-\theta}\,dt, \tag{9}$$

$$\Omega(\theta,\tau,u) = \int_L \frac{K(t,\tau,u)}{t-\theta}\,dt. \tag{9'}$$

According to the assumptions (4) and to the theorems on the Cauchy type integrals on pp. 439-443, the functions (9) and (9′) satisfy Hölder's condition with exponent μ with respect to each of the variables. Hence, using the lemma on p. 495, it follows that the functions (8) can be expressed in the following manner

$$\begin{aligned} F(\theta,\tau) &= \frac{F^*(\theta,\tau)}{|\tau-\theta|^{1-\alpha}}, \\ \Phi(\theta,\tau,u) &= \frac{\Phi^*(\theta,\tau,u)}{|\tau-\theta|^{1-\alpha}} \quad (\theta\neq\tau), \end{aligned} \tag{10}$$

where the functions F^* and Φ^* are bounded and satisfy Hölder's condition with respect to each of the variables for the exponent $\mu-\alpha$, where α is an arbitrarily chosen positive number, smaller than μ.

The integral equation (6) is insoluble by means of the classical method of successive approximations under the less restrictive assumptions (4), since the Hölder exponent of the function Φ with respect to u is less than unity. Therefore, we apply to equation (6) Schauder's fixed point theorem (see Part 1, p. 201).

Assume that $N(\theta, \theta) \neq 0$ at each point $\theta \in L$, and write equation (6) in an equivalent form

$$\varphi(\theta) - \frac{1}{\pi^2} \int_L \frac{F(\theta, \tau)}{N(\theta, \theta)} \varphi(\tau)\, d\tau = -\frac{\lambda}{N(\theta, \theta)} K[\theta, \theta, \varphi(\theta)] + $$

$$+ \frac{\lambda}{\pi^2} \int_L \frac{\Phi[\theta, \tau, \varphi(\tau)]}{N(\theta, \theta)}\, d\tau - \frac{f_1(\theta)}{\pi^2 N(\theta, \theta)}. \tag{11}$$

Consider, now, the function space Λ, the points of which are all complex *continuous* functions $\varphi(t)$ defined on the set L. The sum of two points of this space $f(t)$ and $\varphi(t)$, and the product of a point by a real number λ is defined by formulae

$$\{f\} + \{\varphi\} = \{f + \varphi\}, \quad \lambda\{f\} = \{\lambda f\}.$$

The norm of f is defined by

$$\|f\| = \sup_L |f(t)|, \tag{12}$$

and the distance between two points by the formula

$$\delta(f, \varphi) = \|f - \varphi\|. \tag{13}$$

Under these definitions the space Λ is linear, normed, and complete, and thus this is a Banach space (see Part 2, p. 200).

Let us now consider in the space Λ the set E of all points $\varphi(t)$ of the space Λ satisfying the inequalities

$$\|\varphi\| \leqq R, \tag{14}$$

$$|\varphi(t) - \varphi(t_1)| < \kappa_\varphi |t - t_1|^{\mu/2} \tag{14'}$$

where R and μ are positive numbers, given in the assumptions (3″) and (4), while κ_φ is an arbitrary fixed positive number.

The set E is convex since if f and g are two points of this set, i.e. satisfying inequalities (14) and (14′), then all points of the form $\gamma f(t)+(1-\gamma)\, g(t)$, for $0 \leqq \gamma \leqq 1$, also belong to the set E because they satisfy the conditions (14) and (14′). Moreover, the set E, is *closed* since its limit points also satisfy the conditions (14) and (14′).

In view of the integral equation (11) we now transform the set E by means of the relation

$$\psi(\theta)-\frac{1}{\pi^2}\int_L \frac{F(\theta,\tau)}{N(\theta,\theta)}\,\psi(\tau)\,d\tau$$

$$=-\frac{\lambda}{N(\theta,\theta)}K[\theta,\theta,\varphi(\theta)]+\frac{\lambda}{\pi^2}\int_L \frac{\Phi[\theta,\tau,\varphi(\tau)]}{N(\theta,\theta)}\,d\tau-$$

$$-\frac{f_1(\theta)}{\pi^2 N(\theta,\theta)}. \qquad (15)$$

By the assumption that the kernel $N(t,\tau)/(t-\tau)$ is closed, the homogeneous equation

$$\psi(\theta)-\frac{1}{\pi^2}\int_L \frac{F(\theta,\tau)}{N(\theta,\theta)}\,\psi(\tau)\,d\tau=0$$

possesses the zero solution only, and consequently, on the basis of the First Fredholm Theorem and weak singularity of the kernel $F(\theta,\tau)/N(\theta,\theta)$ (see formula (10)), relation (15) assigns to each point $\varphi(\tau)$ of the set E a definite continuous function $\psi(\theta)$, in other words, a definite point of the space Λ. Let us establish a set of sufficient conditions that each transformed point ψ belongs to the set E, i.e. that it satisfies inequalities (14) and (14′).

Note that on the basis of the theory of weakly-singular equations, the only solution of the problem

$$\psi(\theta)-\frac{1}{\pi^2}\int_L \frac{F(\theta,\tau)}{N(\theta,\theta)}\,\psi(\tau)\,d\tau=g(\theta)$$

takes the form

$$\psi(\theta)=g(\theta)+\int_L \mathfrak{N}(\theta,\tau)\,g(\tau)\,d\tau \qquad (16)$$

where $\mathfrak{N}(\theta, \tau)$ is the usual function (being a combination of iterated kernels and the resolvent kernel) independent of the function $g(t)$ and dependent on the function $F(\theta, \tau)/N(\theta, \theta)$ only, moreover, having a singularity of the same form (10) as this function for $\theta = \tau$. Thus the solution (16) satisfies an inequality of the form

$$|\psi(\theta)| \leqq (1+k_{\mathfrak{N}}) \sup |g| \tag{17}$$

where

$$k_{\mathfrak{N}} = \sup_{\theta \in L} \int_L |\mathfrak{N}(\theta, \tau)| \, dl_\tau . \tag{17'}$$

Hence, it follows that the function $\psi(\theta)$ corresponding to the function $\varphi(\theta)$, on account of relation (15), satisfies the inequality

$$\psi(\theta) \leqq \frac{1+k_{\mathfrak{N}}}{m_N} \left[|\lambda| M_K + \frac{\lambda}{\pi^2} M_\Phi + (C' M_f + C'' k_f) \right] \tag{18}$$

where M_K, m_N, M_Φ, M_f denote the following positive constants:

$$\begin{aligned} M_K &= \sup_{(t, \tau \in L,\ |u| \leqq R)} |K(t, \tau, u)|, \qquad m_N = \inf_{t \in L} |N(t, t)|, \\ M_\Phi &= \sup_{(t \in L,\ |u| \leqq R)} \int_L |\Phi(t, \tau, u)| \, d\tau, \qquad M_f = \sup_{t \in L} |f(t)|; \end{aligned} \tag{19}$$

k_f is the Hölder coefficient of the function f in condition (4), and C' and C'' are certain positive constants depending on the contour L.

Now, let us examine whether the transformed function $\psi(\theta)$ satisfies Hölder's condition, and estimate its coefficient. Thus taking into account the considerations on p. 496 and using only the continuity of the function ψ, we can assert that the integral on the left-hand side of equation (15) satisfies Hölder's condition with exponent $\mu/2$. In the same way, the integral on the right-hand side also satisfies Hölder's condition for the exponent $\mu/2$. Next, the first component of the right-hand side, on account of the third of the assumptions (4) and inequality (14'), satisfies Hölder's condition for the exponent $\mu/2$, and finally, the third component on the right-hand side of equation (15), on account of the Plemelj–Privalov Theorem, satisfies Hölder's condition for the exponent μ. Thus we can assert that each of the functions $\psi(\theta)$, corresponding to the functions $\varphi(\theta)$ of the set E, satisfies Hölder's condition

$$|\psi(\theta)-\psi(\theta_1)| < k_\psi |\theta-\theta_1|^{\mu/2} \tag{20}$$

for the same exponent $\mu/2$ as the functions $\varphi(\theta)$.

From the form of the separate terms of equation (15), we obtain the estimate for the Hölder coefficient k_ψ,

$$\begin{aligned} k_\psi \leqq C_N \sup|\psi| + |\lambda|\, m_N^{-1}[\kappa_\varphi + 2|L|^{\mu/2}] + \\ + 2|\lambda|\, M_k k_N m_N^{-2} |L|^{\mu/2} + |\lambda|\, C_K + D m_N^{-1} k_f |L|^{\mu/2} + \\ + 2(C' M_f + C'' k_f)\, m_N^{-2} k_N |L|^{\mu/2}, \end{aligned} \tag{21}$$

where C_N denotes a positive constant depending on the function N and the contour L, C_K is a positive constant depending on the functions K, N and the contour L, D is a positive constant which depends on the contour L, and finally, $|L|$ denotes the diameter of the set L.

We can assert, on account of inequalities (18) and (21), that the set E' of transformed points ψ is a subset of E, provided that the constants of the problem satisfy the two inequalities

$$(1+k_{\mathfrak{N}})\, m_N^{-1}[|\lambda|\, M_K + |\lambda|\, \pi^{-2} M_\Phi + (C' M_f + C'' k_f)] \leqq R, \tag{22}$$

$$\begin{aligned} C_N R + |\lambda|\, m_N^{-1}[\kappa_\varphi + 2|L|^{\mu/2} + \\ + 2|\lambda|\, M_K k_N m_N^{-2} |L|^{\mu/2} + |\lambda|\, C_K + D m_N^{-1} k_f |L|^{\mu/2} + \\ + 2(C' M_f + C'' k_f)\, m_N^{-2} k_N |L|^{\mu/2} \leqq \kappa_\varphi. \end{aligned} \tag{22'}$$

Since the choice of the constant κ_φ is arbitrary, it is evident that the above conditions are always satisfied, provided that the constants $|\lambda|$, M_f, k_f are sufficiently small, for fixed values of the remaining coefficients.

The set E' is *relatively compact*, on account of Arzela's Theorem, since all its points are uniformly bounded by the inequality $|\psi| \leqq R$ and equicontinuous in view of Höldrr's inequality (20).

It still remains to prove that the transformation defined by relation (15) is continuous in the space Λ. In fact, if $\{\varphi_n\}$ is an arbitrary sequence of points of the set E convergent to φ, then the sequence of corresponding points $\{\psi_n\}$ tends to the point ψ which corresponds to φ, according to relation (15), on the basis of the well-known property of the solution of Fredholm's equation.

Thus all the conditions of Schauder's Theorem are satisfied (see Part 2, p. 201), and therefore we can assert that there exists at least one fixed point $\varphi^*(t)$ of the transformation (15), i.e. that there exists a solution of the integral equation (5), and consequently, also of the given equation (2). Thus, we have the following theorem:

THEOREM. *If the given functions $f(t), N(t,\tau), K(t,\tau,u)$ satisfy the Hölder conditions* (4), *if the kernel $N(t,\tau)/(t-\tau)$ is closed, and if the constants $|\lambda|, M_f, k_f$ are sufficiently small such that inequalities* (22) *and* (22′) *hold, then the integral equation* (2) *possesses at least one solution $\varphi^*(t)$ in the set of complex functions satisfying Hölder's condition.*

§ 2. Non-linear singular equations of the second kind investigated by Schauder's topological method

A non-linear singular integral equation of the second kind has the form

$$\varphi(t) = \lambda \int_L \frac{K[t,\tau,\varphi(\tau)]}{\tau - t}\, d\tau. \tag{23}$$

It is assumed that the complex function $K(t,\tau,u)$, defined in the closed domain

$$t \in L, \qquad \tau \in L, \qquad |u| \leqq R, \tag{24}$$

satisfies the Hölder–Lipschitz condition in the form

$$|K(t,\tau,u) - K(t_1,\tau_1,u_1)| < k[|t-t_1|^{\nu} + |\tau-\tau_1|^{\mu} + |u-u_1|], \tag{25}$$

where $0 < \mu < \nu \leqq 1$, $k > 0$.

Equation (23) cannot be solved by the classical method under the assumption (25). The proof of the existence of its solution can, however, be obtained by Schauder's topological method. Recently, equation (23) was examined, using the above method, by a Soviet mathematician A. Guseinov who considered a particular case when the path of integration is a segment of the real axis. In the general case, when the domain of integration L is a set of smooth contours, equation (23) has been investigated by the author [59], basing on the properties of the Cauchy type integrals and Schauder's Theorem. This proof will be given below.

Equation (23) cannot be reduced to an equivalent weakly-singular equation, and thus we shall apply Schauder's Theorem directly. Let us consider the space Λ the points of which are all complex *continuous* functions $\varphi(t)$ defined on the set L. We assume the same definitions for the operations and for the norm as in the preceding section, thereby the space Λ is a Banach space.

Consider, in this space, the set E of all points $\varphi(t)$ satisfying the inequalities

$$|\varphi(t)| \leqq R, \tag{26}$$

$$|\varphi(t) - \varphi(t')| \leqq \kappa_\varphi |t - t_1|^\mu \tag{26'}$$

where the given constants appear in the assumption (24) and (25), while the positive coefficient κ_φ is fixed arbitrarily. The set E is *closed* since its limit points also satisfy inequalities (26) and (26'). The set E is *convex*, because, if φ and g are two of its points, i.e. satisfying conditions (26) and (26'), then each point

$$\Phi(t) = (1-\gamma)\varphi(t) + \gamma g(t) \qquad (0 \leqq \gamma \leqq 1)$$

of the segment connecting the points φ and g belongs also to the set E, since we have

$$|\Phi(t)| \leqq (1-\gamma)|\varphi(t)| + \gamma|g(t)| \leqq R,$$

$$|\Phi(t) - \Phi(t_1)|$$
$$\leqq (1-\gamma)|\varphi(t) - \varphi(t_1)| + \gamma|g(t) - g(t_1)| \leqq \kappa_\varphi |t - t_1|^\mu .$$

In view of the integral equation (23) we now transform the set E, assigning to each point φ of this set the point ψ, according to the formula

$$\psi(t) = \lambda \int_L \frac{K[t, \tau, \varphi(\tau)]}{\tau - t}\, d\tau. \tag{27}$$

Let us find the conditions that the transformed points ψ belong to the set E. For this purpose, we write

$$\psi(t) = \lambda \int_L \frac{K[t, \tau, \varphi(\tau)] - K[t, t, \varphi(t)]}{\tau - t}\, d\tau + \\ + K[t, t, \varphi(t)] \int_L \frac{d\tau}{\tau - t}, \tag{28}$$

and hence, according to the assumptions (25) and (26′), it follows that:

$$|\psi(t)| \leqq |\lambda|\, k(1+\kappa_\varphi) \int_L \frac{dl_\tau}{|\tau - t|^{1-\mu}} + \pi |\lambda|\, M_K \tag{29}$$

where M_K denotes the upper bound of the function $|K(t, \tau, u)|$ on the set (24).

Next, let us note that we have

$$|K[t, \tau, \varphi(\tau)] - K[t_1, \tau_1, \varphi(\tau_1)]| \\ \leqq k\,|t - t_1|^\nu + (1+\kappa_\varphi)\,|\tau - \tau_1|^\mu].$$

Hence we can conclude, using Theorem 2 on p. 443, which is a generalization of the Privalov's Theorem, that the function (27) satisfies Hölder's condition of the form

$$|\psi(t) - \psi(t_1)| \leqq k\,|\lambda|\,(1+\kappa_\varphi)\, C\,|t - t_1|^\mu, \tag{30}$$

where the positive constant C does not depend on the functions φ, but does depend on the contours L. We emphasize that the fundamental fact concerning the behaviour of the Hölder exponent after the transformation (27) is due to the assumption (25) where it is assumed that $\mu < \nu$, and that the Hölder exponent with respect to the variable u is equal to *unity*.

It follows from inequalities (29) and (30) that all the transformed points ψ of the set E belong to E, provided that the constants of the problem satisfy the following two inequalities

$$|\lambda|\, k(1+\kappa_\varphi)I+\pi|\lambda|\, M_K \leqq R, \quad |\lambda|\, k(1+\kappa_\varphi)C \leqq \kappa_\varphi \tag{31}$$

or when the absolute value of the parameter λ does not exceed the smaller of the two numbers

$$|\lambda| \leqq \min\left(\frac{R}{k(1+\kappa_\varphi)I+\pi M_K}, \frac{\kappa_\varphi}{k(1+\kappa_\varphi)C}\right) \tag{32}$$

where I denotes the upper bound of the integral

$$\int_L \frac{dl_\nu}{|\tau-t|^{1-\mu}}$$

on the set L.

We now prove that the transformation (27) of the set E is *continuous* in the space Λ. To do this, it is necessary and sufficient to prove that if the sequence of the functions $\{\varphi_n(t)\}$ of the set E is uniformly convergent to the function $\varphi(t)$, then the sequence of transformed functions

$$\psi_n(t) = \lambda\int_L \frac{K[t,\tau,\varphi_n(\tau)]}{\tau-t}\,d\tau$$

$$= \lambda\int \frac{K[t,\tau,\varphi_n(\tau)]-K[t,\tau,\varphi_n(t)]}{\tau-t}\,d\tau+\lambda K[t,t,\varphi_n(t)] \tag{33}$$

is uniformly convergent to the function $\psi(t)$ which corresponds to the limit function $\varphi(t)$ according to formula (27). Thus we obtain

$$\psi_n(t)-\psi(t) = \lambda\pi i\{K[t,t,\varphi_n(t)]-K[t,\tau,\varphi(t)]\}+$$

$$+\lambda\left\{\int_L \frac{K[t,\tau,\varphi(t)]-K[t,t,\varphi_n(t)]}{\tau-t}\,d\tau-\right.$$

$$\left.-\int_L \frac{K[t,\tau,\varphi_n(\tau)]-K[t,t,\varphi_n(t)]}{\tau-t}\,d\tau\right\}. \tag{34}$$

The first difference on the right-hand side tends uniformly to zero for $\varphi_n \to \varphi$, and thus it remains to examine the second difference denoted by I_n.

Suppose we are given a circle with centre t and radius ρ, so small that inside the circle lies the single arc of the line L only. We decompose the difference I_n into two parts

$$I_n = I_n^l + I_n^{L-l}$$

where the integration is taken over the arc l and the remaining part $L-l$. The inequality

$$\left| \int_l \frac{K[t, \tau, \varphi_n(\tau)] - K[t, t, \varphi_n(t)]}{\tau - t} \, d\tau \right|$$

$$\leq k(1+\kappa_\varphi) \int_l \frac{dl_\tau}{|\tau - t|^{1-\mu}} \leq \frac{\varepsilon}{3}$$

holds for each n, and consequently in the limit, for all points $t \in L$, provided the length of the arc is sufficiently small, depending on arbitrary positive ε. Thus we have for each n and t

$$|I_n^l| \leq \frac{2}{3} \varepsilon .$$

Since the point t lies outside the arc of integration $L-l$, the integrands (34) are continuous. Therefore, after choosing the length of the arc l, and making use of the property that the functions φ_n tend uniformly to the function φ, we can select an N_ε such that for each t the inequality

$$|I_n^{L-l}| \leq \frac{\varepsilon}{3}$$

holds for $n > N_\varepsilon$. Hence it follows that $|I_n| \leq \varepsilon$ for $n > N_\varepsilon$, the difference $\psi_n - \psi$ tends uniformly to zero, and the transformation (27) is continuous. It still remains to prove that the transformed set E' of points is *relatively compact*. This property follows, at once, on account of Arzela's Theorem, from the fact that all functions $\psi(t)$ are uniformly bounded by the inequality $|\psi| \leq R$, and equicontinuous in view of Hölder's inequality (30).

In this way all the conditions of Schauder's Theorem are satisfied, and consequently, there exists at least one fixed point $\varphi^*(t)$ of the transformation (27), i.e. that in the set E there exists at least one function $\varphi^*(t)$ which is a solution of the integral equation (23) for sufficiently small $|\lambda|$. Thus we have the following theorem:

THEOREM. *If a given complex function* $K(t, \tau, u)$, *defined in the domain* (24), *satisfies Hölder's condition* (25) *and the parameter* λ *satisfies condition* (32), *then there exists at least one solution* $\varphi(t)$ *of the integral equation of the second kind* (23) *in the set of functions satisfying Hölder's condition with exponent* μ.

However, the set of the values of the parameter λ for which the existence of the solution of equation (23) has been proved depends upon the Hölder coefficient κ_φ the choice of which is arbitrary. Making use of this arbitrariness we can choose the value of κ_φ in such a way that the range of variation of the absolute value of $|\lambda|$ be as large as possible. Note that if κ_φ increases from zero to infinity, then the first of the two numbers (32) decreases from the value $R/(kI+\pi M_K)$ to zero, while the second one increases from zero to the limit value $1/kC$. Hence we conclude that the greatest admissible range of the absolute value of $|\lambda|$ is obtained when the value $\kappa_\varphi = \kappa_\varphi^{(0)}$ is chosen in such a way that the numbers (32) are equal

$$\frac{R}{k(1+\kappa_\varphi^{(0)})I+\pi M_K} = \frac{\kappa_\varphi^{(0)}}{k(1+\kappa_\varphi^{(0)})C}\,. \qquad (34')$$

Hence, it follows that "the most expedient" value of the coefficient is

$$\kappa_\varphi^{(0)} = \frac{(RkC-a)+\sqrt{(RkC-a^2)+4k^2IRC}}{2kI}\,, \qquad (34'')$$

where $a = kI+\pi M_K$.

In a similar fashion one can examine a system of n singular integral equations of the form

$$\varphi_\nu(t) = \int\limits_L \frac{F_\nu[t, \tau, \varphi_1(\tau), \ldots, \varphi_n(\tau)]}{\tau-t}\, d\tau \qquad (\nu = 1, 2, \ldots, n)$$

with n unknown functions $\varphi_1, \varphi_2, \ldots, \varphi_n$.

§ 3. Non-linear singular equations of the second kind investigated by the method of successive approximation

The proof of the existence of the solution of singular equation by means of the method of successive approximation requires a different and much more sensitive approach than that for weakly-singular equations, discussed in Part 2.

Under a very restrictive assumption that the function $K(t, \tau, u)$ in equation (23) be holomorphic in a certain strip containing the contour L, the author proved in the paper [60] the existence of the solution of the singular equation of the form (23) by means of the method of successive approximations. For this purpose, the author replaced the singular integral over the contour L by the sum of regular integrals over the pair of closed curves enclosing L. Taking a sequence of pairs of such curves tending to the contour L, it was possible to obtain, in the limit, the solution of a given singular equation.

In a particular case, when the curve of integration L is a segment of the real axis, the singular equation of the form (23) was solved by GUSEINOV [18]. The solution was obtained by the method of successive approximations, the assumptions being less restrictive than that of the holomorphy, but more restrictive compared with those in Schauder's topological method. Namely, GUSEINOV assumes that the real function $K(t, \tau, u)$, defined for real values t, τ, u satisfies Hölder's condition with respect to the variables t, τ

$$|K(t, \tau, u)-K(t_1, \tau_1, u_1)| < k[|t-t_1|^{\nu}+|\tau-\tau_1|^{\mu}] \quad (0<\mu<\nu\leqq 1) \tag{35}$$

and possesses a derivative with respect to the variable u satisfying the Hölder–Lipschitz condition in the form

$$|K_u'(t, \tau, u)-K_u'(t_1, \tau_1, u)| < k'[|t-t_1|^{\nu}+|\tau-\tau_1|^{\mu}+|u-u_1|]. \tag{35'}$$

Recently, D. PRZEWORSKA–ROLEWICZ developed, in her papers [73] and [74], the method of successive approximation (i.e. Banach's method of the fixed point) in the theory of singular equations, using concepts of functional analysis. Below, we present these investigations in a simplified form. The reader, who wishes to be acquainted with this method, is referred to the papers cited above.

Thus, let there be given a singular equation of the second kind

$$\varphi(t) = \lambda \int_L \frac{K[t, \tau, \varphi(\tau)]}{\tau - t} d\tau \tag{36}$$

where L is a finite set of smooth non-intersecting contours L in the complex plane.

We assume that the complex function $K(t, \tau, u)$ of three complex variables defined in the domain

$$t \in L, \quad \tau \in L, \quad |u| = |\xi + i\eta| \leqq R \tag{37}$$

satisfies the Hölder–Lipschitz condition with respect to the variables t, τ, u

$$|K(t, \tau, u) - K(t_1, \tau_1, u_1)| \leqq k[|t-t_1|^{\nu} + |\tau - \tau_1|^{\mu} + |u - u_1|] \tag{38}$$

where $0 < \mu < \nu \leqq 1$, as before. Moreover, we assume that the real part $K^{(\mathrm{re})}$ and the imaginary part $K^{(\mathrm{im})}$ of the function

$$K(t, \tau, u) = K^{(\mathrm{re})}(t, \tau, \xi, \eta) + iK^{(\mathrm{im})}(t, \tau, \xi, \eta) \tag{39}$$

have partial derivatives with respect to the variables ξ and η in the domain (37), satisfying the Hölder–Lipschitz condition in the form

$$\begin{aligned} &|K_{\xi}^{(\alpha)}(t, \tau, \xi, \eta) - K_{\xi}^{(\alpha)}(t_1, \tau_1, \xi_1, \eta_1)| \\ &\qquad \leqq k'[|t-t_1|^{\nu} + |\tau-\tau_1|^{\mu} + |\xi - \xi_1| + |\eta - \eta_1|], \\ &|K_{\eta}^{(\alpha)}(t, \tau, \xi, \eta) - K_{\eta}^{(\alpha)}(t_1, \tau_1, \xi_1, \eta_1)| \\ &\qquad \leqq k'[|t-t_1|^{\nu} + |\tau-\tau_1|^{\mu} + |\xi - \xi_1| + |\eta - \eta_1|] \end{aligned} \tag{40}$$

where the symbol α has to be replaced either by the symbol re or by im.

These assumptions are analogous to the Guseinov assumptions (35) and (35′).

According to the method of successive approximation, we compose the sequence

$$\varphi_0(t), \varphi_1(t), \ldots, \varphi_n(t), \ldots \tag{41}$$

of the complex functions for $t \in L$ by means of the recurrence relation

$$\varphi_{n+1}(t) = \lambda \int_L \frac{K[t, \tau, \varphi_n(\tau)]}{\tau - t} d\tau . \tag{42}$$

Suppose that the first approximation $\varphi_0(t)$ is a complex function arbitrarily defined on L, satisfying the inequalities

$$|\varphi_0(t)| \leqq R, \quad |\varphi_0(t) - \varphi_0(t_1)| \leqq \kappa |t - t_1|^\mu, \tag{43}$$

where R and κ are given constants in the assumptions (37) and (38), while κ is an arbitrarily fixed positive coefficient. Similarly, as in the preceding section, we conclude that the functions of the sequence (40) defined for an arbitrary n satisfy the inequalities

$$|\varphi_n(t)| \leqq R, \quad |\varphi_n(t) - \varphi_n(t_1)| \leqq \kappa |t - t_1|^\mu \tag{44}$$

when the absolute value of the parameter λ is sufficiently small such that the inequalities analogous to inequalities (31)

$$|\lambda| [k(1+\kappa) I + \pi M_K] \leqq R, \quad |\lambda| k(1+\kappa) C \leqq \kappa \tag{45}$$

are satisfied. Thus the assumption (38) is sufficient for the proof of the existence of the sequence of successive approximation. However, it is not sufficient for the proof of its convergence. For this purpose, the additional more restrictive assumption (40) is introduced, and thus the proof of the convergence of the sequence (41) can be obtained. We obtain this proof in another way as compared with the classical method of successive approximations, by means of the combined examination of the convergence of the two series

$$\sum_{n=0}^{\infty} |\varphi_{n+1}(t) - \varphi_n(t)|, \quad \sum_{n=0}^{\infty} H_n[\varphi_{n+1}(t) - \varphi_n(t)], \tag{46}$$

where $H[\psi(t)]$ denotes the Hölder coefficient, in an exact meaning (at the exponent μ) of the function ψ, i.e. the upper bound of the following quotient:

$$H[\psi(t)] = \sup_{(t,t_1 \in L)} \frac{|\psi(t)-\psi(t_1)|}{|t-t_1|^{\mu}}. \tag{47}$$

Thus, this is the least coefficient in the set of all coefficients k_{ψ} which can be inserted in the Hölder inequality

$$|\psi(t)-\psi(t_1)| \leqq k_{\psi}|t-t_1|^{\mu}$$

for the given function.

In order to estimate the difference of successive approximations $\varphi_{n+1}-\varphi_n$ and their Hölder coefficient, in the sense (47), we first prove the following lemma, which is another form of the lemma on p. 531:

LEMMA. *If a complex valued function $f(\xi,\eta;t,\tau)$ of the real variables ξ,η and complex parameters t,τ, defined in the domain*

$$|\xi+i\eta| \leqq R, \quad t\in L, \quad \tau\in L \tag{48}$$

possesses partial derivatives with respect to the variables ξ and η satisfying the Hölder–Lipschitz conditions in the form

$$\begin{aligned} &|f'_{\xi}(\xi,\eta,t,\tau)-f'_{\xi}(\xi_1,\eta_1,t_1,\tau_1)| \\ &\qquad \leqq k_f[|\xi-\xi_1|+|\eta-\eta_1|+|t-t_1|^{\nu}+|\tau-\tau_1|^{\mu}], \\ &|f'_{\eta}(\xi,\eta,t,\tau)-f'_{\eta}(\xi_1,\eta_1,t_1,\tau_1)| \\ &\qquad \leqq k_f[|\xi-\xi_1|+|\eta-\eta_1|+|t-t_1|^{\nu}+|\tau-\tau_1|^{\mu}] \end{aligned} \tag{49}$$

$(0<\mu<\nu\leqq 1)$, *then the equality*

$$\begin{aligned} &f(\tilde{\xi},\tilde{\eta},t,\tau)-f(\xi,\eta,t,\tau) \\ &\quad =(\tilde{\xi}-\xi)F_1(\xi,\tilde{\xi},\eta,\tilde{\eta},t,\tau)+(\eta-\eta)F_2(\xi,\tilde{\xi},\eta,\tilde{\eta},t,\tau) \end{aligned} \tag{50}$$

holds. Here the complex functions F_1 and F_2 determined in the domain

$$|\xi+i\eta| \leqq R, \quad |\tilde{\xi}+i\tilde{\eta}| \leqq R, \quad t\in L, \quad \tau\in L \tag{51}$$

satisfy the Hölder–Lipschitz condition

$$\begin{aligned} &|F_{\alpha}(\xi,\tilde{\xi},\eta,\tilde{\eta},t,\tau)-F_{\alpha}(\xi',\tilde{\xi}',\eta',\tilde{\eta}',t',\tau')| \\ &\leqq k_f[|\xi-\xi'|+|\tilde{\xi}-\tilde{\xi}'|+|\eta-\eta'|+|\tilde{\eta}-\tilde{\eta}'|+|t-t'|^{\nu}+|\tau-\tau'|^{\mu}]. \end{aligned} \tag{52}$$

Proof. The proposition of the lemma follows immediately from the following obvious integral representation of the difference between two arbitrary values of the function $f(\xi, \eta, t, \tau)$:

$$f(\tilde{\xi}, \tilde{\eta}, t, \tau) - \ (\xi, \eta, t, \tau)$$

$$= (\tilde{\xi}-\xi) \int_0^1 f'_\xi[\xi+s(\tilde{\xi}-\xi), \tilde{\eta}, t, \tau]\, ds +$$

$$+ (\tilde{\eta}-\eta) \int_0^1 f'_\eta[\xi, \eta+s(\tilde{\eta}-\eta), t, \tau]\, ds. \qquad (53)$$

Let us now return to the differences $\varphi_{n+1} - \varphi_n$ which, on account of formula (42), can be written in the form

$$\varphi_{n+1}(t) - \varphi_n(t) = \lambda \int_L \frac{\delta_n(t, \tau)}{\tau - t}\, d\tau, \qquad (54)$$

where we have used the notation

$$\delta_n(t, \tau) = K[t, \tau, \varphi_n(\tau)] - K[t, \tau, \varphi_{n-1}(\tau)], \qquad (55)$$

and applying to this difference the proved lemma, substituting

$$K[t, \tau, \xi+i\eta] = f(\xi, \eta, t, \tau),$$

$$\varphi_n(\tau) = \tilde{\xi}+i\tilde{\eta}, \quad \varphi_{n-1}(\tau) = \xi+i\eta$$

we obtain that the difference δ_n can be expressed in the form

$$\delta_n = \mathrm{re}\,[\varphi_n(\tau) - \varphi_{n-1}(\tau)]\, F_1(\xi, \tilde{\xi}, \eta, \tilde{\eta}, t, \tau) +$$

$$+ \mathrm{im}\,[\varphi_n(\tau) - \varphi_{n-1}(\tau)]\, F_2(\xi, \tilde{\xi}, \eta, \tilde{\eta}, t, \tau) \qquad (56)$$

where the functions F_1 and F_2 are expressed by the integrals (53) and satisfy the conditions (52).

In view of the assumed property (38) we define the Hölder coefficient of the function of two variables $\delta_n(t, \tau)$ as the following upper bound:

$$H[\delta_n(t, \tau)] = \sup_{\substack{t, \tau \in L \\ t_1, \tau_1 \in L}} \frac{|\delta_n(t, \tau) - \delta_n(t_1, \tau_1)|}{|t-t_1|^\nu + |\tau-\tau_1|^\mu}. \qquad (57)$$

Hence, in view of formula (56) and the assumption (40) we obtain

$$H[\delta_n(t,\tau)]$$
$$\leqq 4H[\varphi_n(t)-\varphi_{n-1}(t)]\,M'_K+4(2\kappa+1)\,k'\sup|\varphi_n-\varphi_{n-1}| \qquad (58)$$

where M'_K denotes the upper bound of the set of the absolute values of the derivatives of the functions $K^{(\mathrm{re})}$ and $K^{(\mathrm{im})}$ with respect to the variables ξ and η, while k' is the positive coefficient given in (40).

Note that the difference (55) also satisfies, on account of (38), the following inequality:

$$\sup|\delta_n(t,\tau)| \leqq k'\sup|\varphi_n-\varphi_{n-1}|. \qquad (57')$$

Now, applying to the Cauchy type integral (54) Privalov's Generalized Theorem on p. 443 (see inequalities (39) and (40)) we obtain the following properties of the differences between successive approximations:

$$\sup|\varphi_{n+1}(t)-\varphi_n(t)| \leqq \pi|\lambda|\sup|\delta_n|+C'|\lambda|\,H\,\llcorner\delta_n],$$
$$H[\varphi_{n+1}(t)-\varphi_n(t)] \leqq C|\lambda|\,H[\delta_n],$$

where C is a positive constant depending only on the contours L, whereas

$$C' = \sup\int_L |t-\tau|^{\mu-1}\,dl_\tau.$$

Hence, on account of the definition (57) and inequality (58), the fundamental estimates follow:

$$\sup|\varphi_{n+1}(t)-\varphi_n(t)|$$
$$\leqq [\pi k+4C'k'(2\kappa+1)]\,|\lambda|\sup|\varphi_n(t)-\varphi_{n-1}(t)|+$$
$$+4|\lambda|\,IM'_K\,H[\varphi_n(t)-\varphi_{n-1}(t)], \qquad (58)$$

$$H[\varphi_{n+1}(t)-\varphi_n(t)]$$
$$\leqq 4C(2\kappa+1)\,k'|\lambda|\sup|\varphi_n(t)-\varphi_{n-1}(t)|+$$
$$+4CM'_K|\lambda|\,H[\varphi_n(t)-\varphi_{n-1}(t)].$$

By virtue of these inequalities, we immediately conclude that the series (46) converges, and moreover, the first one uniformly, provided the absolute value of the parameter λ is sufficiently small.

The easiest way to obtain a sufficient test for convergence is to note that the inequality

$$\sup|\varphi_{n+1}-\varphi_n|+H[\varphi_{n+1}-\varphi_n] \leqq |\lambda| P\{\sup|\varphi_n-\varphi_{n-1}|+H[\varphi_n-\varphi_{n-1}]\} \tag{59}$$

follows from inequality (58'). P denotes the greater of the two positive numbers:

$$P = \max[\pi k+4(2\kappa+1)(C+C')k'; 4M'_K(C+C')]. \tag{60}$$

Hence, we conclude that the series

$$\sum_{n=0}^{\infty}\{\sup|\varphi_{n+1}-\varphi_n|+H[\varphi_{n+1}-\varphi_n]\}$$

is convergent, and consequently, the series (46) also converges, provided the parameter λ and the constants k, k', M'_K, appropriate for the given function K, satisfy the inequality

$$|\lambda| P<1 \tag{61}$$

as well as inequality (45).

The uniform convergence of the functional sequence (41) to the limit function $\varphi(t)$, which is the solution of the given integral equation (36), follows from the above considerations.

Similarly, as in the classical method of successive approximations, we prove that the obtained solution is unique in the set of functions satisfying Hölder's condition in the form

$$|\varphi(t)-\varphi(t_1)| \leqq \kappa|t-t_1|^{\mu}, \tag{62}$$

i.e. for which the Hölder coefficient $H[\varphi]$, in the exact meaning, in not greater than κ.

In fact, if there exists another solution $\psi(t)$ of integral equation (36) satisfying the condition

$$|\psi(t)-\psi(t_1)| \leqq \kappa|t-t_1|^{\mu},$$

i.e. such that

$$\psi(t) = \lambda \int_L \frac{K[t, \tau, \varphi(\tau)]}{\tau - t} d\tau$$

we then obtain

$$\varphi(t) - \psi(t) = \lambda \int_L \frac{K[t, \tau, \varphi(\tau)] - K[t, \tau, \psi(\tau)]}{\tau - t} d\tau .$$

This relation is analogous to relation (54) between successive approximations, and thus, proceeding as above, we obtain the inequality

$$\sup|\varphi - \psi| + H|\varphi - \psi| \leqq |\lambda| P\{\sup|\varphi - \psi| + H[\varphi - \psi]\} \qquad (63)$$

analogous to inequality (59). Inequality (63), however, is impossible since in order to prove the existence of the solution $\varphi(t)$ we assumed that $|\lambda| P < 1$. It is the existence of the second distinct solution that leads to the contradiction, and hence there exists one solution only in the set of functions satisfying condition (62), for a fixed κ.

It is seen from inequalities (45) and (61) that the range of the parameter λ for which there exists a solution of equation (36) depends on the coefficient κ, the choice of which was arbitrary. It is obvious that we make use of this arbitrariness, and that κ will be so selected that the corresponding admissible range of the parameter λ would be as large as possible. As far as it concerns inequalities (45), identical with conditions (31), we have seen that the most expedient value of κ (34″) is that satisfying equation (34′). In this problem, however, we have one more condition (61), and therefore we are not able to determine exactly the most expedient numerical value of κ, but we can only assert that such a value exists, since when the coefficient κ increases, then the first of the numbers (60) tends to infinity.

We now show that the above investigation has an interesting and clear interpretation in a certain Banach space.

Namely, let us consider a functional space Λ_μ the points of which are all complex functions $\varphi(t)$ defined on the set L

and satisfying Hölder's condition of the form

$$|\varphi(t)-\varphi(t_1)| \leqq \kappa |t-t_1|^{\mu}, \tag{64}$$

where the exponent μ has a positive value, less than unity, fixed for the whole space Λ_μ, while the coefficient κ should take all positive values.

We assume the same definitions of the numerical operations for the space Λ_μ as before for the space of continuous functions, and thus, the space Λ_μ will be linear.

If we assumed the same definitions of the norm and the distance between two points, as for the space of continuous functions,

$$\|\varphi\| = \sup|\varphi|, \quad \delta(\varphi, \psi) = \sup|\varphi-\psi|,$$

then the space Λ_μ would not be complete, since the limit of the uniformly convergent sequence of functions $\{\varphi_n\}$ satisfying condition (64) does not necessarily satisfy the Hölder condition, when the coefficient κ is not fixed.

Thus we assume the following definitions of the norm of the point φ and the distance between two points φ and ψ in the space Λ_μ:

$$\begin{aligned} \|\varphi\| &= \sup_{t\in L}|\varphi(t)|+H[\varphi], \\ \delta(\varphi, \psi) = \|\varphi-\psi\| &= \sup_{t\in L}|\varphi(t)-\psi(t)|+H[\varphi-\psi], \end{aligned} \tag{65}$$

where $H[\varphi(t)]$ is the Hölder coefficient, in the exact meaning, for the exponent μ, in other words

$$H[\varphi] = \sup_{t,t_1\in L} \frac{|\varphi(t)-\varphi(t_1)|}{|t-t_1|^{\mu}}. \tag{66}$$

In view of the definitions (65) the space Λ_μ is *normed* and *complete*. In fact, let there be given, in the space Λ_μ, a sequence of points φ_n satisfying the Cauchy condition, i.e. such that

$$\|\varphi_{n+p}-\varphi_n\| \leqq \varepsilon \tag{67}$$

for $n \geqq N(\varepsilon)$, where p is an arbitrary positive integer, and $N(\varepsilon)$ depends on the choice of an arbitrary $\varepsilon > 0$. According to the definition of the norm (65), it follows from (67) that the functional sequence $\{\varphi_n(t)\}$ is convergent uniformly and absolutely, in the usual meaning, to a certain continuous function $\varphi(t)$:

$$\lim \varphi_n = \varphi\,.$$

Since, we likewise have

$$H[\varphi_{n+p} - \varphi_n] \leqq \varepsilon$$

for $n > N(\varepsilon)$, when p is arbitrary, then we get for the limit function φ that

$$H[\varphi - \varphi_n] \leqq \varepsilon$$

for $n > N(\varepsilon)$. Hence, according to the definition (66), we obtain

$$\sup_{t,t' \in L} \frac{|[\varphi(t) - \varphi(t')] - [\varphi_n(t) - \varphi_n(t')]|}{|t - t'|^{\mu}} \leqq \varepsilon$$

for $n \geqq N(\varepsilon)$. Thus the quotient $|\varphi(t) - \varphi(t')|/|t - t'|^{\mu}$ is bounded for $t, t' \in L$ and the limit function $\varphi(t)$ also satisfies Hölder's condition for the exponent μ, consequently the point φ belongs to the space Λ_{μ} and the space is complete. The space Λ_{μ} is thus a Banach space.

Returning to the method of successive approximations, the sequence of successive approximations (41) can be interpreted as a certain sequence of points $\{\varphi_n\}$ in the function space Λ_{μ}. Then inequality (59) means that the norm of the difference between the successive points satisfies the inequality

$$\|\varphi_{n+1} - \varphi_n\| \leqq |\lambda|\, P\, \|\varphi_n - \varphi_{n-1}\| \tag{68}$$

and, in accordance with Banach's Theorem (Part 2, p. 197), the limit point of the sequence $\{\varphi_n\}$ exists, which is at the same time the fixed point of the transformation

$$\psi(t) = \lambda \int_L \frac{K[t, \tau, \varphi(\tau)]}{\tau - t}\, d\tau$$

for $|\lambda|\, P < 1$.

§ 4. The generalized Hilbert problem

Let there be given a system of smooth contours $L_0, L_1, \ldots, L_p$ as in Fig. 6.

The generalized Hilbert problem, investigated by the author [61], consists in the determination of the system of m functions

$$\Phi_1(z), \Phi_2(z), \ldots, \Phi_m(z) \quad (m \geqq 1)$$

sectionally holomorphic in $S^+, S_0^-, S_1^-, \ldots, S_p^-$, the boundary values of which $\Phi_\alpha^+(t), \Phi_\alpha^-(t)$ satisfy, at each point $t \in L = L_0 + L_1 + \ldots + L_p$, the system of m equations

$$\Phi_\alpha^+(t) = G_\alpha(t)\Phi_\alpha^-(t) + \\ + \lambda F_\alpha[t, \Phi_1^+(t), \ldots, \Phi_m^+(t), \Phi_1^-(t), \ldots, \Phi_m^-(t)] \\ (\alpha = 1, 2, \ldots, m), \quad (69)$$

where $G_\alpha(t)$ and $F_\alpha(t, u_1, \ldots, u_m, u_{m+1}, \ldots, u_{2m})$ are given complex functions for which the following two assumptions are valid:

1. The complex functions $G_\alpha(t)$ defined for $t \in L$ satisfy Hölder's condition

$$|G_\alpha(t) - G_\alpha(t_1)| < k_G |t - t_1|^\mu \quad (70)$$

for a positive exponent $\mu < 1$, and are everywhere different from zero.

2. The complex functions $F_\alpha(t, u_1, \ldots, u_m, u_{m+1}, \ldots, u_{2m})$ are defined in the domain

$$t \in L, \quad |u_\nu| \leqq R \quad (\nu = 1, 2, \ldots, 2m), \quad (71)$$

where R is a prescribed positive number, and satisfy the Hölder-Lipschitz conditions in the form

$$|F_\alpha(t, u_1, \ldots, u_m, u_{m+1}, \ldots, u_{2m}) - \\ - F_\alpha(t', u_1', \ldots, u_m', u_{m+1}', \ldots, u_{2m}')| \\ < k_F \left[|t - t'|^\mu + \sum_{\nu=1}^{2m} |u_\nu - u_\nu'|\right]. \quad (72)$$

In accordance with the theory of linear Hilbert problem discussed in the preceding chapter, if the solution $\Phi_1(z), \ldots, \Phi_m(z)$ of the generalized problem (69) exists, then such a solution satisfies the equation

$$\Phi_\alpha(z) = \frac{\lambda}{2\pi i} X_\alpha(z) \int\limits_L \frac{F_\alpha[\tau, \varphi_1(\tau), \ldots, \varphi_{2m}(\tau)]}{X_\alpha^+(\tau)(\tau - z)} d\tau + X_\alpha(z) P_\alpha(z) \quad (73)$$

($z \in S^+ + S^-$, $\alpha = 1, 2, \ldots, m$) where $\varphi_\nu(t)$ denote the boundary values

$$\varphi_\nu(t) = \Phi_\nu^+(t), \quad \varphi_{\nu+m}(t) = \Phi_\nu^-(t) \quad (\nu = 1, 2, \ldots, m) \quad (74)$$

which, by the assumption, satisfy Hölder's condition; $P_\alpha(z)$ are suitably chosen entire functions. The functions $X_\alpha(z)$ are the fundamental solutions of the homogeneous Hilbert problems

$$X_\alpha^+(t) = G_\alpha(t) X_\alpha^-(t)$$

defined by the formulae

$$X_\alpha(z) = \begin{cases} \Pi_\alpha^{-1}(z) \exp[\Gamma_\alpha(z)] & \text{for} \quad z \in S^+, \\ z^{-\kappa_\alpha} \exp[\Gamma_\alpha(z)] & \text{for} \quad z \in S^-, \end{cases} \quad (75)$$

where κ_α is the index of the problem corresponding to the function $G_\alpha(t)$, i.e. such that

$$\kappa_\alpha = \sum_{\nu=0}^{p} \lambda_\nu^{(\alpha)}, \quad \lambda_\nu^{(\alpha)} = [\arg G_\alpha(t)]_{L_\nu}.$$

Moreover, we have

$$\Pi_\alpha(z) = (z - a_1)^{\lambda_1^{(\alpha)}} \ldots (z - a_p)^{\lambda_p^{(\alpha)}}, \quad G_\alpha^{(0)}(t) = t^{-\kappa_\alpha} G_\alpha(t),$$
$$\Gamma_\alpha(z) = \frac{1}{2\pi i} \int\limits_L \frac{\log G_\alpha^{(0)}(t)}{t - z} dt; \quad (76)$$

a_ν is a point arbitrarily fixed inside the region S_ν^-, whereas the point $z = 0$ lies inside the region S^+.

If we assume in formulae (73) that the point z tends to any point $t \in L$ then, on account of the Plemelj formulae (p. 438). we obtain that the boundary functions (74) satisfy the following system of singular integral equations:

$$\varphi_\alpha(t) = \lambda F^*_\alpha[t, \varphi_1(t), \ldots, \varphi_{2m}(t)] + f_\alpha(t) +$$

$$+\lambda \int_L \frac{F^*_\alpha [t, \tau, \varphi_1(\tau), \ldots, \varphi_{2m}(\tau)]}{\tau - t} d\tau \qquad (\alpha = 1, 2, \ldots, 2m). \quad (77)$$

The functions $F^*_\alpha, F^{**}_\alpha, f_\alpha$ are defined in the domain (71) by the formulae

$$F^*_\alpha(t, u_1, \ldots, u_{2m})$$

$$= \begin{cases} \dfrac{1}{2} F_\alpha(t, u_1, \ldots, u_{2m}) & \text{for} \quad \alpha = 1, 2, \ldots, m, \\ -\dfrac{1}{2} \cdot \dfrac{X^+_{\alpha-m}(t)}{X^-_{\alpha-m}(t)} F_{\alpha-m}(t, u_1, \ldots, u_{2m}) & \text{for } \alpha = m+1, \ldots, 2m; \end{cases}$$

$$F^{**}_\alpha(t, u_1, \ldots, u_{2m}) \qquad (78)$$

$$= \begin{cases} \dfrac{1}{2\pi i} \cdot \dfrac{X^+_\alpha(t)}{X^+_\alpha(\tau)} F_\alpha(\tau, u_1, \ldots, u_m) & \text{for} \quad \alpha = 1, 2, \ldots, m, \\ \dfrac{1}{2\pi i} \cdot \dfrac{X^-_{\alpha-m}(t)}{X^+_{\alpha-m}(\tau)} F_{\alpha-m}(\tau, u_1, \ldots, u_{2m}) & \text{for } \alpha = m+1, \ldots, 2m, \end{cases}$$

$$f_\alpha(t) = \begin{cases} X^+_\alpha(t) P_\alpha(t) & \text{for} \quad \alpha = 1, 2, \ldots, m, \\ X^-_\alpha(t) P_{\alpha-m}(t) & \text{for} \quad \alpha = m+1, \ldots, 2m. \end{cases}$$

According to formulae (75), the known functions $X^\pm_\alpha(t)$ satisfy the Hölder condition

$$|X^\pm_\alpha(t) - X^\pm_\alpha(t_1)| < k_X |t - t_1|^\mu \qquad (79)$$

where k_X is a given positive constant. Moreover, there exist positive constants q and s such that

$$0 < q \leqq |X^+_\alpha(t)| \leqq s. \qquad (80)$$

Let us now regard the functions $\varphi_1(t), \ldots, \varphi_{2m}(t)$ in equations (77) as unknowns in the domain $t \in L$, the functions $P_\alpha(z)$ as arbitrarily chosen entire functions, and let us examine the existence of the solutions of the system of singular integral equations of the form (77). The conditions (70) and (72) are not sufficient for solving the system of equations (77), by means of the classical method, and thus, we apply Schauder's topological method, as in Section 2.

Let us now consider the function space Λ composed of all systems of the complex *continuous* functions $U = [\varphi_1, \ldots, \varphi_{2m}]$ defined at each point $t \in L$. The norm of the point U is defined as the sum

$$\|U\| = \sum_{\alpha=1}^{2m} \sup |\varphi_\alpha(t)|; \tag{81}$$

the sum of two points

$$U = [\varphi_1, \ldots, \varphi_{2m}], \qquad V = [g_1, \ldots, g_{2m}]$$

is given by formula

$$U + V = [\varphi_1 + g_1, \ldots, \varphi_{2m} + g_{2m}],$$

the product of a point U by a real number λ by the formula

$$\lambda U = [\lambda\varphi_1, \ldots, \lambda\varphi_n]$$

and the distance between two points U and V is defined as the norm

$$\delta(U, V) = \|U - V\|.$$

Thus, Λ is a Banach space.

Consider, now, in this space the set E of all the points $U = [\varphi_1, \ldots, \varphi_{2m}]$ satisfying the inequalities

$$\begin{gathered} |\varphi_\alpha(t)| \leqq R, \\ |\varphi_\alpha(t) - \varphi_\alpha(t_1)| \leqq \kappa |t - t_1|^\mu \quad (\alpha = 1, 2, \ldots, 2m), \end{gathered} \tag{82}$$

where R and μ are positive numbers given in the assumed inequalities (70), (71), (72), whereas κ is an arbitrarily fixed, positive coefficient.

The set E is *closed* since the limit point of each sequence of points satisfying conditions (82) also satisfies these conditions, and consequently, it belongs to the set E. The set E is *convex*, since all the points

$$\gamma U+(1-\gamma)V \quad (0 \leqq \gamma \leqq 1)$$

of the segment connecting two arbitrary points U and V of E satisfy conditions (82) and therefore they also belong to this set.

In view of the form of the system (77), we now transform the set E by means of the relations

$$\psi_\alpha(t) = \lambda F_\alpha^*[t, \varphi_1(t), \dots, \varphi_{2m}(t)]+f_\alpha(t)+ \\ +\lambda \int_L \frac{F_\alpha^{**}[t, \tau, \varphi_1(\tau), \dots, \varphi_{2m}(\tau)]}{\tau-t}\, d\tau \quad (\alpha = 1, 2, \dots, 2m), \tag{83}$$

which assign to each point $(\varphi_1, \dots, \varphi_{2m})$ of the set E a certain point $(\psi_1, \dots, \psi_{2m})$ of the space Λ.

Let us find a necessary condition such that each transformed point $(\psi_1, \dots, \psi_{2m})$ belongs to the set E. We write the integral in relations (83) in the following manner:

$$\int_L \frac{F_\alpha^{**}[t, \tau, \varphi_1(\tau), \dots, \varphi_{2m}(\tau)]}{\tau-t}\, d\tau \\ = \pi i F_\alpha^{**}[t, t, \varphi_1(t), \dots, \varphi_{2m}(t)]+ \\ + \int_L \left\{ \frac{F_\alpha^{**}[t, \tau, \varphi_1(\tau), \dots, \varphi_{2m}(\tau)]}{\tau-t} - \right. \\ \left. - \frac{F_\alpha^{**}[t, t, \varphi_1(t), \dots, \varphi_{2m}(t)]}{\tau-t} \right\} d\tau. \tag{84}$$

In accordance with formula (78) and inequalities (70), (72), (79), (80) we obtain

$$|F_\alpha^{**}[t, \tau, \varphi_1(\tau), \dots, \varphi_{2m}(\tau)]-F_\alpha^{**}[t, t, \varphi_1(t), \dots, \varphi_{2m}(t)]| \\ \leqq \frac{s}{2\pi q} k_F [|t-\tau|^\mu + \sum_{\nu=1}^{2m} |\varphi_\nu(t)-\varphi_\nu(\tau)|]+\frac{s}{2\pi q^2} k_X M_F |t-\tau|^\mu \\ \leqq \frac{s}{2\pi q^2} [k_F q(2m\kappa+1)+k_X M_F] |t-\tau|^\mu. \tag{85}$$

Hence, we have the following estimate of the integral (84)

$$\left| \int_L \frac{F_\alpha^{**}[t, \tau, \varphi_1(\tau), \ldots, \varphi_{2m}(\tau)]}{\tau - t} dt \right|$$

$$\leqq \frac{s}{2\pi q^2} [k_F q D(2m\kappa+1) + M_F(\pi q + k_X D)] \quad (86)$$

where

$$D = \sup_{t \in L} \int_L \frac{dl_\tau}{|\tau - t|^{1-\mu}}, \quad M_F = \sup |F_\alpha| . \quad (86')$$

Using (86), we conclude that the components (83) of the transformed point satisfy the inequality

$$|\psi_\alpha(t)|$$

$$\leqq |\lambda| \frac{s}{2\pi q^2} [k_F q D(2m+1) + M_F(\pi q + k_X D)] + M_p s , \quad (87)$$

where

$$M_P = \sup_{t \in L} |P_\alpha(t)| . \quad (87')$$

Note that the Cauchy type integral

$$\psi(z) = \int_L \frac{\varphi(\tau)\, d\tau}{\tau - z},$$

on account of the Plemelj–Privalov Theorem, by the assumption that the complex function $\varphi(\tau)$ given on L satisfies the Hölder condition

$$|\varphi(\tau) - \varphi(\tau_1)| \leqq k_\varphi |\tau - \tau_1|^\mu \quad (0 < \mu < 1)$$

possesses boundary values $\psi^\pm(t)$, at each point $t \in L$, satisfying Hölder's condition in the form

$$|\psi^\pm(t) - \psi^\pm(t_1)| \leqq K k_\varphi |t - t_1|^\mu \quad (88)$$

for the same exponent $\mu < 1$ as the function φ, and for the coefficient proportional to the k_φ; moreover, the positive constant K depends on the contours L and is independent of the function φ.

The value of the Cauchy integral $\psi(t)$ on the curve L, as a principal value of an improper integral, is the arithmetic mean of the boundary values

$$\psi(t) = \int_L \frac{\varphi(\tau)\,d\tau}{\tau - t} = \frac{1}{2}[\psi^+(t) + \psi^-(t)]$$

and likewise satisfies the Hölder condition (88).

Taking into account property (88), we can conclude that the components $\psi_\alpha(t)$ of the transformed point determined by formulae (83) satisfy the Hölder inequality

$$\begin{aligned}|\psi_\alpha(t) - \psi_\alpha(t_1)| \leqq (M_P k_X + s k_P)\,|t - t_1|^\mu + \\ + \frac{|\lambda|\,s}{2\pi q^2}[k_F q(\pi + K q^2)(2m\kappa + 1) + \\ + (2\pi k_X + K)M_F + 2k_F k_X D]\,|t - t_1|^\mu, \qquad (89)\end{aligned}$$

where k_p denotes the Hölder coefficient in the inequality

$$|P_\alpha(t) - P_\alpha(t_1)| \leqq k_P |t - t_1|^\mu \qquad (90)$$

which is satisfied for $t, t_1 \in L$.

On account of inequalities (87) and (89) we can assert that all the transformed points $[\psi_1, \ldots, \psi_{2m}]$ of the set E will belong to this set, provided the absolute value of the parameter λ and the constants M_p, k_p are sufficiently small such that the following inequalities hold:

$$|\lambda|\,\frac{s}{2\pi q^2}[k_F D_q(2m\kappa + 1) + M_F(2\pi q + k_X D)] + M_P s \leqq R,$$
$$(91)$$
$$\begin{aligned}|\lambda|\,\frac{s}{2\pi q^2}[k_F q(\pi + K q^2)(2m\kappa + 1)(2\pi k_X + K)M_F + \\ + 2k_F k_X D] + (M_P k_X + s k_P) \leqq \kappa.\end{aligned}$$

In the same way as in Section 2, it can be proved that the transformation of the set E defined by relations (83) is *continuous* in the space Λ. This proof will not be repeated.

Finally, it is obvious, on the account of Arzèla's Theorem, that the set E', transformed from the set E, is *relatively compact* since the components $\psi_\alpha(t)$ of its points satisfying the Hölder inequality (89) are equicontinuous and uniformly bounded.

Consequently, on the basis of Schauder's Theorem, we conclude that there exists at least one fixed point $[\varphi_1^*(t), \ldots, \varphi_{2m}^*(t)]$ of the transformation (83), or in other words, a solution of the system of integral equations (77). The functions $\varphi_\alpha^*(t)$, by construction, satisfy the Hölder condition (82), and thus, substituting the solution $[\varphi_1^*(t), \ldots, \varphi_{2m}^*(t)]$ in formulae (73), we obtain the system of functions $\Phi_1(z), \ldots, \Phi_m(z)$, which, in view of equations (77), satisfy the boundary conditions (69) of the generalized Hilbert problem. Thus we have the following theorem:

THEOREM. *If the given functions* $G_\alpha(t), F_\alpha(t, u_1, \ldots, u_{2m})$ *satisfy conditions* (70), (72), *and the absolute value of the parameter* λ *and the constants* M_p, k_p *relating to the entire functions* $P_\alpha(z)$ *are sufficiently small such that inequalities* (91) *hold, then there exists at least one system of the functions* $\Phi_1(z), \ldots, \Phi_{2m}(z)$, *sectionally holomorphic in the regions* $S^+, S_0^-, \ldots, S_p^-$ *the boundary values of which satisfy the system of equations* (69).

Note, that making use of the arbitrariness of the choice of the coefficient κ in inequalities (91), its value κ_0 can be so chosen that the corresponding range of variation of $|\lambda|$ be as large as possible. To calculate the value of κ_0 we proceed in the same way as in § 2.

The system of integral equations (77) can be solved by the method of successive approximations, as in the preceding section, under more restrictive assumptions for the functions F_α, analogous to the assumptions (40).

§ 5. The generalized Riemann problem

The boundary problem in the theory of analytic functions stated by GUSEINOW [19] is a generalization of the Riemann boundary problem discussed in Chapter XVI. This problem consists of determining the function

$$\Phi(z) = u(x, y) + iv(x, y) \quad (z = x + iy)$$

holomorphic in the circle S^+ ($|z| < 1$) and continuous in the closure of the circle $S^+ + L$, which at each point t of the circumference of the circle L ($|z| \leqq 1$) satisfies a non-linear relation

$$\mathrm{re}\,[(a+ib)\,\Phi(t)] = a(t)\,u - b(t)\,v = \lambda F(t, u, v) \tag{92}$$

between the boundary values of its real and imaginary parts, $u(t)$ and $v(t)$, respectively.

The given real functions $a(t)$ and $b(t)$ are defined on the circumference of the circle L, the real function $F(t, u, v)$ is determined in the domain

$$t \in L, \quad |u| \leqq R, \quad |v| \leqq R, \tag{93}$$

where R is a given positive number, and λ is a real parameter.

GUSEINOV investigates problem (92) by a direct method of harmonic functions, but he does not introduce the notion of the index κ which is very important in the theory of the Hilbert problem and the Riemann problem. Therefore, the results of Guseinov's investigations are incomplete, even in some parts erroneous, since his problem (92) may not possess a solution even for small values of the parameter λ. The correct investigation of the boundary problem (92) has been carried out by Soviet mathematicians NATALEVITCH [37] and GEKHT [11]. Their method is similar to that given by GUSEINOV.

The author studied the boundary problem (92) using another method based on the solution of the Riemann problem, given by MUSKHELISHVILI (see Chapter XVI). We present this results here, and, for the sake of generality, we consider the problem, analogous to (92), for a system of functions.

Thus, our problem consists in the determination of the system of m functions

$$\Phi_\nu(z) = u_\nu(x, y) + i v_\nu(x, y) \quad (\nu = 1, 2, \ldots, m)$$

holomorphic inside the circle S^+ and continuous in the closure $S^+ + L$ of this circle. The functions satisfy at each point t of the circumference of the circle L the system of m relations

$$a_\nu(t)\,u_\nu - b_\nu(t)\,v_\nu = \lambda F_\nu(t, u_1, \ldots, u_m, v_1, \ldots, v_m) \quad (\nu = 1, 2, \ldots, m) \tag{94}$$

between the boundary values of their real and imaginary parts u_ν and v_ν.

It is assumed that the given real functions $a_\nu(t)$ and $b_\nu(t)$, determined on the circumference of the circle L, satisfy the Hölder conditions

$$\begin{aligned} |a_\nu(t)-a_\nu(t_1)| &< \text{const}\,|t-t_1|^h \\ |b_\nu(t)-b_\nu(t_1)| &< \text{const}\,|t-t_1|^h \end{aligned} \qquad (0<h<1) \qquad (95)$$

and the relation

$$[a_\nu(t)]^2+[b_\nu(t)]^2 \neq 0 \qquad (\nu=1,2,\dots,m) \qquad (96)$$

at each point t on L.

Next we assume that the given real functions $F_\nu(t, u_1, \dots, u_m, v_1, \dots, v_m)$ of the complex variable t and of the real variables $u_1, \dots, u_m, v_1, \dots, v_m$ are determined in the domain

$$t\in L, \quad -R \leqq u_\nu \leqq R, \quad -R \leqq v_\nu \leqq R \quad (\nu=1,2,\dots,m), \qquad (97)$$

and, moreover, that they satisfy Hölder's condition with respect to the variable t and the Lipschitz condition with respect to the variables $u_1, \dots, u_m, v_1, \dots, v_m$:

$$\begin{aligned} &|F_\nu(t, u_1, \dots, u_m, v_1, \dots, v_m)-F_\nu(t', u_1', \dots, u_m', v_1', \dots, v_m')| \\ &\qquad \leqq k_F\Big[|t-t'|^h+\sum_{\alpha=1}^{m}|u_\alpha-u_\alpha'|+\sum_{\alpha=1}^{m}|v_\alpha-v_\alpha'|\Big]. \qquad (98) \end{aligned}$$

Note, that conditions (94) are equivalent to the equalities

$$\begin{aligned} &(a_\nu+ib_\nu)\Phi^+(t)+(a_\nu-ib_\nu)\overline{\Phi^+(t)} \\ &\quad =2\lambda F_\nu\Bigg[t, \frac{\Phi_1^+(t)+\overline{\Phi_1^+(t)}}{2}, \dots, \frac{\Phi_m^+(t)+\overline{\Phi_m^+(t)}}{2}, \\ &\quad \frac{\Phi_1^+(t)-\overline{\Phi_1^+(t)}}{2i}, \dots, \frac{\Phi_m^+(t)-\overline{\Phi_m^+(t)}}{2i}\Bigg] \quad (\nu=1,2,\dots,m) \qquad (99) \end{aligned}$$

at each point t on L, where $\Phi^+(t)$ denotes the boundary value of the function $\Phi_\nu(z)$ with respect to the region S^+. Introducing the functions $\Phi_\nu^*(z)$ complementary with respect to the functions

$\Phi_\nu(z)$, defined in the region S^- outside the circle S^+ by the formula

$$\Phi^*(z) = \overline{\Phi_\nu\left(\frac{1}{\bar{z}}\right)}, \quad z \in S^-, \tag{100}$$

conditions (99) may be rewritten as follows

$$(a_\nu + ib_\nu)\Phi^+(t) + (a_\nu - ib_\nu)\overline{\Phi_\nu^*}(t)$$
$$= 2\lambda F_\nu\left[t, \frac{\Phi_1^+(t) + \overline{\Phi_1^*}(t)}{2}, \ldots, \frac{\Phi_m^+(t) + \overline{\Phi_m^*}(t)}{2},\right.$$
$$\left.\frac{\Phi_1^+(t) - \overline{\Phi_1^*}(t)}{2i}, \ldots, \frac{\Phi_m^+(t) - \overline{\Phi_m^*}(t)}{2i}\right], \tag{101}$$

where $\overline{\Phi_\nu^*}(t)$ denotes the boundary value of the function $\overline{\Phi_\nu^*}(z)$ with respect to the region S^-.

Equations (101) are the boundary conditions of a certain generalized Hilbert problem, investigated in the preceding section. Thus, our problem has been reduced to the determination of the system of holomorphic functions $[\Phi_\nu(z), \Phi_\nu^*(z)]$ $(\nu = 1, 2, \ldots, m)$ *bounded at infinity* and satisfying conditions (100), (101).

The indices of the homogeneous Hilbert problems

$$(a_\nu + ib_\nu)\Phi_\nu^+(t) + (a_\nu - ib_\nu)\overline{\Phi_\nu^*}(t) = 0$$

are called *the indices* $\kappa_1, \ldots, \kappa_m$ *of the problem* (94).

These numbers, determined by formulae

$$\kappa_\nu = \frac{1}{\pi i}[\log(a_\nu - ib_\nu)]_L = \frac{1}{\pi}[\arg(a_\nu - ib_\nu)]_L$$
$$(\nu = 1, 2, \ldots, m), \tag{102}$$

are either even or equal to zero.

We first assume that all the indices $\kappa_1, \ldots, \kappa_m$ are *non-negative*. Then, according to the linear theory of the Riemann boundary problem, discussed in Chapter XVI, each system of functions

$$\Phi_1(z), \ldots, \Phi_m(z)$$

holomorphic inside the circle S^{+}, with boundary values $\Phi_\nu^{+}(t)$, $\overline{\Phi_\nu^{+}(t)}$ satisfying equations (99) and the Hölder conditions. also satisfy, at each point z inside the circle S^{+}, the equations

$$\Phi_\nu(z) = \hat{\Psi}_\nu[z, \{\Phi_\alpha^{+}\}] + \Psi_\nu^{*}[z, \{\Phi_\alpha^{+}\}] + X_\nu(z) P(z) \qquad (\nu = 1, 2, \ldots, m), \tag{103}$$

where

$$\hat{\Psi}_\nu[z, \{\Phi_\alpha^{+}\}] = \frac{\lambda X_\nu(z)}{2\pi i} \int_L \frac{\tilde{F}_\nu[\tau, \Phi_1^{+}(\tau), \ldots, \Phi_m^{+}(\tau)]\, d\tau}{X_\nu^{+}(\tau)(\tau - z)},$$

$$\hat{\Psi}_\nu^{*}[z, \{\Phi_\alpha^{+}\}] = \frac{\lambda z^{\kappa_\nu} X_\nu(z)}{2\pi i} \left\{ \int_L \frac{\tilde{F}_\nu[\tau, \Phi_1^{+}(\tau), \ldots, \Phi_m^{+}(\tau)]\, d\tau}{\tau^{\kappa_\nu} X_\nu^{+}(\tau)(\tau - z)} - \right.$$

$$\left. - \int_L \frac{\tilde{F}_\nu[\tau, \Phi_1^{+}(\tau), \ldots, \Phi_m^{+}(\tau)]\, d\tau}{\tau^{\kappa_\nu + 1} X_\nu^{+}(\tau)} \right\}; \tag{104}$$

$$\tilde{F}_\nu(\tau, w_1, \ldots, w_m)$$

$$= [a_\nu(\tau) + i b_\nu(\tau)]^{-1} F_\nu\left(\tau, \frac{w_1 + \bar{w}_1}{2}, \ldots \right.$$

$$\left. \ldots, \frac{w_m + \bar{w}_m}{2}, \frac{w_1 - \bar{w}_1}{2i}, \ldots, \frac{w_m - \bar{w}_m}{2i}\right),$$

$$X_\nu(z) = \begin{cases} C_\nu e^{\Gamma_\nu(z)}, & z \in S^{+}, \\ C_\nu z^{-\kappa_\nu} e^{\Gamma_\nu(z)}, & z \in S^{-}, \end{cases}$$

$$\Gamma_\nu(z) = \frac{1}{2\pi} \int_L \frac{\Theta_\nu(t)\, dt}{t - z}, \qquad \Theta_\nu(t) = \arg\left[-t^{\kappa_\nu} \frac{a_\nu - i b_\nu}{a_\nu + i b_\nu}\right]; \tag{105}$$

$$\rho_\nu = \frac{1}{2\pi} \int_0^{2\pi} \Theta_\nu(e^{i\theta})\, d\theta, \qquad C_\nu = e^{-i\rho_\nu/2},$$

$$P_\nu(z) = C^{(0)} z^{\kappa_\nu} + C^{(1)} z^{\kappa_\nu - 1} + \ldots + C^{(\kappa_\nu)},$$

where the constants $C_\nu^{(\mu)}$, suitably chosen, satisfy the conditions

$$C_\nu^{(\mu)} = \overline{C_\nu^{(\kappa_\nu - \mu)}} \qquad (\mu = 0, 1, \ldots, \kappa_\nu). \tag{106}$$

The functions $\tilde{F}_\nu$ of the complex variables τ and $w_\gamma = u_\gamma + iv_\gamma$ are defined in the domain

$$\tau \in L, \quad |u_\gamma| \leqq R, \quad |v_\gamma| \leqq R \quad (\gamma = 1, 2, \ldots, m).$$

Conversely, each system of functions

$$\Phi_1(z), \ldots, \Phi_m(z)$$

holomorphic in the circle S^+ (the boundary values of the functions $\Phi_1^+(t), \ldots, \Phi_m^+(t)$ satisfy Hölder's condition on the circumference of the circle L) satisfying equations (103), where $P_\nu(z)$ are the polynomials satisfying conditions (106), satisfies the boundary conditions (99) at each point t of the circumference of the circle L. (In the examined case for $\kappa \geqq 0$).

Since the integrals (104) are also determined at points z of the external region S^-, we then complete the functions $\Phi_1(z), \ldots$ $\ldots, \Phi_m(z)$ to the region S^-. Thus equations (103) will be valid in the set $S^+ + S^-$.

Taking into account the properties of the integrals (104) and (105) we conclude that the functions $\Phi_\nu(z)$, sectionally holomorphic in the set $S^+ + S^-$, are identical with the associated functions (see p. 475) $\Phi_\nu^*(z)$, i.e.

$$\Phi_\nu(z) = \Phi_\nu^*(z) = \overline{\Phi_\nu\left(\frac{1}{\bar{z}}\right)} \tag{107}$$

at each point $z \in S^+ + S^-$.

It follows from the above that the boundary values, interior $\Phi_\nu^+(t)$ and exterior $\Phi_\nu^-(t)$, of the functions $\Phi_\nu(z)$ satisfying equations (103) are related by the equations

$$\Phi_\nu^-(t) = \overline{\Phi_\nu^+(t)} \quad (\nu = 1, 2, \ldots, m) \tag{108}$$

which hold at each point t of the circumference of the circle L.

Using the notation

$$\varphi_\nu(t) = \Phi_\nu^+(t) \quad (\nu = 1, 2, \ldots, m) \tag{109}$$

and applying the known Plemelj formulae (p. 438) to the Cauchy type integrals in formulae (104) we obtain that the functions (109) on the circumference of the circle L satisfy the following system of non-linear, singular, integral equations

$$\varphi_\nu(t) = \lambda \tilde{F}_\nu[t, \varphi_1(t), \dots, \varphi_m(t)] +$$
$$+\frac{\lambda}{2\pi i} X_\nu^+(t) \int\limits_L \frac{(1+t^{\kappa_\nu+1}\tau^{-\kappa_\nu-1})\tilde{F}_\nu[\tau, \varphi_1(\tau), \dots, \varphi_m(\tau)]\, d\tau}{X_\nu^+(\tau)(\tau-t)} +$$
$$+X_\nu^+(t) P_\nu(t) \quad (\nu = 1, 2, \dots, m) \tag{110}$$

where the singular integral has a meaning as its Cauchy principal value.

We now regard the functions $\varphi_1(t), \dots, \varphi_m(t)$ in the integral equations (110) as *unknown*, and we examine the existence of the solution of this system. Here, $P_\nu(t)$ are polynomials with *arbitrary* coefficients $C_\nu^{(\mu)}$ satisfying only the conditions (106).

Note, that $m + \sum_{\nu=1}^{m} \kappa_\nu$ arbitrary constants appear in the polynomials $P_\nu(t)$ in equation (110), on account of conditions (166).

The system of integral equations (110) is of the same kind as that considered in the preceding section under analogous assumptions concerning the functions F_ν. We examine this system by the Schauder method, in the same way as before. It turns out that the system (110) has a solution when the absolute value of the parameter λ is sufficiently small; namely, when the inequalities

$$\begin{aligned} |\lambda| [c_1 M_F + c_2 (1+m\kappa) k_F] &\leqq R - R_1, \\ |\lambda| [c_3 M_F + c_4 (1+m\kappa) k_F] &\leqq \kappa - H \end{aligned} \tag{111}$$

hold. Here, κ is an arbitrarily chosen Hölder coefficient for the functions $\varphi_\nu(t)$

$$|\varphi_\nu(t) - \varphi_\nu(t_1)| \leqq \kappa |t-t_1|^h;$$

next, we get that

$$M_F = \sup |F|, \qquad R_1 = \sup_{t \in L} |X_\nu^+(t) P_\nu(t)|;$$

H denotes the Hölder coefficient for the functions $X_\nu^+(t) P_\nu(t)$:

$$|X_\nu^+(t) P_\nu(t) - X_\nu^+(t_1) P_\nu(t_1)| \leqq H |t-t_1|^h$$

and c_1, c_2, c_3, c_4 are positive constants depending on the functions $a_\nu(t)$ and $b_\nu(t)$. We assume that the constants $C_\nu^{(\mu)}$ in the polynomials $P_\nu(z)$ are sufficiently small such that

$$R_1 < R, \qquad H < \kappa. \tag{112}$$

Similarly, as in the preceding section, we make use of the arbitrariness in the choice of the parameter $\kappa > H$. Its value is chosen in such a way that the range of the parameter λ is as large as possible. Inserting the obtained solution $[\varphi_1(t), \dots, \varphi_m(t)]$ of the integral equations (110) in the formulae

$$\Phi_\nu(z) = \frac{\lambda}{2\pi i} X_\nu(z) \times$$

$$\times \int_L \frac{1+z^{\kappa_\nu+1}\tau^{-\kappa_\nu-1}}{X_\nu^+(\tau)(\tau-z)} \tilde{F}_\nu[\tau, \varphi_1(\tau), \dots, \varphi_m(\tau)]\, d\tau +$$

$$+ X_\nu(z) P_\nu(z) \qquad (\nu = 1, 2, \dots, m) \tag{113}$$

we obtain the system of the functions $\Phi_1(z), \dots, \Phi_m(z)$, holomorphic inside the circle S^+, which is the solution of the stated boundary problem (94). In fact, by the properties (100) of the functions (113), by the fulfilment of the integral equations (110), and by Plemelj formulae, the boundary values of the functions determined in the set $S^+ + S^-$ by formulae (113) satisfy the equalities

$$\Phi_\nu^+(t) = \varphi_\nu(t),$$

$$\Phi_\nu^-(t) = \overline{\varphi_\nu(t)} = \overline{\Phi_\nu^+(t)} \qquad (\nu = 1, 2, \dots, m) \tag{114}$$

at each point of the circumference of the circle L.

In this way, the functions (113) and their boundary values (114) satisfy equations (103), and consequently, the boundary values of the obtained functions (113) satisfy equations (99) or (94) at each point t of the circumference of the circle L.

In accordance with previous considerations, formulae (113) give all the solutions of the examined problem (94) provided we insert in these formulae all the values of the constants $C_\nu^{(\mu)}$ in the polynomials $P_\nu(z)$ satisfying conditions (106) and (112) and all the corresponding solutions $[\varphi_1(t), \ldots, \varphi_{2m}(t)]$ of the system of integral equations (110). Thus, we have the following theorem:

THEOREM. *If the given functions $a_\nu(t), b_\nu(t), F_\nu$ satisfy conditions* (95), (96), (98), (111), *and if all the indices κ_ν are non-negative, then there exist systems of functions $\Phi_1(z), \ldots, \Phi_m(z)$, holomorphic inside the circle S^+, defined by formulae* (113), *the boundary values of which $\Phi_\nu^+(t) = u_\nu(t)+iv_\nu(t)$ satisfy the given system of equations* (94) *at each point t of the circumference of the circle L.*

We now proceed to the case when not all the indices $\kappa_1, \ldots, \kappa_m$ are positive or zero. Then our problem may not have a solution. Assume that some indices

$$\kappa_{\alpha_1}, \kappa_{\alpha_2}, \ldots, \kappa_{\alpha_r} \qquad (r \geqq 1)$$

are negative, i.e. that

$$\kappa_{\alpha_\nu} \leqq -2 \qquad (\nu = 1, 2, \ldots, r),$$

while the remaining indices

$$\kappa_{\beta_1}, \kappa_{\beta_2}, \ldots, \kappa_{\beta_s} \qquad (r+s = m)$$

are positive or zero.

On the basis of the theory of the Riemann problem, derived previously, we can assert that if there exists a solution $[\Phi_1(z), \ldots$ $\ldots, \Phi_m(z)]$ of the given problem (94), then it satisfies the equations

$$\Phi_\alpha(z) = \frac{\lambda}{\pi i} X_\alpha(z) \int_L \frac{\tilde{F}_\alpha[\tau, \varphi_1(\tau), \ldots, \varphi_m(\tau)]}{X_\alpha^+(\tau)(\tau - z)} d\tau,$$

$$\Phi_\beta(z) = \frac{\lambda}{2\pi i} X_\beta(z) \int_L \frac{1+z^{\kappa_\beta+1}\tau^{-\kappa_\beta-1}}{X_\beta^+(\tau)(\tau-z)} \times$$
$$\times \tilde{F}_\beta[\tau, \varphi_1(\tau), \ldots, \varphi_m(\tau)]\, d\tau +$$
$$+ X_\beta(z) P_\beta(z) \qquad (\alpha = \alpha_1, \alpha_2, \ldots, \alpha_r;\ \beta = \beta_1, \beta_2, \ldots, \beta_s) \tag{115}$$

where the system of functions $[\varphi_1(\tau), \ldots, \varphi_m(\tau)]$ is a certain (but not each) solution of the following system of integral equations:

$$\varphi_\alpha(t) = \lambda\tilde{F}_\alpha[t, \varphi_1(t), \dots, \varphi_m(t)] + \\ + \frac{\lambda}{\pi i} X_\alpha^+(t) \int_L \frac{\tilde{F}_\alpha[\tau, \varphi_1(\tau), \dots, \varphi_m(\tau)]}{X_\alpha^+(\tau)(\tau-t)} d\tau,$$

$$\varphi_\beta(t) = \lambda\tilde{F}_\beta[t, \varphi_1(t), \dots, \varphi_m(t)] + \frac{\lambda}{2\pi i} X_\beta^+(t) \times \\ \times \int_L \frac{(1+t^{\kappa_\beta+1}\tau^{-\kappa_\beta-1})\tilde{F}_\beta[\tau, \varphi_1(\tau), \dots, \varphi_m(\tau)]}{X_\beta^+(\tau)(\tau-t)} d\tau + X_\beta^+(t) P_\beta(t) \tag{116}$$

$$(\alpha = \alpha_1, \alpha_2, \dots, \alpha_r;\ \beta = \beta_1, \beta_2, \dots, \beta_s).$$

Repeating for this system the same procedure as for the system (110), we draw the conclusion that a solution $[\varphi_1(t), \dots, \varphi_m(t)]$ of the system (116) exists provided that the absolute value of the parameter λ, and that the coefficients of the polynomials $P_\beta(t)$ are sufficiently small. If any solution of the system (116) with arbitrary coefficients satisfying the conditions (106) is substituted in formulae (115), then the obtained system of functions $\Phi_1(z), \dots, \Phi_m(z)$, holomorphic inside the circle S^+, is not always a solution of the given problem (94). Namely, a necessary and sufficient condition is that the integrals $\Phi_\alpha(z)$ in formulae (116) are bounded at infinity. Thus, we have the following theorem:

THEOREM. *If not all the indices of the problem* (94) *are positive, i.e. when*

$$\kappa_{\alpha_\nu} \leqq -2 \quad (\nu = 1, 2, \dots, r),$$
$$\kappa_{\beta_\nu} \geqq 0 \quad (\nu = 1, 2, \dots, m-r),$$

then the non-linear problem (94) *has a solution* $\Phi_1(z), \dots, \Phi_m(z)$ *if, and only if, there exists at least one solution* $[\varphi_1(t), \dots, \varphi_m(t)]$ *of the system of integral equations* (116) *satisfying the equalities*

$$\int_L \frac{t^{k_\alpha}\tilde{F}_\alpha[t, \varphi_1(t), \dots, \varphi_m(t)]}{X_\alpha^+(t)} dt = 0 \tag{117}$$

where

$$k_\alpha = 0, 1, 2, \dots, -\kappa_\alpha - 2, \quad \alpha = \alpha_1, \alpha_2, \dots, \alpha_r.$$

Then the solution $\Phi_1(z), \dots, \Phi_m(z)$ *is defined by formulae* (115).

The validity of the theorem follows from the property (107) of functions (115), bounded at infinity in view of equalities (117), and then by the Plemelj formulae for the boundary values of Cauchy type integrals.

§ 6. The generalized Poincaré problem

The generalized Poincaré problem, examined by the author [62], consists of determining a function $u(x, y)$, harmonic in a certain region D, which, on the boundary L of this region, satisfies a prescribed relation

$$\frac{du}{dn}+a(s)u = F\left(a, u, \frac{du}{ds}\right) \tag{118}$$

between the boundary values of: (1) the derivative in the direction of the normal to the curve L, (2) the derivative in the direction of the tangent du/ds, (3) the function u itself. The s in equality (118) is the length of the arc of the curve L, determining the position of a varying point on this curve.

We make the following assumptions:

1. A closed Jordan curve L possesses a continuous tangent at each point and the angle between the tangents at any two points (s) and (s_1) satisfies the inequality

$$|\delta_{ss_1}| < c|s-s_1|^{\gamma} \quad (0<\gamma \leqq 1). \tag{119}$$

2. The function $F(s, u, v)$ of three real variables is defined in a closed domain

$$(s)\in L, \quad |u| \leqq R_1, \quad |v| \leqq R_2. \tag{120}$$

This function satisfies Hölder's condition with respect to the variables s and u, and the Lipschitz condition with respect to the variable v:

$$|F(s, u, v)-F(s_1, u_1, v_1)| \leqq k_{F\,L}|s-s_1|^{\alpha}+|u-u_1|^{\beta}+|v-v_1|]. \tag{121}$$

3. The function $a(s)$, defined on L satisfies Hölder's condition

$$|a(s)-a(s_1)| \leqq k_a |s-s_1|^\alpha . \tag{122}$$

We assume that the Hölder exponents satisfy the inequalities

$$\alpha < \beta \leqq 1, \quad \alpha < \gamma \leqq 1 . \tag{123}$$

In order to solve the problem we seek the unknown function $u(A)$ in the form of the logarithmic potential of a simple layer

$$u(A) = \int_L \log \frac{1}{r_{A\sigma}} \mu(\sigma)\, d\sigma , \tag{124}$$

where $\mu(\sigma)$ is an unknown real density.

Then, assuming that the function $\mu(\sigma)$ satisfies Hölder's condition, we obtain

$$\begin{aligned} \left(\frac{du}{dn}\right)_s &= -\pi\mu(s) + \int_L \frac{\sin \varphi_{s\sigma}}{r_{s\sigma}} \mu(\sigma)\, d\sigma , \\ \left(\frac{du}{ds}\right)_s &= \int_L \frac{\cos \varphi_{s\sigma}}{r_{s\sigma}} \mu(\sigma)\, d\sigma , \end{aligned} \tag{125}$$

where $\varphi_{s\sigma}$ denotes the angle between the vector connecting points (s) and (σ) on the contour L and the positive direction of the tangent at the point (s). The first integrand (125) has a weak singularity for $r_{s\sigma} \to 0$. The second integrand possesses a singularity, and consequently, the second integral is taken as its Cauchy principal value. Substituting expressions (125) in the boundary condition (118) we obtain the following integral equation for the unknown function $\mu(s)$:

$$-\pi\mu(s) + \int_L \frac{\sin \varphi_{s\sigma}}{r_{s\sigma}} \mu(\sigma)\, d\sigma + a(s) \int_L \log \frac{1}{r_{s\sigma}} \mu(\sigma)\, d\sigma$$

$$= F\left[s, \int_L \log \frac{1}{r_{s\sigma}} \mu(\sigma)\, d\sigma , \int_L \frac{\cos \varphi_{s\sigma}}{r_{s\sigma}} \mu(\sigma)\, d\sigma \right]. \tag{126}$$

The above integral equation is non-linear and singular. Under less restrictive assumptions (121), (122) this equation cannot be solved by classical methods, but it can be solved by the Schauder topological method.

We first formulate two auxiliary theorems.

THEOREM 1. *If a real function $\mu(s)$, defined on L, satisfies Hölder's condition*

$$|\mu(s)-\mu(s_1)| < \kappa |s-s_1|^\alpha, \tag{127}$$

while the contour L satisfies condition (119) $(0 < \alpha < \gamma \leqq 1)$, *then the integral of the singular function*

$$\Phi(s) = \int_L \frac{\cos \varphi_{s\sigma}}{r_{s\sigma}} \mu(\sigma)\, d\sigma \tag{128}$$

satisfies the inequality

$$|\Phi(s)| < c_1 M_\mu + c_2 \kappa \tag{129}$$

and Hölder's condition in the form

$$|\Phi(s)-\Phi(s_1)| < (C_1 M_\mu + C_2 \kappa)|s-s_1|^\alpha \tag{130}$$

for the same exponent $\alpha < 1$ as the function μ; where c_1, c_2, C_1, C_2 are positive constants, independent of the function μ.

The proof of this theorem is given by the author [62]. The proof of the more general case for the potential with respect to an elliptic equation in n-dimensional space will be given in Chapter XXII.

Note that the estimate (129) of the function $\Phi(z)$ follows immediately from the following decomposition:

$$\Phi(s) = \int_L \frac{\cos \varphi_{s\sigma}}{r_{s\sigma}} [\mu(\sigma)-\mu(s)]\, d\sigma + \mu(s) \int_L \frac{\cos \varphi_{s\sigma}}{r_{s\sigma}}\, d\sigma .$$

THEOREM 2. *If a real function $\mu(s)$ is bounded and integrable, then the integrals*

$$J_1(s) = \int_L \log \frac{1}{r_{s\sigma}} \mu(\sigma)\, d\sigma, \qquad J_2(s) = \int_L \frac{\sin \varphi_{s\sigma}}{r_{s\sigma}} \mu(\sigma)\, d\sigma \tag{131}$$

satisfy the inequalities

$$|J_1(s)| \leqq q_1 M_\mu, \quad |J_2(s)| \leqq q_2 M_\mu \tag{132}$$

and Hölder's condition in the form

$$\begin{aligned} |J_1(s)-J_1(s_1)| &< q_1' M_\mu |s-s_1|^\theta, \\ |J_2(s)-J_2(s_1)| &< q_2' M_\mu |s-s_1|^{\theta'\gamma}, \end{aligned} \tag{133}$$

where $M_\mu = \sup|\mu(s)|$, θ *and* θ' *are arbitrary positive constants less than unity, and* q_1, q_2, q_1', q_2' *are positive constants independent of the function* μ.

The proof of the theorem is considerably simpler than the preceding one. We shall omit it, since it is analogous to the proofs given in Part 2 for the integrals of a similar type.

Let us return to the integral equation (126). According to Schauder's topological method, we consider, as usual, the space Λ consisting of all continuous real functions $\mu(s)$ defined on the contour L. We define as usual the linear operations, the norm, and distance between two points, and consequently, the space Λ becomes a Banach space. Next, we consider in the space Λ the set E consisting of all functions $\mu(s)$ which satisfy the inequalities

$$|\mu(s)| \leqq \rho, \quad |\mu(s)-\mu(s_1)| \leqq \kappa |s-s_1|^\alpha \tag{134}$$

for the exponent $\alpha < 1$ appearing in (121) and (122). The positive constants are chosen in such a way that:

$$\rho q_1 \leqq R_1, \quad c_1\rho + c_2\kappa \leqq R_2. \tag{135}$$

Then according to the properties (129) and (132) each function $\mu(s)$ of the set E satisfies the inequalities

$$\left|\int_L \log\frac{1}{r_{s\sigma}}\,\mu(\sigma)\,d\sigma\right| \leqq R_1, \quad \left|\int_L \frac{\cos\varphi_{s\sigma}}{r_{s\sigma}}\,\mu(\sigma)\,d\sigma\right| \leqq R_2. \tag{136}$$

Repeating the argument on p. 569, we conclude that the set E is closed and convex.

In view of the integral equation (126), we now transform the set E, assigning to each point $\mu(s)$ of this set the point $\psi(s)$ of the space Λ, by the relation

$$-\pi\psi(s)+\int\limits_L \frac{\sin\varphi_{s\sigma}}{r_{s\sigma}}\psi(\sigma)\,d\sigma+a(s)\int\limits_L \log\frac{1}{r_{s\sigma}}\psi(\sigma)\,d\sigma$$

$$=F\left[s,\int\limits_L \log\frac{1}{r_{s\sigma}}\mu(\sigma)\,d\sigma,\int\limits_L \frac{\cos\varphi_{s\sigma}}{r_{s\sigma}}\mu(\sigma)\,d\sigma\right]. \qquad (137)$$

For the given function $\mu(s)$, equation (137) takes the form of a weakly-singular Fredholm equation with unknown function $\psi(s)$. If we assume that the homogeneous integral equation, obtained from equation (137), has the zero solution $\psi = 0$ only, then, on account of equation (137), the point $\psi(s)$ determined by the known Fredholm formula corresponds to each point $\mu(\sigma)$ of the set E. This occurs, for example, when the function $a(s)$ (not constant) is not positive: $a(s) \leqq 0$. (This is a well-known fact from classical potential theory.)

Note that on account of Theorems 1 and 2, the function of the variable s on the right-hand side of equation (137), being the result of substituting the integrals (132) instead of the variables u and v in the expression $F(s, u, v)$, satisfies Hölder's condition with exponent α. In fact, we have, according to inequalities (121), (130), (133), (134)

$$|F[s,u(s),v(s)]-F[s_1,u(s_1),v(s_1)]|$$

$$\leqq k_F(1+q_1'+c_1\rho+c_2\kappa)\,|s-s_1|^{\alpha} \qquad (138)$$

where $\theta = \alpha$, $\theta'\gamma = \alpha$. Next, we have by the Fredholm formula, the inequality

$$|\psi(s)| \leqq PM_F, \qquad (139)$$

where the constant P is independent of the function $\mu(s)$ and depends only on the contour L and the function $a(s)$. From inequalities (132), (133), (138), (139) we conclude that the solution

ψ of equation (137) satisfies Hölder's condition with index α, in the form

$$|\psi(s)-\psi(s_1)| \leqq \pi^{-1}[(q_2'+k_a q_1+M_a q_1')PM_F+ +k_F(1+q_1'+c_1\rho+c_2\kappa)]\,|s-s_1|^{\alpha}, \qquad (140)$$

where $M_a = \sup|a(s)|$.

It is seen from inequalities (134), (139) and (140) that the transformed function $\psi(s)$ belongs to the set E, provided that the constants of the problem satisfy the following inequalities:

$$\begin{gathered} PM_F \leqq \rho, \\ \pi^{-1}[(q_2'+k_a q_1+M_a q_1')PM_F+k_F(1+q_1'+c_1\rho+c_2\kappa)] \leqq \kappa. \end{gathered} \qquad (141)$$

These inequalities are always satisfied if the constants M_F and k_F are sufficiently small.

The proof that the transformation of the set E, defined by relations (137), is *continuous* in Λ can be obtained by a method similar to that in the section on singular integral equation and we will not repeat it. Finally, it is evident, on account of properties (139) and (140), that the transformed functions $\psi(s)$ are uniformly bounded and equicontinuous, and consequently, the set transformed from E is *relatively compact*.

Since all the conditions of Schauder's Theorem are satisfied, we conclude that there exists at least one fixed point $\mu^*(s)$ of the transformation (137), i.e. there exists a solution of the integral equation (126). Substituting the obtained solution $\mu^*(s)$ in formula (125), we obtain the harmonic function

$$u(A) = \int_L \log\frac{1}{r_{A\sigma}}\,\mu^*(\sigma)\,d\sigma \qquad (142)$$

which is the solution of the given problem, i.e. it satisfies the boundary condition (118).

Thus we formulate the following theorem:

THEOREM 3. *If the given contour L satisfies condition* (119), *if the given functions $a(s)$ and F satisfy conditions* (121) *and* (122), *if the constants M_F and k_F of the problem satisfy conditions* (141), *and finally, if the homogeneous boundary problem*

$$\frac{du}{dn}+a(s)u=0$$

has the zero solution only, then there exists at least one function $u(x,y)$, harmonic in the region D, satisfying the boundary condition (118) *at each point of the contour L bounding the region D.*

The problem for the boundary condition (118) has been examined by J. WOLSKA–BOCHENEK (see [91]) for the more general equation of the form

$$\frac{\partial^2 u}{\partial x^2}+\frac{\partial^2 u}{\partial^2 y^2}=\Phi\left(x, y, u, \frac{\partial u}{\partial x}, \frac{\partial u}{\partial y}\right).$$

The above problem can be generalized in the case of an elliptic equation in the complete form

$$a_{11}(x,y)\frac{\partial^2 u}{\partial x^2}+2a_{12}(x,y)\frac{\partial^2 u}{\partial x\,\partial y}+$$

$$+a_{22}(x,y)\frac{\partial^2 u}{\partial y^2}+a(x,y)\frac{\partial u}{\partial x}+$$

$$+b(x,y)\frac{\partial u}{\partial y}+c(x,y)u=\Phi\left(x, y, u, \frac{\partial u}{\partial x}, \frac{\partial u}{\partial y}\right),$$

where the coefficients $a_{11}, a_{12}, a_{22}, a, b, c$ satisfy Hölder's condition. We will not consider this problem, since it is a special case of the problem on the tangential derivatives, which will be investigated in Chapter XXII for elliptic equation in n-dimensional space.

Chapter XX

DISCONTINUOUS BOUNDARY PROBLEMS IN THE THEORY OF ANALYTIC FUNCTIONS. SINGULAR INTEGRAL EQUATIONS FOR A SYSTEM OF NON-CLOSED ARCS

§ 1. On a certain class of complex functions defined on a system of non-closed arcs

Boundary problems in the theory of analytic functions will be called *discontinuous* if the boundary functions entering these problem are discontinuous, and the boundaries of the regions are the systems of non-closed arcs. These problems were first investigated by N. I. Muskhelishvili [33] for a system of disconnected arcs.

The author of this monography investigated discontinuous problems by introducing a certain class $\mathfrak{H}$ of complex discontinuous functions defined on a more general system of non-closed arcs. These functions, in view of their important and interesting properties, play a central rôle in the theory of discontinuous boundary problems and in the theory of singular integral equations for a system of non-closed arcs. Below, we give the definition of the functions of the class $\mathfrak{H}$ and their properties, which are result of the author's investigations in papers [63, 66–68].

Suppose we are given a set of points $L = l_1 + l_2 + \ldots + l_m$ in the complex plane, consisting of a finite number of arbitrarily ordered arcs $l_1, l_2, \ldots, l_m$. The end-points $c_1, c_2, \ldots, c_p$ of these arcs are also ordered arbitrarily but independently of the order of arcs; they may belong to one arc or may be common to several arcs, however, no pair of arcs possesses common

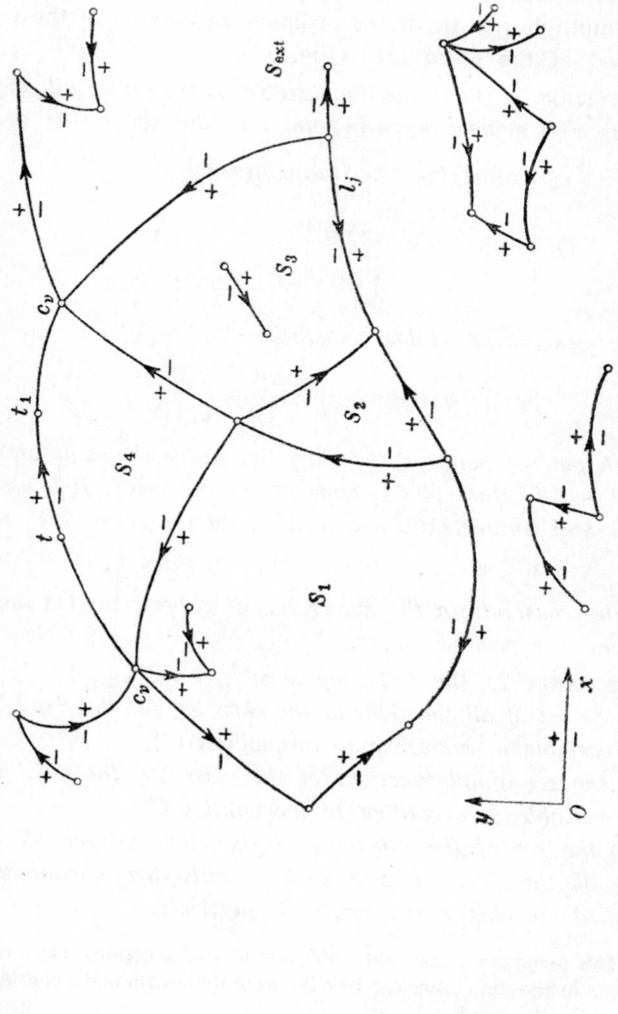

Fig. 15

interior points.* Some parts of the given system of arcs may form one or several nets of closed lines.

We assume that each of the arcs $l_1, \ldots, l_m$ has a tangent continuous at each interior point, and the one-sided tangents at the vertices c_ν, the limits of the corresponding internal tangents. Thus the points $c_1, \ldots, c_p$ are angular points, salient points, multiple points, or the ordinary end-points of the curves composed of the given arcs (Fig. 15).

DEFINITION 1. *We define the class* $\mathfrak{H}_\alpha^\mu$ *as the set of all complex functions* $\varphi(t)$ *defined at each point* t *of the set* L *(or the set* $L' = L - \sum_{\nu=1}^{p} c_\nu$*) satisfying the inequality*

$$|\varphi(t)| < \frac{\text{const}}{\prod_{j=1}^{p} |t-c_j|^\alpha} \qquad (t \in L') \tag{1}$$

and the generalized Hölder condition

$$|\varphi(t)-\varphi(t_1)| < \frac{\text{const}\,|t-t_1|^\mu}{[|t-c_\nu|\,|t_1-c_{\nu_1}|]^{\alpha+\mu}} \tag{1'}$$

for each pair of points t, t_1 *which lies inside the same arbitrary arc* $l = \frown c_\nu c_{\nu_1}$, *the point* t_1 *lying on the arc* $\frown tc_\nu$. *It is assumed that the real parameters* α *and* μ, *fixed for the given class, satisfy*

$$0 \leqq \alpha < 1, \quad 0 < \mu < 1, \quad \alpha + \mu < 1, \tag{2}$$

while the constants in the numerator of expressions (1) *and* (1') *may take any positive values.*

DEFINITION 2. *The following sets,*

(i) *the set of all functions of the class* $\mathfrak{H}_\alpha^\mu$ *for the fixed* α *and variable* μ, *according to inequalities* (2),

(ii) *the set of all functions of the class* $\mathfrak{H}_\alpha^\mu$ *for fixed* μ *and variable* α, *according to inequalities* (2)

(iii) *the set of the functions of the class* $\mathfrak{H}_\alpha^\mu$ *for all values of the parameters* α *and* μ *satisfying conditions* (2),

are called the classes $\mathfrak{H}^\alpha$, $\mathfrak{H}^\mu$, $\mathfrak{H}$, *respectively.*

---

* This assumption does not cause any loss of generality, since the case of the arcs intersecting inside can be reduced to the system under consideration by increasing the number of arcs.

Assume for each arc l_j, in an arbitrary way, a positive direction independent of the other arcs. Even if a certain group of arcs forms a closed line it is not necessary that the directions on that line be compatible with a certain direction of rotation (Fig. 15). Consider a Cauchy type integral

$$\Phi(z) = \int_L \frac{\varphi(\tau)\,d\tau}{\tau - z} = \sum_{\nu=1}^{m} \int_{l_\nu} \frac{\varphi(\tau)\,d\tau}{\tau - z}, \tag{3}$$

which is the sum of the Cauchy type integrals over all the arcs l_ν of the set L, $\varphi(\tau)$ being a function given in the class $\mathfrak{H}$. Integral (3) has a meaning at each point of the plane not lying on L and represents a function $\Phi(z)$ sectionally holomorphic in all the finite regions $S_1, \ldots, S_p$ bounded by the arcs $l_1, \ldots, l_m$ and in the infinite region S_{ext} outside the arcs l_j (see Fig. 15). Note, that the regions $S_1, \ldots, S_p$ may be non-existent if the arcs l_j are disconnected.

According to inequality (1′) the function $\varphi(\tau)$ satisfies Hölder's condition for a bounded coefficient on each closed arc lying inside an arbitrary arc l_j. Hence, according to the Plemelj formulae (Chapter XV, § 3), it follows that function (3) has boundary values $\Phi^+(t)$ and $\Phi^-(t)$ at each point t on L, distinct from the end-points c, defined by the formulae

$$\Phi^{\pm}(t) = \pm\pi i\varphi(t) + \int_L \frac{\varphi(\tau)\,d\tau}{\tau - t} \tag{4}$$

where the singular integral has a meaning as its Cauchy principal value. The signs $\pm$ relate to the two sides of each arc l_j, which are situated with respect to the positive direction of the arc in the same way as the half-planes, upper $\operatorname{im}(z) > 0$ and lower $\operatorname{im}(z) < 0$ are situated with respect to the positive direction of the real axis. We emphasize that the distinction of two sides, positive and negative, of each arc l_j is closely connected with its direction and is an individual property independent of the other arcs.

THEOREM 1. *The class* $\mathfrak{H}_\alpha^\mu$ *is a subset of the class* $\mathfrak{H}_{\alpha_1}^{\mu_1}$, *i.e.*

$$\mathfrak{H}_\alpha^\mu \subset \mathfrak{H}_{\alpha_1}^{\mu_1} \quad (\alpha+\mu < 1,\ \alpha_1+\mu_1 < 1),$$

if the parameters of these classes satisfy the inequalities

$$0 < \mu_1 \leqq \mu, \quad 0 \leqq \alpha \leqq \alpha_1.$$

Proof. In fact, if the function $\varphi(t)$ satisfies inequalities (1) and (1′), then it obviously satisfies the inequalities obtained for greater values of the exponent α. It is more difficult to investigate the effect of change of the exponent μ appearing in the numerator and denominator of the right-hand side of inequality (1′). Thus, consider on each of the arcs $\frown c_\nu c_{\nu_1}$, two arbitrary arcs $\frown c_\nu T_\nu'$ and $\frown T_\nu'' c_{\nu_1}$ which do not have common points, and examine the only two possible cases:

1. The point $t \neq c_\nu$ lies on the arc $\frown c_\nu T_{\nu_1}$, and the point $t_1 \neq c_{\nu_1}$ lies on the arc $\frown T_\nu'' c_{\nu_1}$. Then the absolute value of the difference $|t-t_1|$ has a positive lower bound, and it directly follows from the estimate (1) of the function itself that one can choose sufficiently large positive constant K such that

$$|\varphi(t)-\varphi(t_1)| < K \frac{|t-t_1|^{\mu_1}}{[|t-c_\nu|\,|t_1-c_{\nu_1}|]^{\alpha+\mu_1}}$$

for any μ_1 smaller than unity, and thus, also for $\mu_1 < \mu$.

2. The points t and t_1 lie both either on arc $\frown c_\nu T_\nu''$ or on the arc $\frown T_\nu' c_{\nu_1}$. We assume that

$$t \in \frown c_\nu T_\nu'', \quad t_1 \in \frown t T_\nu''.$$

If, in the given case, $|t-t_1| \leqq |t-c_\nu|$, then we have

$$\frac{|t-t_1|^\mu}{|t-c_\nu|^\mu} \leqq \frac{|t-t_1|^{\mu_1}}{|t-c_\nu|^{\mu_1}} \quad \text{for} \quad \mu_1 < \mu.$$

Since the distance $|t_1-c_{\nu_1}|$ has a positive lower bound, one can choose a sufficiently large constant K_1 such that

$$\frac{|t-t_1|^\mu}{[|t-c_\nu|\,|t_1-c_{\nu_1}|]^{\alpha+\mu}} < K_1 \frac{|t-t_1|^{\mu_1}}{[|t-c_\nu|\,|t_1-c_{\nu_1}|]^{\alpha+\mu_1}}$$

for any positive $\mu_1 < \mu$. If in Case 2 we get that $|t-t_1| > |t-c_\nu|$, then it follows directly from estimate (1) of the function itself that one can choose a sufficiently large constant K_2 such that

$$|\varphi(t)-\varphi(t_1)| < K_2 \frac{|t-t_1|^{\mu_1}}{[|t-c_\nu|\,|t_1-c_{\nu_1}|]^{\alpha+\mu_1}}$$

for any positive $\mu_1 < 1$. This completes the proof of Theorem 1.

Remark. The most interesting class is the class $\mathfrak{H}_0^\mu$. To it there belong all functions $\varphi(t)$ bounded in the neighbourhood of each end-point c_ν which satisfy the generalized Hölder inequality of the form

$$|\varphi(t)-\varphi(t_1)| < \frac{\text{const}\,|t-t_1|^\mu}{[|t-c_\nu|\,|t_1-c_{\nu_1}|]^\mu}.$$

The functions of this class do not necessarily possess one-side limits at the points c_ν.

THEOREM 2. *If the function $\varphi(t)$ belongs to the class $\mathfrak{H}_\alpha^\mu$, i.e. if it satisfies the inequalities*

$$|\varphi(t)| < \frac{M_\varphi}{\prod_{j=1}^{p} |t-c_j|^\alpha}, \tag{5}$$

$$|\varphi(t)-\varphi(t_1)| < \frac{k_\varphi |t-t_1|^\mu}{[|t-c_\nu|\,|t_1-c_{\nu_1}|]^{\alpha+\mu}} \tag{5'}$$

where $t \in \frown c_\nu c_{\nu_1}$, $t_1 \in \frown t c_{\nu_1}$, M_φ and k_φ are positive constants, then the function $F(t)$ defined at each point $t \in L - \sum_{\nu=1}^{p} c_\nu$ by the Cauchy singular integral

$$F(t) = \int_L \frac{\varphi(\tau)\,d\tau}{\tau - t} \tag{6}$$

also belongs to the class $\mathfrak{H}_\alpha^\mu$ for $\alpha > 0$; namely, it satisfies the inequalities of the form

$$|F(t)| < \frac{C_0 M_\varphi + C_0' k_\varphi}{\prod_{j=1}^{p} |t-c_j|^\alpha}, \tag{7}$$

$$|F(t)-F(t_1)| < \frac{(CM_\varphi + C' k_\varphi)\,|t-t_1|^\mu}{[|t-c_\nu|\,|t_1-c_{\nu_1}|]^{\alpha+\mu}} \tag{7'}$$

($t \in \frown c_\nu c_{\nu_1}$, $t_1 \in \frown t c_{\nu_1}$, $\nu = 1, \ldots, p$), where the positive constants C_0, C_0', C, C' depend only on arcs $l_1, \ldots, l_m$ and do not depend on the function $\varphi(t)$. In the particular case of $\alpha = 0$, the function (6) belongs to the class $\mathfrak{H}_{\Sigma}^{\mu}$ where Σ is positive and arbitrarily small. We say that such a function is almost bounded in the neighbourhood of the points of discontinuity c_ν.

Proof. The above theorem gives a most important property of the functions of the class $\mathfrak{H}_{\alpha}^{\mu}$. In view of applications, we particularly emphasize the behaviour of the two parameters α and μ of the class in the Cauchy transformation (6). The proof, rather complicated and long, consists of two parts: the proofs of inequalities (7) and (7′).

It is sufficient to restrict our attention to the integral

$$\psi(t) = \int\limits_{cc'} \frac{\varphi(\tau)\, d\tau}{\tau - t}, \tag{8}$$

where $\frown cc'$ denotes any of the arcs $l_1, \ldots, l_m$. We should distinguish two cases; the first where the point t lies inside the arc of integration $\frown cc'$, and the second one, where it lies on the smooth arc $\frown cc''$ which reaches as for as the point c but has no other points in common with the arc $\frown cc'$. The case where the point t lies on one of the arcs l_j which has no common end-point with the arc $\frown cc'$, needs no special considerations, since integral (8) is then regular and the absolute value of the denominator $\tau - t$ has a positive lower bound.

Part 1. In order to prove inequality (7) we first examine the case where $t \in \frown cc'$. It is sufficient to confine our attention to the case where the point t lies inside the arc $\frown cT$ whose length is equal to one quarter of the length of $\frown cc'$. We decompose integral (8) into the sum of three components

$$\int\limits_{c}^{c'} \frac{\varphi(\tau)\, d\tau}{\tau - t} = \int\limits_{ct_c} \frac{\varphi(\tau) - \varphi(t)}{\tau - t}\, d\tau + \varphi(t) \int\limits_{ct_c} \frac{d\tau}{\tau - t} + \int\limits_{t_c c'} \frac{\varphi(\tau)\, d\tau}{\tau - t}, \tag{9}$$

where the arcs $\frown ct$ and $\frown tt_c$ have equal lengths. The first of the integrals on the right-hand side of equality (9), $J(t)$, will be decomposed into the sum of two integrals with weak singularity:

$$J(t) = \int_{ct} \frac{\varphi(\tau)-\varphi(\tau)}{\tau-t}\, d\tau + \int_{tt_c} \frac{\varphi(\tau)-\varphi(t)}{\tau-t}\, d\tau .$$

Applying the assumed inequality (5), we obtain the estimate

$$|J(t)| < \int_{ct} \frac{k_\varphi |\tau-t|^{\mu-1}\, dl_\tau}{[|\tau-c|\,|t-c'|]^{\alpha+\mu}} + \int_{tt_c} \frac{k_\varphi |\tau-t|^{\mu-1}\, dl_\tau}{[|t-c|\,|\tau-c'|]^{\alpha+\mu}}$$

from which it follows that

$$|J(t)| < \frac{Ak_\varphi}{|t-c|^\alpha} \qquad (\alpha > 0) \tag{10}$$

for $t \in \frown cT$, where the positive constant A depends on the arc $\frown cc'$ and does not depend on the function φ. Examination of the second and third of the integrals (9) provides the following inequality:

$$\left| \varphi(t) \int_{ct_c} \frac{d\tau}{\tau-t} + \int_{t_c c'} \frac{\varphi(\tau)\, d\tau}{\tau-t} \right|$$

$$< \frac{M_\varphi}{\prod\limits_{\nu=1}^{p} |t-c_\nu|^\alpha} \left| \log \frac{t-c}{t_c-t} \right| + \int_{t_c c'} \frac{M_\varphi\, dl_\tau}{\prod\limits_{\nu=1}^{p} |\tau-c_\nu|^\alpha |\tau-t|} . \tag{11}$$

Thus, the absolute value of the logarithmic function in the above inequality is bounded for $t \to c$ in view of the equality of the lengths of the arcs $\frown ct$ and $\frown tt_c$. The second term is a regular integral and does not exceed the sum of integrals in the form

$$\int_{t_c T_0} \frac{\text{const}\, M_\varphi\, dl_\tau}{|\tau-c|^\alpha |\tau-t|} + \int_{T_0 c'} \frac{\text{const}\, M_\varphi\, dl_\tau}{|\tau-c'|^\alpha} , \tag{12}$$

where T_0 divides the arc $\frown cc'$ into two arcs $\frown cT_0$ and $\frown T_0c'$ of equal length. The second of the integrals (12) does not require a discussion, while the first one is comparable with the integral

$$\int_{2s}^{|cT_0|} \frac{d\sigma}{\sigma^\alpha(\sigma-s)} = \frac{1}{s^\alpha} \int_{2}^{|cT_0|/s} \frac{d\lambda}{\lambda^\alpha(\lambda-1)},$$

where s denotes the length of the arc $\frown ct$, σ is the length of the arc $\frown c\tau$, while $|cT_0|$ is the length of the arc $\frown cT_0$. Since the last integral is bounded for $s \to 0$, combining the above results we can assert that integral (9) satisfies the inequality

$$\left| \int_{cc'} \frac{\varphi(\tau)\,d\tau}{\tau-t} \right| < \frac{A' M_\varphi + Bk_\varphi}{|t-c|^\alpha} \qquad (\alpha > 0) \tag{13}$$

for $t \in \frown cT$, where the positive constants A' and B do not depend on the function φ. In view of symmetry, we obtain an inequality of the same form if t lies on the arc $\frown T'c'$, whose length is equal to a quarter of the length of the arc $\frown cc'$. The case where $t \in \frown TT'$ is obvious, and finally, we obtain an estimate of the form

$$\left| \int_{cc'} \frac{\varphi(\tau)\,d\tau}{\tau-t} \right| < \frac{A'_1 M_\varphi + B_1 k_\varphi}{|t-c|^\alpha |t-c'|^\alpha} \tag{13'}$$

for an arbitrary position of the point t inside the arc of integration $\frown cc'$, and $\alpha > 0$.

We now consider the case where the point t lies inside the arc $\frown cc'$, which has only one point c in common with the arc of integration $\frown cc'$. The estimate given below does not depend on the shape of the arc $\frown cc''$ and holds for each point z, not lying on the arc $\frown cc'$ in a sufficiently small neighbourhood D of the end-point c not containing the other end-point c', either inside or on its boundary. Let cR_0 denote the half-tangent at the end c of the arc $\frown cc'$ which is the limit of the secant ray of the arc. We introduce two rays, cR_1 and cR_2, situated on both sides of the half-tangent cR_0 and forming with it arbitrarily chosen equal acute angles. Let the arc $\frown cv$ be a part of the arc $\frown cc'$ situated inside the angle R_1cR_2, and let there be given a triangle Δ bounded by the rays cR_1, cR_2 and the perpendicular to the half-tangent cR_0 passing through the point v, which is the end-point of the arc $\frown cv$. We assume that the arc $\frown cv$ is sufficiently small such that: 1) the tangent at each point t of the arc $\frown cv$ (including the end-point v) forms with the tangent cR_0 an acute angle smaller than the angle between the rays cR_0 and cR_1, 2) the perpendicular to the half-tangent cR_0, passing through arbitrary point z of the triangle Δ intersects the arc $\frown cv$ at one point. Denote by Δ' a triangle bounded by the rays cR_1, cR_2, and the perpendicular to the half-tangent cR_0 intersecting the arc $\frown cv$ at a point v' such that the length of the arc $\frown cv'$ is equal to half the length of the arc $\frown cv$.

In order to estimate integral (8), we assume that z is any point of the triangle Δ', not lying on $\frown cv'$, next, we decompose integral (8) into the sum of the integrals

$$\psi(z) = \psi^{c\zeta_c}(z) + \psi^{\zeta_c v}(z) + \psi^{vc'}(z) \tag{14}$$

over the arcs $\frown c\zeta_c$, $\frown \zeta_c v$, $\frown vc'$, where ζ_c is the point of the arc $\frown cv$ such that the lengths of the arcs $\frown c\zeta$ and $\frown \zeta\zeta_c$ are equal; here ζ denotes the point of the intersection of the perpendicular to the half-tangent cR_0 passing through the point $z \in \Delta'$ with the arc $\frown cv'$. Let us express the first of integrals (14) in the following manner:

$$\psi^{c\zeta_c}(z) = \int\limits_{c\zeta_c} \frac{\varphi(\tau)-\varphi(\zeta)}{\tau - z}\, d\tau + \varphi(\zeta) \int\limits_{c\zeta_c} \frac{d\tau}{\tau - z}. \tag{15}$$

The first of these integrals, according to assumption (5′), satisfies the inequality

$$\left| \int\limits_{c\zeta_c} \frac{\varphi(\tau)-\varphi(\zeta)}{\tau - z}\, d\tau \right|$$

$$< \int\limits_{c\zeta} \frac{k_\varphi |\tau-\zeta|^{\mu-1}\, dl_\tau}{|\tau-c|^{\alpha+\mu}\, |\zeta-c'|^{\alpha+\mu}} + \int\limits_{\zeta\zeta_c} \frac{k_\varphi |\tau-\zeta|^{\mu-1}\, dl_\tau}{|\zeta-c|^{\alpha+\mu}\, |\tau-c'|^{\alpha+\mu}} \tag{16}$$

since the ratio $|\tau-\zeta|/|\tau-z|$ has an upper bound for $z \in \Delta'$. Hence, in view of the upper bound of the ratio $|z-c|/|\zeta-c|$ for $z \in \Delta'$

we obtain the estimate ($\alpha > 0$):

$$\left| \int_{c\zeta_c} \frac{\varphi(\tau)-\varphi(\zeta)}{\tau - z}\, d\tau \right| < \frac{\text{const}\, k_\varphi}{|\zeta - c|^\alpha} < \frac{\text{const}\, k_\varphi}{|z-c|^\alpha}. \tag{16'}$$

The second term of the sum (15) satisfies the inequality

$$\left| \varphi(\zeta) \int_{c\zeta_c} \frac{d\tau}{\tau - z} \right| < \frac{\text{const}\, k_\varphi}{|\zeta - c|^\alpha} \left| \log \frac{\zeta_c - z}{c - z} \right| < \frac{\text{const}\, k_\varphi}{|z-c|^\alpha}, \tag{17}$$

since the logarithmic function is bounded, in view of the equality of the lengths of the arcs $\frown c\zeta$ and $\frown \zeta\zeta_c$. The second of integrals (14) is regular. We obtain an estimate for it, denoting by s and σ the lengths of the arcs $\frown c\zeta$ and $\frown c\tau$, and taking into account that $(\sigma - s)/\sigma \geqq 1/2$ for $\sigma \geqq 2s$. Then we have

$$|\psi^{\zeta_c v}(z)| < \int_{\zeta_c v} \frac{M_\varphi\, dl_\tau}{|\tau - c|^\alpha |\tau - c'|^\alpha |\tau - \zeta|}$$

$$< \text{const}\, M_\varphi \int_{2s}^{|cv|} \frac{d\sigma}{\sigma^{\alpha+1}} < \frac{\text{const}\, M_\varphi}{|z-c|^\alpha}. \tag{18}$$

The third of integrals (14) is obviously bounded for $z \in \Delta'$. Combining the results (16'), (17), (18) we obtain the estimate of integral (8)

$$|\psi(z)| < \frac{aM_\varphi + bk_\varphi}{|z-c|^\alpha} \qquad (\alpha > 0) \tag{19}$$

for $z \in \Delta'$, where the positive constants a and b do not depend on φ. We now consider the case when the point z lies in the region which is common for a sufficiently small neighbourhood D of the end-point c and the concave angle between the rays cR_1 and cR_2, not containing the half-tangent cR.

It can be proved by an elementary calculation that if the point τ lies on the arc $\frown cv$ and the point z in the region Ω, then the three distances $|z-c|$, $|z-\tau|$, $|\tau - c|$ satisfy the inequality

$$\frac{|\tau - z|}{|z-c| + |\tau - z|} \geqq \sin \frac{\vartheta}{2} \tag{20}$$

where ϑ denotes the lower positive bound of the measure of the acute angle which is formed by the vector $\tau - c$, for $\tau \in \frown cv$, with the ray cR_1 and cR_2. Hence for the part of (8) over the arc $\frown cv$, in the case $z \in \Omega$, and for arbitrarily small $|z-c|$ we get the following inequality:

$$\left| \int_{cv} \frac{\varphi(\tau)\, d\tau}{\tau - z} \right| < \left(\sin \frac{\vartheta}{2} \right)^{-1} \int_{cv} \frac{\operatorname{const} M_\varphi \, dl_\tau}{|\tau - c|^\alpha [|z-c| + |\tau - c|]}$$

$$< \frac{\operatorname{const} M_\varphi}{|z-c|^\alpha} \quad (\alpha > 0). \tag{21}$$

Combining the results (13), (19), (21) we obtain the first part (7) of the proposition of Theorem 2 in the case $\alpha > 0$. It is seen from the above argument that for $\alpha = 0$, the function $|F(t)|$ is comparable with the function $|\log \prod_\nu (t - c_\nu)|$.

Part 2. To prove the second part (7′) of the proposition, it is sufficient to consider integral (8) also in the case when the points t, t_1 lie on the arc of integration $\frown cc'$ and in the case when they lie on the arc $\frown cc''$ approaching the common end-point c. In the first case, we first assume, like we did before, that the length of the arc $\frown ct$ is at most equal to a quarter of the length of the arc $\frown cc'$, and that the point t_1 lies on the arc $\frown tc'$. By s and s_1 we denote the lengths of the arcs $\frown ct$ and $\frown ct_1$, respectively. It is a known fact that there exists a positive constant χ less than unity, such that the inequalities

$$0 < \chi \leqq \frac{|t - t_1|}{|s - s_1|} \leqq 1 \tag{22}$$

hold for arbitrary points t and t_1 on the arc $\frown cc'$. By the assumption, we have

$$s < s_1, \quad 4s < l, \tag{23}$$

where l denotes the length of the chosen arc $\frown cc'$.

We assume that the length of the arc $\frown tt_1$ is at most equal to a quarter of the length of the arc $\frown ct$,

$$s_1 - s \leqq \tfrac{1}{4} s. \tag{24}$$

We confine ourselves to examination of this case, since for $s_1 - s > \frac{1}{4}s$, the property (7′) for integral (8) follows immediately from the property (7), proved above.

Now decompose integral (8) into the sum of two integrals

$$\psi(t) = I_1(t) + I_2(t), \tag{25}$$

$$I_1(t) = \int\limits_{ct_0} \frac{\varphi(\tau)\,d\tau}{\tau - t}, \qquad I_2(t) = \int\limits_{t_0c'} \frac{\varphi(\tau)\,d\tau}{\tau - t} \tag{26}$$

over the arcs $\frown ct_0$ and $\frown t_0c$, where t_0 is a point of the arc $\frown t_1c'$ such that the lengths of the arcs $\frown t_1t_0$ and $\frown ct$ are equal. Denoting the length of the arc $\frown ct_0$ by s_0 we obtain

$$s_0 = s_1 + s \leqq \frac{9}{16}\,l. \tag{27}$$

In order to examine the integral $I_1(t)$ we write

$$I_1(t) = \int\limits_{ct_0} \frac{\varphi(\tau) - \varphi(t)}{\tau - t}\,d\tau + \varphi(t) \int\limits_{ct_0} \frac{d\tau}{\tau - t}, \tag{28}$$

and denote the two above terms by $J_1(t)$ and $J_2(t)$. Similarly, for the point t_1 we have

$$I_1(t_1) = J_1(t_1) + J_2(t_1). \tag{28′}$$

In order to estimate the difference $J_1(t) - J_1(t_1)$, each integral possessing a weak singularity, we consider the circle Γ with centre at t and radius $2|t - t_1|$. Besides assumption (24), we take the distance $|t - t_1|$ to be smaller than the smaller of the two numbers

$$|t - t_1| < \min\left[\tfrac{1}{4}|t - c|;\ \delta\right], \tag{29}$$

where the positive constant δ is sufficiently small such that the circumference of the circle Γ intersects the arc $\frown ct_0$ at two internal points t' and t''. It is sufficient to consider the case (29), since otherwise, on account of inequality (22), the property (7′) follows from the property (7). Let us write the decomposition

$$J_1(t) = \int\limits_{t't''} \frac{\varphi(\tau)-\varphi(t)}{\tau - t}\, d\tau + \int\limits_{ct'+t''t_0} \frac{\varphi(\tau)-\varphi(t)}{\tau - t}\, d\tau ,$$

$$J_1(t_1) = \int\limits_{t't''} \frac{\varphi(\tau)-\varphi(t_1)}{\tau - t_1}\, d\tau \int\limits_{ct'+t''t_0} \frac{\varphi(\tau)-\varphi(t_1)}{\tau - t_1}\, d\tau . \tag{30}$$

The first component, $J_1'(t)$, relating to the point t, on account of inequality (5′), satisfies the inequality

$$J_1'(t) < \int\limits_{s'}^{s} \frac{k_\varphi |\tau - t|^{\mu-1}\, dl_\tau}{[|\tau - c|\, |t-c'|]^{\alpha+\mu}} + \int\limits_{s}^{s''} \frac{k_\varphi |\tau - t|^{\mu-1}\, dl_\tau}{[|t - c|\, |\tau-c'|]^{\alpha+\mu}} , \tag{31}$$

where s' and s'' denote the lengths of the arcs $\frown ct'$ and $\frown ct''$. Hence, on the basis of inequality (22), it follows that

$$|J_1'(t)| < \text{const}\, k_\varphi \Bigg[\int\limits_{s'}^{s} \frac{d\sigma}{\sigma^{\alpha+\mu}(s-\sigma)^{1-\mu}} +$$

$$+ \int\limits_{s}^{s''} \frac{d\sigma}{(t-c)^{\alpha+\mu}(\sigma - s)^{1-\mu}} \Bigg], \tag{32}$$

where σ denotes the length of the variable arc $\frown c\tau$. Next, in view of the inequality

$$|t-t'| = |t''-t| = 2\,|t-t_1|$$

and inequalities (22), (24), (29) we have

$$\int\limits_{s'}^{s} \frac{d\sigma}{\sigma^{\alpha+\mu}(s-\sigma)^{1-\mu}} < \frac{(s-s')^\mu}{\mu s'^{\alpha+\mu}} < \frac{\text{const}}{|t-c|^{\alpha+\mu}}\, |t-t_1|^\mu ,$$

$$\int\limits_{s}^{s''} \frac{d\sigma}{(\sigma - s)^{1-\mu}} = \frac{(s''-s)^\mu}{\mu} < \text{const}\, |t-t_1|^\mu .$$

Thus we conclude that integral (31) satisfies the inequality

$$|J_1'(t)| < \frac{\text{const}\, k_\varphi |t-t_1|^\mu}{|t-c|^{\alpha+\mu}}. \tag{33}$$

for $t \in \frown cT$. For the integral $J_1'(t_1)$ we obtain an analogous inequality.

We shall now investigate the difference between the regular integrals $J_1''(t)$ and $J_1''(t_1)$ appearing in the sums (30)

$$J_1''(t) - J_1''(t_1) = \int\limits_{ct'+t''t_0} \frac{\varphi(t_1)-\varphi(t)}{\tau - t}\, d\tau + \\ + \int\limits_{ct'+t''t_0} \frac{t-t_1}{(\tau-t)(\tau-t_1)} [\varphi(\tau)-\varphi(t_1)]\, d\tau. \tag{34}$$

The first of the above integrals D_1, according to the assumption (5′), satisfies the inequality

$$|D_1| < \frac{k_\varphi |t-t_1|^\mu}{[|t-c|\,|t_1-c'|]^{\alpha+\mu}} \left| \int\limits_{ct'+t''t_0} \frac{d\tau}{\tau - t} \right| \\ < \frac{\text{const}\, k_\varphi |t-t_1|^\mu}{[|t-c|\,|t_1-c'|]^{\alpha+\mu}}, \tag{35}$$

since the absolute value of the integral in the right-hand side remains bounded for $|t-t_1| \to 0$, in view of the equal lengths of the arcs $\frown ct$ and $\frown t_1 t_0$. For the second integral D_2 in the sum (34), we obtain the inequality

$$|D_2| < \int\limits_{ct'} \frac{k_\varphi |t-t_1|\, dl_\tau}{|t_1-c'|^{\alpha+\mu} |\tau-c|^{\alpha+\mu} |\tau-t_1|^{1-\mu} |\tau-t|} + \\ + \int\limits_{t''t_0} \frac{k_\varphi |t-t_1|\, dl_\tau}{|t_1-c|^{\alpha+\mu} |\tau-c'|^{\alpha+\mu} |\tau-t_1|^{1-\mu} |\tau-t|}. \tag{36}$$

According to the inequality $|\tau-t_1| \geqq \frac{1}{2}|\tau-t|$, the first component D_2' of the sum (36) satisfies the inequality

$$|D_2'| \; \frac{\text{const}\, k_\varphi\, |t-t_1|}{|t_1-c'|^{\alpha+\mu}} \int_0^{s'} \frac{d\sigma}{\sigma^{\alpha+\mu}(s-\sigma)^{2-\mu}}$$

$$= \frac{\text{const}\, k_\varphi\, |t-t_1|}{|t_1-c'|^{\alpha+\mu}} \left[\int_0^{\frac{1}{2}s'} \frac{d\sigma}{\sigma^{\alpha+\mu}(s-\sigma)^{2-\mu}} + \int_{\frac{1}{2}s'}^{s'} \frac{d\sigma}{\sigma^{\alpha+\mu}(s-\sigma)^{2-\mu}} \right]$$

$$< \frac{\text{const}\, k_\varphi\, |t-t_1|}{|t_1-c'|^{\alpha+\mu}} \left[\frac{1}{s'^{\alpha+1}} + \frac{1}{s'^{\alpha+\mu}(s-s')^{1-\mu}} \right]. \tag{37}$$

Using the inequalities

$$s' \geqq 2\,|t-t_1|, \quad 2s' \geqq |t-c|, \quad |s-s'| \geqq 2\,|t-t_1|,$$

we obtain

$$|D_2'| < \frac{\text{const}\, k_\varphi\, |t-t_1|^\mu}{|t-c|^{\alpha+\mu}\, |t_1-c'|^{\alpha+\mu}}. \tag{38}$$

An inequality of the same form is also valid for the second term D_2'' of the sum (36). Combining the results (33), (35), (38) we obtain the estimate

$$|J_1(t)-J_1(t_1)| < \frac{\text{const}\, k_\varphi\, |t-t_1|^\mu}{[|t-c|\, |t_1-c'|]^{\alpha+\mu}}, \tag{39}$$

where the constant factor does not depend on the function φ.

It remains to estimate the difference between the second integrals in the sums (28) and (28′), which can be written as follows:

$$J_2(t)-J_2(t_1) = [\varphi(t)-\varphi(t_1)] \int_{ct_0} \frac{d\tau}{\tau-t} +$$

$$+\varphi(t_1)\{[\log(t_0-t)-\log(t_0-t_1)]-$$

$$-[\log(t-c)-\log(t_1-c)]\}. \tag{40}$$

Thus, the absolute value of the singular integral

$$\int_{ct_0} \frac{d\tau}{\tau-t} = \log \frac{t_0-t}{t-c}$$

is bounded for $|t-c| \to 0$, on account of the equal lengths of the arcs $s_0-s_1 = s$. Next, in order to estimate the difference between the logarithms, we apply the theorem on absolute value of an integral, bearing in mind that the points t and t_1 lie on the same side of the point c and that the point t lies between the points c and t_1; we then have

$$|\log(t-c)-\log(t_1-c)| = \left| \int_t^{t_1} \frac{d\tau}{\tau-c} \right| \leqq \frac{|t-t_1|}{\chi|\tau'-c|}$$

where χ is the positive constant in inequalities (22), while τ' is the point on the arc $\frown tt_1$ at which the absolute value $|\tau-c|$ assumes its lower bound. Hence, we have

$$|\log(t-c)-\log(t_1-c)| \leqq \frac{|t-t_1|}{\chi^2|t-c|} \leqq \frac{|t-t_1|^\mu}{\chi^2|t-c|^\mu} \tag{41}$$

for $|t-t_1| \leqq |t-c|$. For the second difference between the logarithms in formula (40) we obtain an analogous inequality.

Thus it follows that

$$|J_2(t)-J_2(t_1)| < \frac{A_1 M_\varphi + B_1 k_\varphi}{[|t-c|\,|t_1-c'|]^{\alpha+\mu}} |t-t_1|^\mu, \tag{42}$$

where the positive constants A_1 and B_1 depend on the arc cc' and are independent of the function φ.

It remains to examine the second of integrals (26), which is regular. Thus, we have

$$I_2(t)-I_2(t_1) = \int_{t_0c'} \frac{\varphi(\tau)\,d\tau}{\tau-t} - \int_{t_0c'} \frac{\varphi(\tau)\,d\tau}{\tau-t_1}$$

$$= \int_{t_0c'} \frac{(t-t_1)\,\varphi(\tau)\,d\tau}{(\tau-t)(\tau-t_1)}.$$

Hence, on account of inequality (5), it follows that

$$I_2(t)-I_2(t_1) < \frac{\text{const}\, M_\varphi}{s^\alpha} \int\limits_{s_0}^{l} \frac{|t-t_1|\, d\sigma}{(\sigma-s)^2(l-\sigma)^\alpha}$$

$$< \frac{\text{const}\, M_\varphi |t-t_1|^\mu}{|t-c|^\alpha} \int\limits_{s_0}^{l} \frac{d\sigma}{(\sigma-s)^{1+\mu}(l-\sigma)^\alpha}. \tag{43}$$

Taking into account the inequalities

$$s_0 \leqq \frac{9}{16}\, l, \quad s \leqq \frac{1}{4}\, l,$$

we obtain for the last integral the estimate

$$\int\limits_{s_0}^{l} \frac{d\sigma}{(\sigma-s)^{1+\mu}(l-\sigma)^\alpha}$$

$$< \left(\frac{16}{7l}\right)^\alpha \int\limits_{s_0}^{(9/16)l} \frac{d\sigma}{(\sigma-s)^{1+\mu}} + \left(\frac{16}{5l}\right)^{1+\mu} \int\limits_{(9/16)l}^{l} \frac{d\sigma}{(l-\sigma)^\alpha}$$

thus, for the difference (43) we have

$$|I_2(t)-I_2(t_1)| < \frac{\text{const}\, M_\varphi}{|t-c|^{\alpha+\mu}}\, |t-t_1|^\mu. \tag{44}$$

Combining the results (39), (42), (44), for integral (8), we obtain an inequality of the form

$$|\psi(t)-\psi(t_1)| < \frac{\tilde{A} M_\varphi + \tilde{B} k_\varphi}{[|t-c|\,|t_1-c'|]^{\alpha+\mu}}\, |t-t_1|^\mu \tag{45}$$

for $t \in \frown cT$, $t_1 \in \frown tc'$. In the same way, we obtain a similar inequality when $t \in \frown ct_1$, $t_1 \in \frown T'c'$, where the length of the arc $\frown T'c'$ is equal to a quarter of the length of the arc $\frown cc'$. In the case, when the points t, t_1 lie on the arc $\frown TT'$, we note, that the function $f(t)$ satisfies the ordinary Hölder condition on the arc $\frown TT'$, and consequently, the Plemelj Theorem (given on p. 433) may be applied to the integral $\psi(t)$. Finally, we conclude that integral (8) satisfies the inequality of the form (45) for each $t \in \frown cc'$, $t_1 \in \frown t_1 c'$, where positive constants A, B do not depend on the function φ.

We shall now consider the property of integral (8) when the points t and t_1 lie on the smooth arc $\frown cc''$ which only has the end-point c in common with the arc of integration $\frown cc'$. Let cR_0' denote the half-tangent to the arc $\frown cc''$ at the point c, as the limit of the ray which is secant of the arc. We first consider the case when the half-tangent cR_0' to the arc $\frown cc''$ is different from the half-tangent cR_0 to the arc $\frown cc'$. In this case, we introduce two rays cR_1 and cR_2 forming with the half-tangent cR_0 to the arc $\frown cc'$ sufficiently small acute angles such that the part $\frown cc_0''$ of the arc $\frown cc''$ lying in a sufficiently small neighbourhood D of the end c be external with respect to the angle between the rays cR_1 and cR_2, containing cR_0. Since the function $\psi(z)$ defined by integral (8) is holomorphic outside the arc $\frown cc'$ and has the derivative

$$\psi'(z) = \int_{cc'} \frac{\varphi(\tau)\, d\tau}{(\tau - z)^2},$$

using the theorem on the estimation of the difference between the values of the holomorphic function and on the assumed inequality (5'), we can write, for any two points t and t_1 of the arc $\frown cc_0''$ ($t \in \frown tc_0''$), the inequality

$$|\psi(t) - \psi(t_1)| < \text{const}\, M_\varphi |t - t_1| \sup_{\xi \in \frown tt_1} \left[\int_{cc_0} \frac{dl_\tau}{|\tau - c|^\alpha |\tau - \xi|^2} \right], \tag{46}$$

where $\frown cc_0'$ is the fixed part of the arc $\frown cc'$ inside the angle cR_1R_2. Note that when the point ξ is on the arc $\frown cc_0''$ and the point τ inside the angle cR_1R_2, then the three distances $|\xi - c|$, $|\xi - \tau|$, $|\tau - c|$ satisfy the inequality

$$\frac{|\tau - \xi|}{|\xi - c| + |\tau - c|} \geqq \sin \frac{\vartheta}{2}, \tag{47}$$

where ϑ is the lower positive bound of the measure of the acute angles generated by the vector $\tau - c$ with the rays cR_1 and cR_2. Hence it follows that

$$|\psi(t) - \psi(t_1)| < \text{const}\, M_\varphi |t - t_1| \int\limits_{cc_0'} \frac{dl_\tau}{|\tau - c|^\alpha [|t - c| + |\tau - c|]^2}$$

$$< \frac{\text{const}\, M_\varphi |t - t_1|}{|t - c|^{\alpha+1}}$$

if $|t-c| \leqq |t_1 - c|$. Next, we can assume that $|t - t_1| \leqq |t - c|$, since, otherwise, the required property follows immediately from the estimate of the function $\psi(z)$. Thus we have the inequality

$$|\psi(t) - \psi(t_1)| < \frac{\text{const}\, M_\varphi |t - t_1|^\mu}{|t - c|^{\alpha+\mu}} \tag{48}$$

which is valid on the arc $\frown cc''$ in the neighbourhood of the end-point c.

We still have to consider the most difficult case, namely when the arc $\frown cc''$ has the half-tangent cR_0 in common, at the point c, with the arc $\frown cc'$. Suppose that in this case we are given the part $\frown cc_0'$ of the arc $\frown cc'$ lying in a sufficiently small neighbourhood D of the point c such that:

(i) each perpendicular intersecting the half-tangent cR_0 in the neighbourhood D intersects the arc $\frown cc_0'$ at one point ζ, and the corresponding arc $\frown cc''$, being a part of the arc $\frown cc''$, at one corresponding point t;

(ii) the tangents at each point of the arcs $\frown cc_0'$ and $\frown cc_0''$ form with the half-tangent cR_0 angles smaller than an arbitrary given acute angle ϑ_0.

Let there be given two points t and t_1 of the arc $\frown cc_0''$ and two corresponding points ζ and ζ_1 of the arc $\frown cc_0'$. We denote by s and s_1 the lengths of the arcs $\frown c\zeta$ and $\frown c\zeta_1$ ($s_1 > s$). Note that the ratios $|t - t_1|/|\zeta - \zeta_1|$, $|r - c|/|\zeta - c|$, $|s_1 - s|/|\zeta_1 - \zeta|$ have the positive lower and upper bounds for $t, t_1 \in \frown cc_0''$. It is sufficient to consider the case when the length of the arc $\frown c\zeta$ is at most equal to a third of the length of the arc $\frown cc_0'$. Next, it is sufficient, as we know, to consider the case when $s_1 - s \leqq s/4$. We now decompose the integral

$$\psi(t) = \int_{cc'} \frac{\varphi(\tau)\, d\tau}{\tau - t} \qquad (t \in \frown cc_0'') \tag{49}$$

into the sum

$$\psi(t) = \psi^{(c\zeta_0)}(t) + \psi^{(\zeta_0 c_0')}(t) + \psi^{(c_0' c')}(t) \tag{50}$$

of integrals over the arcs $\frown c\zeta_0, \frown \zeta_0 c_0', \frown c_0' c'$, where ζ_0 is the point of the arc $\frown cc_0$ such that the arcs $\frown c\zeta$ and $\frown \zeta_1 \zeta_0$ have equal length. Then, let Γ be the circle with centre at the point ζ, and radius $2|\zeta_1 - \zeta|$. Besides the assumption that $s_1 - s < s/4$ we take the distance $|\zeta_1 - \zeta|$ to be smaller than the smaller of the two numbers $|t - c|/4$ and δ, where the positive constant δ is sufficiently small such that the circle Γ intersects the arc $\frown c\zeta_0$ at two internal points ζ' and ζ'' (it suffices to restrict the considerations to this case only). Thus we write

$$\psi^{(c\zeta_0)}(t) = \int_{c\zeta_0} \frac{\varphi(\tau) - \varphi(\zeta)}{\tau - t}\, d\tau + \varphi(\zeta) \int_{c\zeta_0} \frac{d\tau}{\tau - t}, \tag{51}$$

and decompose the first integral $J_1(t)$ into the sum of the integrals

$$J_1(t) = \int_{\zeta'\zeta''} \frac{\varphi(\tau) - \varphi(\zeta)}{\tau - t}\, d\tau + \int_{c\zeta' + \zeta''\zeta_0} \frac{\varphi(\tau) - \varphi(\zeta)}{\tau - t}\, d\tau. \tag{52}$$

The first of the above integrals $J_1'(t)$, in view of the assumption (5′), satisfies the inequality

$$|J_1'(t)| < \int_{\zeta'\zeta} \frac{\operatorname{const} k_\varphi |\tau - \zeta|^{\mu - 1}\, dl_\tau}{[|\tau - c|\, |\zeta - c'|]^{\alpha + \mu}} + \int_{\zeta\zeta''} \frac{\operatorname{const} k_\varphi |\tau - \zeta|^{\mu - 1}\, dl_\tau}{|\zeta - c|\, |\tau - c'|]^{\alpha + \mu}}$$

$$< \frac{\operatorname{const} k_\varphi |t - t_1|^\mu}{[|\zeta - c|\, |\zeta_1 - c'|]^{\alpha + \mu}} \qquad (t, t_1 \in cc_0'') \tag{53}$$

since the ratio $|t-\tau|/|\zeta-\tau|$ has a positive lower bound. A similar inequality is satisfied by the integral $J_1'(t_1)$. In order to examine the second integral $J_1''(t)$ in (52), we write

$$J_1''(t)-J_1''(t_1) = \int_{c\zeta'+\zeta''\zeta_0} \frac{\varphi(\zeta_1)-\varphi(\zeta)}{\tau-t}\,d\tau + \\ + \int_{c\zeta'+\zeta''\zeta_0} \frac{(t-t_1)[\varphi(\tau)-\varphi(\zeta_1)]}{(\tau-t)(\tau-t_1)}\,d\tau. \quad (54)$$

The first component $D_1(t)$ satisfies the inequality

$$|D_1(t)| < \frac{\text{const}\, k_\varphi |\zeta-\zeta_1|^\mu}{[|\zeta-c|\,|\zeta_1-c'|]^{\alpha+\mu}} \left| \int_{c\zeta'+\zeta''\zeta_0} \frac{d\tau}{\tau-t} \right| \quad (55)$$

where the integral is obviously bounded for $|\zeta-\zeta_1| \to 0$, on account of equality of the lengths of the arcs $\frown c\zeta$ and $\frown \zeta_1\zeta_0$. The second integral $D_2(t)$ on the right-hand side of equality (54) satisfies the inequality

$$|D_2(t)| < \text{const}\, k_\varphi |t-t_1| \left[\int_{c\xi'} \frac{|\tau-\zeta_1|^{1-\mu}\,dl_\tau}{[|\tau-c|\,|\zeta_1-c'|]^{\alpha+\mu}|\tau-\zeta|} + \\ + \int_{\zeta''\zeta_0} \frac{|\tau-\zeta_1|^{1-\mu}\,dl_\tau}{[|\zeta_1-\tau|\,|\tau-c'|]^{\alpha+\mu}|\tau-\zeta|} \right]. \quad (56)$$

Taking into account that each point τ outside the circle Γ satisfies the inequalities $(1/2) < |\tau-\zeta_1|/|\tau-\zeta| < (3/2)$, we obtain for the first integral D'_2 on the right-hand side of inequality (56) the estimate

$$|D_2'| < \frac{\text{const}}{|\zeta_1-c'|^{\alpha+\mu}} \left[\int_0^{\frac{1}{2}s'} \frac{d\sigma}{\sigma^{\alpha+\mu}(s-\sigma)^{2-\mu}} + \int_{\frac{1}{2}s'}^{s'} \frac{d\sigma}{\sigma^{\alpha+\mu}(s-\sigma)^{2-\mu}} \right] \\ < \frac{\text{const}\,|\zeta-\zeta_1|^{\mu-1}}{[|\zeta-c|\,|\zeta_1-c'|]^{\alpha+\mu}}, \quad (57)$$

while for the second integral D_2'' we have

$$|D_2''| < \frac{\text{const}}{[|\zeta-c|\,|\zeta_1-c'|]^{\alpha+\mu}} \int_{s''}^{s_0} \frac{d\sigma}{(\sigma-s)^{2-\mu}}$$

$$< \text{const}\,\frac{|\zeta-\zeta_1|^{\mu-1}}{[|\zeta-c|\,|\zeta_1-c'|]^{\alpha+\mu}}. \tag{58}$$

Combining the results (53), (57), (58) we obtain the following property of the first of integrals (51) on the arc $\frown cc''$ in the neighbourhood of the point c,

$$|J_1(t)-J_1(t_1)| < \frac{\text{const}\,k_\varphi\,|t-t_1|^\mu}{|t-c|^{\alpha+\mu}}. \tag{59}$$

For the second $J_2(t)$ of integrals (51) we write the equality

$$J_2(t)-J_2(t_1)$$
$$= \varphi(\zeta)\{[\log(\zeta_0-t)-\log(\zeta_0-t_1)]-[\log(c-t)-\log(c-t_1)]\}+$$
$$+[\varphi(t)-\varphi(t_1)]\log\frac{\zeta_0-t_1}{c-t_1}. \tag{60}$$

According to the estimate (41), we have

$$|\log(c-t)-\log(c-t_1)| \leqq \frac{|t-t_1|^\mu}{\chi^2\,|t-c|^\mu},$$

and then

$$|\log(\zeta_0-t)-\log(\zeta_0-t_1)| = \left|\int_{tt_1}\frac{d\xi}{\zeta_0-\xi}\right| < \frac{|t-t_1|}{\inf\limits_{\xi\in tt_1}|\zeta_0-\xi|}$$

$$< \text{const}\,\frac{|t-t_1|^\mu}{|t-c|^\mu}.$$

Finally, we note that the ratio $|\zeta_0-t_1|/|c-t_1|$ has positive lower and upper bounds, and consequently, the difference (60) satisfies the following inequality in the neighbourhood of the end-point c

$$|J_2(t)-J_2(t_1)| < \frac{a_1 M_\varphi + b_1 k_\varphi}{|t-c|^{\alpha+\mu}}\,|t-t_1|^\mu, \tag{61}$$

where the positive constants, a_1, b_1 are independent of φ.

For the second integral of the sum (50) we have the following inequality:

$$|\psi^{(\zeta_0 c_0)}(t)-\psi^{(\zeta_0 c_0)}(t_1)| < \text{const} \int\limits_{\zeta_0 c_0'} \frac{|t-t_1|\, M_\varphi\, dl_\tau}{|\tau-c|^\alpha\, |\tau-t|\, |\tau-t_1|}$$

$$< \text{const}\, M_\varphi |t-t_1| \int\limits_{\zeta_0 c_0'} \frac{d\sigma}{\sigma^\alpha (\sigma-s)^2} < \text{const}\, M_\varphi \frac{|t-t_1|^\mu}{|t-c|^{\alpha+\mu}}. \tag{62}$$

The last of the integrals in the sum (50) has a bounded derivative for $t \in \frown cc_0''$, and thus

$$|\psi^{(c_0'c')}(t)-\psi^{(c_0'c')}(t_1)| < \text{const}\, M_\varphi |t-t_1|. \tag{63}$$

Combining the results (48), (59), (61), (62), (63) we conclude that integral (49) satisfies, in a sufficiently small neighbourhood of the end-point c on an arbitrary arc $\frown cc''$ the generalized Hölder inequality in the form

$$|\psi(t)-\psi(t_1)| < \frac{\tilde{a} M_\varphi + \tilde{b} k_\varphi}{|t-c|^{\alpha+\mu}} |t-t_1|^\mu \tag{64}$$

($t, t_1 \in \frown cc_0$, $|t-c| \leqq |t_1-c|$), the positive constants $\tilde{a}$ and $\tilde{b}$ being independent of the function $\varphi(t)$.

The examined properties of the difference of integral (8) in all the above considered cases, assert the validity of the second part (7′) of the principal theorem for the functions of the class $\mathfrak{H}_\alpha^\mu$ defined on the system of arcs L, for $\alpha > 0$. If $\alpha = 0$, then the function of the class $\mathfrak{H}_0^\mu$, by Theorem 1, belong to each class $\mathfrak{H}_\varepsilon^\mu$, where ε is an arbitrarily small positive constant, and consequently, according to the above considerations the Cauchy type integral (6) also belongs to the class $\mathfrak{H}_\varepsilon^\mu$.

THEOREM 3. *If a complex function $f(\tau, \rho)$ defined in the domain $[\tau \in L', \rho \in \Omega]$ satisfies the inequalities*

$$|f(\tau, \rho)| < \frac{M_f}{\prod\limits_{j=1}^{p} |\tau-c_j|^\alpha}, \tag{65}$$

$$|f(\tau, \rho)-f(\tau_1, \rho_1)| < \frac{k_f[|\tau-\tau_1|^\mu + |\rho-\rho_1|^{\mu_1}]}{[|\tau-c_\nu|\, |\tau_1-c_{\nu_1}|]^{\alpha+\mu}}, \tag{65'}$$

$\tau\in\frown c_\nu c_{\nu_1}$, $\tau_1\in\frown \tau c_{\nu_1}$, *where the constants* M_f, k_f, α, μ, μ_1 *satisfy the inequalities*

$$M_f, k_f > 0, \quad \alpha+\mu < 1, \quad \alpha > 0, \quad 0 < \mu < \mu_1 < 1 \tag{66}$$

(Ω *is an arc or a region in the complex plane*), *then the Cauchy type integral, as a function of the parameter* ρ,

$$F(t,\rho) = \int\limits_L \frac{f(\tau,\rho)\,d\tau}{\tau-t} \tag{66'}$$

defined in the domain [$t\in L'$, $\rho\in\Omega$], *satisfies the inequalities*

$$|F(t,\rho)| < \frac{C_0 M_f + C_0' k_f}{\prod\limits_{j=1}^{p} |t-c_j|^\alpha}, \tag{67}$$

$$|F(t,\rho)-F(t_1,\rho)| < \frac{(CM_f+C'k_f)[|t-t_1|^\mu + |\rho-\rho_1|^{\theta\mu}]}{[|t-c|\,|t_1-c|]^{\alpha+\mu}}, \tag{67'}$$

where $t\in\frown c_\nu c_{\nu_1}$, $t_1\in\frown tc_{\nu_1}$, *the positive constants* $\tilde{C}$, $\tilde{C}'$ *are independent of the function f, and* θ *is an arbitrary positive constant, less than unity.*

Proof. In the case $\rho = \rho_1\in\Omega$, inequality (67), as well as inequality (67′) follows immediately from the preceding theorem. Thus, it is sufficient to consider the case when $t = t_1\in L'$ and $\rho = \rho_1$. As in the preceding theorem, it is sufficient to examine the integral

$$\psi(t,\rho) = \int\limits_{cc'} \frac{f(\tau,\rho)\,d\tau}{\tau-t} \tag{68}$$

over an arc $\frown cc'$ arbitrarily chosen from the arcs $l_1, \ldots, l_m$.

We first suppose that t lies on the arc of integration, and thus, investigating integral (68) in the neighbourhood of the point c, we assume that the length of the arc $\frown ct$ is not greater than the length of the arc $\frown tc'$. Examining the difference $\psi(t,\rho)-\psi(t,\rho_1)$ it is sufficient to consider the assumption $|\rho-\rho_1| \neq |t-c|$, since otherwise, property (67′) follows immediately from (67).

Let us now decompose integral (68) into the sum

$$\psi(t,\rho)=\int_{t't''}\frac{f(\tau,\rho)-f(t,\rho)}{\tau-t}\,d\tau+$$

$$+f(t,\rho)\int_{t't''}\frac{d\tau}{\tau-t}+\int_{ct'+t''c'}\frac{f(t,\rho)}{\tau-t}\,d\tau, \qquad (70)$$

where the arc $\frown t't''$ contains the point t in such a way that the lengths of the arcs $\frown t't$ and $\frown tt''$ are equal. By assumption (65′) we obtain the following estimate for the first of integrals (70) $J_1(t,\rho)$:

$$|J_1(t,\rho)|$$

$$<\text{const}\,k_f\left[\int_{t't}\frac{|\tau-t|^{\mu-1}\,dl_\tau}{[|\tau-c|\,|t-c'|]^{\alpha+\mu}}+\int_{tt''}\frac{|\tau-t|^{\mu-1}\,dl_\tau}{[|t-c|\,|\tau-c'|]^{\alpha+\mu}}\right]$$

$$<\text{const}\,k_f\left[\int_{s-\frac{1}{2}|\rho-\rho_1|}^{s}\frac{d\sigma}{\sigma^{\alpha+\mu}(s-\sigma)^{1-\mu}}+\frac{1}{s^{\alpha+\mu}}\int_{s}^{s+\frac{1}{2}|\rho-\rho_1|}(\sigma-s)^{\mu-1}d\sigma\right]$$

$$<\frac{\text{const}\,k_f|\rho-\rho_1|^{\mu}}{|t-c|^{\alpha+\mu}}. \qquad (71)$$

The value of the function $J_1(t,\rho)$ satisfies an analogous estimate. For the second, $J_2(t,\rho)$, of integrals (70) we obtain the inequality

$$|J_2(t,\rho)-J_2(t,\rho_1)|=|f(t,\rho)-f(t,\rho_1)|\left|\log\frac{t''-t}{t-t'}\right|$$

$$<\frac{\text{const}\,k_f|\rho-\rho_1|^{\mu_1}}{|t-c|^{\alpha+\mu}}, \qquad (72)$$

since the above logarithm of the quotient is bounded, on account of the equality of the lengths of the arcs $\frown t't$ and $\frown tt''$. The third integral $J_3(t, \rho)$ of (70) yields the inequality

$$|J_3(t,\rho)-J_3(t,\rho_1)| = \left| \int\limits_{ct'+t''c'} \frac{f(\tau,\rho)-f(\tau,\rho_1)}{\tau-t}\,d\tau \right|$$

$$< k_f|\rho-\rho_1|^{\mu} \int\limits_{ct'+t''c} \frac{dl_\tau}{|\tau-c|^{\alpha+\mu}\,|\tau-t|\,|\tau-c'|^{\alpha+\mu}}$$

$$< \text{const}\,k_f|\rho-\rho_1|^{\mu_1}\left[\int\limits_0^{s-\frac{1}{2}|\rho-\rho_1|} \frac{d\sigma}{\sigma^{\alpha+\mu}(s-\sigma)}+\right.$$

$$\left. +\frac{1}{|t-c|^{\mu+\alpha}} \int\limits_{s+\frac{1}{2}|\rho-\rho_1|}^{|cc'|=l} \frac{d\sigma}{(\sigma-s)(l-\sigma)^{\alpha+\mu}}\right]$$

$$< \frac{\text{const}\,k_f|\rho-\rho_1|^{\theta\mu}}{|t-c|^{\alpha+\mu}}, \tag{73}$$

where θ is an arbitrary positive constant less than unity. Combining the results (71), (72), (73) we have the inequality

$$|\psi(t,\rho)-\psi(t,\rho_1)| < \frac{\text{const}\,k_f|\rho-\rho_1|^{\theta\mu}}{|t-c|^{\alpha+\mu}} \tag{74}$$

in the neighbourhood of the point c.

In the case when the point t lies on the arc $\frown cc''$, which has the point c in common with the arc of integration $\frown cc'$, integral (68) is regular. Thus we examine the difference at the points ρ and ρ_1 proceeding as in the first part of the proof of the preceding theorem, retaining the introduced symbols and straight lines, with small alterations only. If t is an arbitrary point of the triangle Δ', not lying on $\frown cv'$, then integral (68) is decomposed into the sum

$$\psi(t,\rho) = \int\limits_{\zeta'\zeta''} \frac{f(\tau,\rho)-f(t,\rho)}{\tau-t}\,d\tau+$$

$$+f(t,\rho)\int\limits_{\zeta'\zeta''}\frac{d\tau}{\tau-t}+\int\limits_{c\zeta'+\zeta''c'}\frac{f(\tau,\rho)\,d\tau}{\tau-t}. \tag{75}$$

The procedure and the estimate of the above three components are similar to the results (71), (72), (73), and consequently, we obtain the following property of integral (68)

$$|\psi(t, \rho)-\psi(t, \rho_1)| < \frac{\text{const}\, k_f\, |\rho-\rho_1|^{\theta\mu_1}}{|t-c|^{\alpha+\mu}} \tag{76}$$

where $t \in \Delta'$ in the neighbourhood of the end-point c. In the remaining case, i.e. when t lies in the concave angle between the rays cR_1 and cR_2, not containing the half-tangent cR_0, we have

$$|\psi(t, \rho)-\psi(t, \rho_1)| < \int_{cc'} \frac{k_f\, |\rho-\rho_1|^{\mu}\, d\tau}{[|t-c|\, |\tau-c'|]^{\alpha+\mu}\, |\tau-t|} .$$

Thus, on account of inequality (20), we obtain the property (77) in the neighbourhood of the point c. Thus, the proposition (67) of Theorem 3 is proved.

THEOREM 4. *If the function $\varphi(\tau)$ belongs to the class $\mathfrak{H}_\alpha^\mu$ then the function*

$$\Phi(z) = \int_L \frac{\varphi(\tau)\, d\tau}{\tau - z}, \tag{77}$$

sectionally holomorphic in the regions $S_{\text{ext}}, S_1, S_2, \ldots,$ satisfies the inequality

$$|\Phi(z)| < \frac{\text{const}}{|z-c_\nu|^\delta}. \tag{78}$$

in the neighbourhood of each point of discontinuity c_ν, where $\delta = \alpha$ for $\alpha > 0$, while δ is a sufficiently small positive constant for $\alpha = 0$.

The proof of the theorem is included in the first part of the principal theorem (p. 614) relating to the case when the point t lies outside the arc of integration.

DEFINITION 3. *We define the class $\mathfrak{H}_\alpha^\mu(c_{k_1}, \ldots, c_{k_q})$ as the set of functions $\varphi(t)$ of the class $\mathfrak{H}_\alpha^\mu$, defined on the set L' or L, bounded in the neighbourhood of some chosen end-points of the arcs l_j*

$$c_{k_1}, c_{k_2}, \ldots, c_{k_2} \quad (q \leq p)$$

and consequently, satisfying inequalities of the form

$$|\varphi(t)| < \frac{M_\varphi}{\prod_{\xi=1}^{p} |t-c_j|^{\theta_j \alpha}}, \tag{79}$$

$$|\varphi(t)-\varphi(t_1)| < \frac{k_\varphi |t-t_1|^\mu}{|t-c_\nu|^{\theta_\nu \alpha+\mu} |t_1-c_{\nu_1}|^{\theta_{\nu_1}\alpha+\mu}} \tag{80}$$

$(t \in \frown c_\nu c_{\nu_1}, t_1 \in \frown t c_{\nu_1})$, *where*

$$\theta_\nu = \begin{cases} 0 & \text{for} \quad \nu = k_1, k_2, \ldots, k_q, \\ 1 & \text{for} \quad \nu \neq k_1, k_2, \ldots, k_q. \end{cases}$$

The θ_{ν_1} takes similar values at the point c_{ν_1}. M_φ and k_φ are positive arbitrary constants appropriate for the function φ.

It should be noted that the function $\varphi(t)$ of the class $\mathfrak{H}_\alpha^\mu(c_{k_1}, \ldots, c_{k_q})$ though bounded in the neighbourhood of the ends $(c_{k_1}, \ldots, c_{k_q})$ may not have one-sided limits for the arcs approaching these points.

If the set of chosen end-points $(c_{k_1}, \ldots, c_{k_q})$ contains all the points $c_1, c_2, \ldots, c_p$ then the class $\mathfrak{H}_\alpha^\mu(c_{k_1}, \ldots, c_{k_q})$ is identical with the class $\mathfrak{H}_0^\mu$.

The set of all functions of the class $\mathfrak{H}_\alpha^\mu(c_{k_1}, \ldots, c_{k_q})$ with parameters α and μ take all values satisfying the inequalities $0 \leqq \alpha < 1, 0 < \mu < 1, \mu+\alpha < 1$ is called *the class* $\mathfrak{H}(c_{k_1}, \ldots, c_{k_q})$.

THEOREM 5. *If the function* $\varphi(\tau)$, *defined on the system of arcs* L, *belongs to the class* $\mathfrak{H}_\alpha^\mu(c_{k_1}, \ldots, c_{k_q})$, *then the function defined by the singular integral*

$$\psi(t) = \prod_{j=1}^{p} (t-c_j)^{\gamma_j} \int_L \frac{\varphi(\tau)\, d\tau}{\prod_{j=1}^{p} (\tau-c_j)^{\gamma_j} (\tau-t)} \tag{81}$$

at each point $t \in L'$ *belongs to the class* $\mathfrak{H}_\rho^\mu(c_{k_1}, \ldots, c_{k_q})$. *It is assumed that the complex constants* $\gamma_j = \gamma_j' + i\gamma_j''$ *satisfy the inequalities*

$$\begin{aligned} 0 < \gamma_j' < 1 \quad & \text{for} \quad j = k_1, \ldots, k_q, \\ -1 < \gamma_j' \leqq 0 \quad & \text{for} \quad j \neq k_1, \ldots, k_q, \\ \mu + \max|\gamma_j'| < 1 \quad & \text{for} \quad j = 1, 2, \ldots, p, \end{aligned} \tag{82}$$

and that the positive constant ρ takes the values

$$\begin{aligned} &\rho=\alpha, \quad \text{if} \quad \alpha>\beta=\max|\gamma_j'|,\ j\neq k_1,\ldots,k_q, \\ &\rho=\beta, \quad \text{if} \quad \alpha<\beta. \end{aligned} \tag{82'}$$

Proof. The theorem follows directly from the principal theorem on functions of the class $\mathfrak{H}_\alpha^\mu$. It is sufficient to consider the integral

$$F_\nu(t)=\int\limits_{c_\nu c_{\nu_1}}\frac{\varphi(\tau)\,d\tau}{(\tau-c_\nu)^{\gamma_\nu}(\tau-t)} \qquad (\nu=1,2,\ldots,p) \tag{83}$$

in a sufficiently small closed neighbourhood of the end c_ν, not containing the other end-points.

Taking any continuous branch of the function $(\tau-c_\nu)^{\gamma_\nu}$ on an arbitrary arc $\frown c_\nu c_{\nu_1}$, departing from, or arriving at the point c_ν, we apply the theorem on the absolute value of the integral and property (22) of the arcs. Hence we obtain the inequality

$$|(\tau-c_\nu)^{-\gamma_\nu}-(\tau_1-c_\nu)^{-\gamma_\nu}|<\text{const}\sup|\tau'-c_\nu|^{-\gamma_\nu-1}\,|\tau-\tau_1|,$$

where the upper bound is taken over the set of the points τ' on the arc $\frown\tau\tau_1\subset\frown c_\nu c_{\nu_1}$. Hence we derive the inequalities

$$\left|\frac{1}{(\tau-c_\nu)^{\gamma_\nu}}-\frac{1}{(\tau_1-c_\nu)^{\gamma_\nu}}\right| < \begin{cases} \dfrac{\text{const}\,|\tau-\tau_1|^\mu}{|\tau-c_\nu|^{\gamma_\nu'+\mu}} & \text{for} \quad \gamma_\nu'+\mu>0, \\[2ex] \dfrac{\text{const}\,|\tau-\tau_1|^\mu}{|\tau_1-c_\nu|^{\gamma_\nu'+\mu}} & \text{for} \quad \gamma_\nu'+\mu<0, \end{cases} \tag{84}$$

where $\tau_1\in\frown\tau c_{\nu_1}$. It follows that the function

$$\varphi^*(\tau)=\varphi(\tau)(\tau-c_\nu)^{-\gamma_\nu} \tag{85}$$

satisfies the following inequalities in the neighbourhood of the point c_ν

$$\begin{aligned} &\varphi^*(\tau)<\frac{\text{const}}{|\tau-c_\nu|^{\theta_\nu\alpha+\gamma_\nu'}}, \\ &|\varphi^*(\tau)-\varphi^*(\tau_1)|<\frac{\text{const}\,|\tau-\tau_1|^\mu}{|\tau-c_\nu|^{\theta_\nu\alpha+\gamma_\nu'+\mu}} \end{aligned} \tag{86}$$

for $\theta_\nu \alpha + \gamma'_\nu > 0$, $\theta_\nu = 0$ if $\nu = k_1, \dots, k_q$ and $\theta_\nu = 1$ in the remaining cases.

On account of the principal theorem, it follows from the above argument that in the neighbourhood of the end-point c_ν the function (83) satisfies the inequalities

$$\begin{aligned} |F_\nu(t)| &< \frac{\text{const}}{|t-c_\nu|^{\theta_\nu \alpha + \gamma'_\nu}}, \\ |F_\nu(t) - F_\nu(t_1)| &< \frac{\text{const}\, |t-t_1|^\mu}{|t-c_\nu|^{\theta_\nu \alpha + \gamma'_\nu + \mu}} \end{aligned} \tag{87}$$

for $\alpha + \gamma'_\nu > 0$. In the case $\alpha + \gamma'_\nu < 0$, but $\alpha + \gamma'_\nu + \mu > 0$ (this may happen only if $\nu \neq k_1, \dots, k_q$) we apply a similar argument as in the proof of the principal theorem, and consequently, we obtain that in the neighbourhood of the end-point c the function $F_\nu(t)$ satisfies the inequalities

$$\begin{aligned} |F_\nu(t)| &< \text{const}, \\ |F_\nu(t) - F_\nu(t_1)| &< \frac{\text{const}\, |t-t_1|^\mu}{|t-c_\nu|^{\theta_\nu \alpha + \gamma'_\nu + \mu}}. \end{aligned} \tag{88}$$

Finally, when $\alpha + \gamma'_\nu + \mu < 0$, function (85) and its Hölder coefficient tend to zero for $\tau \to c_\nu$, and function (83) satisfies Hölder's condition in the neighbourhood of the end-point c_ν, the coefficient being bounded.

The above properties of function (83) imply the validity of Theorem 5, i.e. that function (81) belongs to the class $\mathfrak{H}_\rho^\mu$. It should be mentioned that the inequalities referring to the function $\psi(t)$, according to the proof of Theorem 2, have the form

$$\begin{aligned} |\psi(t)| &< \frac{C_1 M_\varphi + C_2 k_\varphi}{\prod_{j=1}^{p} |t-c_j|^{\theta_j \rho}}, \\ |\psi(t) - \psi(t_1)| &< \frac{(C'_1 M_\varphi + C'_2 k_\varphi)\, |t-t_1|^\mu}{|t-c_\nu|^{\theta_\nu \rho + \mu}\, |t_1 - c_{\nu_1}|^{\theta_{\nu_1} \rho + \mu}} \end{aligned} \tag{89}$$

($t \in \frown c_\nu c_{\nu_1}$, $t_1 \in \frown t c_{\nu_1}$) where M_φ and k_φ are the positive constants, appropriate to the function $\varphi(\tau)$ given in inequalities (78) and (78'). The positive constants c_1, c_2, c_1', c_2' do not depend on the function φ.

THEOREM 6. *If the function* $\varphi(\tau)$ *belongs to the class* $\mathfrak{H}_\alpha^\mu(c_{k_1}, \ldots, c_{k_q})$, *then each branch of the function*

$$\Phi(z) = \prod_{j=1}^{p} (z-c_j)^{\gamma_j} \int_L \frac{\varphi(\tau)\, d\tau}{\prod_{j=1}^{p} (\tau-c_j)^{\gamma_j} (\tau-z)} \tag{90}$$

(provided the above assumptions concerning the constants are satisfied) is sectionally holomorphic in the regions $S_{\mathrm{ext}}, S_1, S_2, \ldots$ *bounded by the arcs* $l_1, \ldots, l_m$. *Moreover, it is bounded in sufficiently small neighbourhoods of the chosen end-points* $c_{k_1}, \ldots, c_{k_q}$ *and satisfies the following inequality with a weak singularity*

$$|\Phi(z)| < \frac{\text{const}}{|z-c_\nu|^\rho} \tag{91}$$

in the (intersected) neighbourhood of each other end-point c_ν, *the number* $\rho < 1$ *being determined by formulae* (82').

Proof. This theorem follows immediately from Theorem 4 and the property (86) of function (85).

§ 2. The Hilbert boundary problem for a system of arcs

Let there be given a complex function $G(t)$ defined on the set of points $L' = L - \sum_{1}^{p} c_\nu$ which is the sum of arcs on the complex plane as introduced previously. We assume that the function $G(t)$ satisfies Hölder's condition

$$|G(t) - G(t_1)| < k_G |t-t_1|^{h_G} \tag{92}$$

inside each arc l_γ ($\gamma = 1, \ldots, m$). The function $G(t)$ has *one-sided* limits at the end-points of each arc l_γ. The limits corresponding to an arbitrary point of discontinuity c_ν will be denoted by the symbols

$$\lim_{t_j \to c} G(t_j) = G^{(j)}(c_\nu) \qquad (j = 1, \ldots, r_\nu) \tag{93}$$

where $t_1, \ldots, t_{r_\nu}$ are the points lying inside the arcs directed towards or away from the point c_ν (Fig. 16). Thus r_ν, the limit values of the function $G(t)$ ($r_\nu \geqq 1$) correspond to each point c_ν

$$G^{(1)}(c_\nu), \ldots, G^{(r_\nu)}(c_\nu). \tag{94}$$

It is assumed that the function $G(t)$ and all its limit values (94) are *different from zero.*

Next, let there be given a function $g(t)$ defined in the set L, and belonging to the class $\mathfrak{H}_\alpha^\mu(c_{k_1}, \ldots, c_{k_q})$, where $\alpha > 0$.

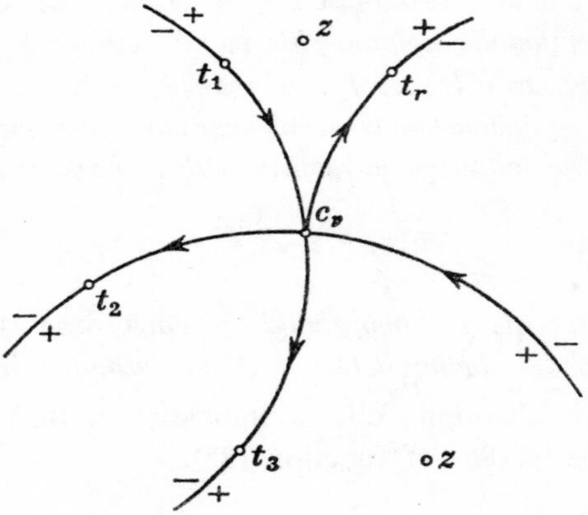

Fig. 16

The Hilbert boundary problem for a system of arcs $l_1, \ldots, l_m$ consists in determining a function $\Phi(z)$, sectionally holomorphic in the regions $S_{ext}, S_1, S_2, \ldots$, (without the point at infinity) bounded by the given arcs, the boundary values of which, i.e. $\Phi^+(t)$ and $\Phi^-(t)$, at each interior point t of any directed arc l_γ (correspondingly to the sides of the arc) satisfy the linear relation

$$\Phi^+(t) = G(t)\Phi^-(t) + g(t) \quad (t \in L'). \tag{95}$$

We recall that the position of two sides of each arc depends on its direction only, and does not depend on the directions of the other arcs. Even in the case when some arcs form a closed line, the boundary values $\Phi^+(t)$ may correspond to the sides lying either inside or outside this line. This is the fundamental difference as compared to the assumptions for the continuous Hilbert problem for contours in Chapter XVI. Besides condition (95) it is required that the function $\Phi(z)$ be bounded in the neighbourhood of the chosen end-points $(c_{k_1}, \ldots, c_{k_q})$, and satisfies the following inequalities with a weak singularity:

$$|\Phi(z)| < \frac{\text{const}}{|z-c_\nu|^\theta}. \tag{96}$$

In the neighbourhood of each other end-point c_ν the arbitrary positive constant θ is less than unity. In accordance with the notation used by MUSKHELISHVILI ([33], p. 231) the above function will be called the *solution of the class* $h(c_{k_1}, \ldots, c_{k_q})$ $(0 \leqq q \leqq p)$. It will be seen that the chosen points $c_{k_1}, \ldots, c_{k_q}$ may not always be chosen arbitrarily from the set of end-points $c_1, \ldots, c_p$. It should also be noted that the set of chosen-points may be empty.

In order to obtain a solution of the above Hilbert problem for a system of arcs, we first prove two lemmas.

LEMMA 1. *If a complex function* $\varphi(\tau)$, *defined on a smooth arc* $\frown cc'$ *(directed from* c *to* c', *or oppositely) satisfies Hölder's condition*

$$|\varphi(\tau)-\varphi(\tau_1)| < \text{const}\,|\tau-\tau_1|^\mu \tag{97}$$

$(0 < \mu < 1)$ *and is equal to zero at one of its end-points, for example* $\varphi(c) = 0$, *then the function holomorphic outside the arc* $\frown cc'$ *and defined by the Cauchy type integral*

$$F(z) = \frac{1}{2\pi i}\int\limits_{cc'} \frac{\varphi(\tau)\,d\tau}{\tau-z} \tag{98}$$

possesses in a sufficiently small closed neighbourhood V *of the end-point* c, *not containing the point* c', *the following properties*: (i) *it is bounded in the neighbourhood* V, (ii) *it tends to the limit*

$$F(c) = \frac{1}{2\pi i}\int\limits_{cc'} \frac{\varphi(\tau)\,d\tau}{\tau-c}$$

when the point z tends, in an arbitrary way, to the point c, (iii) *it has boundary values at each point t of the part* $\frown cv$ *of the arc* $\frown cc'$ *lying in the neighbourhood V on both sides of this arc,* (iv) *satisfies, including the boundary values on both sides of the cut* $\frown cv$*, Hölder's condition*

$$|F(z_1)-F(z_2)| < \text{const}\,|z_1-z_2|^{\mu} \tag{99}$$

for the same $\mu < 1$ *as the given density* $\varphi(\tau)$.

Proof. Consider the Cauchy type integral

$$F^*(z) = \frac{1}{2\pi i}\int_L \frac{\varphi^*(\tau)\,d\tau}{\tau - z} \tag{100}$$

taken over a smooth closed curve L containing the arc $\frown cc'$, where the function $\varphi^*(\tau)$ defined by

$$\varphi^*(\tau) = \begin{cases} \varphi(\tau) & \text{for} \quad \tau \in \frown cc', \\ 0 & \text{for} \quad \tau \in \frown ac. \end{cases}$$

Here $\frown ac$ is a continuation of the arc $\frown cc'$ lying on L, the arcs $\frown ac$ and arc $\frown cc'$ have the only one point in common c. According to the property $\varphi(c) = 0$, we may assume the existence of an extended function $\varphi^*(\tau)$ such that it satisfies Hölder's condition on the whole line L

$$|\varphi^*(\tau)-\varphi^*(\tau_1)| < \text{const}\,|\tau-\tau_1|^{\mu}$$

for the same exponent μ as the function $\varphi(\tau)$. In view of the property of the Cauchy type integral, function (100), has boundary values on both sides of the curve L and satisfies Hölder's condition in the form

$$|F^*(z_1)-F^*(z_2)| < \text{const}\,|z_1-z_2|^{\mu}$$

separately in the two sets $L+S^+$ and $L+S^-$, where S^+ is the interior region while S^- is the exterior region with respect to the contour L. It should be noted that integral (100) is the sum of the integrals

$$F^*(z) = \frac{1}{2\pi i}\int_{cc'} \frac{\varphi(\tau)\,d\tau}{\tau - z} + \frac{1}{2\pi i}\int_{L-ac'} \frac{\varphi^*(\tau)\,d\tau}{\tau - z},$$

where the second integral is a holomorphic function in a certain sufficiently small neighbourhood of the end-point c, as lying outside the arc of integration $L-\frown ac'$. Hence the propositions of the lemma follow immediately.

In the general case, when the density $\varphi(\tau)$ satisfies Hölder's condition (97) on the arc $\frown cc'$, but is not necessarily equal to zero at the point c, we write

$$F(z)=\frac{1}{2\pi i}\int_{cc'}\frac{\varphi(\tau)\,d\tau}{\tau-z}=\frac{\varphi(c)}{2\pi i}\int_{cc'}\frac{d\tau}{\tau-z}+\frac{1}{2\pi i}\int_{cc'}\frac{\varphi(\tau)-\varphi(c)}{\tau-z}\,d\tau$$

hence, on account of the preceding lemma, we conclude that the function $F(z)$, holomorphic in the neighbourhood of the end-point c cut by the arc $\frown cc'$, can be expressed in the form

$$F(z)=\pm\frac{\varphi(c)}{2\pi i}\log(z-c)+\tilde{F}(z)$$

(for the assumed single-valued branch of the logarithm), where the function $\tilde{F}(z)$ is bounded in the neighbourhood of the point c and satisfies all the propositions of the preceding lemma. The upper sign + corresponds to the case when the arc is directed towards the point c, while the lower sign − corresponds to the case when it departs from the point c.

LEMMA 2. *If the function $\varphi(\tau)$ satisfies the Hölder condition* (97) *and is equal to zero at the end-points c ($\varphi(c)=0$), then the principal value of the Cauchy integral*

$$F(t)=\frac{1}{2\pi i}\int_{cc'}\frac{\varphi(\tau)\,d\tau}{\tau-t}$$

at each point $t\in\frown cc'$, has the properties: (i) *it tends to the limit defined by the integral with a weak singularity*

$$F(t)\to F(c)=\frac{1}{2\pi i}\int_{cc'}\frac{\varphi(\tau)\,d\tau}{\tau-c},$$

when the interior point t of the arc $\frown cc'$ tends to its end-point c, (ii) *it satisfies the Hölder condition*

$$|F(t)-F(t_1)| < \text{const}\,|t-t_1|^{\mu} \quad (0<\mu<1)$$

where the coefficient if bounded on the closed arc $\frown cc''$ containing the point c, but not including the point c'.

The proof is analogous to the proof of Lemma 1.

In the more general case, when $\varphi(c)$ is not necessarily zero, the function $F(t)$, near the point c, is expressed by the sum

$$F(t) = \frac{\varphi(c)}{2\pi i}\int\limits_{cc'}\frac{d\tau}{\tau-t}+\frac{1}{2\pi i}\int\limits_{cc'}\frac{\varphi(\tau)-\varphi(c)}{\tau-t}\,d\tau$$

$$= \pm\frac{\varphi(c)}{2\pi i}\log(t-c)+\tilde{F}(t),$$

where the function $\tilde{F}(t)$ tends to the limit

$$\lim_{t\to c}\tilde{F}(t) = \frac{1}{2\pi i}\int\limits_{cc'}\frac{\varphi(\tau)-\varphi(c)}{\tau-c}\,d\tau$$

and satisfies Hölder's condition for the coefficient bounded on the part $\frown cc''$ of the arc $\frown cc'$.

We first solve the Hilbert problem for a system of arcs in the particular case of the homogeneous boundary relation

$$\Phi^{+}(t) = G(t)\,\Phi^{-}(t). \tag{101}$$

We shall apply a method analogous to that given by MUSKHELISHVILI for disconnected arcs ([33], p. 227). Thus, we introduce the Cauchy type integral

$$\Gamma(z) = \frac{1}{2\pi i}\int\limits_{L}\frac{\log G(\tau)\,d\tau}{\tau-z} = \sum_{\gamma=1}^{m}\frac{1}{2\pi i}\int\limits_{l_\gamma}\frac{\log G(\tau)\,d\tau}{\tau-z} \tag{102}$$

where the continuous branches of the logarithmic function $\log G(\tau)$ are arbitrarily chosen for each arc l_γ separately. Taking into account the property (92), we may assert that function (102), sectionally holomorphic in the regions $S_{ext}, S_1, S_2, \ldots,$ has boundary values satisfying the relation

$$\Gamma^+(t) - \Gamma^-(t) = \log G(t) \tag{103}$$

at each point t inside any component arc l_γ of the set L. It is emphasized that in formula (103) we select that continuous branch of the logarithm which is assumed for the arc l_j on which the point t lies. The boundary values $\Gamma^+(t)$, $\Gamma^-(t)$, corresponding to both sides of the arc l_j, depend only on its direction.

In view of the property (103) the function

$$F(z) = \exp[\Gamma(z)], \tag{104}$$

sectionally holomorphic in the regions $S_{ext}, S_1, S_2, \ldots,$ has boundary values satisfying the homogeneous condition

$$F^+(t) = G(t) F^-(t) \tag{105}$$

at each point $t \neq c_\nu$ of the set L. In order to obtain the function which also satisfies condition (96), it should be noted that the part of the Cauchy type integral (102) along the arc $\frown c_\nu c_{\nu_1}$, component of the set L, can be expressed in the neighbourhood of the end-point c_ν as follows

$$\frac{1}{2\pi i} \int_{c_\nu c_{\nu_1}} \frac{\log G(\tau)\, d\tau}{\tau - z} = \pm \frac{\log G^{(j)}(c_\nu)}{2\pi i} \log(z - c_\nu) + \psi_\nu^{(j)}(z) \tag{106}$$

$(j = 1, 2, \ldots, r_\nu)$, where the + sign corresponds to the case when the arc $\frown c_\nu c_{\nu_1}$, corresponding to the boundary value $G^{(j)}(c_\nu)$ is directed towards the point c_ν, while the $-$ sign corresponds to the case when the arc $\frown c_\nu c_{\nu_1}$ departs from the point c_ν. The function $\Psi_\nu^{(j)}(z)$ in a sufficiently small neighbourhood of the end-point c_ν is bounded, the exponent j corresponding to the arc $\frown c_\nu c_{\nu_1}$.

Let us investigate more closely the function $\Psi_\nu^{(j)}(z)$, defined by the formula

$$\Psi_\nu^{(j)}(z) = \frac{1}{2\pi i} \int\limits_{c_\nu c_{\nu_1}} \frac{\log G(\tau) - \log G^{(j)}(c_\nu)}{\tau - z}\, d\tau \pm \frac{\log G^{(j)}(c_\nu)}{2\pi i} \log(z - c_{\nu_1}). \quad (107)$$

The second logarithmic component is regular in the neighbourhood of the point c_ν, while the first is the Cauchy type integral of the density

$$\varphi(\tau) = \log G(\tau) - \log G^{(j)}(c_\nu)$$

satisfying Hölder's condition for the exponent h_G and equal to zero for $\tau = c_\nu$. Hence, on account of Lemma 1, we conclude that function (107) is holomorphic in a sufficiently small neighbourhood of the end-point c_ν cut by the arc $\frown c_\nu c_{\nu_1}$, and that on both sides of the cut, the function possesses the boundary values and the limit value

$$\Psi_\nu^{(j)}(c_\nu) = \frac{1}{2\pi i} \int\limits_{c_\nu c_{\nu_1}} \frac{\log G(\tau) - \log G^{(j)}(c_\nu)}{\tau - c_\nu}\, d\tau \pm \frac{\log G^{(j)}(c_\nu)}{2\pi i} \log(c_\nu - c_{\nu_1}), \quad (108)$$

where for $z \to c_\nu$ the integral corresponds to the function with the weak singularity. Next, according to Lemma 1, function (107) including its boundary values on both sides of the section, satisfies in the neighbourhood of the point c_ν the Hölder condition

$$|\Psi_\nu^{(j)}(z_1) - \Psi_\nu^{(j)}(z_2)| < \text{const}\, |z_1 - z_2|^{h_G} \quad (109)$$

with bounded coefficient.

We now assume, for the constant coefficient in formula (106), the following notation

$$\pm \frac{\log G^{(j)}(c_\nu)}{2\pi i} = \alpha_\nu^{(j)} + i\beta_\nu^j \quad (110)$$

($\nu = 1, 2, \ldots, p, j = 1, \ldots, r_\nu$), where $\alpha_\nu^{(j)}, \beta_\nu^{(j)}$ are real. Moreover, for each point of discontinuity c_ν we adjust the integer λ_ν so that

$$-1 < \lambda_\nu + \sum_{j=1}^{r_\nu} \alpha_\nu^{(j)} < +1. \tag{111}$$

In the particular case when the sum in the above inequalities is a positive integer, it follows from condition (111) that the integer λ_ν is unique and defined by

$$\lambda_\nu = -\sum_{j=1}^{r_\nu} \alpha_\nu^{(j)}. \tag{112}$$

The point of discontinuity c_ν of this type will be called *singular*. Otherwise, condition (111) gives two values of the integers λ_ν, either

$$0 < \lambda_\nu + \sum_{j=1}^{r_\nu} \alpha_\nu^{(j)} < 1 \tag{113}$$

or

$$-1 < \lambda_\nu + \sum_{j=1}^{r_\nu} \alpha_\nu^{(j)} < 0. \tag{113'}$$

In view of the requirement that the solution of the Hilbert problem belongs to the class $h(c_{k_1}, \ldots, c_{k_q})$ we take condition (113) for the chosen end-points $c_{k_1}, \ldots, c_{k_q}$ assuming that neither of them is singular, whereas for the remaining ends we take the condition (113′) or (112).

Using formulae (104), (106), (110) and inequalities (113) and (113′) we prove that the function defined by formula

$$X(z) = \exp\left\{\frac{1}{2\pi i} \sum_{\gamma=1}^{m} \int_{l_\gamma} \frac{\log G(\tau)\, d\tau}{\tau - z}\right\} \prod_{\nu=1}^{p} (z - c_\nu)^{\lambda_\nu} \tag{114}$$

is the solution of the homogeneous Hilbert problem (101) of the class $h(c_{k_1}, \ldots, c_{k_q})$.

Actually, function (114) is sectionally holomorphic in the regions $S_{\text{ext}}, S_1, S_2, \ldots,$ and in view of the property (103) it possesses boundary values $X^{\pm}(t)$ satisfying the relation

$$X^{+}(t) = G(t)X^{-}(t) \tag{115}$$

at each point $t \neq c_\nu$ of the set L. Moreover, function (114), according to the decomposition (106), in the neighbourhood of the point c_ν, can be expressed by the formula

$$X(z) = (z-c_\nu)^{\alpha_\nu^* + \lambda_\nu + i\beta_\nu^*}\Omega_\nu(z) \tag{116}$$

where

$$\Omega_\nu(z) = \exp\left[\sum_{j=1}^{r_\nu} \Psi_\nu^{(j)}(z)\right], \tag{117}$$

$$\alpha_\nu^* = \sum_{j=1}^{r_\nu} \alpha_\nu^{(j)}, \quad \beta_\nu^* = \sum_{j=1}^{r_\nu} \beta_\nu^{(j)}. \tag{118}$$

Function (117), by formula (107), is bounded and different from zero in a sufficiently small neighbourhood of the point c_ν, and is sectionally holomorphic inside the regions into which the arcs departing from the point c_ν intersect the neighbourhood of this point. The function $\Omega_\nu(z)$, appropriate for the point c_ν, has boundary values different from zero on both sides of each section, and satisfies Hölder's condition in the form (109), separately in each of the partial regions in the neighbourhood of the point c_ν. According to the choice of the integers λ_ν and on account of inequalities (113) and (113′), function (116) is bounded in the neighbourhood of the points $c_{k_1}, \ldots, c_{k_q}$ and satisfies the condition (96) in the neighbourhood of the other end-points c_ν, and thus, function (116) is of the class $h(c_{k_1}, \ldots$ $\ldots, c_{k_q})$.

We indicate that in accordance with the existence of the limit (108) the function $\Omega_\nu(z)$, defined in the neighbourhood of the end-point c_ν by formula (117), tends to the unique non-zero limit,

$$\lim_{z\to c_\nu} \Omega_\nu(z) = \exp\left[\sum_{j=1}^{r_\nu} \Psi_\nu^{(j)}(c_\nu)\right], \tag{119}$$

provided the point z, inside any of the component regions of the neighbourhood of the point c_ν, tends in arbitrary way to this point.

We conclude, on the basis of formula (114) and the Plemelj formulae, that the function $X(z)$ tends to the boundary functions

$$X^+(t) = \sqrt{G(t)}\,X(t), \quad X^-(t) = [\sqrt{G(t)}]^{-1}X(t) \tag{120}$$

if the point z tends to any point $t \neq c$ of the set L.

The continuous branch of the function $\sqrt{G(t)}$ is defined on each arc by the formula

$$\sqrt{G(t)} = \exp[\tfrac{1}{2}\log G(t)].$$

We use the notation

$$X(t) = \exp\{\Gamma(t)\}\prod_{\nu=1}^{p}(t-c_\nu)^{\lambda_\nu} \tag{121}$$

where $\Gamma(t)$ is the principal value of integral (102) at the point $t \neq c_\nu$ on L. This function, in the neighbourhood of the point c_ν, can be expressed by the formula of the form

$$\Gamma(t) = \log(t-c_\nu)\sum_{j=1}^{r_\nu}\frac{(\pm 1)}{2\pi i}\log G^{(j)}(c_\nu)+\Gamma^*(t) \tag{122}$$

where the function $\Gamma^*(t)$ is bounded and different from zero, satisfies the Hölder condition with exponent h_G, in the neighbourhood of the point c_ν on each arc commencing from the point c_ν (separately), and has the limit $\Gamma^*(c_\nu) \neq 0$, provided $t \to c_\nu$ along any arc l_γ. On the basis of formulae (116), (117), we conclude that the boundary function $X(t)$, defined by formula (121), can be expressed by the product

$$X(t) = \omega(t)\prod_{\nu=1}^{p}(t-c_\nu)^{\alpha_\nu^*+\lambda_\nu+i\beta_\nu^*} \tag{123}$$

at each point $t \neq c_\nu$ of the set L; here, the definite continuous branches of the function $(t-c_\nu)^{\alpha_\nu^*+\lambda_\nu+i\beta_\nu^*}$ are chosen on each arc l_γ. The function $\omega(t)$, defined and different from zero on the set L satisfies the ordinary Hölder condition

$$|\omega(t)-\omega(t_1)| < \text{const}\,|t-t_1|^{h_G}, \tag{124}$$

the coefficient being bounded on each arc l_γ separately. If the point t tends to the end-point c_ν along an arbitrary arc then, according to the property (119), the function $\omega(t)$ tends to a definite limit different from zero. Taking this limit as the value $\omega(c_\nu) = \lim_{t\to c_\nu}\omega(t)$ of the function $\omega(t)$ at the point c_ν, we can assert that the function $\omega(t)$ is well-defined, everywhere different from zero, and continuous at each point of the set L including the ends c_ν.

The function $X(z)$, defined by formula (114), is called the *fundamental solution of the class* $h(c_{k_1}, \dots, c_{k_q})$ of the homogeneous Hilbert problem for the system of arcs $l_1, \dots, l_m$.

It is seen from formula (116) and the property (119) that the function $X(z)$, defined above, is not only bounded in the neighbourhood of chosen non-singular points $c_{k_1}, \dots, c_{k_q}$ but also it tends to zero when z tends to any of these points.

It can easily be proved that all the solutions of the homogeneous Hilbert problem of the class $h(c_{k_1}, \dots, c_{k_q})$ are determined by the formula

$$\Phi(z) = X(z)P(z), \tag{125}$$

where $P(z)$ is an arbitrary entire function.

In fact, each function determined by formula (125) is obviously a solution of the class $h(c_{k_1}, \dots, c_{k_q})$ of the homogeneous Hilbert problem. Conversely, if a certain function $\Psi(z)$ is a solution of the class $h(c_{k_1}, \dots, c_{k_q})$ of the homogeneous Hilbert problem, then we have

$$\Psi^+(t) = G(t)\Psi^-(t), \quad X^+(t) = G(t)X^-(t)$$

consequently,

$$\frac{\Psi^+(t)}{X^+(t)} = \frac{\Psi^-(t)}{X^-(t)}$$

at each point t of the set $L' = L - \sum_1^p c_\nu$.

Hence it follows (see Chapter XVI, § 1) that the function $\Psi(z)/X(z)$ is holomorphic in the whole plane except the points $c_1, \dots, c_p$. However, in the neighbourhood of these points the above ratio satisfies the inequality with the weak singularity of the form

$$\left|\frac{\Psi(z)}{X(z)}\right| < \frac{\text{const}}{|z-c_\nu|^\theta}, \quad 0 < \theta < 1.$$

Thus, the points $c_1, \ldots, c_p$ are neither the poles, nor the essential singular points of the examined ratio $\Psi(z)/X(z)$, and consequently this ratio is an entire function.

The sum of the integers

$$\kappa = -\lambda_1 - \lambda_2 - \ldots - \lambda_p, \tag{126}$$

appropriate to all the end-points $c_1, \ldots, c_p$ of the given system of arcs is called the *index* of the solution of the Hilbert problem of the class $h(c_{k_1}, \ldots, c_{k_q})$. It is apparent, according to formula (110), that the value of the index κ is independent of the choice of the continuous branches of the function $\log G(t)$ on the arcs l_γ, whereas it depends only on the function $G(t)$ and on the choice of the non-singular points $c_{k_1}, \ldots, c_{k_q}$. In fact, if we arbitrarily change the branch of the function $\log G(t)$ on a certain arc $l_\gamma = \frown c_\nu c_{\nu_1}$ then, in view of formula (110), two components of the sum (126), corresponding to the end-points c_ν and c_{ν_1}, increase and simultaneously decrease by the same integer, and consequently, the sum (126) remains unaltered. The index κ characterizes the behaviour of the function $X(z)$ at infinity, namely, we have the following limit property from formula (114)

$$\lim_{z \to \infty} z^\kappa X(z) = 1. \tag{127}$$

Hence it is seen that when $\kappa > 0$, the function $X(z)$ is regular at infinity and tends to zero as $z^{-\kappa}$, and when $\kappa = 0$, then the function $X(z)$ is regular at infinity. If, however, $\kappa < 0$, then the function $X(z)$ has a pole of order κ at infinity.

If the set of chosen end-points $c_{k_1}, \ldots, c_{k_q}$ is empty, then the class is denoted by h_0, and the fundamental solution of this class, by $X_0(z)$. The index of the solution of the class h_0 is greater than each index κ of another class, namely we have the relation

$$\kappa = \kappa_0 - q. \tag{128}$$

Next, it is readily seen that the fundamental solution $X(z)$ of the class $h(c_{k_1}, \ldots, c_{k_q})$ is connected with the fundamental solution $X_0(z)$ of the class h_0 by the formula

$$X(z) = (z - c_{k_1}) \ldots (z - c_{k_q}) X_0(z). \tag{129}$$

DEFINITION. *By the homogeneous Hilbert problem associated with the problem* (101) *we shall mean the problem with boundary condition*

$$\Psi^{+}(t) = [G(t)]^{-1}\Psi^{-}(t). \tag{101'}$$

The same set of singular ends, and consequently, the same set of all non-singular ends

$$c_{k_1}, \ldots, c_{k_q}, c_{k_{q+1}}, \ldots, c_{k_m}$$

as for the problem (101) corresponds to this problem. The set of all solutions which are bounded in the neighbourhood of all the remaining non-singular ends $c_{k_{q+1}}, \ldots, c_{k_m}$ is called the *associate class* of the solutions of the problem (101′) with the class $h(c_{k_1}, \ldots, c_{k_q})$ of the solutions of the problem (101). This class is denoted by the symbol $h'(c_{k_{q+1}}, \ldots, c_{k_m})$. It is easily seen, on the basis of the preceding formula and the definition of the index (126), that the index κ' of the associate class of solutions has the opposite value $\kappa' = -\kappa$ with respect to the index κ of the given class $h(c_{k_1}, \ldots, c_{k_q})$.

We now determine the solution $\Phi(z)$ of the class $h(c_{k_1}, \ldots, c_{k_q})$ of the non-homogeneous Hilbert problem (95). We recall the assumption that the given function $g(t)$ belongs to the class $\mathfrak{H}_{\alpha}^{\mu}(c_{k_1}, \ldots, c_{k_q})$ and that the chosen points $c_{k_1}, \ldots, c_{k_q}$ are non-singular.

Let us express the boundary condition (95), in view of the fact that $X^{+}(t) \neq 0$ for $t \neq c_{\nu}$, in the equivalent form

$$\frac{\Phi^{+}(t)}{X^{+}(t)} - \frac{\Phi^{-}(t)}{X^{-}(t)} = \frac{g(t)}{X^{+}(t)}. \tag{130}$$

Next we note that if the given function $g(t)$ belongs to the class $\mathfrak{H}_{\alpha}^{\mu}(c_{k_1}, \ldots, c_{k_q})$, then on the basis of formula (123) the ratio $g(t)/X^{\pm}(t)$ belongs to the class $\mathfrak{H}_{\zeta}^{\mu_1}$, where $\mu_1 \leqq \min(\mu, h_G)$, $\zeta = \alpha$ for $\alpha \geqq \beta = \max|\alpha_{\nu}^{*} + \lambda_{\nu}|$ $(\nu = c_{k_1}, \ldots, c_{k_q})$ and $\zeta = \beta$ for $\alpha < \beta$, besides $\mu_1 + \zeta < 1$. Hence it follows that the integral

$$\Psi(z) = \frac{1}{2\pi i} \int_{L} \frac{g(\tau)\, d\tau}{X^{+}(\tau)(\tau - z)} \tag{131}$$

has a definite sense, represents the function sectionally holomorphic in the regions $S_{ext}, S_1, S_2, \ldots$, and takes boundary values satisfying the equality

$$\Psi^+(t) - \Psi^-(t) = \frac{g(t)}{X^+(t)} \tag{132}$$

at each point $t \neq c_\nu$ of the set L. Moreover, according to Theorem 4, function (131) satisfies, in the neighbourhood of each point of discontinuity c_ν, the inequality with weak singularity

$$|\Psi(z)| < \frac{\text{const}}{|z - c_\nu|^\zeta}. \tag{133}$$

Thus, if $\Phi(z)$ is a function of the class $h(c_{k_1}, \ldots, c_{k_q})$ satisfying the non-homogeneous boundary condition (95) or (130), then the difference between the functions $\Psi(z)$ and $\Phi(z)/X(z)$ is a certain entire function $P(z)$, and consequently it can be written in the form

$$\Phi(z) = \frac{X(z)}{2\pi i} \int_L \frac{g(\tau)\, d\tau}{X^+(\tau)(\tau - z)} + X(z) P(z). \tag{134}$$

Conversely, if $P(z)$ is an arbitrary entire function, then the function defined by formula (134) is sectionally holomorphic in the regions $S_{ext}, S_1, S_2, \ldots$ (excluding the point at infinity), has boundary values satisfying conditions (95) and (130), and moreover, on account of Theorem 6 it is bounded in the neighbourhood of the non-singular chosen end-points $c_{k_1}, \ldots, c_{k_q}$ and in the neighbourhood of the other ends c_ν it satisfies the inequality of weak singularity

$$|\Phi(z)| < \frac{\text{const}}{|z - c_\nu|^\rho} \tag{135}$$

where

$$\rho = \begin{cases} \alpha & \text{for} \quad \alpha > \delta = \max|\alpha_\nu^* + \lambda_\nu|, \ \nu \neq k_1, \ldots, k_q, \\ \delta & \text{for} \quad \alpha < \delta \end{cases} \tag{135'}$$

(furthermore μ is sufficiently small such that $\mu + \max|\alpha_\nu^* + \lambda_\nu| < 1$, $\nu = 1, \ldots, p$).

Formula (134), given by MUSKHELISHVILI, thus represents the general solution of the class $h(c_{k_1}, \ldots, c_{k_q})$ of the non-homogeneous discontinuous Hilbert problem (95).

The exponents $\alpha_\nu^* + \lambda_\nu$ in formulae (116) and (123) are equal to zero at the singular ends c_ν, therefore function (134) in the neighbourhood of these points behaves as $\log(z - c_\nu)$ even if the function $g(\tau)$ is bounded at these points. This property explains why we have assumed that the chosen points $c_{k_1}, \ldots, c_{k_q}$ are not singular.

In the case when this condition is not satisfied, i.e. when the points $c_{k_1}, \ldots, c_{k_q}$ are arbitrarily chosen from the set of end-points $c_1, \ldots, c_p$, then as it follows from the preceding reasoning, formula (134) represents all the solutions of the non-homogeneous Hilbert problem (95) of the class $\tilde{h}(c_{k_1}, \ldots, c_{k_q})$. In this way we denote the class of solutions which are bounded or *almost bounded* in the neighbourhood of the points $c_{k_1}, \ldots, c_{k_q}$ and satisfy the inequality with the weak singularity in the neighbourhood of the other points.

We now investigate the solution (134) for $z \to \infty$. In the case when $\kappa \geqq 0$ formula (134) represents all solutions equal to zero at infinity if instead of $P(z)$ an arbitrary polynomial of degree at most $\kappa - 1$ is substituted, or $P = 0$ for $\kappa = 0$. In the case $\kappa < 0$ there exists only one solution of the Hilbert problem equal to zero at infinity. It can be represented by the formula

$$\Phi(z) = \frac{X(z)}{2\pi i} \int_L \frac{g(\tau)\, d\tau}{X^+(\tau)(\tau - z)}. \tag{136}$$

Here, a necessary and sufficient condition is that the given function $g(t)$ satisfies the integral equations

$$\int_L \frac{t^j g(t)\, dt}{X^+(t)} = 0 \quad (j = 0, 1, \ldots, -\kappa - 1). \tag{137}$$

Formally, formula (134) has the same form as the formula for the solution of the continuous Hilbert problem for contours (p. 469) but its essence is different in view of the fact that the fundamental solution $X(z)$, at the chosen end-points $c_{k_1}, \ldots, c_{k_q}$, tends to zero, and that the function $g(\tau)$ is not bounded. Finally, we note that our formula (134) is different from the formula given in MUSKHELISHVILI's monograph for a contour L with the points of discontinuity. Namely, there it is substituted

$$\Gamma(z) = \frac{1}{2\pi i} \int_L \frac{\log G_0(\tau)}{\tau - z} d\tau$$

where $G_0(t) = t^{-\kappa} G(t)$. This transformation which is important in the case of the continuous Hilbert problem, in this case is not expedient, since all the closed lines belonging to L contain at least one point of discontinuity of the function $G(t)$.

§ 3. The inversion of a Cauchy integral for systems of arcs

The inversion of the Cauchy type integral for a system $L = l_1, \ldots, l_m$ of arcs consists in solving a singular integral equation of the first kind of the form

$$\int_L \frac{\varphi(\tau)\, d\tau}{\tau - t} = f(t) \tag{138}$$

where $f(t)$ is a complex function given on the set $L' = L - \sum_1^p c_\nu$, φ being an unknown function. We make the same assumptions for the set L as before. It is required that equation (138) be satisfied at each point $t \neq c_\nu$ of the set L.

Equation (138) is a generalization of the equation in the particular form

$$\int_{-a}^{+a} \frac{\varphi(\xi)\, d\xi}{\xi - z} = f(x), \tag{139}$$

where the integral is taken along the segment of the real axis. This equation appears in the theory of thin aerofoils. Equation (139) was the subject of investigations by numerous authors by means of complicated special methods. MUSKHELISHVILI [33] was first to give a general method for the solution of equation (138) for a system of disconnected arcs, basing it on his theory of the discontinuous Hilbert problem. Below, we present this method in a somewhat altered form, namely we take more general assumptions for the functions $f(t)$, $\varphi(t)$, the system L, and the method is based on previously discussed theory of the functions of the class $\mathfrak{H}$ (see POGORZELSKI [66]).

We assume that the given function $f(t)$ belongs to the class $\mathfrak{H}^{\mu}_{\alpha}(c_{k_1}, \ldots, c_{k_q})$ where the arbitrary points $c_{k_1}, \ldots, c_{k_q}$ are previously chosen.

Let us suppose that there exists a solution $\varphi(\tau)$ of equation (138) in the class $\tilde{\mathfrak{H}}(c_{k_1}, \ldots, c_{k_q})$ which contains all these functions of the class $\mathfrak{H}$ which are bounded or *almost bounded* in the neighbourhood of the points $c_{k_1}, \ldots, c_{k_q}$. Consider the auxiliary function

$$\Phi(z) = \frac{1}{2\pi i}\int_L \frac{\varphi(\tau)\,d\tau}{\tau - z} \tag{140}$$

sectionally holomorphic in the regions $S_{\text{ext}}, S_1, S_2, \ldots$ Function (140) has boundary values satisfying, according to the Plemelj formulae, the equalities

$$\Phi^+(t) - \Phi^-(t) = \varphi(t), \quad \Phi^+(t) + \Phi^-(t) = \frac{1}{\pi i}\int_L \frac{\varphi(\tau)\,d\tau}{\tau - t} \tag{141}$$

at each point $t \neq c_\nu$ of the set L. Thus, (140) is the solution of a particular Hilbert problem of the form

$$\Phi^+(t) + \Phi^-(t) = f(t) \tag{142}$$

which is equal to zero at infinity, is almost bounded in the neighbourhood of the points $c_{k_1}, \ldots, c_{k_q}$ and satisfies the inequalities with weak unboundedness in the neighbourhood of each other point c_ν. We determine all solutions of the class $\tilde{h}(c_{k_1}, \ldots, c_{k_q})$ of the particular Hilbert problem (142), equal to zero at infinity.

We find first the fundamental solution of the class $h(c_{k_1}, \ldots \ldots, c_{k_q})$ which satisfies the boundary condition

$$X^+(t) + X^-(t) = 0. \tag{143}$$

Inserting $G(t) = -1$ in formulae (102), (110), (114), and taking into account condition (111), we conclude that these points are singular for which the difference between the number of divergent and convergent arcs is even. For the other points c_ν the sum $\lambda_\nu + \alpha_\alpha^*$ takes the values $+1/2$ or $-1/2$. The fundamental solution of the class $h(c_{k_1}, \ldots, c_{k_q})$ satisfying the condition (143) is thus

$$X(z) = \prod_{\nu=1}^{p} (z-c_\nu)^{\gamma_\nu} \tag{144}$$

where $\gamma_\nu = 0$ or $1/2$ for the chosen points $c_{k_1}, \ldots, c_{k_q}$ and $\gamma_\nu = -\frac{1}{2}$ for the remaining points. It is also assumed that the branches of the factors $(z-c_\nu)^{\gamma_\nu}$ are holomorphic outside the sections l_j.

According to the property (127), the index of the solution (144) has the value $\kappa = -\sum_{1}^{p} \gamma_\nu$.

In view of formula (134), it follows from the above that the general solution of the class $\tilde{h}(c_{k_1}, \ldots, c_{k_q})$ of the non-homogeneous problem (142), equal to zero at infinity, has the following form

$$\Phi(z) = \frac{1}{2\pi i} \prod_{\nu=1}^{p} (z-c_\nu)^{\gamma_\nu} \int_L \frac{f(\tau)\, d\tau}{\prod_{\nu=1}^{p} (\tau-c_\nu)^{\gamma_\nu} (\tau-z)} + P(z) \prod_{\nu=1}^{p} (z-c_\nu)^{\gamma_\nu} \tag{145}$$

where $P(z)$ is an arbitrary polynomial of degree at most $\kappa-1$ for $\kappa > 0$, or $P = 0$ for $\kappa = 0$. In the case $\kappa < 0$ there exists only one solution in the class $\tilde{h}(c_{k_1}, \ldots, c_{k_q})$, equal to zero at infinity, defined by formula (145) with the substitution $P = 0$. A necessary and sufficient condition is that the given function $f(t)$ satisfies the integral equations

$$\int_L \frac{\tau^\beta f(\tau)\, d\tau}{\prod_{\nu=1}^{p} (\tau-c_\nu)^{\gamma_\nu}} = 0 \quad (\beta = 0, 1, \ldots, -\kappa-1). \tag{146}$$

We shall determine, using the solution (145), all solutions in the class $\tilde{\mathfrak{H}}(c_{k_1}, \ldots, c_{k_q})$ of the integral equation (138). Namely, according to the Plemelj formulae, function (145) has, at each point $t \neq c_\nu$ of the set L, boundary values determined by the formulae

$$\Phi^+(t) = \frac{1}{2} f(t) + \frac{1}{2\pi i} \prod_{\nu=1}^{p} (t-c_\nu)^{\gamma_\nu} \int_L \frac{f(\tau)\, d\tau}{\prod_{\nu=1}^{p} (\tau-c_\nu)^{\gamma_\nu} (\tau-t)} + $$

$$+ P(t) \prod_{\nu=1}^{p} (t-c_\nu)^{\gamma_\nu}, \quad (147)$$

$$\Phi^-(t) = \frac{1}{2} f(t) - \frac{1}{2\pi i} \prod_{\nu=1}^{p} (t-c_\nu)^{\gamma_\nu} \int_L \frac{f(\tau)\, d\tau}{\prod_{\nu=1}^{p} (\tau-c_\nu)^{\gamma_\nu} (\tau-t)} + $$

$$+ P(t) \prod_{\nu=1}^{p} (t-c_\nu)^{\gamma_\nu} \quad (147)$$

where we took these branches of the functions $(t-c_\nu)^{\gamma_\nu}$ which correspond to the positive sides of the arcs, and equalities (143) are also taken into account. Let

$$\Psi(t) = \Phi^+(t) - \Phi^-(t) \quad (148)$$

and consider the function

$$\Psi(z) = \frac{1}{2\pi i} \int_L \frac{\psi(\tau)\, d\tau}{\tau - z} \quad (149)$$

sectionally holomorphic in the regions $S_{\text{ext}}, S_1, S_2, \ldots$ and equal to zero at infinity. The function $\Psi(t)$, according to Theorem 5, belongs to the class $\tilde{\mathfrak{H}}(c_{k_1}, \ldots, c_{k_q})$, where $\rho = \alpha$ for $\alpha > 1/2$ and $\rho = 1/2$ for $\alpha < 1/2$, and moreover, μ is sufficiently small such that $1/2+\mu < 1$.

Next, we have

$$\Psi^+(t) - \Psi^-(t) = \psi(t) \qquad (t \neq c_\nu)$$

thus

$$[\Phi(t) - \Psi(t)]^+ = [\Phi(t) - \Psi(t)]^-$$

for $t \neq c_\nu$, and hence we conclude that $\Psi(z) = \Phi(z)$ in the regions $S_{ext}, S_1, S_2, \ldots$ Further, we have

$$\Psi^+(t)+\Psi^-(t) = \frac{1}{\pi i}\int_L \frac{\psi(\tau)\,d\tau}{\tau - t} = \Phi^+(t)+\Phi^-(t) = f(t).$$

Thus, the function

$$\psi(t) = \Phi^+(t)-\Phi^-(t)$$
$$= \frac{1}{\pi i}\prod_{\nu=1}^{p}(t-c_\nu)^{\gamma_\nu}\int_L \frac{f(\tau)\,d\tau}{\prod_{\nu=1}^{p}(\tau-c_\nu)^{\gamma_\nu}(\tau-t)} + 2P(t)\prod_{\nu=1}^{p}(t-c_\nu)^{\gamma_\nu} \quad (150)$$

in the case $\kappa \geqq 0$, is a solution of the integral equation (138), belonging to the class $\tilde{\mathfrak{H}}_\rho^\mu(c_{k_1}, \ldots, c_{k_q})$. $P(t)$ is an arbitrary polynomial of degree at most $\kappa - 1$ for $\kappa > 0$ or $P = 0$ for $\kappa = 0$. In the case $\kappa < 0$, formula (150) with the substitution $P = 0$ is the only solution, provided a necessary and sufficient condition is satisfied, i.e. that equalities (146) hold. The foregoing argument indicates that formula (150) gives all solutions of equation (138) for $t \neq c_\nu$ in the class $\tilde{\mathfrak{H}}(c_{k_1}, \ldots, c_{k_q})$.

We also note that if none of the chosen points $c_{k_1}, \ldots, c_{k_q}$ is singular ($\gamma_\nu = 1/2$), then solution (150) of the integral equation (138) belongs to the class $\mathfrak{H}_\rho^\mu(c_{k_1}, \ldots, c_{k_q})$, i.e. it is bounded in the neighbourhood of the points $c_{k_1}, \ldots, c_{k_q}$. Formula (150) is compatible with that given by MUSKHELISHVILI in the more general case.

If the given function $f(\tau)$ belongs to the class $\mathfrak{H}_0^\mu$ then formula (150) represents all solutions of the integral equation (138) in the class $\mathfrak{H}$ with arbitrarily chosen points $c_{k_1}, \ldots, c_{k_q}$.

We close this section with the particular case when the set L is a closed Jordan curve consisting of the arcs l_j directed in accordance with the positive direction of rotation along the curve L. Thus, the curve L may possess angular points or salient points $c_1, \ldots, c_p$, ordered in accordance with the positive direction on L. Suppose we are given a function $f(t)$ of the class $\mathfrak{H}_\alpha^\mu(c_{k_1}, \ldots, c_{k_q})$. In this case, all the points of discontinuity c_ν are singular and we obtain that $\gamma_\nu = 0$, and consequently $\kappa = 0$. Substituting, $P = 0$ in formula (150), we obtain the only solution of equation (138) in the set $\tilde{\mathfrak{H}}(c_{k_1}, \ldots, c_{k_q})$ in the form

$$\varphi(t) = \frac{1}{\pi i} \int_L \frac{f(\tau)\, d\tau}{\tau - t}. \tag{151}$$

According to Theorem 2 (principal), this function belongs to the class $\tilde{\mathfrak{H}}^\mu_\alpha(c_{k_1}, \ldots, c_{k_q})$ for $\alpha > 0$.

§ 4. Linear and singular integral equations for a system of arcs

We shall consider linear singular integral equations for the previously introduced system of arcs in the following form, where the separated part has been singled out:

$$\mathbf{K}\varphi \equiv A(t)\varphi(t) + \frac{B(t)}{\pi i} \int_L \frac{\varphi(\tau)\, d\tau}{\tau - t} + \int_L k(t, \tau)\varphi(\tau)\, d\tau = f(t). \tag{152}$$

The following assumptions are adopted:

(i) The functions $A(t)$ and $B(t)$, defined on the set L, satisfy the ordinary Hölder condition for the exponent μ inside each arc l_j separately, and may possess points of discontinuity of the first kind $c_1, c_2, \ldots, c_p$. These functions also satisfy, at each point of the set L, the condition $A^2(t) - B^2(t) \neq 0$,

(ii) The function $k(t, \tau)$, defined and bounded in the domain $[t \in L, \tau \in L]$, satisfies Hölder's condition with respect to both variables, separately on each arc, i.e. we have

$$|k(t, \tau) - k(t', \tau')| < \text{const}\,[|t - t'|^\mu + |\tau - \tau'|^\mu] \tag{152'}$$

where $t, t' \in l_\nu$, $\tau, \tau' \in l_{\nu_1}$,

(iii) The given function $f(t)$ belongs to the class $\mathfrak{H}^\mu_\alpha(c_{k_1}, \ldots, c_{k_q})$.

The equation

$$\mathbf{K}^\circ\varphi \equiv A(t)\varphi(t) + \frac{B(t)}{\pi i} \int_L \frac{\varphi(\tau)\, d\tau}{\tau - t} = f(t) \tag{153}$$

is called the *dominant equation* with respect to equation (152).

This equation can be solved effectively, as in the preceding section, on the basis of the solution of the Hilbert problem for a system of arcs. Let us suppose that the solution $\varphi(t)$ of equation (153) exists in the class $\tilde{\mathfrak{H}}(c_{k_1}, \ldots, c_{k_q})$, and introduce an auxiliary function

$$\Phi(z) = \frac{1}{2\pi i} \int_L \frac{\varphi(\tau)\, d\tau}{\tau - z}, \tag{154}$$

sectionally holomorphic in the regions $S_{\text{ext}}, S_1, S_2, \ldots$ The boundary values of function (154) exist and satisfy the equalities

$$\begin{aligned} \Phi^+(t) - \Phi^-(t) &= \varphi(t), \\ \Phi^+(t) + \Phi^-(t) &= \frac{1}{\pi i} \int_L \frac{\varphi(\tau)\, d\tau}{\tau - t} \end{aligned} \tag{155}$$

at each point $t \neq c_\nu$ of the set L. Function (154) is thus the solution of the Hilbert problem with boundary condition

$$\Phi^+(t) = \frac{A(t) - B(t)}{A(t) + B(t)} \Phi^-(t) + \frac{f(t)}{A(t) + B(t)}. \tag{156}$$

This solution is equal to zero at infinity, is almost bounded in the neighbourhood of the points $c_{k_1}, \ldots, c_{k_q}$, and satisfies the inequality with weak non-boundedness in the neighbourhood of each other point c_ν. According to what has been said in Section 2, all solutions of the class $\tilde{h}(c_{k_1}, \ldots, c_{k_q})$ of the Hilbert problem (156) which are equal to zero at infinity, are determined by the formula

$$\Phi(z) = \frac{X(z)}{2\pi i} \int_L \frac{f(\tau)\, d\tau}{[A(\tau) + B(\tau)]\, X^+(t)(\tau - t)} + X(z) P(z), \tag{157}$$

where $X(z)$ is the fundamental solution of the class $h(c_{k_1}, \ldots, c_{k_q})$ satisfying the homogeneous boundary condition

$$X^+(t) = \frac{A(t) - B(t)}{A(t) + B(t)} X^-(t) \tag{157'}$$

determined by formula (114), where $G(t)$ is replaced by the ratio $(A-B)/(A+B)$. The function $P(z)$ is an arbitrary polynomial of degree at most $\kappa-1$ for $\kappa > 0$, or $P = 0$ for $\kappa = 0$. In the case $\kappa < 0$ there exists only one solution in the class $\tilde{h}(c_{k_1}, \ldots, c_{k_q})$ equal to zero at infinity, determined by formula (157) where $P = 0$ has been substituted, provided that the following necessary and sufficient condition for the function $f(\tau)$ is satisfied:

$$\int_L \frac{\tau^\beta f(\tau)\,d\tau}{[A(\tau)+B(\tau)]\,X^+(\tau)} = 0 \quad (\beta = 0, 1, 2, \ldots, -\kappa-1). \quad (158)$$

Using formula (157) and the same argument as in the preceding section, we find that all solutions of the dominant equation (153) in the class $\tilde{\mathfrak{H}}(c_{k_1}, \ldots, c_{k_q})$ are determined by the formula

$$\varphi(t) = \frac{X^+(t)-X^-(t)}{2\pi i}\int_L \frac{f(\tau)\,d\tau}{[A(\tau)+B(\tau)]\,X^+(\tau)(\tau-t)} + \\ + \frac{f(t)}{A(t)+B(t)} + [X^+(t)-X^-(t)]\,P(t) \quad (159)$$

where $P(t)$ depends on κ in the above manner. In particular, for $\kappa < 0$, there exists only one solution determined by formula (159) for $P = 0$, provided that equalities (158) hold. The solutions (159), obtained above, belong to the class $\mathfrak{H}^\mu_\rho(c_{k_1}, \ldots, c_{k_q})$, where ρ is determined by formulae (135) when μ is sufficiently small.

When none of the chosen points $c_{k_1}, \ldots, c_{k_q}$ is singular, then the solution (159) of the dominant equation belongs to the class $\mathfrak{H}^\mu_\rho(c_{k_1}, \ldots, c_{k_q})$, i.e. it is bounded in the neighbourhood of the points $c_{k_1}, \ldots, c_{k_q}$ as is the given function $f(t)$.

If the given function $f(\tau)$ belongs to the class $\mathfrak{H}^\mu_0$, then formula (159) represents all solutions of the integral equation (153) in the class $\mathfrak{H}$ with arbitrarily chosen points $c_{k_1}, \ldots, c_{k_q}$.

When the integral equation (153) is homogeneous ($f = 0$), then in the case $\kappa > 0$ all its solutions in an arbitrary class $\mathfrak{H}(c_{k_1}, \ldots, c_{k_q})$ are determined by the formula

$$\varphi(t) = [X^+(t)-X^-(t)]\,P(t), \quad (160)$$

where $P(t)$ is a polynomial of degree at most $\kappa-1$; on the other hand, if $\kappa \leqq 0$, then the equation has the zero solution only, $\varphi = 0$.

We conclude, in the same way, that to the class $h'(c_{k_{q+1}}, \ldots, c_{k_m})$ of solutions of the Hilbert problem associated with the problem (157′), for the index $\kappa' = \kappa$, there corresponds the class of solutions $\tilde{\mathfrak{H}}(c_{k_{q+1}}, \ldots, c_{k_m})$ of the equation $\mathbf{K}^\circ\psi = 0$, associated with equation (153).

Using the obtained solution (159) of the dominant equation, we now determine the solution of the given equation (152). We can assert that when equation (152) has the solution $\varphi(t)$ in the class $\tilde{\mathfrak{H}}(c_{k_1}, \ldots, c_{k_q})$, then this function satisfies the equation

$$\varphi(t) = \frac{X^+(t) - X^-(t)}{2\pi i} \int_L \frac{[f(\tau) - \int_L k(\tau, \xi)\varphi(\xi)\,d\xi]\,d\tau}{[A(\tau)+B(\tau)]X^+(\tau)(\tau - t)} + \frac{1}{A(t)+B(t)}[f(t) - \int_L k(t,\tau)\varphi(\tau)\,d\tau] + [X^+(t) - X^-(t)]P(t), \quad (161)$$

and consequently the integral equation

$$\varphi(t) = \int_L N(t,\tau)\varphi(\tau)\,d\tau + \frac{X^+(t) - X^-(t)}{2\pi i} \int_L \frac{f(\tau)\,d\tau}{[A(\tau)+B(\tau)]X^+(\tau)(\tau - t)} + \frac{f(t)}{A(t)+B(t)} + [X^+(t) - X^-(t)]P(t), \quad (162)$$

where

$$N(t,\tau) = -\frac{k(t,\tau)}{A(t)+B(t)} - \frac{X^+(t) - X^-(t)}{2\pi i} \int_L \frac{k(\theta,\tau)\,d\theta}{[A(\theta)+B(\theta)]X^+(\theta)(\theta - \tau)}. \quad (163)$$

We have assumed that the index of the fundamental solution $X(z)$ of the class $h(c_{k_1}, \ldots, c_{k_q})$ is non-negative, while $P(t)$ is a certain polynomial of degree at most $\kappa-1$ when $\kappa > 0$, or $P = 0$ for $\kappa = 0$. In the case when $\kappa < 0$, equation (162), with the substitution $P = 0$, is satisfied if, and only if, the functions f and φ satisfy the equalities

$$\int_L \frac{t^\nu [f(t) - \int_L k(t,\tau)\varphi(\tau)\,d\tau]\,dt}{[A(t)+B(t)]\,X^+(t)} = 0 \tag{164}$$

$(\nu = 0, 1, \ldots, -\kappa-1)$.

Let us examine the integral equation (162) regarding $P(t)$ as the given polynomial of degree $\kappa-1$ for $\kappa > 0$, or setting $P = 0$ for $\kappa = 0$. The kernel (163) of equation (162) is bounded for $t-\tau \to 0$, and bounded in the neighbourhood of the chosen end-points $c_{k_1}, \ldots, c_{k_q}$, on account of Theorem 5 (p. 636), while it may not be bounded, with a weak singularity at the other ends. For, according to formula (123), we have

$$|N(t,\tau)| < \frac{\text{const}}{\prod\limits_{\nu=1}^{p} (t-c_\nu)^{\delta\theta_\nu}} \tag{165}$$

where $\delta = \max\limits_{\nu \neq k_j} |\alpha_\nu^* + \lambda_\nu|$, $\theta_\nu = 0$ for $\nu = k_1, \ldots, k_q$, and $\theta = 1$ for $\nu \neq k_1, \ldots, k_q$. Next, according to Theorem 5, the kernel N satisfies the generalized Hölder condition in the form

$$|N(t,\tau) - N(t_1,\tau_1)| < \frac{\text{const}\,[|t-t_1|^\mu + |\tau-\tau_1|^{\mu'}]}{|t-c_\nu|^{\delta\theta_\nu+\mu}\,|t_1-c_{\nu_1}|^{\delta\theta_{\nu_1}+\mu}} \tag{166}$$

where $\mu' < \mu$, $\delta+\mu < 1$. The kernel $N(t,\tau)$ thus belongs to the class $\mathfrak{H}_\delta^\mu(c_{k_1}, \ldots, c_{k_q})$ with respect to the variable t.

Equation (162) can be reduced to the Fredholm equation with a bounded kernel, by the substitution

$$\varphi(t) = \frac{\psi(t)}{T(t)}, \quad \text{where} \quad T(t) = \prod_{\nu \neq k_j} |t-c_\nu|^{\alpha_\nu^*+\lambda_\nu}. \tag{167}$$

Integral equation (162) then takes the form

$$\psi(t) = \int_L N(t, \tau) \frac{T(t)}{T(\tau)} \psi(\tau)\, d\tau + \tilde{f}(t)\, T(t), \tag{168}$$

where $\tilde{f}(t)$ denotes the known function, which is the sum of all three components following after the integral term in equation (162). Introducing a new variable ρ (or r) dependent on the variable τ (or t) by the formulae

$$\begin{aligned} \rho &= \sum_{j=1}^{\nu-1} \int_{l_j} \frac{d\tau}{T(\tau)} + \int_{c_\mu}^{\tau} \frac{d\tau}{T(\tau)}, \qquad \tau \in l_\nu = \frown c_\mu c_{\mu'} \\ r &= \sum_{j=1}^{\nu-1} \int_{l_j} \frac{d\tau}{T(\tau)} + \int_{c_\mu}^{t} \frac{d\tau}{T(\tau)}, \qquad t \in l_\nu = \frown c_\mu c_{\mu'} \end{aligned} \tag{169}$$

($\nu = 1, \ldots, m$), the integral equation (168) takes the form

$$\tilde{\psi}(\tau) = \int_L N(t, \tau)\, T(t)\, \tilde{\psi}(\rho)\, d\rho + f(t)\, T(t) \tag{170}$$

where $N(t, \tau)\, T(t)$ is the bounded kernel satisfying the Hölder condition.

If the First Fredholm Theorem is applied to equation (170) and $\kappa \geqq 0$, we obtain the definite solution $\tilde{\psi}(r)$, and consequently the solution $\varphi(t)$ of equation (162), for an arbitrary choice of coefficients of the polynomial $P(t)$ of degree $\kappa - 1$, or $P = 0$ for $\kappa = 0$. It is apparent that this solution, on account of the theorems cited many times, belongs to the class $\tilde{\mathfrak{H}}^{\mu}_{\zeta}(c_{k_1}, \ldots, c_{k_q})$ where $\zeta = \alpha$ for $\alpha > \delta$, and $\zeta = \delta$ for $\alpha < \delta$. This function is also the solution of the original equation (152). In the case $\kappa < 0$, one should insert $P = 0$, and, moreover, the solution φ of equation (162) must satisfy the conditions (164). When these conditions are satisfied, the function φ is also the solution in the class $\tilde{\mathfrak{H}}^{\mu}_{\zeta}(c_{k_1}, \ldots, c_{k_q})$ of the given equation (152).

If the homogeneous equation, corresponding to equation (170), has a non-zero solution, then on account of the third Fredholm theorem, the existence of the solution requires that the given function $\tilde{f}(t)\,T(t)$ satisfies the known necessary and sufficient conditions of orthogonality.

If the given function $f(t)$ in the integral equation (152) belongs to the class $\mathfrak{H}_0^{\mu}$, then the above argument can be applied for an abitrary choice of the chosen points $c_{k_1}, \ldots, c_{k_q}$ which affect the form of the fundamental function $X(z)$, and thus we obtain all solutions of the integral equation (152) in the class $\mathfrak{H}$.

Below, we give without proof, two theorems which are analogous to those on pp. 513 and 515 for singular integral equations for contours.

THEOREM 1. *The singular equation* $\mathbf{K}\varphi = f(t)$, *for the system of arcs L, has a solution in the class* $\tilde{\mathfrak{H}}(c_{k_1}, \ldots, c_{k_q})$ *if and only if the given function* $f \in \mathfrak{H}(c_{k_1}, \ldots, c_{k_q})$ *is orthogonal,*

$$\int_L f(t)\,\psi_j(t)\,dt = 0 \quad (j = 1, 2, \ldots, k'),$$

to all linearly independent solutions ψ_j *of the associate class* $\mathfrak{H}'(c_{k_{q+1}}, \ldots, c_{k_m})$ *of the associated homogeneous equation* $\mathbf{K}'\psi = 0$.

THEOREM 2. *If k is the number of linearly independent solutions in the class* $\mathfrak{H}(c_{k_1}, \ldots, c_{k_q})$ *of the homogeneous equation* $\mathbf{K}\varphi = 0$, *and* k' *is the number of linearly independent solutions in the associated class* $\mathfrak{H}'$ *of the associated equation* $\mathbf{K}'\psi = 0$, *then the difference between these numbers is equal to the index* κ *of the given class* $\mathfrak{H}(c_{k_1}, \ldots, c_{k_q})$.

We close this section with some remarks concerning general singular linear integral equation for a system of arcs, written in the form

$$A(t)\,\varphi(t) + \int_L \frac{K(t, \tau)}{\tau - t}\,\varphi(\tau)\,d\tau = f(t). \tag{171}$$

We adopt the same assumptions for the functions $A(t)$ and $f(t)$ as for equation (152) while the function $K(t, \tau)$ will satisfy Hölder's condition

$$|K(t, \tau) - K(t', \tau')| < \text{const}\,[|t - t'|^{\mu} + |\tau - \tau'|^{\mu}] \tag{172}$$

where $t, t' \in l_\nu$, $\tau, \tau' \in l_{\nu_1}$, and thus, the function K is bounded but may possess discontinuities of the first kind at the points $c_1, c_2, \ldots, c_p$ similarly as the function $A(t)$.

Equation (171) can be written in the equivalent form

$$A(t)\varphi(t) + K(t, t)\int_L \frac{\varphi(\tau)\,d\tau}{\tau - t} + \int_L k(t, \tau)\varphi(\tau)\,d\tau = f(t) \tag{173}$$

where

$$k(t, \tau) = \frac{K(t, \tau) - K(t, t)}{\tau - t} \tag{174}$$

however, by the assumptions (172), function (174), as a rule, will not satisfy the restrictive conditions (152′) which were adopted for the analogous function in equation (152). Function (174) may even be unbounded as $(\tau - t)^{-1}$ when the points t and τ lie on two different arcs commencing from the point c_ν.

Thus, in the general case, equation (171) cannot be reduced to the Fredholm equation, as was done for equation (152), and consequently, we cannot solve generally the linear singular equation (171) for an arbitrary system of arcs, as was done in Chapter XVII for contours.

In this case the Schauder topological method is very useful. By means of this method one can obtain the solution of equation (171) for any system of arcs, by the assumption (172), and also by the assumptions limiting the magnitude of the absolute value of the function K and its Hölder coefficient. Here, we omit these investigations since they are a special case of those for a non-linear integral equation and will be discussed in the next section.

§ 5. Non-linear singular integral equation for a system of arcs, investigated by the topological method

We now consider a non-linear singular integral equation for the previously introduced system of arcs in the form

$$\varphi(t) = \int_L \frac{K[t, \tau, \varphi(\tau)]}{\tau - t}\,d\tau \tag{175}$$

such as in Chapter XIX. The investigation of this equation presents new difficulties, in view of the possibility, that the unknown function may be unbounded in the neighbourhood of the end-points $c_1, \ldots, c_p$.

This equation was investigated by A. I. GUSEINOV [18] for the case when the line of integration was an interval on the real axis. The author considered equation (175) in a more general case when L is a system of disconnected arcs (see POGORZELSKI [63]). Now, we consider the theory of equation (175) for an arbitrary system of arcs L, generalizing the assumptions and eliminating some deffects of the paper cited above.

We assume that the given complex function $K(t, \tau, u)$ is defined in the domain

$$t \in L', \quad \tau \in L', \quad u \in \Pi \tag{176}$$

(where Π denotes the complex plane, and $L' = L - \sum_1^p c_\nu$), and satisfies the inequality

$$|K(t, \tau, u)| < m_K |u| + \frac{m'_K}{\prod_{j=1}^{p} (\tau - c_j)^\alpha} \tag{177}$$

as well as the generalized Hölder–Lipschitz condition

$$|K(t, \tau, u) - K(t_1, \tau_1, u_1)| < k_K |u - u_1| + k'_K \frac{|t - t_1|^{\mu_1} + |\tau - \tau_1|^\mu}{[|\tau - c_\nu|\, |\tau_1 - c_{\nu_1}|]^{\alpha+\mu}}. \tag{178}$$

Here m_K, m'_K, k_K, k'_K are given positive constants, and the positive exponents α, μ, μ_1 satisfy the inequalities

$$\alpha + \mu < 1, \quad 0 < \mu < \mu_1 \leqq 1; \tag{179}$$

and moreover, $\tau \in \frown c_\nu c_{\nu_1}$, $\tau_1 \in \frown \tau c_{\nu_1}$, $t, t_1 \in l_\gamma$ $(\gamma = 1, \ldots, m)$.

We prove the existence of the solution of equation (175) by the Schauder topological method, using previously proved properties of the functions of the class $\mathfrak{H}$ for a system of arcs. This proof is a particularly fine achievement of the Schauder topological method, but it requires more sensitive investigation than for the contours in Chapter XIX, in view of the unboundedness of the functions appearing in the open domain (176). The possibility of the application of the Schauder theorems to equation (175) is mainly due to the behaviour of the class $\mathfrak{H}_\alpha^\mu$ in the Cauchy transformation, proved in Section 1 of this chapter. Thus, consider a function space Λ consisting of complex functions φ, defined and continuous in the open set L', and satisfying the inequalities *

$$\sup_{t\in L'}\Big[\prod_{j=1}^{p} |t-c_j|^{\alpha+\mu}\,|\varphi(t)|\Big] < \infty \tag{180}$$

where the constants α and μ are those appearing in the assumed properties (177) and (178). The definitions of the sum of two points φ_1 and φ_2, and the product of the point $\varphi(t)$ by a real number are obvious.

The norm of the point φ is defined as the upper bound of the product

$$\|\varphi\| = \sup_{t\in\alpha'}\Big[\prod_{j=1}^{p} |t-c_j|^{\alpha+\mu}\,|\varphi(t)|\Big] \tag{181}$$

which exists by assumption (180). The distance between two points φ_1 and φ_2 is defined by the formula

$$\delta(\varphi_1, \varphi_2) = \|\varphi_1 - \varphi_2\|\,. \tag{182}$$

The space Λ is obviously linear, metric and normed. We next show that it is complete, i.e. that in Λ the Cauchy condition is both necessary and sufficient for the convergence (in the sense of the norm) of a sequence of points.

In fact, suppose that a sequence of points $\{\varphi_n\}$ of the space Λ satisfies the Cauchy condition:

$$\|\varphi_{n+n'} - \varphi_n\| < \varepsilon \tag{183}$$

for $n > N(\varepsilon)$, where n' is an arbitrary positive integer. We consider the sequence of functions

$$\Phi_n(t) = \prod_{j=1}^{p} |t-c_j|^{\alpha+\mu}\,\varphi_n(t)$$

---

* The reason why in the definitions (180) and (181) the exponent $\alpha+\mu$ instead of α has been introduced will be explained below.

which, by assumption (180), are continuous and bounded in the set L'. In view of the assumed inequality (183), we have

$$\sup_{t \in L'} |\Phi_{n+n'}(t) - \Phi_n(t)| < \varepsilon \quad \text{for} \quad n > N(\varepsilon)$$

and consequently, the sequence of functions $\{\Phi_n(t)\}$ is uniformly convergent (in the usual meaning) to a certain function $\Phi(t)$ continuous and bounded in the open set L'. Thus, the point $\varphi \in \Lambda$ defined by

$$\varphi(t) = \prod_{j=1}^{p} |t - c_j|^{-\alpha-\mu} \Phi(t)$$

is the limit point of the sequence $\{\varphi_n\}$ in the sense of the norm (181), and condition (183) is sufficient. Thus, the space Λ defined above is a Banach space.

We now consider in the space Λ the set $\mathscr{E}$ of all points φ for which

$$\begin{gathered} \prod_{\zeta=1}^{p} |t - c_j|^{\alpha} |\varphi(t)| \leqq \rho, \\ [|t - c_\nu| \, |t_1 - c_{\nu_1}|]^{\alpha+\mu} |\varphi(t) - \varphi(t_1)| \leqq \kappa |t - t_1|^{\mu} \end{gathered} \tag{184}$$

where t, t_1 is an arbitrary pair of points lying on the same arbitrary arc $\frown c_\nu c_{\nu_1}$, and moreover $t_1 \in \frown t c_{\nu_1}$. The positive numbers ρ and κ are fixed arbitrarily. According to the definition on p. 610 the functions φ of the set $\mathscr{E}$ belong to the class $\mathfrak{H}_\alpha^\mu$.

The set $\mathscr{E}$ is *closed*, since the limit point of the sequence of points satisfying inequalities (184) also satisfies these inequalities. In fact, it is sufficient to note that if the sequence of points $\{\varphi_n\}$ is convergent in norm (181) to the point φ, then the sequence of functions $\varphi_n(t)$ in each closed part of the set L tends uniformly to the function $\varphi(t)$.

The set $\mathscr{E}$ is *convex*, since if two points φ_1 and φ_2 satisfy inequality (184), then each point $\gamma\varphi_1 + (1-\gamma)\varphi_2$ of the segment connecting these points also satisfies inequality (184) $(0 \leqq \gamma \leqq 1)$.

In view of the form of the integral equation (175), the set $\mathscr{E}$ will be transformed according to the relation

$$\psi(t) = \int_L \frac{K[t, \tau, \varphi(\tau)]}{\tau - t} \, d\tau \tag{185}$$

which, as will be shown, assignes to each point φ of the set $\mathscr{E}$ a certain point ψ of the space Λ. Let us find a necessary condition that each transformed point ψ also belongs to the set $\mathscr{E}$. We note that on the basis of the assumption (177) and the first of inequalities (184), we obtain, for each point φ of the set $\mathscr{E}$ the inequality

$$|K[t,\tau,\varphi(\tau)]| < m_K|\varphi(\tau)| + \frac{m'_K}{\prod_{j=1}^{p}|t-c_j|^\alpha} < \frac{m_K\rho+m'_K}{\prod_{j=1}^{p}|t-c_j|^\alpha}. \tag{186}$$

Next, according to the assumed inequality (178) and the second of inequalities (184) the function $K[t,\tau,\varphi(\tau)]$ satisfies, for the points of the set $\mathscr{E}$, the generalized Hölder condition

$$|K[t,\tau,\varphi(\tau)]-K[t_1,\tau_1,\varphi(\tau_1)]| < \frac{(k_K\kappa+k'_K)[|t-t_1^\mu|+|\tau-\tau_1^\mu|]}{[|\tau-c_\nu|\,|\tau_1-c_{\nu_1}|]^{\alpha+\mu}}. \tag{187}$$

Using Theorem 2 (principal) (p. 613) and Theorem 3 (p. 631) in which we substitute $\rho = t$, we conclude that on account of the property (187) the transformed function (185), continuous in the open set L', satisfies the inequality

$$|\psi(t)| < \frac{C_0(m_K\rho+m'_K)+C'_0(k_M\kappa+k'_K)}{\prod_{j=1}^{p}|t-c_j|^\alpha}, \tag{188}$$

where the positive constants C_0 and C'_0, independent of the functions K, φ appear in Theorems 2 and 3. Thus, the point ψ belongs to the space Λ. On the basis of the same Theorems 2 and 3, the transformed function satisfies Hölder's condition

$$|\psi(t)-\psi(t_1)| < \frac{C_1(m_K\rho+m'_K)+C'_1(k_K\kappa+k'_K)}{[|t-c_\nu|\,|t_1-c_{\nu_1}|]^{\alpha+\mu}}\,|t-t_1|^\mu, \tag{189}$$

where the positive constants C_1, C'_1 can be expressed in a simple way by constants $C, C', \tilde{C}, \tilde{C}'$ appearing in Theorems 2 and 3, and moreover $t \in \frown c_\nu c_{\nu_1}$, $t_1 \in \frown t c_{\nu_1}$. The fundamental fact is that the transformed functions also belong to the class $\mathfrak{H}_\alpha^\mu$ as do the functions φ of the set $\mathscr{E}$. Comparing inequalities (188), (189) with inequalities (184), we conclude that the set $\mathscr{E}'$ of all the transformed points ψ is a subset of set $\mathscr{E}$ provided the constants of the problem satisfy the following inequalities:

$$\begin{aligned} C_0(m_K\rho+m_K')+C_0'(k_K\kappa+k_K') &\leqq \rho, \\ C_1(m_K\rho+m_K')+C_1'(k_K\kappa+k_K') &\leqq \kappa. \end{aligned} \tag{190}$$

For the given ρ and κ satisfying the inequalities

$$\rho > C_0 m_K' + C_0' k_K', \qquad \kappa > C_1 m_K' + C_1' k_K', \tag{191}$$

condition (190) is satisfied provided the positive constants m_K and k_K are sufficiently small. Since, however, the choice of the constants ρ and κ in conditions (184) was arbitrary, we make use of this arbitrariness and determine the sets of all values m_K and k_K for which inequalities (190) are satisfied when ρ and κ take all the values of the above right-hand side expressions (191). First of all, we note that a necessary condition for inequalities (190) to be satisfied is that the inequalities

$$C_0 m_K < 1, \qquad C_1' k_K < 1 \tag{192}$$

hold.

Next, we note that when ρ and κ are regarded as rectangular coordinates in the plane, then the set of all points (ρ, κ) satisfying the first of inequalities (190) is a half-plane lying "below" the straight line with equation

$$\kappa = \frac{1-C_0 m_K}{C_0' k_K}\,\rho - \frac{C_0 m_K' + C_0' k_K'}{C_0' k_K}, \tag{193}$$

while the set of all the points (ρ, κ) satisfying the second of inequalities (190) is a half-plane lying "above" the straight line with equation

$$\kappa = \frac{C_1 m_K}{1-C_1' k_K}\,\rho + \frac{C_1 m_K' + C_1' k_K'}{1-C_1' k_K}. \tag{194}$$

A necessary and sufficient condition for the existence of a set of points (ρ, κ) possessing positive coordinates, and satisfying inequalities (190) simultaneously, is the *strict* inequality

$$\frac{1-C_0\, m_K}{C_0'\, k_K} > \frac{C_1\, m_K}{1-C_1'\, k_K} \tag{195}$$

or the equivalent inequality

$$C_0\, m_K + C_1'\, k_K + (C_0'\, C_1 - C_0\, C_1')\, m_K\, k_K < 1\,. \tag{196}$$

Finally, when an appropriate pair of numbers ρ and κ is chosen, then inequalities (190) will be satisfied for all pairs of positive, sufficiently small numbers (m_K, k_K) satisfying inequalities (192), (196) and only for such pairs. The set of all points (ρ, κ) corresponding to any pair (m_K, k_K) satisfying inequalities (192) and (196) forms a quadrant of the plane bounded by straight lines (193) and (194), or a part of this quadrant in which inequalities (191) are satisfied.

Before applying Schauder's Theorem we prove following two lemmas.

LEMMA 1. *The transformation of the set $\mathscr{E}$ by formula* (185) *is continuous in the space Λ.*

Proof. Consider an arbitrary sequence $\{\varphi_n\}$ of points of the set $\mathscr{E}$ convergent in norm (181) to the point φ, i.e. such that

$$\lim_{n\to\infty} \|\varphi_n - \varphi\|$$

$$= \lim_{n\to\infty} \sup_{t \in L'} \Big[\prod_{j=1}^{p} |t-c_j|^{\alpha+\mu}\, |\varphi_n(t) - \varphi(t)|\Big] = 0\,. \tag{192}$$

According to the definition of the continuity of a transformation, it is necessary and sufficient to prove that the sequence $\{\psi_n\}$ of points transformed by using formula (185) is convergent to the point ψ which corresponds to the limit point φ, also according to formula (185). Let us now examine the difference

$$\psi_n(t) - \psi(t) = \int_L \frac{K[t, \tau, \varphi_n(\tau)]\, d\tau}{\tau - t} - \int_L \frac{K[t, \tau, \varphi(\tau)]\, d\tau}{\tau - t} \tag{193}$$

as $n \to \infty$. We consider the arc $l = \frown l'l''$ which is a part of the arc $\frown c_\nu c_{\nu_1}$ with a point t lying on it. One of the end-points l' or l'' may coincide with the end-point c_ν or c_{ν_1}. Without loss of generality we assume that: (i) the point t divides the arc l into two parts of equal length, provided this arc, together with the end-points l' and l'' lies inside the arc $\frown c_\nu c_{\nu_1}$, (ii) the point t lies inside the arc l such that the length of the arc $\frown l't$ is at most equal to the length of the arc $\frown tl''$ when the end-point l' coincides with the end-point c_ν, (iii) the length of the arc $\frown l't$ is at least equal to the length of the arc $\frown tl''$ when the l'' coincides with c_{ν_1}.

We now decompose each of integrals (193) into two integrals

$$\begin{aligned} \psi_n(t) &= \psi_n^l(t)+\psi_n^{L-l}(t), \\ \psi(t) &= \psi^l(t)+\psi^{L-l}(t) \end{aligned} \tag{194}$$

taken over the arc l and the remaining part $L-l$. Now, we write

$$\begin{aligned} \psi_n^l &= \int\limits_l \frac{K[t,\tau,\varphi_n(\tau)]-K[t,t,\varphi(t)]}{\tau-t}\,d\tau + \\ &\qquad + K[t,t,\varphi_n(t)]\int\limits_l \frac{d\tau}{\tau-t}, \\ \psi^l(t) &= \int\limits_l \frac{K[t,\tau,\varphi(\tau)]-K[t,t,\varphi(t)]}{\tau-t}\,d\tau + \\ &\qquad + K[t,t,\varphi(t)]\int\limits_l \frac{d\tau}{\tau-t}. \end{aligned} \tag{195}$$

The first integral $I_n(t)$ of the first sum refers to the function having a weak singularity and, according to the estimate (187) it satisfies the inequality

$$\begin{aligned} |I_n(t)| &< \int\limits_{l't} \frac{k_K(\kappa+1)\,|\tau-t|^{\mu-1}\,dl_\tau}{[|\tau-c_\nu|\,|t-c_{\nu_1}|]^{\alpha+\mu}} + \\ &\qquad + \int\limits_{tl''} \frac{k_K(\kappa+1)\,|\tau-t|^{\mu-1}\,dl_\tau}{[|t-c_\nu|\,|\tau-c_{\nu_1}|]^{\alpha+\mu}}. \end{aligned} \tag{196}$$

Hence it follows that for each $\varepsilon > 0$ there exists a sufficiently small positive number η_ε, such that for each arc $l \subset L$, the length of which is not greater than η_ε, the inequality

$$\sup_{t\in L'} \{ \prod_{j=1}^{p} |t-c_j|^{\alpha+\mu} |I_n(t)| \} \leqq \frac{\varepsilon}{5} \tag{197}$$

holds for any $t \in L'$ and any n; consequently, the same is true for the limit function $\varphi(t)$.

The second of the integrals in the first of formulae (195), according to the estimate (186), satisfies the inequality

$$\left| K[t, t, \varphi_n(t)] \int_l \frac{d\tau}{\tau - t} \right| < \frac{m_K \rho + m_K'}{\prod_{j=1}^{p} |t-c_j|^\alpha} \left| \log \frac{t-l''}{l'-t} \right|. \tag{198}$$

Hence it follows, in view of the assumed position of the point t on arc $l = \frown l'l''$, that for each $\varepsilon > 0$ there exists a sufficiently small positive number η_ε' such that for each arc $l \subset L$, the length of which is not greater than η_ε, we have for every n

$$\sup_{t\in L'} \left\{ \prod_{j=1}^{p} |t-c_j|^{\alpha+\mu} K[t, t, \varphi_n(t)] \int_l \frac{d\tau}{\tau - t} \right\} \leqq \frac{\varepsilon}{5} \tag{199}$$

and consequently, for the limit function $\varphi(t)$. The integrals (195) taken over the exterior part $L - l$ are regular, and by the assumption (178) satisfy the inequality

$$|\psi_n^{L-l}(t) - \psi^{L-l}(t)| < \int_{L-l} \frac{k_K |\varphi_n(\tau) - \varphi(\tau)| \, dl_\tau}{|\tau - t|}. \tag{200}$$

According to the assumed position of the point t inside the arc l, the distance $|\tau - t|$ has a positive lower bound for $t \in L - l$. Consequently, when the length l of the arc, equal to the smaller of numbers η_ε and η_ε', is fixed, we can choose, by the assumption (192), for the number $\varepsilon > 0$, an index N_ε such that

$$\sup_{t\in L'} \{ \prod_{j=1}^{p} |t-c_j|^{\alpha+\mu} |\psi_n^{L-l}(t) - \psi^{L-l}(t)| \} \leqq \frac{\varepsilon}{5} \tag{201}$$

for $n \geqq N_\varepsilon$. Combining the results (197), (199), (201) we conclude that

$$\|\psi_n - \psi\| \leqq \varepsilon \quad \text{for} \quad n \geqq N_\varepsilon$$

which proves the proposition of Lemma 1.

LEMMA 2. *The set $\mathscr{E}'$ transformed from the set $\mathscr{E}$ by relation* (185) *is relatively compact.*

Proof. By the definition the set $\mathscr{E}$ is relatively compact if from any sequence $\{\psi_n\}$ of its points one can choose a subsequence $\{\psi_{k_n}\}$ convergent in the norm (181). Thus, we consider on each arc $l_\gamma = \frown c_\nu c_{\nu_1}$ two disconnected arcs $\frown c_\nu t_\gamma$ and $\frown t'_\gamma c_\nu$ of length sufficiently small such that the inequality

$$\sup_{t \in L_0} \{ \prod_{j=1}^{p} |t - c_j|^{\alpha+\mu} |\psi_n(t)| \} < \frac{\varepsilon}{2} \tag{202}$$

holds for all terms of the arbitrarily chosen sequence $\{\psi_n\}$ of points of the set $\mathscr{E}'$. L_0 denotes the set of points of all the arcs $\frown c_\nu t_\gamma$ and $\frown t'_\gamma c_\nu$. It is emphasized that this inequality holds because of inequality (188) which is satisfied for all points of the set $\mathscr{E}'$.

We now observe that the functions ψ_n are bounded on the set of arcs $\frown t_\gamma t'_\gamma$, and according to inequality (189), satisfy the Hölder inequality

$$|\psi_n(t) - \psi_n(t_1)| < k_\psi |t - t_1|^\mu$$

for the same fixed coefficient k_ψ. Thus, the functions of the sequence $\{\psi_n\}$ are equicontinuous and uniformly bounded on the set of arcs $\frown t_\gamma t'_\gamma$. Hence by Arzèla's Theorem, we conclude that one can select a subsequence $\{\psi_{k_n}\}$, uniformly convergent (in the usual sense) in the set of arcs $\frown t_\gamma t'_\gamma$. From the above, it follows that for each $\varepsilon > 0$ there exists N_ε such that the inequality

$$\sup_{t \in L - L_0} \{ \prod_{j=1}^{p} |t - c_j|^{\alpha+\mu} |\psi_{k_n}(t) - \psi_{k_m}(t)| \} < \varepsilon \tag{203}$$

holds for $n > N_\varepsilon, m > N_\varepsilon$. Since inequality (202) is satisfied by all terms of the sequence $\{\psi_n\}$, we conclude that the sequence of points ψ_{k_n} satisfies the Cauchy criterion for convergence,

$$\sup_{t \in L'} \{ \prod_{j=1}^{p} |t-c_j|^{\alpha+\mu} |\psi_{k_n}(t)-\psi_{k_m}(t)| \}$$
$$= \|\psi_{k_n}-\psi_{k_m}\| < \varepsilon \quad \text{for} \quad n, m > N_\varepsilon, \tag{204}$$

in accordance with the definition of the norm (181). Now, taking into account that the space Λ is complete, which implies that the Cauchy criterion is sufficient for the convergence of the sequence of points, and we finally conclude that the selected subsequence $\{\psi_{k_n}\}$ is convergent in the space Λ and consequently the transformed set $\mathscr{E}'$ is relatively compact. This completes the proof of the theorem.

From Lemmas 1 and 2 it can now be understood why the exponent $\alpha+\mu$ has been adopted in the definitions (180) and (181) while the exponent α in the first of inequalities (184).

The following conclusion can be drawn from the proved properties and Schauder's Theorem: in the set $\mathscr{E}$ there exists at least one point $\varphi^*(t)$ fixed with respect to the transformation (185), provided inequalities (192) and (196) are satisfied by the constants m_K and k_K. In other words, there exists, in the class $\mathfrak{H}_\alpha^\mu$, at least one solution $\varphi^*(t)$ of the singular integral equation (175). Thus we can state the following theorem:

THEOREM. *If the given function $K(t, \tau, u)$ satisfies the conditions* (177), (178), (179) *and the constants m_K and k_K are sufficiently small such that the conditions* (192) *and* (196) *hold, then there exists, in the class $\mathfrak{H}_\alpha^\mu$, at least one solution of the singular integral equation* (175) *for the system of arcs.*

§ 6. Non-linear singular integral equation for a system of arcs, investigated by the method of successive approximation

A non-linear singular integral equation

$$\varphi(t) = \int_L \frac{K[t, \tau, \varphi(\tau)]}{\tau - t} \, d\tau \tag{205}$$

for a system L of smooth arcs can be solved by the method of successive approximation when more restrictive assumptions are imposed on the function $K(t, \tau, u)$, as in Section 3 of Chapter XIX (p. 574). This problem, however, requires a certain modification of the investigation since the singular integral is unbounded in the neighbourhood of the end-points of the arcs. A. I. GUSEINOV [18] was the first to examine the equation in the form (205) by the method of successive approximation, but however, only in the case when the arcs L was a segment of the real axis. The general problem for a system of arcs L has been recently examined by D. PRZEWORSKA–ROLEWICZ [75] by the method of successive approximation using concepts of functional analysis. Below, we present this problem in a different way, without introducing ideas from functional analysis.

Thus we assume that the function $K(t, \tau, u)$ is defined in an open domain

$$t, \tau \in L', \qquad u = \xi + i\eta \in \Pi \tag{206}$$

(Π denotes a plane of a complex variable), and it satisfies the inequalities

$$|K(t, \tau, u)| < m_K |u| + m_K' \tag{207}$$

and the Hölder–Lipschitz condition

$$|K(t, \tau, u) - K(t_1, \tau_1, u_1)| < k_K [|t-t_1|^{\mu_1} + |\tau-\tau_1|^{\mu} + |u-u_1|] \tag{208}$$

where $0 < \mu < \mu_1 \leqq 1$. Moreover, we assume that the real part $K^{(re)}$ and the imaginary part $K^{(im)}$ of the given function

$$K(t, \tau, u) = K^{(re)}(t, \tau, \xi, \eta) + iK^{(im)}(t, \tau, \xi, \eta) \tag{209}$$

have partial derivatives with respect to the variables ξ and η, bounded in the domain (206), satisfying the Hölder–Lipschitz condition in the form

$$\begin{aligned} &|K_\xi^{(\beta)}(t, \tau, \xi, \eta) - K_\xi^{(\beta)}(t_1, \tau_1, \xi_1, \eta_1)| \\ &\qquad < k' [|t-t_1|^{\mu_1} + |\tau-\tau_1|^{\mu} + |\xi-\xi_1| + |\eta-\eta_1|], \end{aligned} \tag{210}$$

$$\begin{aligned} &|K_\eta^{(\beta)}(t, \tau, \xi, \eta) - K_\eta^{(\beta)}(t_1, \tau_1, \xi_1, \eta_1)| \\ &\qquad < k' [|t-t_1|^{\mu_1} + |\tau-\tau_1|^{\mu} + |\xi-\xi_1| + |\eta-\eta_1|] \end{aligned}$$

where the symbol β must be replaced by either re or im. In accordance with the method of successive approximation, we form the sequence of complex functions of the class $\mathfrak{H}_\alpha^\mu$

$$\varphi_0(t),\ \varphi_1(t),\ \ldots,\ \varphi_n(t) \tag{211}$$

by means of the recursive relation

$$\varphi_{n+1}(t) = \int_L \frac{K[t, \tau, \varphi_n(\tau)]}{\tau - t} d\tau \tag{212}$$

where α is an arbitrarily chosen positive constant satisfying the condition

$$0 < 2\alpha < 1 - \mu. \tag{213}$$

In order to prove the existence of the sequence (211), we assume that $\varphi_0(t)$ is any function of the class $\mathfrak{H}_\alpha^\mu$, i.e. that it satisfies the inequalities (for $n = 0$)

$$\prod_{j=1}^{p} |t - c_j|^\alpha |\varphi_n(t)| \leqq \rho \tag{214}$$

$$[|t - c_\nu| \, |t_1 - c_{\nu_1}|]^{\alpha+\mu} |\varphi_n(t) - \varphi_n(t_1)| \leqq \kappa |t - t_1|^\mu \tag{214'}$$

$t \in \frown c_\nu c_{\nu_1}$, $t_1 \in \frown t c_{\nu_1}$, where ρ and κ are arbitrarily chosen positive constants.

Relation (212) is analogous to the transformation (185), and consequently, proceeding as in the previous section, we obtain that all functions of the sequence (211) are well-defined in the class $\mathfrak{H}_\alpha^\mu$ and satisfy inequalities (214), (214') provided the constants of the problem satisfy the inequalities (analogous to (190))

$$\begin{aligned} &C_0(m_K \rho + C_2 m_K) + C_0 k_K(\kappa + C_3) \leqq \rho, \\ &C_1(m_K \rho + C_2 m_K) + C_1 k_K(\kappa + C_3) \leqq \kappa, \end{aligned} \tag{215}$$

where

$$\begin{aligned} &C_2 = \sup_{t \in L} \Big[\prod_{j=1}^{p} |t - c_j|^\alpha \Big], \\ &C_3 = \max_\gamma \sup_{t, t_1 \in L} [|t - c_\nu| \, |t_1 - c_{\nu_1}|]^{\alpha+\mu} \quad (l_\gamma = \frown c_\nu c_{\nu_1}). \end{aligned} \tag{216}$$

Here, the behaviour of the class $\mathfrak{H}_\alpha^\mu$ under the transformation (212), due to the principal theorem on p. 613, is the fundamental fact. As before, making use of the arbitrary choice of the positive constants ρ and κ, we can show that the inequalities

$$
\begin{gathered}
C_0 m_K + C_1' k_K + (C_0' C_1 - C_0 C_1') m_K k_K < 1, \\
C_0 m_K < 1, \quad C_1' k_K < 1
\end{gathered}
\tag{217}
$$

are both necessary and sufficient for the existence of the positive values ρ and κ for which inequalities (215) hold.

It is seen from the above that inequalities (207) and (208) are sufficient for the existence of the sequence of successive approximations (211).

In order to prove the convergence of sequence (211) we make use of the more restrictive assumptions (210), introducing not only the numerical series $\sum_{n=0}^{\infty} S^*[\varphi_{n+1} - \varphi_n]$ of the upper bounds of the products

$$
\sup_{t \in L'} \Big[\prod_{j=1}^{p} |t - c_j|^\alpha \, |\varphi_{n+1}(t) - \varphi_n(t)| \Big] = S^*[\varphi_{n+1}(t) - \varphi_n(t)] \tag{218}
$$

but also the series

$$
\sum_{n=0}^{\infty} H^*[\varphi_{n+1}(t) - \varphi_n(t)], \tag{219}
$$

the terms of which are determined by the formula

$$
H^*[\psi(t)] = \max_{\gamma} \sup_{t, t_1 \in c_\nu c_{\nu_1}} \Big\{ [|t - c_\nu| \, |t_1 - c_{\nu_1}|]^{2\alpha + \mu} \times \times \frac{|\psi(t) - \psi(t_1)|}{|t - t_1|^\mu} \Big\} \tag{220}
$$

$(\frown c_\nu c_{\nu_1} = l_\gamma, \, t_1 \in \frown t c_{\nu_1})$.

In order to prove the convergence of the series (218) and (219), we proceed in the same way as in Section 3 of Chapter XIX, using the important lemma given on p. 577.

Thus we write

$$\varphi_{n+1}(t)-\varphi_n(t) = \lambda \int_L \frac{\delta_n(t,\tau)}{\tau-t}\,d\tau, \qquad (221)$$

where

$$\delta_n(t,\tau) = K[t,\tau,\varphi_n(\tau)]-K[t,\tau,\varphi_{n-1}(\tau)]. \qquad (222)$$

Next, we define the generalized Hölder coefficient of the function of two variables

$$H^*[\delta_n(t,\tau)] = \max_{\gamma,\gamma'} \sup_{\substack{t,t_1\in l_\gamma\\ \tau,\tau_1\in l_{\gamma'}}} \Big\{[|\tau-c_\nu|\,|\tau_1-c_{\nu_1}|]^{2\alpha+\mu}\times$$

$$\times \frac{|\delta_n(t,\tau)-\delta_n(t_1,\tau_1)|}{|t-t_1|^{\mu_1}+|\tau-\tau_1|^{\mu}}\Big\} \qquad (223)$$

($\frown c_\nu c_{\nu_1} = l_\gamma$, $\tau_1 \in \frown \tau c_{\nu_1}$).

Hence, on account of the lemma on p. 577, and proceeding as we did for inequality (58) on p. 579, we obtain an inequality of the same form

$$H^*[\delta_n(t,\tau)]$$

$$\leqq 4M_k' H^*[\varphi_n(t)-\varphi_{n-1}(t)]+4(2\kappa+1)\,k'\,S^*[\varphi_n(t)-\varphi_{n-1}(t)] \qquad (224)$$

where the meaning of the symbol H^* is different as compared with H, for it is defined by formulae (220) and (223). M_K' also denotes the least upper bound of the absolute values of the derivatives of the functions $K^{(\mathrm{re})}$ and $K^{(\mathrm{im})}$ with respect to the variables ξ and η while k' is the positive coefficient given in the assumptions (210). Using the notation

$$S_\tau^*[\delta_n(t,\tau)] = \sup_{\substack{\tau\in L\\ t\in L}} \Big\{\prod_{j=1}^{p} |\tau-c_j|^\alpha\,|\delta_n(t,\tau)|\Big\}, \qquad (225)$$

we obviously have

$$S_\tau^*[\delta_n(t,\tau)] \leqq k_K S^*[\varphi_n-\varphi_{n-1}]. \qquad (226)$$

Applying Theorems 2 and 3 of Section 1 of this chapter to the Cauchy type integral (221), we obtain

$$S^*[\varphi_{n+1}-\varphi_n] \leqq C_1 S_\tau^*[\delta_n(t,\tau)]+C_1' H^*[\delta_n(t,\tau)], \quad (227)$$

$$H^*[\varphi_{n+1}-\varphi_n] \leqq C_2 S_\tau^*[\delta_n(t,\tau)]+C_2' H^*[\delta_n(t,\tau)] \quad (227')$$

(see formulae (188) and (189)). Hence, in view of inequality (224) and the definition (223) we get the fundamental inequalities

$$\begin{aligned} &S^*[\varphi_{n+1}(t)-\varphi_n(t)] \\ &\quad \leqq [C_0 k_K+4(2\kappa+1) C_0' k'] S^*[\varphi_n(t)-\varphi_{n-1}(t)]+ \\ &\qquad\qquad +4C_0' M_K' H^*[\varphi_n(t)-\varphi_{n-1}(t)], \\ &H^*[\varphi_{n+1}(t)-\varphi_n(t)] \\ &\quad \leqq [C_1 k_K+4(2\kappa+1) C' k'] S^*[\varphi_n(t)-\varphi_{n-1}(t)]+ \\ &\qquad\qquad +4C' M_K' H^*[\varphi_n(t)-\varphi_{n-1}(t)]. \end{aligned} \quad (228)$$

From these inequalities it follows immediately that the numerical series

$$\sum_{n=0}^{\infty} S^*[\varphi_{n+1}(t)-\varphi_n(t)], \quad \sum_{n=0}^{\infty} H^*[\varphi_{n+1}(t)-\varphi_n(t)] \quad (229)$$

converge, provided the constants k_K, k', M_K' are sufficiently small. In order to find a more precise sufficient criterion for convergence, we estimate the rate of the decrease of the sum of terms (228). Summing both sides of inequality (228) we obtain

$$\begin{aligned} &S^*[\varphi_{n+1}(t)-\varphi_n(t)]+H^*[\varphi_{n+1}(t)-\varphi_n(t)] \\ &\qquad \leqq P\{S^*[\varphi_n(t)-\varphi_{n-1}(t)]+H^*[\varphi_n(t)-\varphi_{n-1}(t)]\}, \end{aligned} \quad (230)$$

where

$$\begin{aligned} P = \max\{[(C_0+C_1) k_K+ \\ +4(2\kappa+1) k'(C_0'+C_1')], 4(C_0'+C_1') M_K'\}. \end{aligned} \quad (231)$$

Finally, it is seen that the numerical series (229) converges, provided that

$$P<1. \quad (232)$$

Hence, on account of the definition (228), we conclude that the functional series

$$\sum_{n=0}^{\infty} [\varphi_{n+1}(t) - \varphi_n(t)] \tag{233}$$

is absolutely and uniformly convergent in each set of points L_0 which is a closed subset of L excluding the end-points c_ν.

Hence, the existence of the limit function

$$\varphi(t) = \lim_{n\to\infty} \varphi_n(t), \tag{234}$$

continuous at each point $t \in L'$, is established. This function belongs to the class $\mathfrak{H}_\alpha^\mu$, i.e. it satisfies inequalities (214) and (214′), and consequently it is the required solution of the singular integral equation (205). In the same way as for the contours on p. 580, it can be proved that the above solution is unique in the class $\mathfrak{H}_\alpha^\mu$. Thus we may formulate the following theorem:

THEOREM. *If a given complex function* $K(t, \tau, u)$ *is defined in the domain* (206) *and satisfies conditions* (207), (208), (210), *if the constants of the problem* m_K, k_K, k, M_K *are sufficiently small such that inequalities* (217) *and* (232) *hold, then there exists a unique solution of the integral equation* (205), *in the class* $\mathfrak{H}_*^\mu$, *being the limit of the sequence* (211) *at each interior point* t *of the set* L'. $\mathfrak{H}_*^\mu$ *denotes the set of all functions of the class* $\mathfrak{H}_\alpha^\mu$ *for which* α *takes all values such that* $0 < \alpha < (1-\mu)/2$.

§ 7. Generalized Hilbert problem for a system of arcs

As in the case of contours, the generalized Hilbert problem for a system of arcs L consists in the determination of a system $\Phi_1(z), \ldots, \Phi_n(z)$ of functions, sectionally holomorphic in the regions $S_{\text{ext}}, S_1, S_2, \ldots$ (without the point at infinity), bounded by the arcs $l_1, \ldots, l_m$. The boundary values of these functions, i.e. $\Phi_\nu^+(t)$ and $\Phi_\nu^-(t)$, on both sides of each arc satisfy the system of n non-linear equations

$$\Phi_\nu^+(t)$$
$$= G_\nu(t)\Phi_\nu^-(t) + F_\nu[t, \Phi_1^+(t), \ldots, \Phi_n^+(t), \Phi_1^-(t), \ldots, \Phi_n^-(t)] \tag{235}$$

($\nu = 1, \ldots, n$) at each point $t \in L' = L - \sum_0^p c_j$. It is required that all the functions $\Phi_\nu(z)$ belong to the class $h(c_{k_1}, \ldots, c_{k_q})$, i.e. that they are bounded in the neighbourhood of the chosen non-singular end-points $c_{k_1}, \ldots, c_{k_q}$ and that in the neighbourhood of each other end-point c_j they satisfy an inequality of the form

$$|\Phi_\nu(z)| < \frac{\text{const}}{|z-c_j|^\theta} \qquad (0 < \theta < 1). \tag{236}$$

We make the following assumptions:

1. The complex functions $G_\nu(t)$, defined on the set L', satisfy Hölder's condition

$$|G_\nu(t) - G_\nu(t_1)| < k_G |t-t_1|^{h_G} \qquad (\nu = 1, \ldots, n). \tag{237}$$

separately on each component arc. The functions $G_\nu(t)$ have one-sided limits at the end-points of each arc. These limits, corresponding to any point of discontinuity c_γ, will be denoted by symbols

$$\lim_{t_j \to c_\gamma} G_\nu(t_j) = G_\nu^{(j)}(c_\gamma) \qquad (j = 1, \ldots, r_\gamma), \tag{238}$$

where $t_1, \ldots, t_{r_\gamma}$ are the points lying inside the arcs either departing from the point c_γ or arriving at it. Thus the $n.r_\gamma$ limit values

$$G_\nu^{(1)}(c_\gamma), \ldots, G_\nu^{(r_\gamma)}(c_\gamma) \qquad (\nu = 1, \ldots, n) \tag{239}$$

of the functions $G_1(t), \ldots, G_n(t)$ correspond to each point of discontinuity c_γ. It is assumed that all the values of each function $G_\nu(t)$, including the limit values (239), *are not equal to zero.* It is also assumed that neither of the chosen points $c_{k_1}, \ldots, c_{k_q}$ is singular with respect to the functions $G_\nu(t)$.

2. The complex functions $F_\nu(t, u_1, \ldots, u_{2n})$, defined in the domain

$$t \in L', \qquad u_j \in \Pi \quad (j = 1, \ldots, 2n) \tag{240}$$

(Π denotes the complex plane), satisfy the inequalities

$$|F_\nu(t, u_1, \dots, u_{2n})| < m_F \sum_{j=1}^{2n} |u_j| + \frac{m'_F}{\prod_{j=1}^{p} |t-c_j|^{\alpha\theta_j}} \tag{241}$$

($\nu = 1, \dots, n$) and the generalized Hölder–Lipschitz condition

$$|F_\nu(t, u_1, \dots, u_{2n}) - F_\nu(t', u'_1, \dots, u'_{2n})|$$
$$< k_F \sum_{j=1}^{2n} |u_j - u'_j| + \frac{k'_F |t-t'|^{h_F}}{[|t-c_\gamma|^{\alpha\theta_\gamma+\mu} |t-c_{\gamma_1}|]^{\alpha\theta_{\gamma_1}+h_F}} \tag{242}$$

($t \in \frown c_\gamma c_{\gamma_1}$, $t' \in \frown tc_\gamma$), where m_F, m'_F, k_F, k'_F are given positive constants. The given positive exponents α and h_F satisfy the condition $\alpha + h_F < 1$, moreover, the following equalities hold:

$$\theta_j = \begin{cases} 0 & \text{for} \quad j = k_1, \dots, k_q, \\ 1 & \text{for} \quad j \neq k_1, \dots, k_q. \end{cases} \tag{243}$$

According to formula (134), we can assert that if there exists a solution of the problem (235) formed by the functions $\Phi_1(z), \dots$ $\dots, \Phi_n(z)$ the boundary functions of which belong to the class $\mathfrak{H}(c_{k_1}, \dots, c_{k_q})$, then these functions satisfy the relations

$$\Phi_\nu(z) = \frac{X_\nu(z)}{2\pi i} \int_L \frac{F_\nu[\tau, \varphi_1(\tau), \dots, \varphi_{2n}(\tau)]\, d\tau}{X_\nu^+(\tau)(\tau - z)}$$
$$+ X_\nu(z) P_\nu(z) \quad (\nu = 1, \dots, n), \tag{244}$$

where $\varphi_1(\tau), \dots, \varphi_{2n}(\tau)$ are the boundary values of the functions $\Phi_\nu(z)$, at any point $\tau \in L'$, on both sides of the component arcs l_j

$$\varphi_\nu(\tau) = \Phi_\nu^+(\tau), \qquad \varphi_{n+\nu}(\tau) = \Phi_\nu^-(\tau) \qquad (\nu = 1, \dots, n). \tag{245}$$

$X_\nu(z)$ is the fundamental solution in the class $h(c_{k_1}, \dots, c_{k_q})$ corresponding to the function $G_\nu(t)$; $P_\nu(t)$ are certain entire functions.

When the point z tends to any point $t \in L'$, then functions (244) tend to the boundary values (245) which, on account of the Plemelj formulae, satisfy the following system of singular integral equations

$$\varphi_\nu(t) = \frac{X_\nu^+(t)}{2\pi i} \int_L \frac{F_\nu[\tau, \varphi_1(\tau), \dots, \varphi_{2n}(\tau)]\, d\tau}{X_\nu^+(\tau)(\tau - t)} +$$

$$+\tfrac{1}{2} F_\nu[t, \varphi_1(t), \dots, \varphi_{2n}(t)] + X_\nu^+(t) P_\nu(t), \tag{246}$$

$$\varphi_{n+\nu}(t) = \frac{X_\nu^-(t)}{2\pi i} \int_L \frac{F_\nu[\tau, \varphi_1(\tau), \dots, \varphi_{2n}(\tau)]\, d\tau}{X_\nu^+(\tau)(\tau - t)} -$$

$$-\tfrac{1}{2}[G_\nu(t)]^{-1} F_\nu[t, \varphi_1(t), \dots, \varphi_{2n}(t)] + X_\nu^-(t) P_\nu(t)$$

($\nu = 1, \dots, n$), where the integrals have a meaning as their Cauchy principal values.

We now investigate the existence of a solution of the system of non-linear singular integral equations (246) assuming that the functions $\varphi_1, \dots, \varphi_{2n}$ are unknown and instead of $P_\nu(t)$ substituting arbitrary entire functions.

In view of the less restrictive assumptions for the functions F_ν, the existence of the solutions of the system (246) will be studied by Schauder's topological method using the same procedure as in the case of the integral equation (175) in Section 5.

Consider the function space Λ of all systems of $2n$ continuous complex functions

$$[\varphi_1(t), \dots, \varphi_{2n}(t)]$$

which are defined in the open set L' and which satisfy the inequalities

$$\sup_{t \in L'} \Big\{ \prod_{j=1}^{p} |t - c_j|^{A\theta_j + \mu} |\varphi_\nu(t)| \Big\} < \infty \tag{247}$$

($\nu = 1, \dots, 2n$), where θ_j take the values (243). The positive constant A has an assumed value for the whole space Λ, in accordance with the inequalities

$$\max |\lambda_\gamma^{(\nu)} + \sum_{j=1}^{r_\gamma} \alpha_\gamma^{(\nu)j}| < A < 1, \qquad \alpha < A \tag{248}$$

($\nu = 1, \ldots, n$), where the constants $\lambda_\gamma^{(\nu)}$ and $\alpha_\gamma^{(\nu)j}$ concern the points of discontinuity c_γ for the function $G_\nu(t)$, when $\gamma \neq k_1, \ldots$ $\ldots, k_q$, according to formula (110) and inequality (113′). Thus we have

$$\alpha_\gamma^{(\nu)j} = \mathrm{re}\left[\pm\frac{\log G_\nu^j(c_\gamma)}{2\pi i}\right] -1 < \lambda_\gamma^{(\nu)} + \sum_{j=1}^{r_\gamma} \alpha_\gamma^{(\nu)j} \leqq 0$$

$$(\gamma \neq k_1, \ldots, k_q) \quad (249)$$

($\nu = 1, \ldots, n, j = 1, \ldots, r_\gamma$), the + sign refers to an arc arriving at the point c_γ while the − sign refers to an arc departing from this point.

The exponent α has the value occurring in the assumptions (241) and (242). The exponent μ has a fixed value, sufficiently small such that

$$\tilde{A} + \mu < 1, \quad \mu \leqq \min(h_G, h_F) \quad (250)$$

where $\tilde{A}$ denotes the greatest of the numbers

$$|\lambda_\gamma^{(\nu)} + \sum_{j=1}^{r_\gamma} \alpha_\gamma^{(\nu)j}| \quad (\nu = 1, \ldots, n,\ \gamma = 1, \ldots, p). \quad (250')$$

As usual, the sum of two points in the space Λ and the product of a point by a real number are defined by the formulae

$$[\varphi_1, \ldots, \varphi_{2n}] + [\varphi_1', \ldots, \varphi_{2n}'] = [\varphi_1 + \varphi_1', \ldots, \varphi_{2n} + \varphi_{2n}'],$$
$$\lambda[\varphi_1, \ldots, \varphi_{2n}] = [\lambda\varphi_1, \ldots, \lambda\varphi_{2n}]. \quad (251)$$

Next, we define the norm of a point $U = [\varphi_1, \ldots, \varphi_{2n}]$ by

$$\|U\| = \max_{1 \leqq \nu \leqq 2n} \sup_{t \in L'} \left\{ \prod_{j=1}^{p} |t - c_j|^{A\theta_j + \mu} |\varphi_\nu(t)| \right\}. \quad (252)$$

The distance between two points U and V in the space Λ is defined, as usual, by the norm of the difference of these points:

$$\delta(U, V) = \|U - V\|. \quad (253)$$

The space Λ is linear, metric, and normed, and it can be proved, in the same way as in Section 5, that it is complete. Consequently Λ is a Banach space.

We now consider in the space A the set $\mathscr{E}$ of all points $U = [\varphi_1, \ldots, \varphi_{2n}]$ satisfying the inequalities

$$\prod_{j=1}^{p} |t-c_j|^{A\theta_j} |\varphi_\nu(t)| \leqq \rho,$$
$$|t-c_\gamma|^{A\theta_\gamma+\mu} |t_1-c_{\gamma_1}|^{A\theta_{\gamma_1}+\mu} |\varphi_\nu(t)-\varphi_\nu(t_1)| \leqq \kappa |t-t_1|^\mu \tag{254}$$

$(\nu = 1, \ldots, 2n)$, $t \in \frown c_\gamma c_{\gamma_1}$, $t_1 \in \frown t c_{\gamma_1}$, where ρ and κ are arbitrarily fixed numbers. The functions $\varphi_\nu(t)$ connected with the set $\mathscr{E}$ belong to the class $\mathfrak{H}_A^\mu(c_{k_1}, \ldots, c_{k_q})$ in accordance with the definition on p. 635. The set $\mathscr{E}$ is closed and convex.

Taking into account the form of the integral equations (246), we transform the set $\mathscr{E}$ by means of the relations

$$\psi_\nu(t) = \frac{1}{2\pi i} X_\nu^+(t) \int_L \frac{F_\nu[\tau, \varphi_1(\tau), \ldots, \varphi_{2n}(\tau)]\, d\tau}{X_\nu^+(\tau)(\tau-t)} -$$
$$+\tfrac{1}{2} F_\nu[t, \varphi_1(t), \ldots, \varphi_{2n}(t)] + X_\nu^+(t) P_\nu(t), \tag{255}$$
$$\psi_{n+\nu}(t) = \frac{1}{2\pi i} X_\nu^-(t) \int_L \frac{F_\nu[\tau, \varphi_1(\tau), \ldots, \varphi_{2n}(\tau)]\, d\tau}{X_\nu^+(\tau)(\tau-t)} -$$
$$-\tfrac{1}{2} [G_\nu(t)]^{-1} F_\nu[t, \varphi_1(t), \ldots, \varphi_{2n}(t)] + X_\nu^-(t) P_\nu(t)$$

$(\nu = 1, 2, \ldots, n)$. The functions F_ν, entering the above integrals, according to the assumed properties (241), (242) and inequalities (254), satisfy the inequalities

$$F_\nu[\tau, \varphi_1(\tau), \ldots, \varphi_{2n}(\tau)] < \frac{2nm_F\rho + Dm_F'}{\prod_{j=1}^{p} |t-c_j|^{A\theta_j}} \tag{256}$$

and the generalized Hölder condition

$$|F_\nu[\tau, \varphi_1(\tau), \ldots, \varphi_{2n}(\tau)] - F_\nu[\tau_1, \varphi_1(\tau_1), \ldots, \varphi_{2n}(\tau_1)]|$$
$$< \frac{2nk_F\kappa + D'k_F'}{|\tau-c_\gamma|^{A\theta_\gamma+\mu} |\tau_1-c_{\gamma_1}|^{A\theta_{\gamma_1}+\mu}} |\tau-\tau_1|^\mu. \tag{257}$$

The positive constants D and D' depend on the system of arcs L and are independent of the functions F_ν and φ_ν. Hence, on the basis of Theorem 5 on the functions of the class $\mathfrak{H}(c_{k_1}, \ldots, c_{k_q})$ (see inequalities (89)), and on account of formulae (123) the (124) and the assumptions (248), (250), we conclude that the functions (255) satisfy the following inequalities:

$$|\psi_\nu(t)| < \frac{D_1(2nm_F\rho + Dm'_F) + D_2(2nk_F\kappa + D'k'_F) + D_3 M_P}{\prod_{j=1}^{p} |t-c_j|^{A\theta_j}}, \tag{258}$$

$$|\psi_\nu(t) - \psi_\nu(t_1)|$$
$$< \frac{D'_1(2nm_F\rho + Dm'_F) + D'_2(2nk_F\kappa + D'k'_F) + D_3 M_p + D_4 k_p}{|t-c_\gamma|^{A\theta_\gamma+\mu}\,|t_1-c_\gamma|^{A\theta_{\gamma_1}+\mu}} \times$$
$$\times |t-t_1|^\mu. \tag{259}$$

The positive constants $D_1, D_2, D_3, D'_1, D'_2, D'_3, D_4$ do not depend upon F_ν and φ_ν, but depend on the system of arcs L and on $G_\nu(t)$. We use the notation $M_p = \sup P_\nu(t)$, and k_p denotes the Hölder coefficient of the functions $P_\nu(t)$ on the set L. Consequently, the functions $\psi_\nu(t)$ belong to the class $\mathfrak{H}^\mu_A(c_{k_1}, \ldots, c_{k_q})$ as well as the functions $\varphi_\nu(t)$. Comparing inequalities (258), (259) with inequalities (254) defining the set $\mathscr{E}$ we conclude that a sufficient condition for the transformed set $\mathscr{E}'$ to be a subset of $\mathscr{E}$ is that the inequalities

$$\begin{aligned} &D_1(2nm_F\rho + Dm'_F) + D_2(2nk_F\kappa + D'k'_F) + D_3 M_p \leqq \rho, \\ &D'_1(2nm_F\rho + Dm'_F) + D'_2(2nk_F\kappa + D'k'_F) + D_3 M_p + D_4 k_p \leqq \kappa \end{aligned} \tag{260}$$

hold.

For the prescribed values ρ and κ satisfying the inequalities

$$\begin{aligned} &\rho > D_1 Dm'_F + D_2 D' k'_F + D_3 M_p, \\ &\kappa > D'_1 Dm'_F + D'_2 D' k'_F + D'_3 M_p + D_4 k_p \end{aligned} \tag{261}$$

we can always find sufficiently small constants m_F and k_F such that inequalities (260) are satisfied. Since, however, the choice of the constants ρ and κ in the conditions (254) is arbitrary, we make use of this arbitrariness and determine the sets of all values m_F and k_F, for which inequalities (260) are satisfied when

ρ and κ increase from the right-hand side values of (261) up to infinity.

Thus, proceeding in the same way as for the system of inequalities (190) in Section 5, it is readily seen that inequalities (260) hold if, and only if, the constants m_F and k_F are sufficiently small such that the strict inequalities

$$\begin{gathered} 2n\,D_1 m_F < 1\,, \qquad 2n\,D_2' k_F < 1\,, \\ 2n\,D_1 m_F + 2n\,D_2' k_F + 4n^2 (D_2 D_1' - D_1 D_2')\, m_F k_F < 1 \end{gathered} \tag{262}$$

are satisfied.

As in Section 5 one can prove two lemmas, namely: the transformation of the set $\mathscr{E}$ defined by formulae (255) is continuous in the space Λ, and the transformed set $\mathscr{E}'$ is compact.

Hence, when conditions (262) are satisfied, we conclude, on the basis of Schauder's Theorem, that there exists in the set $\mathscr{E}$ at least one point $[\varphi_1^*, \ldots, \varphi_{2n}^*]$ fixed with respect to the transformation (255), i.e. that there exists a solution of the system of integral equations (246) for arbitrary entire functions $P_\nu(z)$.

The functions $\varphi_\nu^*(t)$ belong to the class $\mathfrak{H}_A^\mu(c_{k_1}, \ldots, c_{k_q})$ since they satisfy inequalities (254), and consequently, substituting these functions in formulae (244) we obtain the system of functions $\Phi_1(z), \ldots, \Phi_n(z)$, sectionally holomorphic in the regions $S_{\text{ext}}, S_1, S_2, \ldots$ (without the point at infinity), bounded by the arcs l_γ. The boundary values of these functions $\Phi_\nu^+(t)$ and $\Phi_\nu^-(t)$, according to the Plemelj formulae and the system of integral equations (246) satisfy the given system of equations (235) at each point $t \in L'$. Moreover, on account of inequalities (256) and (257) and Theorem 6 on p. 639, the functions $\Phi_\nu(z)$ are bounded in the neighbourhood of the chosen non-singular end-points $c_{k_1}, \ldots, c_{k_q}$ and satisfy the inequality

$$|\Phi_\nu(z)| < \frac{\text{const}}{|z - c_\gamma|^A}$$

with a weak boundedness in the neighbourhood of each end-point $c_\gamma \neq c_{k_1}, \ldots, c_{k_q}$. Thus we can formulate the following theorem:

THEOREM. *If the given functions G_ν and F_ν satisfy conditions 1 and 2, and if the constants of the problem, m_F and k_F, are sufficiently small such that inequalities* (262) *hold, then there exists a system of functions $\Phi_1(z), \ldots, \Phi_n(z)$, sectionally holomorphic in the regions $S_{ext}, S_1, S_2, \ldots$, bounded by the system of arcs L, the boundary values of which satisfy the given system of equations* (235) *at each point $t \in L'$, and which belong to the class $h(c_{k_1}, \ldots, c_{k_q})$. All such systems of functions are defined by formulae* (244), *where $P_\nu(z)$ are arbitrary entire functions, while $[\varphi_1(t), \ldots, \varphi_{2n}(t)]$ is a solution of the system of integral equations* (246).

At the end of this section we mention that the above non-linear Hilbert problem was solved by W. ŻAKOWSKI [94] for a system composed of open arcs and contours on which the boundary values are continuous. The problem was solved by the topological method and by the method of successive approximation.

§ 8. Discontinuous Riemann boundary problem

The discontinuous Riemann boundary problem consists in the determination of the function $\Phi(z) = u(x, y) + iv(x, y)$, holomorphic inside the circle S^+ with circumference L, the boundary values of which $\Phi^+(t)$ satisfy the linear relation

$$\operatorname{re}[(a+ib)\Phi^+(t)] = a(t)u(t) - b(t)v(t) = f(t) \tag{263}$$

at each point $t \in L$ which is distinct from the points of discontinuity $c_1, \ldots, c_p$ of the real functions $a(t), b(t), f(t)$ defined on the circumference of the circle. We require also that the function $\Phi(z)$ satisfies the following inequality with a weak singularity

$$|\Phi(z)| < \frac{\text{cons}_t}{|z-c_\nu|^\theta} \quad (0 < \theta < 1) \tag{264}$$

in the neighbourhood of each point of discontinuity c_ν. If, in particular, the solution $\Phi(z)$ of the discontinuous Riemann problem is bounded in the neighbourhood of non-singular chosen points of discontinuity $c_{k_1}, \ldots, c_{k_q}$ it will be said to belong to the class $h(c_{k_1}, \ldots, c_{k_q})$.

The solution of this problem is given by MUSKHELISHVILI in his monograph [33]. He uses the method of reduction to the Hilbert problem, as it was done for the continuous problem on p. 473. Below, we give the solution of this problem under more general assumptions and in a somewhat different way. We assume that the given functions $a(t)$ and $b(t)$ have points of discontinuity $c_1, \ldots, c_p$ of the first kind on the circumference of the circle L, ordered according to its positive direction. We make more general assumption for the function $f(t)$, namely, we assume that this function belongs to the class $\mathfrak{H}_\alpha^\mu$ with respect to the points $c_1, \ldots, c_p$.

We denote by $a(c_\nu - 0)$ and $a(c_\nu + 0)$ the left and the right hand side limits of the function $a(t)$ at the point c_ν, respectively. In the same way for the function $b(t)$, we have $b(c_\nu - 0)$ and $b(c_\nu + 0)$. It is assumed that the functions $a(t)$ and $b(t)$ inside of each of the arcs $\frown c_\nu c_{\nu+1}$ $(c_{p+1} = c_1)$ satisfy Hölder's condition

$$|a(t) - a(t_1)| < \text{const}\,|t - t_1|^h,$$
$$|b(t) - b(t_1)| < \text{const}\,|t - t_1|^h,$$

and that $a^2 + b^2 \neq 0$ at each point $t \in L$, including the limits.

As in Section 4 on p. 584, we introduce the function $\Phi(z)$ sectionally holomorphic in the regions S^+ and S^- and identical with the associate function $\Phi_*(z)$, i.e. we have

$$\Phi(z) = \Phi(1/\bar{z}). \tag{265}$$

Thus the given Riemann problem can be reduced to the determination of the discontinuous solution of the Hilbert problem in the class $h(c_{k_1}, \ldots, c_{k_q})$ with boundary condition

$$(a + ib)\,\Phi^+(t) + (a - ib)\,\Phi^-(t) = 2f(t) \quad (t \neq c_\nu). \tag{266}$$

The solution is regular at infinity but not necessarily equal to zero.

Here, we have

$$G(t) = -\frac{a - ib}{a + ib}, \quad g(t) = \frac{f(t)}{a + ib};$$

writing

$$\alpha_\nu^+ = -\frac{1}{2\pi i}\log G(c_\nu+0), \quad \alpha_\nu^- = +\frac{1}{2\pi i}\log G(c_\nu-0), \tag{267}$$

we choose an integer $\lambda_\nu = -(\alpha_\nu^+ + \alpha_\nu^-)$ at the singular points c_ν, i.e. such that the ratio $G(c_\nu+0)/G(c_\nu-0)$ is positive; next, we assign to the chosen points $c_{k_1}, \ldots, c_{k_q}$ integers λ_ν such that

$$0 < \lambda_\nu + (\alpha_\nu^+ + \alpha_\nu^-) < 1$$

and to the remaining points c_ν integers λ_ν such that

$$-1 < \lambda_\nu + (\alpha_\nu^+ + \alpha_\nu^-) < 0.$$

The index of the problem is determined by the formula

$$\kappa = -\sum_{\nu=1}^{p} \lambda_\nu$$

and does not depend on the choice of the branch of the function $\log G(t)$ on the arcs $\frown c_\nu c_{\nu+1}$.

In this case the index is not necessarily even, as it was in the continuous problem.

The fundamental solution $X(z)$ of the class $h(c_{k_1}, \ldots, c_{k_q})$ corresponding to the homogeneous problem (266) is defined by formula (114). Assuming now that the given function $f(t)$ belongs to the class $\mathfrak{H}_\alpha^\mu(c_{k_1}, \ldots, c_{k_q})$, we obtain, on account of formula (134), the general solution of the class $h(c_{k_1}, \ldots, c_{k_q})$ of the discontinuous Hilbert problem (266) in the form

$$\Psi(z) = \frac{1}{\pi i} X(z) \int_L \frac{f(\tau)\,d\tau}{X^+(\tau)(a+ib)(\tau-z)} + X(z)P(z), \tag{268}$$

where the limit function $X^+(\tau)$ is defined by formulae (120) and (123). The integral (268) has a meaning due to weak singularities of the integrand at the points c_ν. We first consider the case $\kappa \geqq 0$. Substituting

$$P(z) = P^\kappa(z) = C_0 + C_1 z + \ldots + C_\kappa z^\kappa$$

where $C_0, C_1, \ldots, C_\kappa$ are arbitrary constants, we obtain all solutions regular at infinity. Hence it follows that for $z \in S^+ + S^-$ the formula

$$\Phi(z) = \tfrac{1}{2}[\Psi(z) + \overline{\Psi(1/\bar{z})}] \tag{269}$$

represents all solutions from the class $h(c_{k_1}, \ldots, c_{k_q})$ of the discontinuous Hilbert problem (266) which are identical with their associate solutions $\Phi_*(z) = \Phi(z)$.

Thus, formula (269) gives, for $z \in S^+$ in the case $\kappa \geqq 0$, all solutions from the class $h(c_{k_1}, \ldots, c_{k_q})$ of the discontinuous Riemann problem (264). This solution depends on $\kappa+1$ arbitrary constants $C_0, C_1, \ldots, C_\kappa$. After calculation, the function (269) becomes

$$\Phi(z) = \frac{1}{2\pi i}\int_L \frac{Z(z,\tau) f(\tau)\,d\tau}{[a^2(\tau)+b^2(\tau)](\tau - z)} + $$

$$+\tfrac{1}{2} X(z) P^\kappa(z) + \tfrac{1}{2} X_*(z) P_*^\kappa(z), \tag{270}$$

where

$$Z(z,\tau) = \frac{X(z)[a(\tau) - ib(\tau)]}{X^+(\tau)} - \frac{zX_*(z)\overline{[a(\tau)+ib(\tau)]}}{X^+(\tau)\tau}. \tag{271}$$

In the case $\kappa < 0$ the Hilbert problem (266) may not have solutions in the class $h(c_{k_1}, \ldots, c_{k_q})$ regular at infinity, and then the corresponding Riemann problem may not have a solution, either.

The solution of the Hilbert problem (266) in the case $\kappa < 0$, regular at infinity, exists if and only if the function $f(t) \in \mathfrak{H}_\alpha^\mu(c_{k_1}, \ldots, c_{k_q})$ satisfies the equalities

$$\int_L \frac{\tau^j f(\tau)\,d\tau}{X^+(\tau)(a+ib)} = 0 \quad (j = 0, 1, \ldots, -\kappa - 2). \tag{272}$$

Then the solution is unique and is defined by the formula

$$\Phi(z) = \frac{1}{\pi i} X(z) \int_L \frac{f(\tau)\,d\tau}{X^+(\tau)(a+ib)(\tau - z)}. \tag{273}$$

This function is the only solution in the class $h(c_{k_1}, \ldots, c_{k_q})$ of the discontinuous Riemann problem (263) in the region S^+.

The discontinuous Riemann problem can be generalized to the case when the required system of holomorphic functions satisfies non-linear discontinuous relations on the boundary of the region, similar to the relations on p. 592. This problem leads to the system of singular integral equations the investigation of which was given by NICZYPOROWICZ [38].

§ 9. On a certain class of holomorphic functions

At the end of this chapter devoted to discontinuous boundary problems, we give a short account of a certain class of holomorphic functions (see POGORZELSKI [67]) interesting because of its properties. The introduction of this class gives, in more complicated boundary problems, a certain symmetry concerning the holomorphic functions and their derivatives.

First of all, we now generalize the definition of the class of functions $\mathfrak{H}_\alpha^\mu(c_{k_1}, \ldots, c_{k_q})$ by considering all functions $\varphi(t)$ of the class $\mathfrak{H}_\alpha^\mu$ defined on the set L, bounded or almost bounded, in the neighbourhood of the chosen points of discontinuity $c_{k_1}, \ldots, c_{k_q}$. More precisely, we consider the functions satisfying the inequalities

$$|\varphi(t)| < \frac{\text{const}}{\prod\limits_{\nu=1}^{p} |t-c_\nu|^{\alpha\theta_\nu}},$$

$$|\varphi(t)-\varphi(t_1)| < \frac{\text{const}\, |t-t_1|^\mu}{|t-c_\nu|^{\alpha\theta_\nu+\mu}\, |t_1-c_{\nu'}|^{\alpha\theta_{\nu'}+\mu}}, \tag{274}$$

where θ_ν is an arbitrarily small positive number (in particular, zero) for $\nu = k_1, \ldots, k_q$, while $\theta_\nu = 1$ for $\nu \neq k_1, \ldots, k_q$.

The definition, given below, concerns a more particular system of directed contours $L_0, L_1, \ldots, L_n$ shown in Fig. 6, but with the generalization that the contours may possess a finite number of points of dicontinuity of the tangents $c_1, c_2, \ldots, c_p$.

Thus we have angular and salient points. Taking inequalities (274) for functions of the class $\mathfrak{H}_\alpha^\mu(c_{k_1}, \ldots, c_{k_q})$ determined in the set $L = L_0+L_1+,\ldots,+L_n$ with points of discontinuity $c_1, c_2, \ldots, c_p$, we introduce the following additional assumptions:

1. If there exist, on a certain contour L_j, at least two points of discontinuity, then the second of inequalities (274) always refers to the pair of the points t, t_1 lying on the same smooth arc $\frown c_\nu c_{\nu'}$, between the points of discontinuity, moreover $t_1 \in \frown tc_{\nu'}$.

2. If only one point c_ν of discontinuity exists on a certain contour L_j, then in the denominator of the second of inequalities (274) the second factor $|t_1-c_{\nu'}|$ should be neglected. It is assumed that $|t-c_\nu| < |t_1-c_\nu|$, and that the length of the arc $\frown tt_1$, which does not contain the point c_ν, is less than a certain number less than the whole length of the contour L_j.

3. If, on a certain contour L_j, there are no points of discontinuity, then the second of inequalities (274) holds, when both the factors in the denominator are disregarded for each pair of the points t and t_1 lying on this contour.

DEFINITION 1. *We denote by $\mathfrak{H}_\alpha^\mu$ the class of all functions $\Phi(z)$ sectionally holomorphic in the regions $S^+, S_0^-, S_1^-, \ldots, S_n^-$ (bounded by the contours $L_0, \ldots, L_n$), the boundary values of which*

$$\Phi^\pm(t) = \lim_{z\to t} \Phi(z), \quad t \neq c_\nu,$$

belong to the class $\mathfrak{H}_\alpha^\mu$ on the set L, and which satisfy the inequality with weak boundedness

$$|\Phi(z)| < \frac{\text{const}}{|z-c_\nu|^\theta} \tag{275}$$

in the neighbourhood of each point of discontinuity c_ν, where θ is a positive number less than unity, not yet fixed.

Note that on account of the Theorem 1 on p. 612, the class $\mathfrak{H}_\alpha^\mu$ is a subset of the class $\mathfrak{H}_{\alpha_1}^{\mu_1}$ for $\alpha \leqq \alpha_1, \mu_1 \leqq \mu$.

DEFINITION 2. *The set of all functions $\Phi(z)$ of the class H_α^μ, the boundary functions of which $\Phi^\pm(t)$ belong to the class $\mathfrak{H}_\alpha^\mu(c_{k_1}, \ldots, c_{k_q})$ is called the class $H_\alpha^\mu(c_{k_1}, \ldots, c_{k_q})$.*

Below, we formulate four theorems concerning more important properties of the functions of the class $\mathfrak{H}_\alpha^\mu$. The proofs of these theorems, based mainly on the above properties of the functions of the class $\mathfrak{H}_\alpha^\mu$ are given in the paper of POGORZELSKI [67].

THEOREM 1. *Each function $\Phi(z)$ of the class $\mathfrak{H}_\alpha^\mu(c_{k_1}, \ldots, c_{k_q})$ $(\alpha > 0)$ satisfies, in the neighbourhood of the point of discontinuity c_ν, the inequality*

$$|\Phi(z)| < \frac{\text{const}}{|z-c_\nu|^{\rho_\nu}} \tag{276}$$

where $\rho_\nu = \alpha$ for $\nu \neq k_1, \ldots, k_q$ while ρ_ν is a positive, arbitrarily small number for $\nu = k_1, \ldots, k_q$.

THEOREM 2. *If the function $\varphi(t)$, defined on the set L, belongs to the class $\mathfrak{H}_\alpha^\mu(c_{k_1}, \ldots, c_{k_q})$ $(\alpha > 0)$, then the function defined by the Cauchy type integral*

$$\Phi(z) = \int\limits_L \frac{\varphi(\tau)\, d\tau}{\tau - z} \tag{277}$$

for $z \in S^+ + S^-$ belongs to the class $\mathfrak{H}_\alpha^\mu(c_{k_1}, \ldots, c_{k_q})$.

THEOREM 3. *If the derivative of the function $\Phi(z)$, sectionally holomorphic in the regions $S^+, S_0^-, S_1^-, \ldots, S_n^-$, belongs to the class $\mathfrak{H}_\alpha^\mu$,*

$$\Phi'(z) \in \mathfrak{H}_\alpha^\mu,$$

then the function $\Phi(z)$ has the boundary values

$$\Phi^\pm(t) = \lim_{z \to t} \Phi(z)$$

at each point t on both sides of the contour L, even at the points of discontinuity $c_1, \ldots, c_p$ of the derivative. Moreover, the boundary functions satisfy Hölder's condition

$$|\Phi^\pm(t_1) - \Phi^\pm(t_2)| < \text{const}\,|t_1 - t_2|^\theta$$

on each of the contours $L_0, L_1, \ldots, L_n$, where $\theta = 1-\alpha$ for $\alpha > 0$, while θ is positive and arbitrarily small for $\alpha = 0$.

Now let there be given a single closed smooth Jordan curve L, bounding the interior region S^+. We assume that the tangent to this line forms, with a constant direction, an angle satisfying the Hölder condition for the exponent h_L. Then we have the following theorem which is analogous to Vekua's Theorem on p. 538, on the integral representation of the holomorphic function:

THEOREM 4. *If the m-th order* ($m \geqq 1$) *derivative of the function* $\Phi(z)$, *holomorphic in the region* S^+, *belongs to the class* $\mathfrak{H}_\alpha^\mu(c_{k_1}, \ldots, c_{k_q})$,

$$\Phi^m(z) \in \mathfrak{H}_\alpha^\mu(c_{k_1}, \ldots, c_{k_q}),$$

with respect to the points of discontinuity $c_1, \ldots, c_p$ *on the curve* L, *then this function* $\Phi(z)$ *can be expressed in a unique way by the integral formula*

$$\Phi(z) = \int_L \varphi(\tau)\left(1-\frac{z}{\tau}\right)^{m-1} \log\left(1-\frac{z}{\tau}\right) d\sigma_\tau + \int_L \varphi(\tau)\, d\sigma_\tau + iC, \quad (278)$$

where $\varphi(\tau)$ *is a real function from the class* $\mathfrak{H}_\alpha^{h'}(c_{k_1}, \ldots, c_{k_q})$ *while* C *is a real constant*; $h' = \min(\mu, h_L)$.

Using the above theorem we can solve the discontinuous boundary problem analogous to the Vekua boundary problem for the condition (81) on p. 548, when the real function $f(t)$ belongs to the class $\mathfrak{H}_\alpha^\mu(c_{k_1}, \ldots, c_{k_q})$ with respect to the points $c_1, \ldots, c_p$ on the curve L.

The discontinuous Vekua problem can be generalized to the case of finding the function $\Phi(z)$ holomorphic in the region S^+, the derivative of which $\Phi^{(m)}(z)$ belongs to the class $\mathfrak{H}_\alpha^\delta$ with respect to the points of discontinuity $c_1, \ldots, c_p$ on L, the boundary function of which and the boundary functions of its derivatives satisfy the following non-linear relation:

$$\operatorname{re} \sum_{j=0}^{m} \{a_j(t)\, \Phi^{(j)}(t) + \int_L g_j(t, \tau)\, \Phi^{(j)}(\tau)\, d\sigma\}$$

$$= F[t, \Phi(t), \ldots, \Phi^{(m)}(t)] \qquad (t \in L').$$

We assume for the functions $a(t)$ and $g_j(t, \tau)$ the same hypothesis as in Section 5, Chapter XVIII. We also assume that the function $F(t, u_0, \ldots, u_m)$ is defined in the domain $[t \in L', u_\nu \in$ complex plane] and satisfies the inequalities

$$|F(t, u_0, \ldots, u_m)| < k_F \sum_{\nu=0}^{m} |u_\nu| + \frac{M_F}{\prod_{\nu=1}^{p} |t-c_\nu|^\alpha},$$

$$|F(t, u_0, \ldots, u_m) - F(t', u_0', \ldots, u_m')|$$
$$< k_F \sum_{\nu=0}^{m} |u_\nu - u_\nu'| + \frac{k_F' |t-t'|^h}{|t-c_\gamma|^{\alpha+h} |t'-c_{\gamma_1}|^{\alpha+h}}.$$

These investigations are given by the author in his paper [69].

REFERENCES

1. BANACH, S., Sur les opérations dans les ensembles abstraits et leurs applications aux équations intégrales, *Fundamenta Math.*, **3**, 133–181 (1922).
2. BERTRAND, G., Équations de Fredholm à intégrales principales au sens de Cauchy, *Comptes Rendus*, 1458–1461, Paris 1921.
3. BERTRAND, G., La théorie des marées et les équations intégrales, *Ann. de l'Éc. Norm.*, **40**, 151–258 (1923).
4. CACCIOPOLI, V., Un teorema generale sull' esistenza di elementi uniti in una transformazione funzionale, *Rend. Accad. Lincei*, **2** (1930).
5. CARLEMANN, T., Sur la résolution de certaines équations intégrales, *Arkiv för matematik, astr. o phys.*, **16** (1922).
6. DRESSEL, F. G., The fundamental solution of the parabolic equation, *Duke Math. J.*, **13**, 61–70 (1946).
7. FRÉCHET, M., Quelques propriétés des ensembles abstraits, *Fundamenta Math.*, **12**, 298–310 (1928).
8. GAKHOV, F., On the Riemann boundary problem, *Mat. sb.*, 673–683 (1937) (in Russian).
9. GAKHOV, F., Linear boundary problems of the complex function theory, *Izv. Phiz.-matem. obshch. pri Kazansk. Univers.*, **10**, 39–79 (1938) (in Russian).
10. GAKHOV, F., Boundary problems of the theory of analytic functions and singular integral equations, *Diss. for the degree of Doctor of Phil. in Math.*, Tiflis, 1942 (in Russian).
11. GEKHT, B., Solvability of non-linear singular integral equations by the method of operations, *Uch. zapiski Gos. Kazansk. Univ.*, **116** (1956) (in Russian).
12. GEVREY, M., Détermination et emploi des fonctions de Green dans les problèmes aux limites relatifs aux équations linéaires du type elliptique, *J. de Mathématique*, **95**, 1–80 (1930).
13. GEVREY, M., Intégrales analogues aux potentiels, *Comptes Rendus*, Paris 1927.
14. GEVREY, M., Sur les équations aux dérivées partielles du type parabolique, *J. de Mathématique*, **78**, 305–471 (1913).
15. GIRAUD, G., Sur certaines opérations aux dérivées partielles du type parabolique, *Comptes Rendus*, **195**, 18–100, Paris 1932.
16. GIRAUD, G., Sur les équations du type elliptique, *Bull. de Sc. Mathém.*, **53**, 367–395 (1929).

17. Giraud, G., Équations à intégrales principales, *Ann. de l'Éc. Norm.*, **51**, 251–372 (1934); **56**, 119–172 (1939).

18. Guseinov, A., On a certain integral equation, *Izv. Acad. Nauk S. S. S. R.*, **12**, 193–212 (1948), (in Russian).

19. Guseinov, A., On a certain boundary problem in the theory of analytic functions, *Mat. sb.*, **26** (68) (1950) (in Russian).

20. Hammerstein, A., Nichtlineare Integralgleichungen nebst Anwendungen, *Acta Math.*, **54**, 117–176 (1930).

21. Hilbert, D., *Grundzüge einer allgemeinen Theorie der linearen Integralgleichungen*, Leipzig 1912.

22. Holmgren, E., Sur le problème de Fourier, *Comptes Rendus*, Paris 30. Dec. 1907 et 9. Jan. 1908.

23. Khvedelidze, B., On the Poincaré boundary problem of the theory of the logarithmic potential, *Soobshch. Acad. Nauk Gruz. S. S. R.*, 571–578 (1941) (in Russian).

24. Krzyżański, M., *Partial differential equations of second order*, vol. I, Warsaw 1957, vol. II, Warsaw 1962 (in Polish).

25. Kuratowski, K., *Introduction to Set Theory and Topology*, Warsaw 1962. English edition: (Vol. 13 of this series) Pergamon Press, Oxford/Addison–Wesley, Reading, Mass.

26. Levi, E., Sulla equazioni lineari totalemente ellittiche alle derivati parziali, *Rend. del Circolo Matematico di Palermo*, **24**, 275–317 (1907).

27. Lichtenstein, L., *Nichtlineare Integralgleichungen*, Berlin 1931.

28. Majcher, G., Sur un problème aux limites mixte pour l'équation hyperbolique, *Ann. Pol. Math.* **5**, 121–133 (1958).

29. Mazur, S., Über die kleinste konvexe Menge, die eine gegebene kompakte Menge enthält, *Studia Math.*, 7–10 (1930).

30. Mikhlin, S., *Integral Equations*, Moscow 1949 (in Russian). Revised English edition: Pergamon Press (Vol. 4 of this series).

31. Miranda, C., *Equazioni alle derivati parziali di tipo ellittico*, Berlin 1955.

32. Morera, G., Intorno all' integrale de Cauchy, *Rendiconti del Ist. Lomb.*, **22**, 191–200 (1889).

33. Muskhelishvili, N., *Singular Integral Equations*, P. Nordhoff N. V., Gröningen, Holland, 1953. Translation from the 2nd Russ. ed. Moscow 1946, by J. R. M. Radok.

34. Muskhelishvili, N., Application of the Cauchy type integral to a class of singular integral equations, *Tr. Tbilissk. Mat. Inst.*, **10**, 1–43 (1941) (in Russian).

35. Muskhelishvili, N. and Kveselava, D., Singular integral equations with the Cauchy type kernels for arcs, *Tr. Tbilissk. Mat. Inst.*, **11**, 141–172 (1945) (in Russian).

36. Müntz, H., *Integral Equations*, Moscow 1934 (in Russian).

37. Natalevitch, V., Non-linear singular integral equations and non-linear boundary problems in the theory of analytic functions, *Uch. zapiski Kazansk. Gos. Univ.*, **112** (1952) (in Russian).

38. Niczyporowicz, E., Sur un problème aux limites discontinues dans la théorie des fonctions analytiques, *Ann. Pol. Math.* **14**, 269–288 (1964).
39. Niemytzki, W., Théorèmes d'existence des solutions de quelques équations intégrales non-linéaires, *Mat. sb.*, **41** (1934).
40. Noether, F., Über eine Klasse singulärer Integralgleichungen, *Math. Ann.*, **82**, 42–63 (1921).
41. Plemelj, J., Ein Ergänzungssatz zur Cauchyschen Integraldarstellung analytischer Funktionen, *Monatshefte f. Math. u. Phys.*, 205–210 (1908).
42. Pogorzelski, W., *Mathematical Analysis*, vol. I–IV, Warsaw 1956 (in Polish).
43. Pogorzelski, W., Étude de la solutions fondamentale de l'équation elliptique, *Ann. Pol. Math.*, **4**, 247–284 (1957).
44. Pogorzelski, W., Étude de la solution fondamentale de l'équation parabolique, *Richerche di Matematica*, **5**, 25–57 (1956).
45. Pogorzelski, W., Propriétés des intégrales de l'équation parabolique normale, *Ann. Pol. Math.*, **4**, 61–92 (1957).
46. Pogorzelski, W., Les propriétés du noyau résolvant de l'équation intégrale d'un problème aux limites, *Bibliotheca Universitatis Liberae Polonae*, **1** (1922).
47. Pogorzelski, W., On some boundary problems of potential theory, *Bull. Wojsk. Akad. Techn.*, **18**, 17–24 (1955).
48. Pogorzelski, W., On a certain type of non-linear integro-differential equations, *Wiad. Matemat.*, **22**, 155–166 (1918) (in Polish).
49. Pogorzelski, W., Problème aux limites pour l'équation parabolique normale, *Ann. Pol. Math.*, **4**, 110–126 (1957).
50. Pogorzelski, W., Propriété d'une fonction de Green et ses applications aux équations elliptiques, *Ann. Pol. Math.*, **3**, 46–75 (1956).
51. Pogorzelski, W., Sur la solution de l'équation intégrale dans le problème de Fourier, *Ann. de la Soc. Pol. de Math.*, **24**, 56–74 (1951).
52. Pogorzelski, W., Sur le problème de Fourier généralisé, *Ann. Pol. Math.*, **3**, 126–141 (1956).
53. Pogorzelski, W., Sur les équations résolubles sans limitation, *J. de Math.*, Paris 1958.
54. Pogorzelski, W., Sur les systèmes d'équations intégrales a l'infinité des functions inconnues, *Ann. Pol. Math.*, **2**, 106–117 (1955).
55. Pogorzelski, W., Étude d'une fonction de Green et du problème aux limites pour l'équation parabolique normale, *Ann. Pol. Math.*, **4**, 288–307 (1958).
56. Pogorzelski, W., Problème aux limites de Poincaré, *Ann. de l'Acad. des Sc. Tech.*, Warsaw 1936.
57. Pogorzelski, W., Über die Transformationen einiger iterierten uneigentlichen Integrale und ihre Anwendungen zur Poincaréschen Randwertaufgabe, *Math. Zeitschrift*, **44**, 427–444 (1939).

58. Pogorzelski, W., Sur les équations intégrales non linéaires à singularité polaire, *C. R. Soc. Pol.*, Warsaw 1924.
59. Pogorzelski, W., Investigation of singular integral equations by the fixed point method, *Biul. Wojsk. Akad. Techn.*, Warsaw 1955 (in Polish).
60. Pogorzelski, W., Sur l'équation intégrale non linéaire de second espèce à forte singularité, *Ann. Pol. Math.*, **1**, 138–148 (1954).
61. Pogorzelski, W., Problème aux limites de Hilbert généralisé, *ibid.* **2**, 136–144 (1955).
62. Pogorzelski, W., Problème aux limites de Poincaré généralisé, *ibid.* **2**, 257–270 (1955).
63. Pogorzelski, W., Sur l'équation intégrale singulière non linéaire et sur les propriétés d'une intégrale singulière pour les arcs non fermés, *J. of Math. and Mech.*, **7**, 515–532 (1958).
64. Pogorzelski, W., Sur certaines classes de fonctions complexes définies sur les arcs non fermés, *Bull. Acad. Pol. Sc.*, Cl. III, **7** (1959).
65. Pogorzelski, W., Problème généralisé de Hilbert pour les arcs non fermés, *Ann. Sc. de l'Éc. Norm. Sup.*, Paris 201–222 (1959).
66. Pogorzelski, W., Sur les problèmes aux limites discontinues dans la théorie des fonctions analytiques, *Bull. Acad. Pol. Sc.*, Série math. (1959). *J. of Math. and Mech.* **9** (4), 583–606 (1960).
67. Pogorzelski, W., Propriétés d'une classe de fonctions holomorphes aux fonctions limites discontinues, *Ann. Pol. Math.*, **9**, 189–200 (1960).
68. Pogorzelski, W., Sur une propriété principale d'une classe $\mathfrak{H}$ des fonctions discontinues pour le système d'arcs, *Bull. Acad. Pol. Sc.*, **8** (6) (1960).
69. Pogorzelski, W., Sur certaines problèmes aux limites discontinues d'ordre supérieur dans la théorie des fonctions analytiques, *Ann. Pol, Math.*, **12**, 1–15 (1962).
70. Poincaré, H., *Leçons de Mécanique céleste*, vol. III, Chapt. X, Paris 1910.
71. Privalov, I., *Introduction to the Theory of Functions of a Complex Variable*, 1940.
72. Privalov, I., On a boundary problem in the theory of analytic functions, *Mat. sb.*, **41**, 519–526 (1934).
73. Przeworska-Rolewicz, D., Sur l'application de la méthode des approximations successives à une équation intégrale à forte singularité, *Ann. Pol. Math.*, **6**, 161–170 (1959).
74. Przeworska-Rolewicz, D., Sur le système d'équations intégrales singulières pour les lignes fermées, *Studia Math.*, **18**, 247–268 (1959).
75. Przeworska-Rolewicz, D., Étude des systèmes d'équations intégrales singulières pour les arcs non fermés par la méthode des approximations successives, *Bull. Acad. Pol. Sc.*, Série math., astr. et phys., (1958).
76. Sadowska, D., Sur un problème aux limites de la théorie des fonctions analytiques, *Ann. Pol. Math.*, **8**, 193–200 (1960).
77. Schauder, J., Der Fixpunktsatz in Funktionalräumen, *Studia Math.*, **2**, 171–180 (1930).

78. Sikorski, R., *Real Functions*, Warsaw 1958 (in Polish).
79. Smirnov, V. I., *Course of Higher Mathematics*, vol. IV, Moscow 1951 (in Russian). Revised English edition: (Vols. 57 to 62 in this series) Pergamon Press, Oxford/Addison-Wesley, Reading, Mass.
80. Sternberg, W., Über die lineare elliptische Differentialgleichungen zweiter Ordnung mit drei unabhängigen Veränderlichen, *Math. Zeitschrift*, **21**, 286–311 (1924).
81. Szmydt, Z., Sur un nouveau type de problèmes pour un système d'équations différentielles hyperboliques, *Bull. de l'Ac. Pol. de Sc.*, Cl. III, **4** (2), (1956).
82. Tichonov, A., *Bulletin de l'Université de Moscou*, **1** (1938).
83. Vekua, I., *New Methods of Solution of Elliptic Equations*, Moscow 1948 (in Russian).
84. Vekua, I., On linear singular integral equations containing integrals in the sense of the Cauchy principal value, *Dokl. Acad. Nauk S. S. S. R.*, **26**, 335–338 (1940) (in Russian).
85. Vekua, I., On the theory of singular integral equations, *Soobshch. Acad. Nauk Gruz. S. S. R.*, 869–876 (1942) (in Russian).
86. Vekua, I., On a linear boundary problem of Riemann, *Tr. Tbilissk. Mat. Inst.*, **11**, 109–139 (1942) (in Russian).
87. Vekua, I., On a new integral representation of analytic functions and its application, *Soobshch. Acad. Nauk S. S. S. R.*, **2**, (6), 477–484 (1941) (in Russian).
88. Vekua, I., Boundary problems of the theory of linear elliptic differential equations, *Soobshch. Acad. Nauk Gruz. S. S. R.*, No. 1, 22-34, No. 3, 181–186, No. 7, 497–500 (1940) (in Russian).
89. Wolska, J., Sur les équations intégrales et intégro-différentielles à singularité polaire, *Prace Mat.*, **48**, Warsaw 1952.
90. Wolska, J., Sur un problème généralisé de Vécoua, *Ann. Pol. Math.*, 209–221 (1960).
91. Wolska, J., Problème aux limites à dérivée tangentielle pour l'équation du type elliptique, *Bull. Acad. Pol. Sc.*, Cl. III, **4** (1956).
92. Zaremba, S., Application of the Picard method to the partial differential equations with three variables, *Prace Mat.-Fiz.*, **9**, 1–27 (1898) (in Polish).
93. Żakowski, W., Continuous and discontinuous boundary problem of Hilbert, *Biul. Wojsk. Akad. Techn.* (1959) (in Polish).
94. Żakowski, W., Sur un problème non linéaire de Hilbert, *Ann. Pol. Math.*, **9**, 79–99 (1960).

REFERENCES

78. [illegible], [illegible] Real [illegible] 1966 (in Polish).
79. [illegible] of [illegible] Mathematiques, [illegible] 1967.
[illegible] Ellipticity [illegible] (1962) (in [illegible])
[illegible], Mass. [illegible] Kanthus, Mass.
80. [illegible] [illegible] [illegible] [illegible] [illegible] 84, 364-[illegible] 2, No. 311 (1959).
81. [illegible] [illegible] [illegible] [illegible] [illegible] Sci. C. III, 4, 131 (1956).
82. [illegible] A., [illegible] [illegible] (1909).
83. [illegible] [illegible] [illegible] [illegible] Moscow 1943 (in Russian).
84. [illegible] [illegible] [illegible] equations [illegible] in [illegible] [illegible] and Cauchy [illegible] [illegible] [illegible] 3, 81
[illegible] (in Russian).
85. [illegible] L., On the [illegible] [illegible] [illegible] problem [illegible] [illegible] [illegible] (1932) [illegible]
86. [illegible] L., On [illegible] [illegible] [illegible] of Riemann [illegible] [illegible] [illegible] 11, [illegible] (1927) [illegible] Russian).
87. [illegible] L., On [illegible] [illegible] [illegible] of analytic functions and its [illegible] [illegible] [illegible] 473-494 (1954) (in Russian).
88. [illegible] L., [illegible] of the [illegible] [illegible] differential equations [illegible] [illegible] [illegible] 13, No. 11 (in Russian).
89. [illegible] Sur les [illegible] [illegible] et [illegible] [illegible] 48, [illegible] (1927).
90. [illegible] L., [illegible] problem [illegible] [illegible] [illegible] Math., [illegible] (1960).
91. [illegible], [illegible] [illegible] [illegible] [illegible] pour l'equation [illegible] Bull. Acad. Sci. Cl. III, [illegible] (1960).
92. Zmigrodzki, K., Application of [illegible] method to [illegible] partial differential equations [illegible] [illegible] 3, [illegible] (in Polish).
93. [illegible], W., [illegible] the [illegible] boundary problem of [illegible] [illegible] [illegible] (1959) (in [illegible]).
94. [illegible] W., Sur le problème [illegible] [illegible] [illegible] Math. [illegible] 79 (1957).

INDEX

OTHER TITLES IN THE SERIES IN
PURE AND APPLIED MATHEMATICS

Vol. 78 DITKIN and PRUDNIKOV—*Integral Transforms and Operational Calculus*
Vol. 79 POLOZHII—*The Method of Summary Representations for Numerical Solution of Problems of Mathematical Physics*
Vol. 80 MISHINA and PROSKURYAKOV—*Higher Algebra—Linear Algebra, Polynomials, General Algebra*
Vol. 81 ARAMANOVICH *et al.*—*Mathematical Analysis—Differentiation and Integration*
Vol. 82 REDEI—*The Theory of Finitely Generated Commutative Semigroups*
Vol. 83 MIKHLIN—*Multidimensional Singular Integrals and Integral Equations*
Vol. 84 LEBEDEV, SKAL'SKAYA and UFLYAND—*Problems in Mathematical Physics*
Vol. 85 GAKHOV—*Boundary Value Problems*
Vol. 86 PHILLIPS—*Some Topics in Complex Analysis*
Vol. 87 SHREIDER—*The Monte Carlo Method*